N.B. AUSTIN

STRANGER
THAN FICTION

CORRUPTION AND CRIMES AGAINST
HUMANITY IN THE COVID ERA

MOORE BELL

ISBN: 978-1-946990-08-2

Table of Contents

Chapter 1

From the Author Pt. 1: Introduction

A few years ago, I came upon a memoir written by my long-since-deceased great-grandfather, Nicholas. The content of it wasn't particularly long—maybe 20 pages or so, hand-written—nor was it written with a ton of detail. The fact that he wrote it at all was no small accomplishment however, as my grandfather told me his dad had actually taught himself how to write! Nicholas's memoir told the story of how he'd come to America from Turkey during the early 20th century, due to the oppression of the Greek population at the time. From there it primarily documented different aspects of his life and times in this new country he'd come to love so much.

The most fascinating thing about this book to me, other than the background it gave me on my family, was that it provided a first-hand account of the experiences and attitudes of a different time. This included things like his feelings toward different cultural figures/events and his relationships with his wife and family. Those dynamics were very different from what we experience today. But they were also different from what we understand of that time, based on what we are now told of it by people who weren't there. This was my first real epiphany about the unmatched value of a primary source. And so, having written and self-published three fiction books at that point, I thought it would be a cool idea to transcribe and publish his memoir.[1]

But this book is not an advertisement for that one (the memoir is priced at cost on Amazon, as a matter of fact). This book is simply the result of what my great-grandfather taught me which, given the timing of my coming upon it, I can only attribute to God's plan for me. You see, I am a health data scientist by trade—specifically, a rigorously-trained morbidity and mortality risk expert. The Covid era has been wild enough to live through at all, but to be in this profession at this time has been particularly jarring. No matter what you think about the subject, the amount of data being tossed around and conclusions being made based on that data is unprecedented.

To be honest with you upfront, dear reader, describing my feelings toward it will be a serious challenge. It's simultaneously been one of the most interesting and difficult things I've ever experienced.

As you will find in this incessantly-cited book, the amount of documentation I've gathered since the Covid era began has been like no project I've ever worked on. In that way, I guess you could say I've had a passion for the subject. And while in the final chapters I will outline the personal hardships I've experienced during this time, I cannot say I am bitter about any of the exceptionally heavy information I've gathered in the chapters which will precede that one. It simply is what it is and to despair about it is to be defeated by it, in my opinion. In fact, for all the hardship there has been far more fortune. As such, I will look back on this period fondly.

That said, the information is heavy, so please either prepare yourself for that or stop reading now if your mind isn't open to a new perspective on this subject. I am documenting this now because I feel I must for the sake of future generations. While that might sound dramatic, in a time defined by ubiquitous censorship it isn't remotely so. Because as much as I've learned the importance of primary sources from my great-grandfather's memoir, I've learned the consequences of lacking those sources due to the actions of today's petty tyrants.

In fact, over the past decade I've seen everyone from regular talk-show personalities to even gamers being either muted or outright removed from platforms built on government-subsidization. These people did not commit crimes of any kind. They lawfully exercised their God-given right to free speech, most of the time in an insightful or comedic way. But converged American institutions have increasingly punished them for it. It's gotten so bad at times that my favorite comedian's *wife*, who isn't in the public eye at all, was even prevented from using one such platform to rent out a home. I will cover a lot more on these actions as it relates to the Covid era specifically in the chapters to come. But if the entirely-sourced information I am to present here and the attitudes toward it such as mine are not documented, I see it as a very real risk they will not be made available for the benefit of posterity at all. This cannot be permitted, since such a preventable disaster as this will surely come to pass again.

And that's what Covid was—a disaster of public health. Throughout this book I will document why and how this happened in painstaking detail. Over the course of reading it, you might also recognize changes in how I describe things. For example, if my goal was to prove that birds are actually robots, I would still call them birds until I demonstrated clearly they were robots, at which point I would call them what I felt they'd been shown to be—namely, robots. I do this because I am making a case which I intend to prove. I am simply starting from the perspective of today's prevailing narrative so that the case can be built to demonstrate why that narrative is so very wrong, where it is wrong.

Also, there will be opinions peppered into the analyses throughout the book. All opinions are entirely my own and are simply conclusions drawn based on the documented information I present. Not one opinion I will provide will be given without said supporting documentation. All data presented is as of September 7, 2021 or later. Thank you for reading and I hope it helps you understand what has transpired in some way.

Endnotes

1   Athanasiades, N., 2018. My Biography: The Story of Nicholas Athanasiades. 1st ed. CreateSpace Independent Publishing Platform.

Chapter 2

Lockdowns and Business Closures

"That's something that I don't think we could possibly do in the United States. I can't imagine shutting down New York or Los Angeles, but the judgement on the part of the Chinese health authorities is that given the fact that it's spreading throughout the provinces... it's their judgement that this is something that in fact is going to help in containing it. Whether or not it does or does not is really open to question because ***historically when you shut things down it doesn't have a major effect*** *(my emphasis)."*
—Anthony Fauci, January 24, 2020[1]

"Fifteen days to slow the spread."
—Anthony Fauci and Trump admin. Covid plan, March 16, 2020[2]

"If you look at the trajectory of the curves of outbreaks and other areas, it's at least going to be several weeks. I cannot see that all of a sudden, next week or two weeks from now, it's going to be over. I don't think there's a chance of that. I think it's going to be several weeks."
—Anthony Fauci, March 20, 2020[3]

"So if we can get the overwhelming portion of the population vaccinated by let's say the end of the second, the beginning of the third quarter—by the time we get into mid-fall of 2021, we can be approaching some level of normality."
—Anthony Fauci, December 16, 2020[4]

"... by the end of the year—by Christmas."
—Anthony Fauci, February 19, 2021[5]

"If all things go the way we want them to go, and we get really the overwhelming majority of people vaccinated, I think as we get into the fall and winter, we could start to really get some good control over this as we get back into the fall of 2022."
—Anthony Fauci, August 23, 2021[6]

"When I listen to the tape, I meant to say the spring of 2022, so I did misspeak."
　　　　—Anthony Fauci, later in the day of August 23, 2021[7]

In March of 2020, by the sudden orders of public health officials around the world, society as we know it shut down. Small businesses were deemed, "non-essential," and ordered closed; people were told to remain at home, with non-compliers in some particularly tyrannical places facing financial and/or criminal punishments; masks were made mandatory for customers to attend stores, with non-compliers refused service; and mandatory mass testing campaigns took place to attend workplaces, among other venues. These extraordinary actions were taken in the name of a cluster of patients suffering from pneumonia-like symptoms in Wuhan, China. Those patients were ultimately alleged as having contracted a novel coronavirus, which would go on to be referred to as SARS-CoV-2. The diseases this virus caused would be referred to with the name, "COVID-19."

This is the highest level of the Covid era story. There is much more background to every narrative told, every action taken, and every player involved, if one wishes to understand what actually happened in 2020 and the years that followed. This book will provide as much of this background as humanly possible. For now however, we will start with one of the most jarring, pandemic-defining actions for many people: lockdowns.

So where did this idea to quarantine the entirety of a population come from? Was it a visionary in epidemiology? Was it the result of a successful, disease-mitigating experiment? No and no. As shocking as it may sound, the idea of lockdowns/closures as a strategy for pandemic mitigation originated from a 14-year old girl's science fair project.[8] Per TV personality Dr. Drew Pinsky, her project led her computer-programmer father to model out such a scenario. According to Pinsky, *"he and she then published a paper in 2006 that the Bush Administration adopted as policy."* The unprecedented approach taken by public health organizations in 2020, however, was this young girl's recommendation of, *"regional sorts of closures,"* on steroids.

And countries like Australia are a shocking example where people have been violently arrested for having, "no valid reason," to be walking within a few hundred feet of their homes.[9] Even if we look past the inhumanity of such a situation, it would be reasonable to wonder how the *physical interaction* of a group of officers detaining a person who is outside minding their own business is anything but counterintuitive, especially if the stated goal is keeping humans distant from one another. One might even question how slamming a man on the floor for eating a sandwich outside is contributing to his health and/or teaching him how/why he should be complying with unlawful orders. During our time we did question these things, as we saw a variety of such events captured on video. Some of the officials responsible for these enforcement actions, like Australian Prime Minister Scott Morrison for example, even admitted such policies were, "not a sustainable way to live in this country." But reason and decency have simply not been a consideration or limitation when it comes to public health organizations in the sweeping megalomania of 2020.

Before we continue with the unfathomable, perhaps-unintended consequences however, we can start with the most obvious, necessary question related to these public health organization lockdowns: did these measures work? The answer is that they observably and objectively did not. A January 2022 meta-analysis pre-print by a team including a John's Hopkins economist, for example, concluded the following on the matter[10]:

> *"While this meta-analysis concludes the lockdowns have had little to no public health effects, they have imposed enormous economic and social costs where they have been adopted. In consequence, lockdown policies are ill-founded and should be rejected as a pandemic policy instrument."*

As we saw in the opening quotes, Anthony Fauci said in January 2020 what John's Hopkins, "discovered," two years later—namely, that locking down, "doesn't have a major effect." However, Fauci's pronouncement came just before the US went on to engage in an unprecedented lockdown effort, without any resistance from the head of the US pandemic response. In fact, as we saw in the subsequent quotes, Fauci exploited the public's trust in extending his planned two weeks to, "slow the spread," further and further.

But Fauci wasn't remotely alone in this behavior. Throughout the Covid era, the *opinions* of, "experts," like Fauci were deemed infallible to the point of being worthy of human-rights-violating enforcement. And lockdowns are but one example of the complete lack of benefit those opinions provided to the public's health.

So why did lockdowns happen anyway under the watches of such prominent, "public health," officials? Why did many of them support the lockdowns? And why didn't the rest openly and aggressively oppose something so fruitless which would also have significant consequences? We will discover the answers over the course of this book. But the truth is that the lockdowns didn't just have, "little to no effect," on public health, but rather an overwhelmingly negative effect. In fact, across the entire world the countries/states with the harshest lockdowns tended to experience the most cases and deaths. Per John's Hopkins, the following are the top 3 countries to date by deaths classified as Covid per 100K population to date (September 2021)[11]:

1. Peru – 611
2. Hungary – 308
3. Bosnia and Herzegovina – 300

The Covid-19 government response stringency index is a composite score ranging from 0 to 100 developed by researchers at Oxford University.[12] This index was put together to track the stringency of public health policy measures implemented by countries, including school closures, business closures, travel restrictions, etc. For each of the 3 countries with the most Covid-classed deaths per capita, we will now review how restrictions over time impacted case/death rates.

1. Peru
   a. Peru's stringency index score was > 75 from mid-March through mid-December 2020
   b. For the majority of those months it reached and remained > 90, as one of the harshest countries in the entire world
   c. It was also one of the first to eclipse a score of 90, doing so on March 16, 2020

d. Despite having reached this level of lockdown by March 16, Peru did not register its first Covid-classed deaths or cases until a week later.[13,14] From that point on cases climbed throughout the year, despite all restrictive efforts.

e. After a brief week or so of respite in December, measures soon tightened again in 2021 to 2020 levels, with cases and deaths following suit

f. The bottom line is clear: Peru at the same time had some of the strictest measures taken in the world and also experienced the most death per capita in the world, clearly demonstrating that the measures were an abject failure

2. Hungary

a. Hungary is an interesting case because it remained largely without Covid impact until the winter of 2020. However, it too demonstrates the same story as Peru as far as lockdown effectiveness is concerned.

b. Like Peru, Hungary eclipsed 70 on the strictness scale prior to registering a single death or case.[15] It then experienced a small cluster of deaths and cases, which lasted until measures were reduced in May. Restrictions, cases and deaths then vanished until the fall of 2020.

c. In the fall of 2020, cases and deaths began to rise, and with them, so did restrictions. Hungary soon topped the 70th percentile of the index again, where it remained until mid-April 2021. At this exact time restrictions eased, cases and deaths both dropped off a cliff until today (September 2021), when Hungary is one of the least impacted and least restricted nations in the world.

3. Bosnia and Herzegovina

a. Bosnia and Herzegovina shows the opposite of Peru and Hungary, as it progressively decreased restrictions over time, and experienced the same waves of deaths and cases as those other countries.[16]

b. With no cases or deaths to start with, this country still implemented intense measures, with upticks in incidence soon to follow

c. It remained at a score above 50 leading into its first major spike. From there, as measures eased, spikes up and down continued

d. If nothing else, Bosnia and Herzegovina shows the complete lack of correlation between measures and outcomes both in its timing, as well as when compared to places like Peru and Hungary

In reviewing those with the top death rates, we can clearly see these countries were provided no benefit whatsoever by lockdown in general, or by mitigating inevitable case spikes. To round out this review though, let's look at some of the least restricted countries:

- Belarus
  - Per 100K death rate[17]: 41 (#111)
  - Restriction index: never went above 50 from beginning of pandemic to date (avg. ~30)
- Sweden
  - Per 100K death rate[18]: 143 (#40)
  - Restriction index: never went above 70 from beginning of pandemic to date (avg. ~50)
- Finland
  - Per 100K death rate[19]: 19 (#129)
  - Restriction index: max 71 for 2 weeks in April 2020 (avg. ~40)

These figures are simply not explainable if lockdowns work. The countries with the harshest restrictions during timeframes with no known treatments very frequently saw more per capita deaths. And as we can see in the above examples, countries with far less restrictions did *not* show any clear evidence of worse outcomes. In fact, the empirical evidence seems to point pretty clearly to restrictions actually *worsening* mortality rates attributed to Covid.

Despite Covid era claims to the contrary by the US Centers for Disease Control and Prevention (CDC), the National Institutes of Health (NIH), the mainstream propagandist media, and the mainstream propagandist social media networks, this issue was also hotly contested by thousands of doctors and scientists the world over. Such alternative doctors posited that avoiding human contact, locking people indoors, increasing fear, and otherwise diminishing human productivity is the opposite of a public *health* strategy. In fact, 14,879 medical & public health scientists and 43,804 medical practitioners signed a public declaration affirming their opposition to the draconian actions taken by public health organizations since the beginning of the pandemic.[20] The Great Barrington Declaration, as it was titled, called instead for a strategy of focused-protection for the at-risk populations which desired it, without sabotaging the lives and medical autonomy of those not at-risk. The Declaration was inexplicably ignored by the aforementioned US organizations, however, despite its clear, previously-demonstrated success in places like Sweden.

And so too were the pleas ignored of even those government officials dissenting from the narrative. One such example is former White House senior health advisor, Dr. Scott Atlas, who criticized Fauci, Covid response official Deborah Birx, and CDC director Robert Redfield for refusing to look at scientific data pointing to the futile, harmful effects of lockdowns.[21] Atlas recalled his time addressing these figureheads on the matter as follows:

> *"As I finished, there was silence. No one offered any contrary data. No one spoke of scientific studies. No one even mentioned the discredited Korea study. Zero comments from Dr. Birx. Nothing from Fauci. And as always, not a single mention by Birx or Fauci about the serious harms of school closures. In my mind, this was bizarre. Why was I the only one in the room with detailed knowledge of the literature? Why was I the only one considering the data on such an important topic with a critical eye? Were the others simply accepting bottom lines and conclusions, without any analytical evaluation? Weren't they supposed to be expert medical scientists, too?"*

Atlas also goes on to claim the only responses he did eventually get from the trio in question were empty slanders. He quotes Birx as having said his data and assessments of it were, "out of the mainstream," accused him of being, "fringe," and uttering the blatant lie that, "all experts agreed with her." This lack of scientific justification is particularly damning when considering the extent of the economic and social consequences associated with the, "ends justify the means," approach lockdowns constitute, for which the, "ends," are either a zero or outright negative benefit. Those consequences have been widespread and are now well-documented history as follows:

- Violation of basic human rights including:
    o The right to peaceable assembly[22]
    o The right to free religious worship[23]
    o The right to free speech and expression[24]
    o The right to seek redress of government[25]
    o The right to informed consent
- The surrender of the legislative authority/responsibility of elected-leaders to public-health officials, so long as they declare "emergency"
- Per a 2021 study by Raman et al. in the *British Medical Journal* (BMJ), the lockdowns had a, "significant negative," impact on health and provision of healthcare.[26] The study's multivariable analyses showed that all five dimensions of healthcare provision reviewed (non-affordability, non-accessibility, inadequacy, inappropriateness, and discontinuity of care) were negatively affected. Associated depression and social loneliness were also observed outcomes of the analysis.
- One example of the above includes the negative effect of lockdowns on healthcare outcomes of the UK, where a report concluded up to 740,000 potential cancer cases that should have been urgently referred by physicians have been, "missed," since the first lockdown.[27] Another report claimed that official data showed, "one in 10 people in England," found themselves on waiting lists for various operations, with suspected heart attack victims waiting almost an hour for ambulance care and more than 300,000 patients waiting over a year to receive care.[28]
- Per Federal Reserve estimates, the pandemic response resulted in the permanent closure of roughly an additional 200,000 US establishments compared to normal levels[29]
- Australia, among other countries, developed camps for concentrating its citizens, referred to as, "quarantine facilities."[30] There is, without question, no benefit this provides whatsoever. It is slavery and is reminiscent of the most evil periods of human history.

- Per Human Rights Watch, "Sri Lanka's police are increasingly killing and abusing people under cover of the Covid-19 pandemic measures."[31] This abuse of power is not isolated to one country, however. Per Amnesty International, at least 60 countries demonstrated documented cases of, "authorities adopting punitive and coercive measures," which have, "not only resulted in violations of human rights but also divided societies and failed to tackle the health crisis."[32] Cited violations included arbitrary arrests, unlawful use of force, crackdowns on criticism of pandemic response, and torture.
- Per World Health Organization's Dr. David Nabarro in October 2020, "We really do appeal to all world leaders: stop using lockdown as your primary control method."[33] Reasons cited:
  - Destruction of Caribbean tourism industry
  - Difficulties for farmers (food supply risk)
  - Poverty levels – doubling of world poverty within a year
  - Child malnutrition – doubling of child malnutrition
  - Despite the pleas of this World Health Organization expert, lockdowns around the world did not stop. Even western countries like New Zealand went on to senselessly enforce strict measures over a single case.[34]
- Per analysis by research group Collateral Global, 1.2 million children world-wide could die from disrupted healthcare amid pandemic lockdowns.[35] This is more than a quarter of the total deaths worldwide attributed to Covid as of fall 2021, and only addresses the impact of disrupted healthcare on one demographic—namely, children.
- Per a 2021 study by Hill et al. in *Pediatrics*, youths demonstrated higher incidence of suicidal behavior during the 2020 Covid closures than in 2019.[36] To be clear, this is a group with effectively no Covid risk whatsoever (412 total deaths attributed to Covid under age 17 from 1/1/20 to 9/1/21 … by comparison, there were 924 pneumonia deaths in the same time period in the same age group).[37]

- Per the American Institute for Economic Research, the increase in youth suicide deaths dramatically outpaced those attributed to Covid.[38] A review of CDC mortality data showed a 23% increase in deaths of all causes in the 0-24 age group from 2019 to 2020. And while one might wish to associate this increase with a horrific Covid death toll, Covid-attributed deaths account for only 1.2% of the total deaths in this age group. Based on previously mentioned studies affirming malnutrition, interruption of healthcare, obesity, suicide rates, and depression in this age group, this staggering increase can therefore only be attributed directly to the clearly misguided responses of public health organizations. And to put the death toll in context using a simple calculation:
  - US under 25 population is approximately 30% (slightly higher, per estimates) of the approximately 330M US population. This means there are approximately 99M people in this age bracket.
  - So with a per 100K all-cause death toll rate in 2020 for this age bracket of 131.7, a total year-over-year increase of 23%, minus a Covid-associated rate of 1.2%, this means the incremental increase in death associated with public health malfeasance is 28.7 per 100K
  - Finally, with 99M people in this bracket, at a rate of 28.7 per 100K, this would mean **approximately 28,400 children ages 0-24 were lost due to the effects of public health malfeasance of various forms**.
- Per a 2021 study by Woolford et al. in the *Journal of the American Medical Association (JAMA)*, childhood overweight and obesity saw a relative increase of 23.8% during the pandemic, when compared with a reference period.[39] According to Mayo Clinic, obesity is a risk factor for serious symptoms of the diseases called Covid.[40] This implies the actions taken worsened the danger.
- Per the United Nations, drug abuse increased 22% worldwide during the pandemic[41]

- Per the International Labour Organization, workers lost $3.7 trillion in earnings during the pandemic, with women and young people hardest hit by employment losses[42]
- Per Oxfam, the world's billionaires made $3.9 trillion during the pandemic[43]
- Per Census data, the number of Americans who say they can't afford enough food for themselves or their children is growing, caused by school closings, inflated food prices, and inability of government to fund continued jobless benefits without increasing inflation even more[44]
- A 2020 study by Silverio-Murillo et al. in the *SSRN Electronic Journal* analyzed data from police precincts in several major US cities.[45] It found domestic violence increased by 10 to 27 percent during lockdown periods.
- Per the Mises Institute, the CDC, operating under the US Department of Health and Human Services (DHHS), has asserted jurisdiction over private residential leases nationwide.[46] The CDC has taken this absurd action, for which it has no real authority, in the name of curtailing evictions related to the economic impact of lockdowns it is responsible for encouraging. Not only is this a tremendous perversion of US government authority as a whole by an unelected bureaucracy, but the impact of these eviction moratoriums will continue to have further negative impacts economically on private landowners, who amid skyrocketing home prices will continue to be outbid by large, favored-debtor private companies. More on this in a later chapter.

These damages and their psychological effects were also dragged on and on with no specific, adhered-to objectives or goal posts. As we showed earlier, Anthony Fauci's disorientation was one of the most evident examples of this aimlessness. When combining the shocking amount of devastation resulting from the lockdowns with their way-less-than-zero positive impact, it is clear that the organizations responsible utterly failed in their mandate to, "control disease." In fact, as demonstrated, their actions contributed greatly to senseless suffering and *increased* disease, and will continue to well into the future.

Endnotes

1   Magness, Phillip. 2020. "Twelve Times The Lockdowners Were Wrong". *AIER*. https://www.aier.org/article/twelve-times-the-lockdowners-were-wrong/.

2   Wearp, Matthew. 2021. "It's Been An Entire Year Since 'Fifteen Days To Slow The Spread'". *Dailycaller.Com*. https://www.dailycaller.com/2021/03/16/1-year-anniversary-fifteen-days-slow-the-spread-covid-19-coronavirus-trump-fauci/.

3   Johnson, Marty. 2020. "Fauci: 'It's Going To Be Several Weeks' Of Social Distancing For Coronavirus". *Thehill*. https://www.thehill.com/homenews/administration/488628-fauci-its-going-to-be-several-weeks-of-social-distancing-for.

4   Higgins-Dunn, Noah, and Berkeley Lovelace Jr. 2020. "Dr. Fauci Says U.S. Could Return To Normal By Mid-Fall If Most People Get Covid Vaccine". *CNBC*. https://www.cnbc.com/2020/12/16/dr-fauci-says-us-could-return-to-normal-by-mid-fall-if-most-people-get-covid-vaccine.html.

5   Murphy, Mike. 2021. "Fauci Predicts Return To 'Normal' By Christmas". *Marketwatch*. https://www.marketwatch.com/story/fauci-predicts-return-to-normal-by-christmas-11613707914.

6   Pengelly, Martin, and Richard Luscombe. 2021. "Fauci Says US Could Be Back To Normal By Spring 2022 – If Vaccinations Take Off". *The Guardian*. https://www.theguardian.com/world/2021/aug/24/anthony-fauci-coronavirus-us-normal-spring-2022-americans-vaccinated.

7   Ibid.

8   O'Connor, Larry. 2020. "Misguided Shutdown Policy Began As High School Science Project". *Townhall*. https://townhall.com/columnists/larryoconnor/2020/05/20/misguided-shutdown-policy-began-as-high-school-science-project-n2569154.

9   T., Brett. 2021. "'Indefensible Authoritarianism': Here's How The Coronavirus Lockdowns Are Coming Along In Australia". *Twitchy.Com*. https://www.twitchy.com/brettt-3136/2021/09/27/indefensible-authoritarianism-heres-how-the-coronavirus-lockdowns-are-coming-along-in-australia/.

10   Herby, Jonas, Lars Jonung, and Steve H. Hanke. 2022. "A LITERATURE REVIEW AND META-ANALYSIS OF THE EFFECTS OF LOCKDOWNS ON COVID-19 MORTALITY". Sites.Krieger.Jhu.Edu. https://sites.krieger.jhu.edu/iae/files/2022/01/A-Literature-Review-and-Meta-Analysis-of-the-Effects-of-Lockdowns-on-COVID-19-Mortality.pdf.

11   "Mortality Analyses - Johns Hopkins Coronavirus Resource Center". 2020. *Johns Hopkins Coronavirus Resource Center*. https://coronavirus.jhu.edu/data/mortality.

12   "COVID-19 Government Response Tracker". 2020. *Bsg.Ox.Ac.Uk*. https://www.bsg.ox.ac.uk/research/research-projects/covid-19-government-response-tracker.

13   "Peru COVID - Coronavirus Statistics - Worldometer".
         2020. *Worldometers.Info*.
         https://www.worldometers.info/coronavirus/country/peru/#graph-deaths-daily.

14   "Peru COVID - Coronavirus Statistics - Worldometer".
         2020. *Worldometers.Info*.
         https://www.worldometers.info/coronavirus/country/peru/.

15   "Peru COVID - Coronavirus Statistics - Worldometer".
         2020. *Worldometers.Info*.
         https://www.worldometers.info/coronavirus/country/hungary/.

16   "Peru COVID - Coronavirus Statistics - Worldometer".
         2020. *Worldometers.Info*.
         https://www.worldometers.info/coronavirus/country/bosnia-and-herzegovina/.

17   "Peru COVID - Coronavirus Statistics - Worldometer".
         2020. *Worldometers.Info*.
         https://www.worldometers.info/coronavirus/#countries.

18   Ibid.

19   Ibid.

20   Bhattacharya, Jay, Sunetra Gupta, and Martin Kulldorff. 2020. "Great
         Barrington Declaration - Signature Count". *Great Barrington
         Declaration*. https://gbdeclaration.org/view-signatures/.

21   Huff, Ethan. 2021. "Dr. Atlas Memoir Blasts Birx, Redfield, Fauci For
         Dismissing Covid Science". *Naturalnews.Com*.
         https://www.naturalnews.com/2021-11-22-atlas-blasts-birx-redfield-fauci-dismissing-science.html.

22   Amnesty International Ltd. 2020. "COVID-19 Crackdowns: Police Abuse
         And The Global Pandemic". London: Amnesty International.
         https://www.justice.gov/eoir/page/file/1345736/download.

23   Ibid., 7

24   Ibid., 10

25   Ibid., 16

26   Raman, Rajiv, Ramachandran Rajalakshmi, Janani Surya, Radha
         Ramakrishnan, Sobha Sivaprasad, Dolores Conroy, Jitendra Pal Thethi, V
         Mohan, and Gopalakrishnan Netuveli. 2021. "Impact On Health And
         Provision Of Healthcare Services During The COVID-19 Lockdown In
         India: A Multicentre Cross-Sectional Study". *BMJ Open* 11 (1): e043590.
         doi:10.1136/bmjopen-2020-043590.

27   Donnelly, Laura. 2021. "'Biggest Cancer Catastrophe Ever' To Hit NHS
         As Up To 740,000 Potential Cases Missed". *The Telegraph*.
         https://www.telegraph.co.uk/news/2021/12/01/biggest-cancer-catastrophe-ever-hit-nhs-740000-potential-cases/.

28   Donnelly, Laura. 2021. "One In 10 People In England Now On An NHS
         Waiting List". *Telegraph.Co.Uk*.
         https://www.telegraph.co.uk/news/2021/11/11/patients-lives-risk-record-ambulance-waits-warns-college-paramedics/.

29   Simon, Ruth. 2021. "Covid-19's Toll On U.S. Business? 200,000 Extra Closures In Pandemic's First Year". *The Wall Street Journal*. https://www.wsj.com/articles/covid-19s-toll-on-u-s-business-200-000-extra-closures-in-pandemics-first-year-11618580619.

30   Claire Brimelow, Hannah. 2021. "A Look At Australia's 'Mandatory Supervised Quarantine Facility' | TIMCAST". *TIMCAST*. https://timcast.com/news/a-look-at-australias-mandatory-supervised-quarantine-facility/.

31   "Sri Lanka: Police Abuses Surge Amid Covid-19 Pandemic". 2021. *Human Rights Watch*. https://www.hrw.org/news/2021/08/06/sri-lanka-police-abuses-surge-amid-covid-19-pandemic.

32   Amnesty International Ltd. 2020. "COVID-19 Crackdowns: Police Abuse And The Global Pandemic". London: Amnesty International. https://www.justice.gov/eoir/page/file/1345736/download.

33   Mark Miller, Andrew. 2020. "WHO Official Urges World Leaders To Stop Using Lockdowns As Primary Virus Control Method". *Washington Examiner*. https://www.washingtonexaminer.com/news/who-official-urges-world-leaders-to-stop-using-lockdowns-as-primary-virus-control-method.

34   "New Zealand Enters Nationwide Lockdown Over One Covid Case". 2021. *BBC News*. https://www.bbc.com/news/world-asia-58241619.

35   Polumbo, Brad. 2021. "1.2 Million Children World-Wide Could Die From Disrupted Healthcare: Analysis". *Fee.Org*. https://www.fee.org/articles/12-million-children-world-wide-could-die-from-disrupted-healthcare-amid-pandemic-lockdowns-analysis-finds/.

36   Hill, Ryan M., Katrina Rufino, Sherin Kurian, Johanna Saxena, Kirti Saxena, and Laurel Williams. 2021. "Suicide Ideation And Attempts In A Pediatric Emergency Department Before And During COVID-19". *Pediatrics* 147 (3). doi:10.1542/peds.2020-029280.

37   2020. *Data.Cdc.Gov*. https://data.cdc.gov/NCHS/Provisional-COVID-19-Deaths-by-Sex-and-Age/9bhg-hcku.

38   Gartz, Micha. 2021. "More "Covid Suicides" Than Covid Deaths In Kids". *AIER*. https://www.aier.org/article/more-covid-suicides-than-covid-deaths-in-kids/.

39   Woolford, Susan J., Margo Sidell, Xia Li, Veronica Else, Deborah R. Young, Ken Resnicow, and Corinna Koebnick. 2021. "Changes In Body Mass Index Among Children And Adolescents During The COVID-19 Pandemic". *JAMA* 326 (14): 1434. doi:10.1001/jama.2021.15036.

40   "COVID-19: Who's At Higher Risk Of Serious Symptoms?". 2022. *Mayo Clinic*. https://www.mayoclinic.org/diseases-conditions/coronavirus/in-depth/coronavirus-who-is-at-risk/art-20483301.

41   "COVID Pandemic Fuelling Major Increase In Drug Use Worldwide: UN Report". 2021. *UN News*. https://news.un.org/en/story/2021/06/1094672.

42   Kaplan, Juliana. 2021. "Workers Lost $3.7 Trillion In Earnings During The Pandemic. Women And Gen Z Saw The Biggest Losses.". *Business*

Insider. https://www.businessinsider.com/workers-lost-37-trillion-in-earnings-during-the-pandemic-2021-1.

43   Kaplan, Juliana. 2021. "Billionaires Made $3.9 Trillion During The Pandemic — Enough To Pay For Everyone's Vaccine". *Business Insider.* https://www.businessinsider.com/billionaires-made-39-trillion-during-the-pandemic-coronavirus-vaccines-2021-1.

44   Harrison, David. 2020. "More Americans Go Hungry Amid Coronavirus Pandemic, Census Shows". *WSJ.* https://www.wsj.com/articles/more-americans-go-hungry-amid-coronavirus-pandemic-census-shows-11597570200?mod=hp_lead_pos9.

45   Silverio-Murillo, Adan, Jose Roberto Balmori de la Miyar, and Lauren Hoehn-Velasco. 2020. "Families Under Confinement: COVID-19, Domestic Violence, And Alcohol Consumption". *SSRN Electronic Journal*, 3, 28. doi:10.2139/ssrn.3688384.

46   Deist, Jeff. 2020. "The CDC Is America's New Landlord". *Mises Institute.* https://www.mises.org/power-market/cdc-americas-new-landlord.

Chapter 3

Censorship

Censorship was an official policy of the US government and its public health organizations overseeing the Covid response. They illegally enforced this censorship in collusion with private enterprise. This is not hyperbole. As we saw in the Amnesty International review on policing in the prior chapter, police in many countries are being used to physically arrest and intimidate people for publicly criticizing the pandemic response. However, the tactics used to silence dissent are much further reaching than this. Those tactics, which we will outline in this chapter, have come not just from the public sector, but also from an unholy union of public and private. And this criminal conspiracy, which in the United States is the most blatant possible violation of the First Amendment, has been openly and proudly stated on several occasions.

> *"In terms of actions, Alex, that we have taken—or we're working to take, I should say—from the federal government: we've increased misinformation research and tracking from within the surgeon general's office;* **we're flagging problematic posts for Facebook that spread disinformation** *(my emphasis); we're working with doctors and medical professionals to connect medical experts who are popular with their audiences with accurate information and* **boost trusted content** *(my emphasis), so we're helping get trusted content out there."*
> —Biden Regime Press Secretary Jen Psaki, July 2021[1]

> *"… providing for Facebook or other platforms to measure and publicly share the impact of misinformation on their platform and the audience it's reaching. Also with the public—with all of you—to create robust enforcement strategies which bridge their properties and provide transparency about rules.* **You shouldn't be banned from one platform and not others if you—for providing misinformation out there** *(my emphasis)."*
> —Jen Psaki, the next day

I could provide quotes by more than just the press secretary, too—this brazenness is not isolated to her. But we will get to similar examples as we go. For now, what she is flaunting is as illegal as it is immoral. It is an open confession of criminal corporate-governmental collusion. What she refuses to acknowledge when discussing this anti-science, illogical, un-American idea of, "misinformation," is that over the course of the pandemic the large majority of censored sources *are* the very, "doctors and medical professionals," she refers to. In fact, the term, "misinformation," itself seems to be a weapon in this psychological censorship war just as much as the term, "conspiracy theorist," was weaponized by the CIA to similarly justify dismissal/silencing of dissent.[2] And the truth is that in many ways during the Covid era, it's worked. The following are just a few of thousands—or, as we will find, *millions*—of documented examples of esteemed doctors and medical professionals, being censored by what we have now seen is a confession of an illegal government-corporate union to bury dissent:

- The Great Barrington Declaration, signed by 14,879 medical & public health scientists and 43,804 medical practitioners as discussed previously, was censored by *Google* and *Reddit*[3,4]
- Famed epidemiologist and early opponent of lockdowns Martin Kulldorff was censored by *Twitter* and *LinkedIn*[5,6]
- **Inventor of mRNA technology** Robert Malone was censored by *LinkedIn* and *YouTube*[7,8]
- America's Frontline Doctors, representing a coalition of 600+ medical professionals, was censored by *Facebook*[9]
- The spirit of censorship carried into the medical profession as well, with Dr. Mary Talley Bowden having been suspended and forced to resign her hospital privileges at Houston Methodist Hospital over the hospital's slanderous opposition to her successfully treating, "more than 2,000," patients with ivermectin[10]
- Dr. Meryl Ness had her license suspended and was ordered to undergo a psychiatric evaluation by the Maine Board of Licensure in Medicine for prescribing patients ivermectin and hydroxychloroquine[11]

- Dr. John Witcher, Mississippi physician since 1996, was allegedly threatened with license revocation over opposition to the Covid inoculations[12]
- Dr. Andrew Kaufman was censored by *YouTube*[13]
- *YouTube* also admits to having censored *more than 1 million* Covid-related videos[14]

The dangers of censoring the very types of doctors and experts Psaki referred to seem obvious. Unfortunately, the regime she served admitted to aiding and abetting these censorship efforts despite those dangers. What has been clear to many as a result is that, "misinformation," simply means information this regime disagrees with, especially since there is no shortage of experience/credentials amongst those who do disagree (my own included). In later chapters we will elaborate on the damage this has caused because of just how wrong they were.

But so far we saw this already as it related to the lockdowns and the support of, "authoritative sources," for those disastrous measures. Based on this alone, we can already see without question that the people pushing this notion of, "misinformation," do not have anyone's best interest at heart. And even without analysis of any kind, this is apparent simply by their intentional prevention of people's access to all points of view, which would be necessary for a person to truly draw informed conclusions on matters of science especially. For example, one need only look at Anthony Fauci's monthly change of opinion on mask wearing or the Food and Drug Administration's past approval of Quaaludes, among many other times these organizations changed a stance on something.[15,16] And it is okay to change stances on things if all you are doing is making recommendations. That, of course, is what science is. It changes all the time and any past conclusion can be disproven with any new observation(s).

However, this is also what makes any particular scientific conclusion's enforcement or coercion immoral, but also illegal. And this is laid out in the Nuremberg Code, which those who engage in censorship are in violation of[17]:

"1. The voluntary consent of the human subject is absolutely essential. This means that the person involved should have legal capacity to give consent; should be so situated as to be

able to exercise free power of choice, without the intervention of any element of force, fraud, deceit, duress, over-reaching, or other ulterior form of constraint or coercion; and should have sufficient knowledge and comprehension of the elements of the subject matter involved, as to enable him to make an understanding and enlightened decision."

So, based on this passage, two questions:

1. Does censorship of dissenting opinions, which is what Psaki's quotes above confess engagement in, allow for a person's, "sufficient knowledge and comprehension of the elements of the subject matter involved?"
2. If there is suppression of dissent (alternate points of view), can a person possibly make an, "understanding and enlightened decision?"

The answer to both questions is a resounding, "no." The US government and the companies whose actions it apparently dictates have violated the informed consent of the American people, in open abridgment of its own Constitution. They were not alone, however. This took place all over the world. In the UK, for example, it got even worse, in the form of the 2021 Online Safety Bill.[18] Described as, "the flagship legislation to combat abuse and hatred on the internet," this law would create the concept of a, "knowingly false communication," offense, which would criminalize those who send or post a message they know to be false with the intention to cause harm.

The litany of problems with this criteria come from its intentional obscurity. For example, does it include sarcasm? How can anyone possibly prove an, "intention to cause harm," from a limited online post that isn't a direct threat? They couldn't. And this brings us to the truth of the matter. Per *Summit News*, UK, "government sources," gave the example of, "anti-vaxxers," as a target of the bill. Do, "anti-vaxxers," know the information they post to be false? The majority obviously believe what they are posting to be true, like 99% of people with an opinion would be expected to. Also, who gets to decide what constitutes as, "false," as the bill outlines? Is it the same, "experts," who endorsed lockdowns at the expense of the entire world's health and wellbeing? We will see throughout this book that these, "experts," were wrong and/or lying the majority of the time.

24

But the point remains: it is the opposite of science to suggest alternatives shouldn't be publicly hypothesized and tested. The hallmark scientific practice of peer review is essential for this very reason. So bills such as this are not drafted for science or public protection, but rather to control what is shared publicly to the narrowest possible selection of government-approved ideas.

The Event 201 Pandemic Simulation Recommendation

In order to further understand how censorship became acceptable enough to openly declare it as a source of pride, we must dive into the premeditation to enforce it, specifically as it relates to a coronavirus outbreak. At this point it is well-documented that the Bill & Melinda Gates Foundation, the World Economic Forum (WEF), and the John's Hopkins University Bloomberg School of Medicine held a global pandemic preparedness simulation in the fall of 2019, immediately before the pandemic was identified.[19] This exercise was called Event 201.

What is not as well-known is the content of Event 201's recommendations, provided by the Bill & Melinda Gates foundation and the WEF, for global public health organizations to follow in response to such a pandemic.[20] These recommendations came as live participants in the simulation described, "conspiracy theories that are around about the potential that pharmaceutical companies or the UN have released this [virus] for their own benefit." Another participant added that, "maybe it's time for us to showcase some cases where we are able to bring forward some bad actors and leave it before the courts to decide whether they have actually spread some fake news."

One would wonder, based on these real statements given by the actual people involved, whether this scenario was meant to simulate the North Korean government's response, given how illegal it would be in western countries like the US to put someone before a court for, "fake news." Back to the recommendations though, while each of the seven total recommendations can be thoroughly dissected, the most important one we will focus on here is recommendation #7. It reads as follows:

> *"Governments and the private sector should assign a greater priority to developing methods to combat misinformation and disinformation prior to the next pandemic response.*

Governments will need to partner with traditional and social media companies to research and develop nimble approaches to countering misinformation. **This will require developing the ability to flood media with fast, accurate, and consistent, information.** **Public health authorities should work with private employers and trusted community leaders such as faith leaders, to promulgate factual information to employees and citizens** (my emphasis). *Trusted, influential private-sector employers should create the capacity to readily and reliably augment public messaging, manage rumors and misinformation, and amplify credible information to support emergency public communications.* **National public health agencies should work in close collaboration with the World Health Organization to create the capability to rapidly develop and release consistent health messages. For their part, media companies should commit to ensuring that authoritative messages are prioritized and that false messages are suppressed including through the use of technology** (my emphasis). *"*

It should go without saying that the opposite of, "authoritative," is *not*, "false." Information can be *both* authoritative and false, as we've only just begun to demonstrate with Anthony Fauci. Yet, this recommendation by the Bill & Melinda Gates Foundation shows just how easy it is to pervert language in ones favor. As can be seen in the first bold section above, the Foundation openly ignores both laws against public/private collusion and corruption, as well as the separation of church and state (and business). These ideas fly in the face of foundational western principles and sovereignty in the name of a centralized, global power structure, as identified with the mention of World Health Organization (WHO) coordination.

I cannot tell you how many times over the past year and a half I have been asked, "but if there is global deceit behind this pandemic, then how is it all coordinated?" The aforementioned recommendation answers this question better than anything I can possibly think of. And we don't even have to assume bad-intent to get there. Let's just pretend, for now, that all these actions have just been a long series of tremendous mistakes. Would this degree of centralization of authority lend itself to *more* catastrophe for each erroneous decision made by such a global authority, or less? If the Netherlands prescribes the wrong treatment, for example, the world does not suffer the consequences of what the Netherlands previously deemed, "misinformation." If the WHO prescribes the wrong treatment, however, and the national public health agencies all work in close collaboration with it as the recommendation suggests, the entire world absolutely suffers the consequences of every mistake made by this handful of people. Later chapters will make painfully clear what those consequences have been.

Relevant questions now appear: who are those handful of people responsible for the fate of the world's health and who are ultimately (as seen above) controlling what can or can't be said or amplified in the public square? Who elected them? Who do they represent? Whose interests do they serve? What are the consequences of their failures? I will not answer any of these questions with speculation. My goal in this book is to make no claims whatsoever as to the intent of any of the actors in this story. What I am presenting is strictly means, motive, and opportunity, all of which are present in the case of Event 201 and should be, at minimum, understood by people and businesses who pay any mind to the opinions of these groups.

Besides the simulation itself being well-known at this point, it is also known that the Bill & Melinda Gates Foundation is the largest funder of the WHO, contributing more to the Organization's $4.84 billion biennial budget than any member-state government.[21] I will not get into the documented cases of past corruption by these groups here (though there are several), as this book is focused specifically on decisions made related to the Covid era. For more on the WHO though, one can watch the cited documentary, "TrustWHO," produced by Lilian Franck, and/or the documentary, "Who Is Bill Gates?" by James Corbett, for more on Gates' relationship with the WHO, the pharmaceutical industry, and even the media.[22] The nature of these conflicts of interest are certainly relevant to what is occurring today, so the background is valuable.

"Fact-Checking"

The final issue we will address in this chapter is the brand new, completely dystopian concept of, "fact-checking." The decade of the 2010's could be characterized accurately as involving a war for the internet. During this time period terms like, "fake news," rose to great prominence, as the onset of social media resulted in a mass congestion of information and clashing opinions. Polarization and confusion amplified over this time period to an extent which would have made ex-CIA director William Casey proud.[23] But I digress... As confusion increased, so too did a demand for truth. However, the, "fact-checking," blogs which resulted from this demand arguably made the problem significantly worse.

A primary theme we have discussed in this chapter is the dangers of a centralization of information. As we saw with Event 201, such control is readily attainable through financial conflicts of interest. So when considering the biases of any media, we must consider those conflicts. And they aren't hard to reason out: think of any commercial break you've ever seen on cable TV. How many of the advertisements are for pharmaceuticals, on average? If you're having a hard time remembering, here's a run-down of CNN's Q1 2018 spend for some of their top-15 advertisers[24]:

- Top-15 advertisers total revenue: $25.86M
- Pharmaceutical companies in top-15: $7.61M (29.4% of total)
    o Otezla (Amgen): $2.52M
    o Humira (Abbvie): $2.52M
    o Xarelto (Janssen): $1.31M
    o Harvoni (Gilead): $1.26M

Now, consider you were an executive at a corporate media outlet like CNN. Would you risk nearly 30% of your organization's revenue stream and your job, at the expense of your shareholders, in order to break a story on those pharmaceutical companies and potentially sever ties? Maybe you think you would, but for most people this isn't the case. And this is just for ads. How about paid posts? The following is an actual paid *Twitter* post on behalf of Pfizer by CNBC, a network which also purports to have some degree of journalistic integrity[25]:

> *"After delivering the first COVID-19 vaccine, Pfizer is uniquely positioned to advance mRNA, which could be a breakthrough for other infectious diseases, genetic diseases and cancer. cnb.cx/3A9txfN (Paid Post for @pfizer) #ad"*

And that's not all. Next there's sponsorships of the corporate, "news," shows themselves. The following are some of the shows sponsored by Pfizer alone, possibly the most significant player in the manufacturing of the Covid shots:

- Good Morning America
- CBS Health Watch
- Anderson Cooper 360
- ABC News Nightline
- Making a Difference
- CNN Tonight
- Early Start
- Erin Burnett Out Front
- This Week with George Stephanopolous
- Meet the Press
- CBS This Morning
- 60 Minutes

These same issues apply to an even greater degree as it relates to, "fact-checkers," which are just the newest perception-shifting instrument. An important question which arises from said instrument is: "Who Will Fact-Check the Fact-Checkers?" This question is answered in great detail by James Corbett in his investigative report of the same name.[26] To summarize some of James' findings:

- **Conflicts of Interest** – *Reuters* is part of the Thompson Reuters Corporation, which partners with the Bill & Melinda Gates Foundation on the Generation Africa Program 2020 and the Thompson Reuters Foundation. Africa Check, another, "fact-checking," site which frequently, "debunks," claims about Gates' well-documented (by Corbett in, "Who is Bill Gates?") escapades in Africa, is funded by the Bill & Melinda Gates Foundation and the Open Society Foundation. The International Fact-Checking Network is also funded by the Bill & Melinda Gates Foundation and the Open Society Foundation. Finally, "fact-checker," *Newsguard* was discovered to have been founded by prominent neo-conservative oligarchs such as Tom Ridge (Secretary of Homeland Security under George W. Bush) and retired

General Michael Hayden (former CIA director, NSA director, and principal at the Bush-tied Chertoff Group).

- **"Fact-checkers," tend to, "fact-check," selective bits of strawman claims** – an example provided by Corbett is, "fact-checks," on whether Event 201, "predicted," the SARS-COV-2 coronavirus pandemic, which is alleged to have broken out within weeks of the simulation event taking place. It is obviously irrelevant whether or not Event 201 discussed the specific pandemic pathogen, even if it *did* discuss a novel coronavirus. The timing of the Event 201 pandemic outbreak simulation coinciding exactly with what is believed to be a once-in-a-century pandemic outbreak is incredibly suspect, no matter what specific details were discussed. To, "fact-check," specifics is intentionally misleading, pointless, and demonstrates a bias on the part of the, "fact-checker."

- **"Fact-checkers," take actual, stated plans and "debunk" them** – an example of this comes from *Reuters*, who, "fact-checked," an apparent claim that Bill Gates plans on using, "microchip," implants to fight the coronavirus. Again, the intention to deflect and gaslight those who question an actual statement Bill Gates made about implants and certificates related to vaccines is clear. In the article itself *Reuters* even admits as much, when it acknowledges both a detectable quantum dot vaccine patch technology Gates *has* supported, and a *Reddit* AMA where Gates said, "eventually we will have some digital certificates to show who has recovered or been tested recently or when we have a vaccine, who has received it." These discriminatory goals identified by Gates' observers at the beginning of the pandemic are now clearly being implemented in real-time, and Gates continues to profit from all of them.[27]

- **Outright Falsity and/or Dishonesty**
  - In one of the most ironic of all, "fact-checks," *PolitiFact* on January 31, 2020, said it is *true* that, "the likelihood of people in the United States catching the virus is minimal," while calling *false* claims about, "the virus's source, conspiracies about its connection to biological warfare … information about its spread,

30

and misconceptions about how to treat it."[28] It is objectively impossible, based on the information available at the time, for *Politifact* to have known any of these things were true or false with any degree of certainty.

o "Expert," opinions were proven to not necessarily be, "facts," or, "truth," in an April 3, 2020 *Time Magazine* article, "correction," to previous article opinions on masks[29]: *"A previous version of this article was based on expert guidance at the time of publication, but as the Covid-19 pandemic has grown in the U.S. in recent weeks, public health thinking ... has changed."* What *Time Magazine* is admitting here is that the, "facts," (aka: the opinion of sources who *they* deem credible and who others are entitled to the autonomous discernment of deciding if they feel the same) have changed.

o Articles concluding, "mostly true," or, "half true," facts, which defy all logic and understanding of what the truth is[30]

o *MSN* published on January 1, 2021 that Bill Gates was trying to dim the sun ... then fact checked themselves 2 months later on March 3[31,32]

o Bill Adair, founder of *Politifact*, admitted the following about *Politifact*, "truth rankings"[33]: *"Yeah, we're human. We're making **subjective** (my emphasis) decisions. Lord knows the decision about a Truth-O-Meter rating is entirely subjective."* Thus, affirming *Politifact* is a subjective, entertainment platform.

o *Reuters* presented disagreement between scientists as, "misinformation," and sourced its, "fact checks," with an endless loop of its own, "fact checks."[34] It also slandered the scientist in question in the article as, "anti-vaxx," despite exhaustive claims regularly made by the same scientist that he is pro-vaccine.

o *Reuters* "fact-checkers," admitted they mischaracterized Pfizer/BioNtech, Moderna, and J&J inoculations as, "approved," when they were not approved, in an article about why they feel the inoculations are not experimental—an egregious error given the subject and the implications on mandates (to be discussed)[35]

- *The Independent*, November 4, 2021[36]: *"Fact Check: [Ron] DeSantis falsely claims vaccinated citizens without boosters could be declared unvaccinated and lose their jobs."* Countries like Israel had already taken up this practice months before.[37] And it took less than two weeks for Anthony Fauci to prove the Independent's, "fact-check," absurd in the case of the US as well[38]: *"... when we look back on this, we're going to see that boosters are essential for an optimal vaccine regimen."*

- Demonstrating time and time again these are biased political bodies incapable of determining, "fact," the *Washington Post* in August 2021 also went after popular authoritarian target, Ron DeSantis, claiming his description of Covid as seasonal was, "misleading," according to, "experts."[39] By January 2022 however, the *Washington Post* supported the previously, "misleading," idea of seasonal Covid, without any mention of how the aforementioned, "experts," were wrong.[40]

These types of articles can be picked apart for days. The point of this chapter is not to do that, but to simply demonstrate how dissent is discredited in a lazy fashion by media lackeys, as opposed to taking place in a scientific debate amongst experts. By December 2021 this was even admitted to by *Facebook* itself, which reportedly defended itself in court by claiming the, "fact-check," labels it uses are protected **opinion** under the first amendment.[41] This is a strange defense, considering the company also represents itself as an open platform and therefore not subject to liability as a publisher of said opinions. But we've already established that the government freely admits to working with *Facebook* to violate the free speech of dissenters, so it cannot be expected at this point to enforce the law at the company's expense.

At the expense of respect for the intelligence of the people these efforts shamelessly attempt to propagandize, the, "fact-checking," continues. And the hilarious desperation of those involved was ever so evident in a January 2022 piece in *Poynter*, titled, "An open letter to YouTube's CEO from the world's fact-checkers."[42] I personally cannot even fathom the level of narcissism necessary for people to brand themselves, "the world's fact-checkers." But this is what we live with today—a group of people who if they were not knowingly and intentionally pushing an agenda, would simply be considered a bunch of self-aggrandizing sociopaths who become more of a laughing stock to the sane by the day.

The thing of it is however, that they *are* pushing an agenda. An analysis by Raheem Kassam on the organization behind this open letter revealed its member groups suffer from partisanship and transparency issues, with an undisclosed amount of funding coming from *Google*.[43] Editors/contributors were also hard or impossible to find any background at all on, with one fact-check-cited doctor having no relevant online footprint whatsoever. Still, the, "fact-checks," published by these front groups are used by the social media companies in a type of information laundering effort, to push otherwise reprehensible ideas.

One such example which prompted Kassam's investigation was when he was, "fact-checked," on an article he shared by *Forbes* which—in the spirit of censorship and dissent crushing—discussed the idea of using psychoactive drugs to, "make people more likely to adhere to social norms such as wearing masks and adhering to social distancing guidelines." The, "fact-checkers," simply referred to the *Forbes* article having been revised and claimed the Forbes author didn't actually support the mass-drugging of the population.[44] However, this concept of, "mortality pills," *was* nonetheless a real proposition posited by a so-called, "bioethicist."[45] Such things revealed the lengths to which Covid narrative supporters were willing to go to enforce their will during this time, which the, "fact-checkers," primary mission was clearly to cover for in any way possible.

In summary, one would think we would want to hear from people who disagree. In order to make an informed decision, we would need to know why they have such a different opinion on a subject as important as what we put in our bodies. Science, of course, is simply a method of observation and experimentation, with conclusions drawn from said observation. So a time such as this would be the most important imaginable for a public debate on the methods and conclusions drawn. Instead, bloggers who receive funding from oligarchs slandered (as demonstrated) and spun dishonest narratives. These narratives were then used as a justification by officials for the exact purpose of preventing the full, scientific debate in favor of pushing an agenda. The result was actual, credentialed doctors having their opinions stifled by untouchable bureaucrats, and the cost (which we will tally in great detail in the next few chapters) of that stifling has and will continue to devastate human health well into the future.

Endnotes

1   Freiburger, Calvin. 2021. "Biden Admin Admits It Tells Facebook What To Censor: 'They're Killing People' - Lifesite". *Lifesite*. https://www.lifesitenews.com/news/biden-admin-admits-it-tells-facebook-what-to-censor-theyre-killing-people/.

2   "In 1967, The CIA Created The Label "Conspiracy Theorists"". 2015. *Global Freedom Movement*. https://www.globalfreedommovement.org/in-1967-the-cia-created-the-label-conspiracy-theorists/.

3   Myers, Fraser. 2020. "Why Has Google Censored The Great Barrington Declaration?". *Spiked-Online.Com*. https://www.spiked-online.com/2020/10/12/why-has-google-censored-the-great-barrington-declaration/.

4   Yang, Ethan. 2020. "Reddit's Censorship Of The Great Barrington Declaration". *AIER*. https://www.aier.org/article/reddits-censorship-of-the-great-barrington-declaration/.

5   Tucker, Jeffrey. 2021. "Twitter Censors Famed Epidemiologist Martin Kulldorff". *AIER*. https://www.aier.org/article/twitter-censors-famed-epidemiologist-martin-kulldorff/.

6   "Linkedin Censors Harvard Epidemiologist Martin Kulldorff". 2021. *Brownstone Institute*. https://brownstone.org/articles/linkedin-censors-harvard-epidemiologist-martin-kulldorff/.

7   Koutsobinas, Nick. 2021. "MRNA Vaccine Pioneer: Silenced By Big Tech". *Newsmax*. https://www.https://www.newsmax.com/newsfront/robertmalone-covid19-bigtech-censorship/2021/07/03/id/1027367/.

8   Barkoukis, Leah. 2021. "'The Single Most Qualified' Mrna Expert Censored After Discussing Concerns Over Vaccines". *Townhall*. https://www.townhall.com/tipsheet/leahbarkoukis/2021/06/24/the-single-most-qualified-mrna-expert-censored-after-discussing-concerns-over-vaccine-n2591500.

9   "Footage Of Reputable Medical Doctors Now Being Censored!". 2022. *Prageru.Com*. Accessed February 26. https://www.prageru.com/petition/doctors.

10 "Dr. Bowden Resigns After Hospital Attacks Her For Prescribing Ivermectin". 2021. *MN Freedom Action Network.* https://www.mnfan.org/2021/11/17/dr-bowden-resigns-after-hospital-attacks-her-for-prescribing-ivermectin/.

11 Murphy, James. 2022. "Maine Physician Suspended, Ordered To Undergo Psych Evaluation After Prescribing Ivermectin, HCQ". *The New American.* https://thenewamerican.com/maine-physician-suspended-ordered-to-undergo-psych-evaluation-after-prescribing-ivermectin-hcq/.

12 Peters, Stew. 2021. "Doctors THREATENED, Forced To Support "Vaccine" Narrative". *Red Voice Media.* https://www.redvoicemedia.com/2021/09/doctors-threatened-forced-to-support-vaccine-narrative/.

13 "Censored Scientists: Dr. Andrew Kaufman". 2020. *Internet Archive.* https://archive.org/details/censored-scientists-dr-andrew-kaufman.

14 "Youtube Admits To Censoring 1 Million+ Videos For COVID 'Misinformation'". 2021. *Headline USA.* https://www.headlineusa.com/youtube-censor-1m-videos-covid/.

15 "The Fauci Flip-Flop". 2021. *Rumble.* https://www.rumble.com/vm0wp7-the-great-fauci-flip-flop.html.

16 Stewart, Callie. 2016. "Seven Dangerous Medications The FDA Should Never Have Approved". *All That's Interesting.* https://allthatsinteresting.com/fda-mistakes.

17 "Trials Of War Criminals Before The Nuremberg Military Tribunals Under Control Council Law No. 10". 1949. *U.S. Government Printing Office* 2: 181-182.

18 Watson, Paul. 2021. "People In UK Who Post "False Information" About Vaccines Could Be Jailed For Two Years". *Summit.News.* https://summit.news/2021/11/01/people-in-uk-who-post-false-information-about-vaccines-could-be-jailed-for-two-years/.

19 "About Event 201, A High-Level Pandemic Exercise On October 18, 2019". 2019. *Event 201.* https://www.centerforhealthsecurity.org/event201/about.

20 "Public-Private Cooperation For Pandemic Preparedness And Response". 2019. *Event 201.* https://www.centerforhealthsecurity.org/event201/recommendations.html.

21 Mercola, Joseph. 2021. "New Documentary On WHO Exposes Widespread Corruption, Massive Funding By Bill Gates". *Children's Health Defense.* https://www.childrenshealthdefense.org/defender/trustwho-documentary-who-corruption-funding-bill-gates/.

22 Corbett, James. 2022. "Who Is Bill Gates? (Full Documentary, 2020)". *The Corbett Report - Open Source Intelligence News.* https://www.corbettreport.com/who-is-bill-gates-full-documentary-2020/.

23 "ASL. Primary Sources For Quote Attributed To William Casey". 2022. *An Apocalyptic Synthesis.* Accessed February 26. https://www.amallulla.org/casey/.

24 Ariens, Chris. 2018. "Here's How Much Ad Revenue The Cable Networks Bring In From Their Biggest Advertisers". *Adweek.Com.* https://www.adweek.com/tvnewser/heres-how-much-ad-revenue-the-cable-networks-bring-in-from-their-biggest-advertisers/361164/.

25 "The Shocking Truth: Pfizer Openly Bankrolling Pro-Vaccine Mainstream Media". 2021. *The Shocking Truth.* https://www.theshockingtruth.tv/health/covid-19/pfizer-openly-bankrolling-pro-vaccine-mainstream-media/.

26 Corbett, James. 2020. "Who Will Fact Check The Fact Checkers?". *The Corbett Report - Open Source Intelligence News.* https://www.corbettreport.com/who-will-fact-check-the-fact-checkers/.

27 "Bill Gates' Coronavirus Conflicts Of Interest". 2020. *World Tribune: U.S. Politics And Culture, Geopolitics, East Asia Intelligence, China, Geostrategy, Military, National Security, Corporate Watch, Media Watch, North Korea, Iran, Columnists: Dennis Prager, Michelle Malkin, John Metzler, Jeffrey Kuhner, John Mcnabb, Joe Schaeffer, Bill Juneau, Alexander Maistrovoy, Donald Kirk.* https://www.worldtribune.com/bill-gates-coronavirus-conflicts-of-interest/.

28 Funke, Daniel. 2020. "A Reader's Guide To Misinformation About The Coronavirus". *Politifact.* https://www.politifact.com/article/2020/jan/31/readers-guide-misinformation-about-coronavirus/.

29 Gajanan, Mahita. 2020. "Can Face Masks Prevent Coronavirus? Experts Say That Depends". *Time.* https://www.time.com/5774521/coronavirus-face-mask-prevention/.

30 Berezow, Alex. 2019. "Debunkers Debunked: Who Fact-Checks The Fact-Checkers?". *American Council On Science And Health.* https://www.acsh.org/news/2019/11/04/debunkers-debunked-who-fact-checks-fact-checkers-14378.

31 Beaman, Jeremy. 2021. "Bill Gates Is Trying To Dim The Sun". *Internet Archive Waybackmachine.* https://web.archive.org/web/20210107085137/https://www.msn.com/en-us/weather/topstories/bill-gates-is-trying-to-dim-the-sun/ar-BB1coXrR.

32 Murdock, Jason. 2021. "Fact check: is Bill Gates trying to block the sun". *Msn.Com.* https://www.msn.com/en-us/news/technology/fact-check-is-bill-gates-trying-to-block-the-sun/ar-BB1ea74y.

33 Lucas, Barbara. 2017. "Dishonest Fact-Checkers". *Capitalresearch.Org.* https://www.capitalresearch.org/article/dishonest-fact-checkers/.

34 "Fact Check-Fact Check: Ex-Pfizer Scientist Repeats COVID-19 Vaccine Misinformation In Recorded Speech". 2021. *Reuters.* https://www.reuters.com/article/factcheck-health-coronavirus-idUSL2N2N72CS.

35 "CORRECTED-Fact Check- COVID-19 Vaccines Are Not Experimental And They Have Not Skipped Trial Stages". 2021. *Reuters.* https://www.reuters.com/article/factcheck-covid-vaccines-idUSL1N2M70MW.

36   Feinberg, Andrew. 2021. "Fact Check: Desantis Falsely Claims Vaccinated Citizens Without Boosters Could Be Declared Unvaccinated And Lose Their Jobs". *News.Yahoo.Com.* https://news.yahoo.com/fact-check-desantis-falsely-claims-230846893.html.

37   "Israel Will No Longer Consider Double-Vaxxed 'Vaccinated' - Only Triple-Vaxxed -". 2021. *Weliveinamadworld.Com.* https://weliveinamadworld.com/israel-will-no-longer-consider-double-vaxxed-vaccinated-only-triple-vaxxed/.

38   O'Neill, Jesse. 2021. "Fauci Says COVID Booster Might Be New Standard For Fully Vaccinated". *Nypost.Com.* https://nypost.com/2021/11/17/fauci-says-covid-booster-might-be-new-standard-for-fully-vaccinated/.

39   Kornfield, Meryl. 2021. "Desantis Blames Florida's Surge On 'Covid Season.' That's Misleading, Experts Say.". *The Washington Post.* https://www.washingtonpost.com/health/2021/08/13/desantis-covid-season/.

40   Patel, Kasha. 2022. "Covid-19 May Have Seasons For Different Temperature Zones, Study Suggests". *The Washington Post.* https://www.washingtonpost.com/weather/2022/01/28/covid-seasons-temperature-humidity-study/.

41   "Facebook Admits The Truth: 'Fact Checks' Are Really Just (Lefty) Opinion". 2021. *Nypost.Com.* https://nypost.com/2021/12/14/facebook-admits-the-truth-fact-checks-are-really-just-lefty-opinion/.

42   "An Open Letter To Youtube's CEO From The World's Fact-Checkers". 2022. *Poynter.* https://www.poynter.org/fact-checking/2022/an-open-letter-to-youtubes-ceo-from-the-worlds-fact-checkers/.

43   Kassam, Raheem. 2022. "A Google-Funded 'Fact Check' Team Appears To Be A Handful Of Potentially Non-Existent Indians In An Impoverished Town Near Bangladesh.". *Raheemkassam.Substack.Com.* https://raheemkassam.substack.com/p/a-google-funded-fact-check-team-appears?utm_source=url.

44   "Forbes Edits COVID 'Morality Pill' Article Following National Pulse Report.". 2022. *The National Pulse..* https://thenationalpulse.com/2022/02/09/forbes-corrects-covid-morality-pill-article/.

45   Crutchfield, Parker. 2020. "'Morality Pills' May Be The US's Best Shot At Ending The Coronavirus Pandemic, According To One Ethicist". *The Conversation.* https://theconversation.com/morality-pills-may-be-the-uss-best-shot-at-ending-the-coronavirus-pandemic-according-to-one-ethicist-142601.

Chapter 4

Masks

"They've [public health bureaucrats] *got a personal kind of agenda; they make up their own rules as they go; they change them when they want to and they smugly—like Tony Fauci does not mind going on television in front of the people who pay his salary and lie directly into the camera."*

—Kary Mullis[1]

Anthony Fauci was appointed Director of the National Institute of Allergy and Infectious Diseases (NIAID), a unit of the NIH, in 1984.[2] According to the Institute, over the course of his career he has advised seven Presidents on a variety of public health issues. Fauci has also been in this position over the majority of the life of the CDC, an organization which has existed in some form since July 1, 1946, for the nominal purpose of disease control and prevention.[3] While for now we will focus on Fauci, the CDC and public health organizations all over the world have run in parallel, lock-step fashion during the Covid era.

The year 2020 was the 36th year of Anthony Fauci's directorship in combatting these types of infectious diseases. By this point in any person's career, one would think someone like Fauci would be well aware of a standard, basic set of actions which he would recommend people take during any pandemic. And in a pre-Covid May 22, 2019 *Bloomberg* interview, it appeared he was[4]:

"Interviewer: *'And the best way for me to prevent getting an infectious disease and having to have you as my doctor is what? Wearing a mask? Um—'*
Fauci: [laughing] *'No-no-no-no-no.'*
Interviewer: *'If somebody's—I can see they're getting ready to sneeze or cough—walk away?'*
Fauci: *'You avoid all the paranoid aspects and do something positive. A – good diet; B – you don't smoke, I know; I know you don't drink—at least not very much—so that's pretty good; Get some exercise—I know you don't get as much exercise as you should; get good sleep.* **I think the normal,**

low tech, healthy things are the best thing that you can do, David, to stay healthy *(my emphasis)."*

Unfortunately though, once 2020 arrived, it seems Fauci second-guessed and reversed every single thing he'd known and previously recommended about the actions people should take during such an event. And masks, which above we can see he actually *laughed* at the notion of, were one major example.

> "Fauci: *'Right now in the United States people should not be walking around with masks.'*
> Interviewer: *'You're sure of it? Cause people are listening really closely to this.'*
> Fauci: *'No—right now people should not be—there's no reason to be walking around with a mask. When you're in the middle of an outbreak, wearing a mask might make people feel a little bit better and it might even block a droplet. But it's not providing the perfect protection that people think that it is. And often, there are unintended consequences—people keep fiddling with the mask and they keep touching their face.'*
> Interviewer: *'And can you get some sort of ... schmutz sort of staying inside there?'*
> Fauci: ***'Of course—of course*** *(my emphasis). But when you think masks, you should think of healthcare providers needing them and people who are ill."*
> —Anthony Fauci, March 8, 2020[5]

> "... *I wear it for the reason that I believe it is effective. It's not 100% effective. It's sort of—**respect for another person and have that other person respect you*** *(my emphasis). You wear a mask, they wear a mask, you protect each other. I mean, I do it when I'm in the public for the reasons that, A – I want to protect myself and protect others, and also because I want to make it be for people to see that that's the kind of thing that you should be doing."*
> —Anthony Fauci, May 27, 2020[6]

> "You're using the word 'mandating masks' – yes, if that works, let's do it. I don't think it's gonna happen nationally. If it doesn't happen nationally—the reason is because it might—

it may not come from the White House to do it. And if it doesn't then I think that the mayors and the governors should do it."
—Anthony Fauci, October 2020[7]

"So if you have a physical covering with one layer, you put another layer on—it just makes common sense that it likely would be more effective and that's the reason why you see people either double masking or doing a version of an N-95."
—Anthony Fauci, January 25, 2021[8]

"... it is conceivable that as we go on a year or two more from now that during certain seasonal periods when you have respiratory borne viruses like the flu, people might actually elect to wear masks to diminish the likelihood you'll spread these respiratory borne diseases."
—Anthony Fauci, May 9, 2021[9]

For anyone else in such a leadership position during trying times, this would be viewed as a complete failure, no matter which position a person takes on masks. For example, if you believe they work, Fauci failed to recognize them right off the bat as a standard practice. In fact, with Fauci eventually suggesting masks should be a permanent, if seasonal, garment for cold/flu prevention too, one has to wonder why he was laughing off the notion of wearing them at all in 2019. If, on the other hand, you agree with Fauci's opinion during the *first* 36 years of his career—namely, that masks are counterintuitive—then he obviously failed in even grander fashion by reversing course on all of his, "positive," recommendations.

Despite this obviously dishonest failure from all perspectives, however, Fauci has been incessantly propagandized as a kind of untouchable high priest (more on that later). And since, as we can see in the quotes above, Fauci is clearly the opposite of, "the only one saying facts," as he claims to be, we will take it upon ourselves next to actually make sense of the history and differing perspectives people have on masks.[10]

Bacteria, Chemicals, and Other Things to Not Inhale

In 2008 the NIH published a paper, co-written by Anthony Fauci, in which it claimed the, "majority of deaths during the influenza pandemic of 1918-1919 were not caused by the influenza virus acting

41

alone … Instead, most victims succumbed to bacterial pneumonia following influenza virus infection."[11] According to Fauci himself, "… bacteria delivered the knockout punch." Also, per the CDC, "a common cause of bacterial pneumonia is the bacteria Streptococcus pneumoniae (pneumococcus)."[12]

So with these two official public health opinions in mind, we turn to a story about a group of parents in Florida who sent their kids' face masks to a lab for analysis.[13] The analysis of the masks detected streptococcus pneumoniae, among many other germs associated with a variety of illnesses. This analysis was also confirmed by the experiments of mask-wearing *proponents*. According to local news station WDBJ 7, their team took a trip to Virginia-Maryland College of Veterinary Medicine to test, "how many bacteria are trapped by masks?"[14] Alongside two scientists, director of facilities Peter Jobst and department head of biomedical sciences and pathology Margie Lee, the team coughed into Petri dishes with and without masks. After two days, they then checked the dishes for bacteria growth. Predictably, they found the unmasked Petri dishes to contain bacteria growth, with none in the mask-covered dishes. However, this experiment was ended here with no mention of viral transfer (the intended purpose of mask-wearing in the Covid era) and the conclusion that the masks, "work," because they trapped the spread of bacteria.

Why didn't the scientists check to see how much bacteria was trapped and growing on the *inside* of the mask? Why didn't they wonder whether or not it was a good thing to trap exhaled bacteria right before one's mouth only to be continuously re-inhaled? The otherwise inexplicable questions of how and why such willful incompetence and/or deceit took place will be addressed at length later in this book. But the reality is the harmful effects of mask-wearing have been known since the year of the 1918 Spanish Flu itself, when newspapers headlines such as that from the *Santa Barbara Daily News* read, "Mask is Chief Ally of 'Flu' Physicians Declare: Average Person Doesn't Know How to Take Care of Mask and It Becomes Veritable Bacteria Incubator."[15]

So, when taking the words of the NIH that the, "majority of deaths," during the Spanish Flu were ultimately, "delivered," by bacterial pneumonia, alongside these logical observations and additional studies that masks build up bacteria like streptococcus pneumoniae, as well as doctors who directly affirm the connection between masks and bacterial pneumonia, it becomes clear that masking is a completely counterintuitive measure to take to prevent death and should have been identified as such from the beginning of the Covid era.[16,17]

Bacterial build up is also confirmed as medical professionals cite it as the cause of several other unintended, embarrassing consequences of masking. Miranda Mellos, for example, a registered nurse in a level 2 trauma center emergency department, said, "when you are breathing out in a mask, the bacteria from your mouth gets trapped."[18] Without proper hygiene, which is essentially guaranteed for implementing and mandating a new practice billions worldwide are untrained in, masks are therefore admitted by Mellos to cause acne breakouts, bad breath, tooth decay, gum inflammation, rashes, and even contraction of the illnesses they're intended to prevent.

The case against wearing a mask over your mouth is also made increasingly dire when considering the materials a face mask is comprised of. For example, evidence has been gathered by scientists that masks which are on sale and being used by members of the general public are laced with toxic, cancer-causing chemicals and don't necessarily meet safety standards.[19] These compounds include:

- Formaldehyde – a chemical known to cause watery eyes, burning in the eyes, nose and throat, coughing, wheezing, and nausea
- Aniline – a known carcinogen which is considered both a health and environmental hazard[20]
- Cobalt – a known carcinogen which can cause a variety of health complications[21]
- Hazardous Fluorocarbons[22]
- Optical Brighteners – a chemical considered to cause environmental hazard, with some ties to allergy aggravation[23]
- 2-Butanone Oxime – a known carcinogen
- Acetaldehyde – a probable carcinogen which can cause a variety of health issues[24]
- Microfibers – mid to long term mask use (longer than a single-use), "promotes both fiber abrasion and encourages bacterial colonization over time." Tests find that microfiber abrasion in

43

some masks can be classified as, "hazardous dust," by German Social Accident Insurance.

The dangers of these chemicals is exacerbated by the focus on, "mandating," the use of masks and the complete lack of any effort by public health organizations to caveat the risks of improper use, which we have demonstrated to this point are many. For example, a common argument might be that, "surgeons and doctors wear masks." However, this does not address the following:

1. No surgeon or doctor ever thought it useful to continue wearing their mask in their daily life before, despite the ever-present cold and flu. If there were no negative consequences to mask-wearing at all, why would they *not* have done this their whole lives? What would've been the harm?
2. Surgeons, in particular, but also doctors, do not always wear masks on the job. The primary time they wear masks is when and because they're around open wounds and can be subject to bodily secretions. The usefulness in this situation is to prevent contamination/infection of a wound via the primary source of projectile while a surgeon works: the nose and mouth. After such a surgery a mask would then be discarded.
3. Surgeons and doctors do not, for the safety reasons mentioned above, re-wear masks, nor do they wear a single-use mask long term. Mandating of indefinite mask use encourages the exact opposite behavior.
4. Mass single-use masking is neither a viable or desirable practice, as even at current mid-long term use practices, as an estimated 1.56 billion face masks have entered oceans in 2020, per Oceans Asia.[25] While on a recent vacation in Charleston, South Carolina I even personally witnessed at least 5 separate masks laying in the road—*on a single city block*.

The Psychology of Masks

What we've named so far are only the physical dangers associated with masks. There are also a variety of psychological issues masks are known to cause. The following studies and citations demonstrate this psychological impact:

- Per a 2020 study by van der Westhuizen et al. in the *BMJ*, face-masking[26]:
  - *"can provoke an increase in stress hormones with a negative impact on immune resilience in the long term"*
  - *"prevents the mirroring of facial expressions, a process that facilitates empathetic connections and trust between pupils and teachers"*
  - Lack of mirroring, *"potentially leads to a significant increase in socio-psychological stress ... Several studies show that long-term exposure to socio-psychological stress leaves neuro-epigenetic scars that are difficult to cure in young people and often escalate into mental behavioral problems and a weakened immune system."*
  - And given the objective of masking is to prevent respiratory illness, the practice is revealed to be increasingly counter-intuitive as researchers show a, *"relationship between the increase in stress experiences and the risk of upper respiratory tract infections and mortality."*
  - This being done, again, to an age bracket of approximately 100M in the US, which experienced 412 deaths total attributed to Covid in a year and eight months[27]
- Per the Organization for Autism Research, autistic children face particularly significant problems with mask wearing.[28] Despite these problems, which are both mental and physiological, public health organizations have failed to take a stand in defense of even this most obvious of exceptional classes. As a result, autistic parents in the Covid era have seen their doctors deny them exemption forms for their children, who have been inhumanely kicked out of school, airplanes, and stores as a result.
- Per a 2002 study by Dyer in the *BMJ*, prisoners at Guantanamo Bay were shown in photos to have been subject to torture tactics which included wearing surgical masks.[29] According to Dr. Duncan Forrest of UK-based charity the Medical

Foundation for the Care of Victims of Torture, tactics such as this constitute sensory deprivation, "bordering on torture," which, "could cause immediate and lasting psychological symptoms akin to post-traumatic stress disorder…"

- Per retired Lieutenant Colonel and best-selling author Dave Grossman, masks are used in wartime to create a sense of anonymity for an aggressor, while dehumanizing the victim.[30] In his experience they prevent empathy, empower violence, and lead to violence.

- Jaclyn Theek, clinic director at the Speech and Learning Institute, reported a, "364% increase in patient referrals of babies and toddlers," who were speech delayed during the Covid era.[31] According to Theek, masks are, "most definitely a factor," due to the inability of the child to observe the masked adult's face, which is necessary to help them pick up on speech patterns. This demographic increased from 5% of her patient population pre-Covid, to 20% during the Covid era.

As seen above, perhaps the most inhumane cowardice surrounding mask mandates has come from the masking of children. Several politicians including New York Governor Kathy Hochul and Georgia political figure Stacey Abrams took disgusting public relations photos in classrooms, smiling mask-less in rooms full of masked children.[32,33] The psychological abuse associated with these political stunts represents an unconscionable attack on an entire generation, many of whom will suffer mental consequences for the rest of their lives. And even at a young age, some of them are already well aware of the atrocity which has been committed against them.

One brave 8-year-old girl in Florida, for example, was suspended 38 times for exercising her right to not have her breathing hole covered and spoke up to the vile cowards on her school board for this injustice.[34] Another 10-year-old boy made an impassioned plea about the absurdity of being forced to wear a mask while, "outside at PE [physical education] and on track."[35] These are two among several other examples of children who will not otherwise be remembered for it, but did, in fact, demonstrate heroic courage during a time their elders were willing to condemn them to an evil fate. And make no mistake about it—I use the word, "absurd," frequently, but this was *not* done out of mere stupidity. This was cowardice, this was greed (as we will later prove), and this was evil. Those defining traits were reflected well in the sarcastic words of one Illinois student, who rightfully ridiculed the betrayal her school board committed on her and her fellow students as follows[36]:

> *"Thank you for teaching students that our own mental health is much less important than making triple-vaccinated adults feel safe.*
>
> *Thank you for teaching me that even the most minute risk is not worth taking. Life is best when you take the path of least resistance with no chance of failure and definitely no chance of catching a cold.*
>
> *Thank you for not reaching out to the students to see how we feel about masks, because if you did the majority of students would say that they hate masks and then you might second-guess your decision to make us wear them.*
>
> *Thank you for allowing me to experience the anxiety of never seeing facial expressions.*
>
> *Thank you for teaching us that we should never question authority or think critically, but instead we should follow whatever the people in charge tell us to do—obedience is best. I realize now that thinking for yourself is overrated and not really necessary when you could just make decisions based on fear.*
>
> *Thank you for pushing your irrational anxieties and fears on me, because I didn't already have enough to worry about. I realize now how easy I had it when I only had to worry about my classes, my grades, the SAT, and getting into college.*
>
> *Thank you for teaching me that being a morally superior person only requires that I cover my face for eight hours a day, and that the most morally superior people wear two masks, or even three masks.*
>
> *As you know, states around us—Indiana, Wisconsin, Iowa, Michigan, and Minnesota—which have two and half times more students than Illinois—don't force kids to mask. I'm with you though: these states are out of control, recklessly putting kids at risk of misery and death every day. Masks work, even if these states have the same outcomes as Illinois.*

Speaking of data, thank you for staying silent about masking despite the fact that Covid has a very high survival rate in kids my age. Who needs data though? We all know it will never be safe to see anyone's face ever again."

I include this entire quote because these people deserve the most aggressive of ridicule. To go on a side tangent for a moment, it has been worse than infuriating to watch their irrational fear of death used as a justification to abuse those who choose not to live in fear. Instead of encouraging people to make their own decisions about risk tolerance and leaving the rest to fate, they cheered for state-enforced hypochondria on everyone else, no matter how little they could support their insane position. They screamed in people's mask-free faces, called for their discrimination at stores including to eat, and worst of all, abused children. As someone who has stood opposed to this evil from the outset, it has taken everything in me to wish anything but vengeance upon these lost, child-abusing charlatans. But I know God will see to justice being done in the long run. And until then—or until those who did behave this way acknowledge their actions and apologize—I, for one, will continue to do everything in my power to ensure my family is not dependent on a single one of them for anything in the future. But I digress…

Perhaps one of the most important long term issues surrounding masks comes from German Dr. Margarite Griesz-Brisson MD, PhD, who is a Consultant Neurologist and Neurophysiologist with a PhD in neurotoxicity, environmental medicine, neuro-regeneration, and neuroplasticity, and who is not alone among neurologists sounding the same alarm on masks mandates.[37,38] In a video posted to (and subsequently, inexplicably banned from) *YouTube* in mid-2020, she stated her opinion as follows[39]:

"The re-inhalation of our exhaled air will without a doubt create oxygen deficiency and a flood of carbon dioxide. We know that the human brain is very sensitive to oxygen deprivation. There are nerve cells, for example, in the hippocampus, that can't be longer than 3 minutes without oxygen – they cannot survive. The acute warning symptoms are headaches, drowsiness, dizziness, issues in concentration,

slowing down of reaction time – reactions of the cognitive system.

However, when you have chronic oxygen deprivation, all of those symptoms disappear, because you get used to it. But your efficiency will remain impaired and the under supply of oxygen in your brain continues to progress. We know neurodegenerative diseases take years to decades to develop. If today you forget your phone number, the breakdown in your brain would have already started 20 or 30 years ago.

... The second problem is that the nerve cells in your brain are unable to divide themselves normally. So in case our governments will generously allow us to get rid of the masks and go back to breathing oxygen freely again in a few months, the lost nerve cells will no longer be regenerated. What is gone is gone.

*... **There is no unfounded medical exemption from face masks because oxygen deprivation is very dangerous for every single brain. It must be a free decision of every human being whether they want to wear a mask** (my emphasis)."*

Dr. Griesz-Brisson goes on to discuss how devastating masks will be for the long term physiological development of children— another crime continuing to be forced upon an entire generation of completely riskless people on a daily basis—and how, "oxygen deprivation damages every single organ," in the body.

In an almost comically insulting bit of the, "fact-checking," propaganda we discussed earlier, "fact-check," site *AFP* cites, "experts," in claiming Dr. Griesz-Brisson has been, "debunked."[40] But not only did the professional liar who authored this blog post demonstrate the audacity to suggest the *actual opinion of an actual doctor* was, "debunked," they even went as low, as immature, and as threatening as to show a picture of Dr. Griesz-Brisson with a red, "X," through it. Considering Dr. Griesz-Brisson undeniably *is* an expert, the title of the blog post could just as easily be, "Experts Say Wearing Face Masks Causes Neurological Damage," and it would still be true. In fact, if an actual journalist sought to do their job and not intentionally mislead their readers, they might title their blog post, "Experts Disagree on Whether Face Masks Cause Neurological

49

Damage." *AFP*, however, like we've seen with an endless supply of, "fact-checking," blogs, does not fall into this category.

Furthermore, to call what *AFP* did a, "debunking," is equally silly. Again, *AFP* simply highlights a difference of opinion held by a physician named Philipp Lepper. Imagine going for a second opinion at a doctor and calling the second opinion a, "fact-check." That's what the *AFP* dishonestly does as a business model. In reality, Lepper's entire point is refuted in the *AFP*'s own blog post, when Chief Hospital Physician Dominic Dellweg says:

> *"The mask provides additional resistance for our breathing. Our respiratory muscles have to work harder to breathe the air through the mask. It can be uncomfortable and even cause shortness of breath.*
> *This is not an expression of an insufficient supply of oxygen to the body ... This increased exertion is reported to the brain as shortness of breath via receptors in the respiratory muscles, although the values for oxygen and carbon dioxide are in the normal range."*

The argument Dellweg gives here to oppose the point of reduced oxygen is extremely strange. First of all, according to Mayo Clinic, one of the causes of Hypoxemia (below-normal levels of oxygen in the blood) is the inability of the lungs to inhale the oxygen-containing air.[41] This is exactly the process Dellweg describes when he says the, "respiratory muscles have to work harder to breath the air through the mask." Perhaps what he means is that this struggle does not *imply* a lack of oxygen in the body, which is fair, considering a physically exerted person simply breaths more heavily to compensate for increased oxygen need. However, if a physically exerted person were to continue exercising for say, eight hours, their ability to continue getting the air flow they need, and thus, the oxygen, would obviously worsen over time. Wearing a mask and further inhibiting the breathing process on an ongoing basis would serve as the same needless strain, which Dellweg seems to agree with. And it is not denied whatsoever that masks increase the risk of such oxygen-inhibiting lung injuries, as even avid mask-proponent the Health-Site admits the dangers of exercising with a mask on and highlights a story about a misguided man whose lungs collapsed as a result of doing so.[42]

Scientific Reasoning for Why Masks Do Not Prevent Anything

To go deeper on Lepper's points, *AFP*'s resident expert presents a glaring issue with their own mask-favoring narrative, when they explain how, "air flows freely through the mask." In making this claim, Lepper says that, "the pore size of medical mouth and nose masks is around 100,000 to 1,000,000 times larger than an oxygen molecule." Therefore, he claims, it is impossible for the mask to prevent the flow of oxygen.

So let's review this claim and understand its implications. According to the NIH, the pore size of masks ranges from 80 to 500 micrometers.[43] We will assume Lepper's claim that an oxygen particle is 260 picometers (0.00026 micrometers) is accurate. In this case, he would be correct that oxygen particles are significantly smaller than mask pores, as there are 1,000,000 picometers in a micrometer. However, if he is correct that this means there will be no stagnation of oxygen flow, this would also imply that wearing masks to stop viral transfer is pointless, since SARS-COV-2 is claimed to range from 50 to 140 nanometers (0.05 to 0.14 micrometers, also much smaller than mask pore size).[44] To summarize, if Lepper is right, masks can't stop oxygen intake *or* viral transfer and are therefore pointless. If Lepper is wrong on the other hand, masks could inhibit some degree of oxygen intake and viral transfer, which would cause more harm than good in human bodies which need oxygen to prevent the host of issues previously mentioned (including respiratory illness!).

However, Stanford University researchers found N-95 masks *do actually* reduce oxygen intake, by anywhere from 5 to 20 percent.[45] So this contradicts Lepper's point on oxygen stagnation being impossible, since N-95 masks have a 0.1 to 0.3 micrometer pore size (still much larger than an oxygen molecule).[46] A 5 to 20 percent reduction in oxygen over the long term is a surefire way to break down and destroy a human body. Still, after two years of violating human rights with cloth, surgical, and/or N-95 mask mandates, N-95 masks have become the official CDC pivot policy recommendation in 2022.[47] This is because the futility of cloth and surgical masks has been, "re-discovered," and they've been admitted as having been pointless, "facial decorations," by Fauci and the same Covid collaborators who knew this to be true before the Covid era began.[48] For why they would pretend otherwise, one need only look at Fauci's own words—namely, that masks served as a, "symbol." More on that later though.

Back to the, "fact-checkers," who all have the same exact opinion (narrative) on everything, their commitment to their assigned cause consistently leads them into a pickle of their own, "fact-checking." You see, in a desperate effort to claim some masks still weren't dangerous (cloth and surgical), *Snopes* in May 2020 was forced to acknowledge Stanford's N-95 affirmation that Dr. Griesz-Brisson was *not*, "debunked," as falsely claimed by, "fact-checker," *AFP*.[49] At the same time, *AFP*'s, "fact-check expert opinion," demonstrates in hilarious fashion how, "fact-checkers," can, "fact-check," the, "facts," of, "fact-checkers," to the point where you end up with a perverted version of what would otherwise be a healthy debate.

Does the miniscule size of an oxygen particle mean inhibition is impossible in masks? Clearly *Snopes* and *AFP* do not agree and if they were honest each would, "fact-check," the other. It is also interesting to reflect on this May 2020 *Snopes* propaganda defending cloth and surgical mask mandates, now that they are admitted as having been, "facial decorations," the entire time. Was what they said in 2020 a, "fact," or is what their masters are saying now a, "fact?"

To further expound on the lack of masking effectiveness, we can also look at the same type of epidemiological data we did in relation to lockdowns, which show clearly there was no benefit by location in mask mandates. Denmark, for example, has seen its public health officials openly shun mask mandates, who claimed, "all these countries recommending face masks haven't made their decisions based on new studies."[50] Despite this approach, which the majority of public health organizations and media would deny and gaslight proponents of, Denmark has seen one of the lowest death rates per 100K of any recorded country at 0.45 (compare this to the rates of heavily restrictive countries in our chapter on lockdowns for the eye popping difference).[51] At a case per population rate of 6%, Denmark is also well below many countries in that mark as well (US at 12.5%, UK at 10.8% and Israel at 13.1%, for example).

The timeline of masking policy in the state of Texas is also a tremendous case study in the practice's complete futility. On July 2,

2020, for example, Governor Gregg Abbott issued an executive order requiring face coverings in commercial settings.[52] Despite this policy, however, case rates in Texas hovered within +/- 50% of the same 7-day average (6K) seen on July 2 for the second half of the year … that is, until December, when 7-day case rates skyrocketed to more than 4 times that of July 2, despite the mandates.[53] By March 3, 2021, with 7-day average cases down to 7K, Governor Abbott then removed the mask mandate.[54] By July 2, 2021, 7-day case rates had dropped to 1.5K (the lowest since June 2020). They then rose again by September to the same levels seen in the December with-mandate spike, demonstrating that mask policy has not correlated to case rates whatsoever in the state.

To round out this Chapter, we will now highlight some further studies and information which support our findings and show any perceived benefits of alleged viral transmission prevention by masks are highly debatable:

- Per 2021 study by Kisielinski et al. in the *International Journal Of Environmental Research And Public Health*[55]: *"We objectified evaluation evidenced changes in respiratory physiology of mask wearers with significant correlation of O2 drop and fatigue ($p < 0.05$), a clustered co-occurrence of respiratory impairment and O2 drop (67%), N95 mask and CO2 rise (82%), N95 mask and O2 drop (72%), N95 mask and headache (60%), respiratory impairment and temperature rise (88%), but also temperature rise and moisture (100%) under the masks. **Extended mask-wearing by the general population could lead to relevant effects and consequences in many medical fields** (my emphasis)."*
- Per the Centre for Evidence-Based Medicine, six trials have been published related to mask wearing over the past decade.[56] These trials showed that, "masks alone have no significant effect in interrupting the spread," of influenza-like illness in the general population, nor in healthcare workers.
- A 2021 randomized-controlled study by Bundgaard et al. in *Annals of Internal Medicine* found no statistically significant effect of surgical masks against SARS-CoV-2 in a community setting[57]

- Per the *Washington Examiner*, citing Jeffrey Anderson at *City Journal*, whether or not masks work depends on the study, with the, "best studies," suggesting they don't[58]
  - Anderson makes a key distinction between *observational* studies and *randomized-controlled* studies (RCTs), noting that public health organizations have mostly based their policy on observational studies
  - The problem with such studies, however, is they do not include a control group. Anderson demonstrates the issue with this by comparing to an observational study about a non-mask-wearing gym trainer, who coached 50 members during the time he tested positive, "but not one member developed symptoms."
  - Without a control group, the variable in question (in this case, masks) cannot be truly tested. This principle is fundamental to properly conducting the scientific method and Anderson highlights its use in the Danish study mentioned above.
  - The CDC, however, based their guidance on an observational study following 200 hair dressers. This demonstrates a failure on the part of the organization to follow basic scientific best-practices. But Anderson also demonstrates it is actually a choice borne out of dishonesty when he points out the CDC's dismissal of the Danish study (which had 4,800 participants) as, "inconclusive," and, "too small."
  - It should go without saying that a study with more participants and a control group cannot possibly be, "too small," or, "inconclusive," relative to a study with less participants and no control group
  - Anderson goes on to conclude that: *"In sum, of the 14 RCTs that have tested the effectiveness of masks in preventing the transmission of respiratory viruses, three suggest, but do not provide any statistically significant evidence in intention-to-treat analysis, that masks might be useful. The other eleven suggest that masks are either useless—whether compared with no masks or because they appear not to add to good hand hygiene alone—or actually counterproductive."*

- Per a 2020 study by Klompas et al. in the *New England Journal of Medicine (NEJM)*[59]: *"... we know that wearing a mask outside health care facilities offers little, if any, protection from infection. Public health authorities define a significant exposure to Covid-19 as face-to-face contact within 6 feet with a patient with symptomatic Covid-19 that is sustained for at least a few minutes (and some say more than 10 minutes or even 30 minutes). The chance of catching Covid-19 from a passing interaction in a public space is therefore minimal. In many cases, the desire for widespread masking is a reflexive reaction to anxiety over the pandemic."*

- A 2020 study by Bae et al. in *Annals of Internal Medicine* saw four infected patients cough into a Petrie dish with a mask on and found, "both surgical and cotton masks seem to be ineffective at preventing the dissemination of SARS-CoV-2 from the coughs of patients with COVID-19 to the environment and external face mask"[60]

- UK study reportedly showed children who, "never," or, "sometimes," wear masks at work or school were less likely to test positive than those who, "always," wear them[61]

- A 2011 randomized clinical-trial by MacIntyre et al. in *Influenza and Other Respiratory Viruses* studied standard medical/surgical masks and demonstrated no protection at all from influenza[62]

- Per April 6, 2020 World Health Organization guidance on use of masks related to Covid-19, "wide use of masks by health people in the community setting is not supported by current evidence."[63] Masking also comes with, "uncertainties and critical risks." These risks include a, "false sense of security," as well as, "touching the face under the masks and under the eyes." These risks would, therefore, result in, "unnecessary costs."

The final point I will highlight on masks before closing out is this: the lack of common sense limitations on mask mandates and recommendations led to downright baffling, anti-science, clown-show behavior in society throughout 2020 and 2021. For one, Bill Gates went unquestioned by a panel of his peers when he seriously compared wearing masks to wearing pants—this despite the fact that he was inexplicably *not* wearing a mask but *was* wearing pants during the talk, and was notoriously known for not wearing masks at all despite incessantly endorsing them throughout the Covid era.[64,65] The following are just a few additional examples of absurd practices many fearful people tricked by this dishonesty took upon themselves. Neither the CDC, NIH, FDA, WHO, nor any other public health organization made any effort at all to convince them not to engage in these behaviors, despite their clearly pointless, counterintuitive, and widespread nature. In fact, on many occasions those organizations *encouraged* them:

- Requiring masks to walk from the host stand of a restaurant to the table, and then not at all required during the meal
- Wearing masks alone in the car
- Wearing actual outer-space-type helmets (I personally witnessed someone doing this un-ironically)
- Wearing full-on gas masks (I personally witnessed this as well, though I can't know if it was or wasn't ironic)
- Kissing with masks on
- Staring into each other's eyes from a distance as a substitute for kissing… with masks on[66]
- Having sex with masks on[67]
- Wearing masks while working out
- Wearing masks while running outside
- Wearing masks while outside
- Double and triple masking
- Putting pantyhose on your head to make your mask, "safer."[68] Yes, this really was an un-ironic thing the *Vice* blog posted about, even if it seems like a veiled attempt to mock people and test the extent of their gullibility.
- Oregon Governor Kate Brown turned herself into a meme by sharing a selfie in a way-over-the-top holiday face-covering.[69] It featured thick, Christmas-colored frill and what appeared to resemble a snow globe attached to the front. Perhaps Brown was in the holiday spirit, but it'd be impossible to know considering her entire face was hidden, other than her dead eyes.

Based on all the above information, the unintended consequences of masks are demonstrably worse than any possible benefit. Further, understanding that, "the science," changes every day, mandated masking—along with any mandate based on what oligarchs call, "science," for that matter—constitutes an informed consent violation and should be considered a crime against humanity. During the Covid era, people were forced via economic sanctions, discrimination, and other coercion into a nonsensical action which leads to physical health damage, psychological damage, environmental damage, free expression rights violations, religious violations, and bodily autonomy rights violations.

The societal implications of this coercion have also been so damaging that merely breathing in someone else's presence has become erroneously perceived and literally used in court as a justification for lethal self-defense.[70] Thanks to this, "symbol," the despicable lie was seeded into the subconscious of people all over the world that those around them, including their family and friends, were diseased and to be avoided. The fear of other human beings was then used on too many occasions to count in order to justify discrimination, harassment, assault, and battery. As we've shown, those who pushed that lie and caused that fear knew full-well the damage doing so would result in. With the aims of normalizing the coming discrimination of the mass inoculation campaign (to be covered) and breaking down resistance, they carried ahead anyway. And so, we repeat the words of Kary Mullis, who in his own life experienced the same deceit by the same people, so many years prior:

> *"They have their own personal kind of agenda. They make up their own rules as they go; they change them when they want to..."*

Endnotes

1   "PCR Test Founder Kary Mullis Shares - "Tony Fauci Doesn't Mind Going In Front Of TV And Lying."". 2020. *Bitchute*. https://www.bitchute.com/video/55LBX7rj94eZ/.
2   "Anthony S. Fauci, M.D., NIAID Director". 2022. *Niaid.Nih.Gov*. Accessed March 2. https://www.niaid.nih.gov/about/director.
3   "Our History - Our Story | About | CDC". 2022. *Cdc.Gov*. Accessed March 2. https://www.cdc.gov/about/history/index.html.

4   Rubenstein, David. 2019. "The David Rubenstein Show: Anthony Fauci". *Bloomberg.Com*. https://www.bloomberg.com/news/videos/2019-05-22/david-rubenstein-show-anthony-fauci-video.

5   "Video: Dr. Fauci Admits Face Masks Ineffective Against Coronavirus". 2020. *Newswars*. https://www.newswars.com/video-dr-fauci-admits-face-masks-ineffective-against-coronavirus/.

6   "Dr. Anthony Fauci On Importance Of Masks, Reopening Schools - CNN Video". 2020. *CNN*. https://www.cnn.com/videos/health/2020/05/27/cnngo-dr-anthony-fauci-may-27-interview-sciutto-intv.cnn.

7   O'Kane, Caitlin. 2020. "CBS News". *Cbsnews.Com*. https://www.cbsnews.com/news/fauci-mask-mandate/.

8   Stieg, Cory. 2021. "Dr. Fauci: Double-Masking Makes 'Common Sense' And Is Likely More Effective". *Cnbc.Com*. https://www.cnbc.com/2021/01/25/dr-fauci-double-mask-during-covid-makes-common-sense-more-effective.html.

9   Macias, Amanda. 2021. "Fauci Says Face Masks Could Become Seasonal After Covid Pandemic". *Cnbc.Com*. https://www.cnbc.com/2021/05/09/fauci-says-face-masks-could-become-seasonal-after-covid-pandemic.html.

10   Romero, Dennis. 2020. "'SNL' Presents Fauci As Sex Symbol Because 'I've Been The Only One Saying Facts'". *NBC News*. https://www.nbcnews.com/news/us-news/snl-presents-fauci-sex-symbol-because-i-ve-been-only-n1251023.

11   "Bacterial Pneumonia Caused Most Deaths In 1918 Influenza Pandemic". 2008. *National Institutes Of Health (NIH)*. https://www.nih.gov/news-events/news-releases/bacterial-pneumonia-caused-most-deaths-1918-influenza-pandemic.

12   "Causes Of Pneumonia | CDC". 2020. *Cdc.Gov*. https://www.cdc.gov/pneumonia/causes.html.

13   Morefield, Scott. 2021. "A Group Of Parents Sent Their Kids' Face Masks To A Lab For Analysis. Here's What They Found". *Townhall*. https://www.townhall.com/tipsheet/scottmorefield/2021/06/15/a-group-of-parents-sent-their-kids-face-masks-to-a-lab-for-analysis-heres-what-they-found-n2591047.

14   Boles, Ashley. 2020. "Spreading Germs: How Many Bacteria Are Trapped By Masks?". *Wdbj7.Com*. https://www.wdbj7.com/2020/07/29/spreading-germs-how-many-bacteria-are-trapped-by-masks/.

15   The Santa Barbara Daily News. 1918. "Mask Is Chief Ally Of 'Flu' Physicians Declare", , 1918. https://www.newspapers.com/clip/59044578/mask-is-chief-ally-of-flu-physicians/.

16   Chughtai, Abrar Ahmad, Sacha Stelzer-Braid, William Rawlinson, Giulietta Pontivivo, Quanyi Wang, Yang Pan, Daitao Zhang, Yi Zhang, Lili Li, and C. Raina MacIntyre. 2019. "Contamination By Respiratory

Viruses On Outer Surface Of Medical Masks Used By Hospital Healthcare Workers". *BMC Infectious Diseases* 19 (1). doi:10.1186/s12879-019-4109-x.

17   Dempsey, Ernest. 2020. "Bacterial Pneumonia And Other Health Risks Of Wearing Masks Alarm Doctors – Word Matters!". *Ernestdempsey.Com*. https://www.ernestdempsey.com/bacterial-pneumonia-and-other-health-risks-of-wearing-masks-alarm-doctors/.

18   Wilkinson, Lindsey. 2020. "Full-Time Mask-Wearing Brings Its Own Set Of Problems". *Cw.Ua.Edu*. https://cw.ua.edu/65524/top-stories/full-time-mask-wearing-brings-its-own-set-of-problems/.

19   Pinkstone, Joe. 2021. "Scientists Find Evidence Of Toxic Chemicals In Some Face Masks". *Mail Online*. https://www.dailymail.co.uk/sciencetech/article-9426499/Scientists-evidence-toxic-chemicals-face-masks.html.

20   "Pubchem Compound Summary For CID 6115, Aniline". 2022. *Pubchem.Ncbi.Nlm.Nih.Gov*. Accessed March 2. https://pubchem.ncbi.nlm.nih.gov/compound/aniline.

21   New Jersey Department of Health and Senior Services. 1998. "Hazardous Substance Fact Sheet: Cobalt". Trenton: New Jersey Department of Health and Senior Services.

22   "Chemical Cocktail Found In Face Masks – German Study | The Liberty Beacon". 2021. *The Liberty Beacon | Bringing Alternative Media Sources Together™*. https://www.thelibertybeacon.com/chemical-cocktail-found-in-face-masks-german-study/.

23   Foradori, Sarah. 2018. "3 Dangers Of Optical Brighteners In Laundry Detergent - And What You Can Do About It | Www.Alkuhme.Com". *Www.Alkuhme.Com*. https://www.alkuhme.com/2018/08/28/3-dangers-of-optical-brighteners-in-laundry-detergent/.

24   The Environmental Protection Agency. 2000. "Acetaldehyde Hazard Summary". Online: The Environmental Protection Agency.

25   "Estimated 1.56 Billion Face Masks Will Have Entered Oceans In 2020 - Oceansasia Report". 2020. *OCEANS ASIA*. https://oceansasia.org/covid-19-facemasks/.

26   van der Westhuizen, Helene-Mari, Koot Kotze, Sarah Tonkin-Crine, Nina Gobat, and Trisha Greenhalgh. 2020. "Face Coverings For Covid-19: From Medical Intervention To Social Practice". *BMJ*, m3021. doi:10.1136/bmj.m3021.

27   2020. *Data.Cdc.Gov*. https://data.cdc.gov/NCHS/Provisional-COVID-19-Deaths-by-Sex-and-Age/9bhg-hcku.

28   "THE CHALLENGE OF FACE MASKS". 2020. *Organization For Autism Research*. https://www.researchautism.org/the-challenge-of-face-masks/.

29   Dyer, O. 2002. "Prisoners' Treatment Is "Bordering On Torture," Charity Says". *BMJ* 324 (7331): 187-187. doi:10.1136/bmj.324.7331.187.

30   Grossman, Dave. 2021. "Masks Can Be Murder". *Americanthinker.Com.* https://www.americanthinker.com/articles/2021/01/masks_can_be_murde r.html.

31   D'Souza, Dinesh. 2022. "Speech Delays Have Increased 364% In Children Since The Pandemic Began". *Rumble.* https://www.rumble.com/vtckss-speech-delays-have-increased-364-in-children-since-the-pandemic-began.html.

32   Dent, Alec. 2021. "Did Kathy Hochul Go Maskless In A Classroom With Children?". *Factcheck.Thedispatch.Com.* https://factcheck.thedispatch.com/p/did-kathy-hochul-go-maskless-in-a?s=r.

33   "Stacy Abrams Scrambles To Delete Photo Of Her Grinning Maskless Surrounded By Masked Children". 2022. *Chad Prather.* https://chadprather.com/stacy-abrams-scrambles-to-delete-photo-of-her-grinning-maskless-surrounded-by-masked-children/.

34   Davis, Jack. 2021. "8-Year-Old With 38 Mask-Related Suspensions Gets Roaring Applause After Confronting School Board". *The Western Journal.* https://www.westernjournal.com/8-year-old-girl-38-mask-related-suspensions-appears-school-board-meeting-gets-roaring-applause-defiant-speech/.

35   Miller, Andrew Mark. 2021. "10-Year-Old Goes Viral Begging School Board To End Mask Mandate: The Rules Aren't Fair, 'Don't Make Sense To Me'". *Washington Examiner.* https://www.washingtonexaminer.com/news/4th-grader-viral-begging-end-mask-mandate.

36   "Watch: Student Destroys School Board With Sarcastic Speech Thanking Them For Masks". 2022. *Newswars.* https://www.newswars.com/watch-student-destroys-school-board-with-sarcastic-speech-thanking-them-for-masks/.

37   Mills, Henna. 2020. "German Neurologist On Face Masks: 'Oxygen Deprivation Causes Permanent Neurological Damage'". *Technocracy.News.* https://www.technocracy.news/german-neurologist-on-face-masks-oxygen-deprivation-causes-permanent-neurological-damage/.

38   "Neurologist Rips 'Medical Tyranny' After NY School Forces Medically Exempt Child To Wear Mask". 2021. *Fox News.* https://www.foxnews.com/media/neurologist-rips-medical-tyranny-after-ny-school-forces-medically-exempt-autistic-child-to-wear-mask.

39   "Youtube Deleted This. MASKS ARE DANGEROUS! GERMAN NEUROLOGIST MARGARETA GRIESZ BRISSON". 2020. *Ugetube.* https://ugetube.com/watch/youtube-deleted-this-masks-are-dangerous-german-neurologist-margareta-griesz-brisson_nvGciUKQwgbwyKA.html?lang=german.

40   Russezki, Jan. 2020. "Experts Say Wearing Face Masks Does Not Cause Neurological Damage". *Fact Check.* https://factcheck.afp.com/experts-say-wearing-face-masks-does-not-cause-neurological-damage.

41   "Hypoxemia (Low Blood Oxygen)". 2018. *Mayo Clinic*.
      https://www.mayoclinic.org/symptom/hypoxemia/basics/causes/sym-
      20050930.

42   Sarma, Jahnavi. 2020. "COVID-19: Wearing A Face Mask Is Important
      But Avoid It While Working Out". *Thehealthsite.Com*.
      https://www.thehealthsite.com/news/covid-19-wearing-a-face-mask-is-
      important-but-avoid-it-while-working-out-746877/.

43   Neupane, Bhanu Bhakta, Sangita Mainali, Amita Sharma, and Basant
      Giri. 2019. "Optical Microscopic Study Of Surface Morphology And
      Filtering Efficiency Of Face Masks". *Peerj* 7: e7142.
      doi:10.7717/peerj.7142.

44   Cuffari, Benedette. 2021. "The Size Of SARS-Cov-2 And Its
      Implications". *News-Medical.Net*. https://www.news-
      medical.net/health/the-size-of-sars-cov-2-compared-to-other-things.aspx.

45   Myers, Andrew. 2020. "Stanford Researchers Reengineer COVID-19
      Face Masks | Stanford News". *Stanford News*.
      https://news.stanford.edu/2020/04/14/stanford-researchers-reengineer-
      covid-19-face-masks/.

46   Qian, Yinge, Klaus Willeke, Sergey A. Grinshpun, Jean Donnelly, and
      Christopher C. Coffey. 1998. "Performance Of N95 Respirators:
      Filtration Efficiency For Airborne Microbial And Inert
      Particles". *American Industrial Hygiene Association Journal* 59 (2): 128-
      132. doi:10.1080/15428119891010389.

47   Rutherford, Fiona. 2022. "Bloomberg - Are You A
      Robot?". *Bloomberg.Com*.
      https://www.bloomberg.com/news/articles/2022-01-14/cdc-encourages-
      wider-use-of-medical-grade-face-masks-for-public.

48   Becker, Kyle. 2022. "15 Worst Covid Lies That Are Now Completely
      Exposed For All The World To See". *Thekylebecker.Substack.Com*.
      https://thekylebecker.substack.com/p/15-worst-covid-lies-that-are-
      now?utm_source=url.

49   Ibrahim, Nur. 2020. "Is It Dangerous To Wear A COVID-19 Protective
      Mask For Too Long?". *Snopes.Com*. https://www.snopes.com/fact-
      check/masks-dangerous-health/.

50   Miltimore, Jon. 2020. "Europe's Top Health Officials Say Masks Aren't
      Helpful In Beating COVID-19 | Jon Miltimore". *Fee.Org*.
      https://www.fee.org/articles/europes-top-health-officials-say-masks-
      arent-helpful-in-beating-covid-19/.

51   "COVID-19 Deaths Per Capita By Country | Statista". 2022. *Statista*.
      https://www.statista.com/statistics/1104709/coronavirus-deaths-
      worldwide-per-million-inhabitants/.

52   *Executive Order No. GA-29*. 2020. Vol. 418014. Executive Department:
      Governor of the State of Texas.

53   "Texas Coronavirus Cases And Deaths". 2020. *Usafacts.Org*.
      https://usafacts.org/visualizations/coronavirus-covid-19-spread-
      map/state/texas.

54   Nichols, Robert S., Amy Karff Halevy, and Rebecca L. Baker. 2021.
        "Texas Governor Lifts Mask Mandate, But Employers Must Still Comply
        With The Occupational Safety And Health Act". *Bracewell.Com.*
        https://bracewell.com/insights/texas-governor-lifts-mask-mandate-
        employers-must-still-comply-occupational-safety-and.

55   Kisielinski, Kai, Paul Giboni, Andreas Prescher, Bernd Klosterhalfen,
        David Graessel, Stefan Funken, Oliver Kempski, and Oliver Hirsch.
        2021. "Is A Mask That Covers The Mouth And Nose Free From
        Undesirable Side Effects In Everyday Use And Free Of Potential
        Hazards?". *International Journal Of Environmental Research And Public
        Health* 18 (8): 4344. doi:10.3390/ijerph18084344.

56   Jefferson, Tom, and Carl Heneghan. 2020. "Masking Lack Of Evidence
        With Politics - The Centre For Evidence-Based Medicine". *The Centre
        For Evidence-Based Medicine.* https://www.cebm.net/covid-19/masking-
        lack-of-evidence-with-politics/.

57   Bundgaard, Henning, Johan Skov Bundgaard, Daniel Emil Tadeusz
        Raaschou-Pedersen, Christian von Buchwald, Tobias Todsen, Jakob
        Boesgaard Norsk, and Mia M. Pries-Heje et al. 2021. "Effectiveness Of
        Adding A Mask Recommendation To Other Public Health Measures To
        Prevent SARS-Cov-2 Infection In Danish Mask Wearers". *Annals Of
        Internal Medicine* 174 (3): 335-343. doi:10.7326/m20-6817.

58   White, Kaylee McGhee. 2021. "Do Masks Actually Work? The Best
        Studies Suggest They Don't". *Msn.Com.* https://www.msn.com/en-
        us/health/medical/do-masks-actually-work-the-best-studies-suggest-they-
        don-t/ar-AANfurl.

59   Klompas, Michael, Charles A. Morris, Julia Sinclair, Madelyn Pearson,
        and Erica S. Shenoy. 2020. "Universal Masking In Hospitals In The
        Covid-19 Era". *New England Journal Of Medicine* 382 (21): e63.
        doi:10.1056/nejmp2006372.

60   Bae, Seongman, Min-Chul Kim, Ji Yeun Kim, Hye-Hee Cha, Joon Seo
        Lim, Jiwon Jung, and Min-Jae Kim et al. 2020. "Effectiveness Of
        Surgical And Cotton Masks In Blocking SARS–Cov-2: A Controlled
        Comparison In 4 Patients". *Annals Of Internal Medicine* 173 (1): W22-
        W23. doi:10.7326/m20-1342.

61   Becker, Kyle. 2022. "Another Bombshell Report: U.K. Study Shows
        Maskless Kids *Less Likely* To Test Positive For
        Covid". *Beckernews.Com.* https://beckernews.com/new-another-
        bombshell-report-u-k-study-shows-maskless-kids-less-likely-to-test-
        positive-for-covid-43836/.

62   MacIntyre, Chandini Raina, Quanyi Wang, Simon Cauchemez, Holly
        Seale, Dominic E. Dwyer, Peng Yang, and Weixian Shi et al. 2011. "A
        Cluster Randomized Clinical Trial Comparing Fit-Tested And Non-Fit-
        Tested N95 Respirators To Medical Masks To Prevent Respiratory Virus
        Infection In Health Care Workers". *Influenza And Other Respiratory
        Viruses* 5 (3): 170-179. doi:10.1111/j.1750-2659.2011.00198.x.

63   "Advice On The Use Of Masks In The Context Of COVID-19". 2020. *Apps.Who.Int.* https://apps.who.int/iris/bitstream/handle/10665/331693/WHO-2019-nCov-IPC_Masks-2020.3-eng.pdf?sequence=1&isAllowed=y.

64   Pavlich, Katie. 2022. "Bill Gates Just Made An Absurd Comparison On Mask Mandates". *Townhall.* https://townhall.com/tipsheet/katiepavlich/2022/02/21/bill-gates-compares-wearing-a-mask-to-wearing-pants-n2603556.

65   Ji, Sayer. 2020. "Why Won'T Bill Gates Wear A Mask? | SGT Report". *Sgtreport.Com.* https://www.sgtreport.com/2020/10/why-wont-bill-gates-wear-a-mask/.

66   Wynne, Griffin. 2020. "Your COVID-Safe Kissing Guide". *Bustle.Com.* https://www.bustle.com/wellness/kiss-safely-covid-19-pandemic.

67   "Ahead Of Valentine's Day, Lovers Are Advised To Wear Masks During Sex". 2022. *Big News Network.Com.* https://www.bignewsnetwork.com/news/272292136/ahead-of-valentines-day-lovers-are-advised-to-wear-masks-during-sex.

68   Cole, Samantha. 2022. "Scientists Find Putting Pantyhose On Your Head Makes Your Mask Safer". *Vice.Com.* https://www.vice.com/en/article/akvng5/mask-hacks-better-fit-research.

69   Nightingale, Hannah. 2021. "Oregon Governor Roasted For Wearing INSANE 'Holiday' Mask". *The Post Millennial.* https://thepostmillennial.com/oregon-governor-roasted-for-wearing-insane-holiday-mask.

70   "Security Guard Who Shot Man 3 Times Acted In Self Defense Because The Victim Wasn't Wearing A COVID Mask, Lawyer Says". 2021. *CWB Chicago.* https://www.cwbchicago.com/2021/08/security-guard-who-shot-man-3-times-acted-in-self-defense-because-the-victim-wasnt-wearing-a-covid-mask-lawyer-says.html.

Chapter 5

"Social" Distancing

*"**The six feet rule was arbitrary in and of itself** (my emphasis). Nobody knows where it came from. Most people assume that six feet of distance, the recommendation for keeping six feet apart, comes out of some old studies related to flu, where droplets don't travel more than six feet. We know Covid spreads through aerosols. We've known that for a while, so how operative is that? **The six feet rule is a perfect example of sort of the lack of rigor around how the CDC made recommendations** (my emphasis)."*
—Scott Gottlieb, former commissioner of the Food and Drug Administration (now Pfizer board member), September 2021[1]

"Interviewer: Does this study suggest to you that three feet [distancing] is good enough?
Fauci: *It does, indeed. And that's exactly the point I'm making ... What the CDC wants to do is, they want to accumulate data. And when the data shows that there is an ability to be three feet, they will act accordingly ... **And I can assure you, within a reasonable period of time, quite reasonable, they will be giving guidelines according to the data they have. It won't be very long, I promise you** (my emphasis)."*
—Anthony Fauci, March 12, 2021[2]

"Stay 6 feet away from others ... Inside your home: Avoid close contact with people who are sick. If possible, maintain 6 feet between the person who is sick and other household members. Outside your home: Put 6 feet of distance between yourself and people who don't live in your household."
—CDC Guidance as of April 2022[3]

"Social," Distancing is an absurd term based on outdated science, recommended by today's charlatan public health organizations for no reason other than to promote fear. According to *Study Finds*, 6-feet *separation* was originally proposed in 1897 by a German bacteriologist named Carl Flugge.[4] However, a 2020 report by Jones et al. in the *BMJ* argues that the practice is part of, "oversimplified, overly rigid, and outdated science," which does not take aerosols into account.[5] According to institutions like these, a sneeze can send aerosols as far as 26-feet inside a room and heavy breathing can lead to rooms filled with such aerosols. The shocking thing here is that, while Anthony Fauci admits to this day he never had any scientific justification to recommend 6 feet versus say, 3 feet, the report in the *BMJ* actually suggests *greater than* 6 feet would be ideal, depending on the situation. The problem with this suggestion is how obviously impractical it is, making the entire venture of expanding the normal, "cover your sneeze," best-practices both pointless and reckless.

For example, the *BMJ* report specifically mentions settings like gyms as, "high risk," since they are indoors and involve heavy breathing. If the recommendations of this report were followed, people would separate *more* than 6 feet in gyms for this reason. What this ultimately means, however, is that fewer people would need to be permitted in gyms at any given time, or they'd have to be shut down entirely, which we know they were. Such actions are/were completely counterintuitive and unfathomable for a public health organization to have encouraged during a pandemic for two glaring reasons:

1. The CDC admits about 94.9% of those hospitalized had at least 1 underlying medical condition.[6] Specifically, the CDC even goes on to say that, "obesity, diabetes with complication, anxiety disorders, and the total number of conditions were the strongest risk factors for severe Covid-19 illness." One would think—based on this assertion—that the primary goal of the CDC would therefore have been to get every citizen in a gym daily. Instead, the opposite was done, as gyms were closed and/or people were scared away from them due to the presence of other human beings.

2. Despite the claims of the *BMJ* report, the reality is that over the past year-and-a-half epidemiological studies have shown a lack of any statistically significant link between open gyms and Covid cases. Specifically, a University of Oregon study found that **no outbreaks could be traced to gyms**, despite 8.5 million check-ins by gym patrons in the state over a 32-week period.[7]

Taking these two things together, there are only three reasonable conclusions which can be drawn on the imposition of, "social," distancing and what it reveals about the alleged pandemic itself:

1. Assuming inhalation-of or infection-with the alleged SARS-CoV-2 virus is the *cause* of the *disease* Covid-19, the CDC/*BMJ* transmission theories posited about aerosols, droplets, and distancing benefits are *highly* debatable and are not supported in the real-world—this because healthy people in gyms exposed to those aerosols frequently were not at risk
2. Assuming the CDC/*BMJ* aerosol transmission theories of the SARS-CoV-2 virus *are* true, the assumption that this virus *causes* the *disease* Covid-19 is a bad one. This is due to there being no statistically significant link between actually being *diseased* and frequenting high-transmission-likelihood venues, along with the *significant* link between the disease and pre-existing conditions.
3. Both the transmission and cause of disease assumptions are bad because they are themselves based on bad assumptions and don't reflect the discernable reality of the situation (more on this later)

Unfortunately, the lack of outbreaks during ongoing large and indoor allegedly, "high-risk," events has not led to a society-wide change of course away from these senseless recommendations and/or enforcements. In fact, governments, with the support of their public health organizations, have gone to absurd lengths to punish any lack of compliance. The owners of the Atilis Gym of Bellmawr, New Jersey, for example, have been arrested, visited by police, and hit with over $1 million in fines for not following the governor's closure requirements.[8] In fact, in the name of, "health," the state even took the cruel and unusual step of boarding up and padlocking the gym, only for the owners to have to break in to their own facility. And despite all of that—despite overcoming those inhumane coercions and hosting tens of thousands of patrons anyway—the state of New Jersey, without apology or any sense of irony, failed to link even a single case to the gym.

As we've seen in all previous chapters to this point, this type of unjust behavior in the name of, "public health," has not even remotely been an isolated incident. It has been ubiquitous thanks to the centralization we've pointed to, and has led to a dangerous dysfunction in society. For one thing, many if not most stores still have their, "social," distance floor markers and cash register shield walls, to the undeniable detriment of human interaction. And human interaction is, like exercise as mentioned above, also a crucial thing to maintain for the benefit of human health. MercuryCare Business Health Solutions, a Health Services and Employee Assistance Program provider, highlights some key points on the importance of social interaction[9]:

- Benefits of socialization
  - Improved mental health care
  - Reduced risk of dementia – improved brain health
  - Promotes sense of safety, belonging
  - Allows people to confide in one another
- Physical, in-person connections are important for mental and physical health, as online interaction (see increased use and encouragement of platforms like Zoom during the Covid era) provides a false sense of connectedness

Further, on the note of mental health, a classic sociological study, "Le Suicide," by Emile Durkheim found that the primary factor in suicide is a lack of social integration.[10] We have already quantified the increase in suicide numbers in chapter 2, but this provides further support for the responsibility of public health organizations for that increase. In each of the four types of suicide, Durkheim defines how promoting the view that other human beings are diseased and to be avoided by more than the average body length is cruel and reckless:

- **Anomic suicide**
  - <u>Description</u>: caused by a sense of disconnect from society and a feeling of not belonging resulting from weakened social cohesion
  - <u>Relevance in the Covid era</u>: especially applicable in the context of children whose schools were shut down and who were told to distance from friends at the most crucial ages for social development

- **Altruistic suicide**
  - Description: result of excessive regulation of individuals by societal forces such that the person may be moved to kill themselves for the benefit of a cause or for society at large
  - Relevance in the Covid era: the idea that human beings are a threat to others and the use of collective phraseology ubiquitous during the Covid pandemic
- **Egoistic suicide**
  - Description: occurs when people feel totally detached from the work, family, community, and other social ties in society. Elderly are susceptible.
  - Relevance in the Covid era: a 2020 study by Sepúlveda-Loyola et al. in the *Journal of Nutrition, Health & Aging* on the impact of Covid-19 social isolation on the health of older people found mental and physical health were negatively affected during, "social," distancing.[11] Outcomes included anxiety, depression, poor sleep quality, and physical inactivity, which all contribute to poor physical health and disease.
- **Fatalistic suicide**
  - Description: occurs under conditions of extreme social regulation resulting in oppressive conditions and a denial of the self and of agency
  - Relevance in the Covid era: lockdowns, mask mandates, business closures, church closures, "vaccine mandates," denial of religious exemptions, denial of basic human rights, censorship, "fact-checking," and seemingly every other action taken/encouraged by public health organizations

Throughout the pandemic there has been an absurd amount of hypocrisy in the actions of public health organizations and their political proponents related to each and every action recommended/ordered/mandated. Whether it be Nancy Pelosi's spa day, Gavin Newsome's dinner party, Austin Mayor Steve Adler's recommendation to not travel broadcasted from a resort in Mexico, Lori Lightfoot's makeover, or an endless list of other disingenuous offenses, it has been perfectly clear, "The Science," applies to, "thee," and not to, "me."[12]

That said, "public health experts," are not meant to be a political body. In fact, that they are not political has been their primary, incessant appeal when they beg people to, "trust them," despite the overwhelming destruction their actions have caused with no conceivable or demonstrated benefit whatsoever. Yet one particular set of actions related to, "social," distancing demonstrated that political is all many of them are, at the expense of any scientific credibility they desperately wanted and tried coercing people into believing they had. The hypocrisy to which I am referring is the public health reaction to race protests in the summer of 2020.

Per a report by *Politico*, here are just a few actual, mind-boggling quotes from credentialed, "public health experts," on the topic[13]:

- Jennifer Nuzzo, John's Hopkins epidemiologist: *"**We should always evaluate the risks and benefits** (my emphasis) of efforts to control the virus. In this moment **the public health risks of not protesting to demand an end to systemic racism** (my emphasis) greatly exceed the harms of the virus."*
- Abraar Karan, Brigham and Women's Hospital physician: *"The injustice that's evident to everyone right now needs to be addressed. **While I have voiced concerns that protests risk creating more outbreaks, the status quo wasn't going to stop #covid19 either** (my emphasis)."*
- Tom Frieden, former CDC director and convicted sexual abuser, "loudly warned against efforts to rush reopening but is now supportive of mass protests."[14]
- Jeffrey Flier, former dean of Harvard Medical School: *"It makes it clear that all along there were trade-offs between details of lockdowns and social distancing and other factors that the experts previously discounted and have now decided to reconsider and rebalance."*
- Hundreds of public health workers in an open letter: "[Protests against stay-at-home orders] *not only oppose public health interventions, but are also rooted in white nationalism and run contrary to respect for Black lives. Protests against systemic racism, which fosters the disproportionate burden of COVID-*

*19 on Black communities and also perpetuates police violence, must be supported. **Staying at home, social distancing, and public masking are effective at minimizing the spread of COVID-19. However, as public health advocates, we do not condemn these gatherings as risky for COVID-19 transmission** (my emphasis)."*

- Rochelle Walensky, CDC director, 2021 official statement[15]: *"... the pandemic illuminated inequities that have existed for generations and revealed for all of America a known, but often unaddressed, **epidemic impacting public health: racism. What we all know is this** (my emphasis): racism is a serious public health threat that directly affects the well-being of millions of Americans."*

There isn't much commentary I should have to provide on the absurdity of these statements. For American citizens to be mandated or coerced into doing anything by people who say things this foolish is simply wrong and to be utterly dismissed. There's no other way to say it. These are not scientists. In fact, the CDC director making statements like this should be outright disqualifying, if our goal for the CDC is to *control diseases*. And to see the evil in these statements, your opinion on racism in America doesn't even matter. If you oppose mandates and distancing and want to protest about it, then these, "public health experts," are lying, raging political hypocrites. On the other hand, if you do think racism is an epidemic and want to protest about it, then these, "public health experts," encouraged you to engage in an activity *they believed* would cause you to catch a dangerous, life threatening, extremely infectious disease that a week before was worth shutting the world down for and abusing anyone who disagreed. No matter where you fall, there is no compassion, logic, or science to be found in any of the above quotes, and that is a tremendous problem when these are the people whose directives politicians followed to the detriment of billions worldwide.

The truth of the matter here is this: I'm not even denying that outcomes for, "minorities," in the Covid era were worse. In many cases they were. But in their support for the Covid narrative and the experimentation which underpinned it, many of the very public health officials virtue signaling about race were directly facilitating and/or inflicting those very outcomes. In some cases they were even alleged by first-hand whistleblowers as having done so *knowingly*, the primary account attestations of which I will provide throughout this book.

To close out this chapter, Webster's defines the word *oxymoron* as, "a combination of contradictory or incongruous words."[16] We will get more to the psychological implications of public health organizations using this kind of doublespeak in a later chapter. But the bottom line is: *distancing* is not *social*. In fact, *distancing* is the opposite of *social*. To use such terminology for what, in their own words, is an arbitrary practice, is both condescending and irresponsible. It's even more so when the people spreading it are shown to not actually believe in or follow their own edicts. And while some might try to pass off the phrasing of, "social," distancing as a morale boosting tool, it is impossible to square the good intent this alleges with the passive-aggressive, damaging actions demonstrated to this point by those who have used it.

Endnotes

1   Tillison, Tom. 2021. "Former Head Of FDA Says 6 Ft. Distancing Rule Was 'Arbitrary': 'Nobody Knows Where It Came From'". *Bizpac Review*. https://www.bizpacreview.com/2021/09/20/former-head-of-fda-says-6-ft-distancing-rule-was-arbitrary-nobody-knows-where-it-came-from-1137013/.

2   Jones, Susan. 2021. "Dr. Fauci Now Believes 3 Feet Of Social Distancing May Be Enough". *Cnsnews.Com*. https://cnsnews.com/index.php/article/national/susan-jones/dr-fauci-now-believes-3-feet-social-distancing-may-be-enough.

3   "COVID-19 And Your Health". 2022. *Centers For Disease Control And Prevention*. https://www.cdc.gov/coronavirus/2019-ncov/prevent-getting-sick/prevention.html.

4   Sleezer, Brianna. 2020. "Social Distancing Six Feet Apart Is Based On 'Outdated Science,' Scientists Say". *Study Finds*. https://www.studyfinds.org/social-distancing-six-feet-apart-outdated-science/.

5   Jones, Nicholas R, Zeshan U Qureshi, Robert J Temple, Jessica P J Larwood, Trisha Greenhalgh, and Lydia Bourouiba. 2020. "Two Metres Or One: What Is The Evidence For Physical Distancing In Covid-19?". *BMJ*, m3223. doi:10.1136/bmj.m3223.

6   Kompaniyets, Lyudmyla, Audrey F. Pennington, Alyson B. Goodman, Hannah G. Rosenblum, Brook Belay, Jean Y. Ko, and Jennifer R. Chevinsky et al. 2021. "Underlying Medical Conditions And Severe Illness Among 540,667 Adults Hospitalized With COVID-19, March

2020–March 2021". *The Centers For Disease Control And Prevention.* https://www.cdc.gov/pcd/issues/2021/21_0123.htm.

7   Golden, C. Douglas. 2020. "Colorado Study Finds 'No Statistically Significant' Link Between Gyms And COVID Cases". *The Western Journal.* https://www.westernjournal.com/study-finds-no-statistically-significant-link-gyms-covid-cases/.

8   Ibid.

9   "Health Benefits Of Social Interaction - Mercy Medical Center". 2022. *Mercycare.Org.* Accessed March 2. https://www.mercycare.org/bhs/employee-assistance-program/eapforemployers/resources/health-benefits-of-social-interaction/.

10   Crossman, Ashley. 2020. "Learn About Emile Durkheim's Classic Study Of Suicide In Sociology". *Thoughtco.* https://www.thoughtco.com/study-of-suicide-by-emile-durkheim-3026758.

11   Sepúlveda-Loyola, W., I. Rodríguez-Sánchez, P. Pérez-Rodríguez, F. Ganz, R. Torralba, D. V. Oliveira, and Leocadio Rodríguez-Mañas. 2020. "Impact Of Social Isolation Due To COVID-19 On Health In Older People: Mental And Physical Effects And Recommendations". *The Journal Of Nutrition, Health & Aging* 24 (9): 938-947. doi:10.1007/s12603-020-1500-7.

12   "Data Visualization | COVID Hypocrisy: Policymakers Breaking Their Own Rules | The Heritage Foundation". 2022. *Data Visualizations | The Heritage Foundation.* https://www.heritage.org/data-visualizations/public-health/covid-hypocrisy-policymakers-breaking-their-own-rules/.

13   Diamond, Dan. 2020. "Suddenly, Public Health Officials Say Social Justice Matters More Than Social Distance". *POLITICO.* https://www.politico.com/news/magazine/2020/06/04/public-health-protests-301534.

14   Carrega, Christina. 2019. "Former CDC Director Tom Frieden Pleads Guilty In Sex Abuse Case, Gets No Jail Time". *ABC News.* https://abcnews.go.com/US/cdc-director-pleads-guilty-groping-family-friend-jail/story?id=63478002.

15   Walensky, Rochelle P. 2021. "Media Statement From CDC Director Rochelle P. Walensky, MD, MPH, On Racism And Health". *CDC.* https://www.cdc.gov/media/releases/2021/s0408-racism-health.html.

16   "Oxymoron Definition & Meaning". 2022. *Merriam-Webster.Com.* Accessed March 2. https://www.merriam-webster.com/dictionary/oxymoron.

Chapter 6

Testing for What?

"PCR is ... just a process that's used to make a whole lot of something out of something. That's what it is—it's not—it doesn't tell you that you're sick and it doesn't tell you that the thing you ended up with really is gonna hurt you."
—Kary Mullis, Inventor of Polymerase Chain Reaction (PCR)[1]

This is, in my opinion, the most important chapter in this book. In it we will discuss the basis of the entire Covid era: mass, ubiquitous testing. In order to do this, we will begin with the, "gold standard," test, the PCR, and work our way down to other tests which were also used despite having massive faults. There are several glaring issues with PCR which, when taken together, disqualify it as a meaningful method of diagnosing cases. Despite these issues, it was used anyway as the primary tool used to allege a pandemic and to justify all the damage which precedes and follows this chapter.

The Inventor's Disdain for the Public Health Officials in Question and Their Perversion of his Method

As can be seen in the preceding quote, Kary Mullis is the inventor of the PCR process. The process itself is a, "thermal cycling method used to make up to billions of copies of a specific DNA sample, making it large enough to study."[2] With uses in a variety of fields from biomedical research to criminal forensics, PCR has been considered a discovery for the ages, earning Mullis a Nobel Prize in 1993.

Unfortunately, however, even the most genius of inventions can be subject to misuse. And despite Mullis' death in August 2019, just prior to the first declarations of a pandemic, he was well-versed and outspoken on the abuses of his method by those he deemed unfit to use it[3,4]:

"... these guys like Fauci get up there and start talking and, you know, he doesn't really know anything about anything— and I'd say that to his face—nothing. The man thinks you can take a blood sample and put it under an electron microscope

and if it's got a virus under there you'll know it. He doesn't understand electron microscopy and he doesn't understand medicine and he should not be in a position like he's in. Most of those guys up there are just total administrative people and they don't know anything about what's going on in the body."

Mullis' experience with figureheads like Fauci came during what has turned out to be a very similar situation to today—namely, HIV/AIDS. In other interviews too he had described his revelations about the weak foundations related to that declared pandemic.[5] For example, Mullis recalled being unable to find a single person or study demonstrating conclusively that HIV truly was the cause of AIDS. According to Mullis, even Luc Montagnier, the person who is credited with discovering HIV, did not have more than a completely unrelated study on monkeys to point him to.

As we will demonstrate later, the entire history of public-health-declared pandemics in general is extremely relevant to what we face today and is necessary background to understand what is happening in context. However, the reasons we must now call attention to Mullis' spat with these institutions during AIDS are as follows:

1. To identify the players and to observe that their ideology is the same now as then
2. To further demonstrate the stark contrast and observable conflict between those who practice the Scientific Method (Mullis, Malone, etc.) and those who make claims in the name of, "science" (Fauci, Walensky, etc.)
3. **And, most importantly in the case of this section** – to show conclusively that even though Mullis is not here to object openly to the current abuse of his method, there was clear precedent for the conflict which already existed surrounding it

Indeed, Mullis was well aware of the strengths and weaknesses of his method. One key weakness, as it relates to the use of PCR for the detection of infectious disease, is called out in the following quote by the inventor himself:

*"And with PCR, if you do it well, **you can find almost anything in anybody** (my emphasis). It starts making you*

*believe in the, sort of, Buddhist notion that everything is contained in everything else. Right? I mean, if you can amplify one single molecule up to something that you can really measure—which PCR can do—then **there's just very few molecules that you don't have at least one single one of in your body*** (my emphasis)*, okay? So that can be thought of as a misuse of it, just to claim that it's meaningful."*

Focusing on the bolded parts of the above quote, what Mullis is explaining is that PCR is not a method for demonstrating the *quantification* of a substance in the body. It can take the substance and make copies for improved observation, but it cannot tell you how much of the thing being observed is actually inside you or what impact it's having on you, if any.

The reason this is so relevant in the case of viral illness is that the quantity of viral replication in the body *is* (theoretically) the thing that determines whether or not you actually become ill. The prevailing theory (germ theory) behind why some viruses ultimately make people sick is that they take over our cells and force those cells to replicate the virus.[6] At the same time, the human body is constantly filled with and exposed to millions of viruses (fun fact: there are as many as 10 million viruses in a single drop of ocean water[7]).

Under normal circumstances, the immune system is able to account for the vast majority of viruses, and so this replication is prevented. However, as you can now imagine, it would not be useful under those normal circumstances for you to simply know whether or not a virus is present. You would only become sick when a virus your immune system fails to fight off is sufficiently replicating, which PCR cannot tell you whether that is or isn't the case. And thanks to the weapon PCR has been made into by ignoring the importance of quantification, people have become conditioned during the Covid pandemic (for the first time in germ theory history) to fear, "asymptomatic carriers."

"In all the history of respiratory-borne viruses of any type, asymptomatic transmission has never been the driver of outbreaks. The driver of outbreaks is always a symptomatic person."

—Anthony Fauci, January 2020[8]

"However, only patients with signs and symptoms consistent with pertussis should be tested by PCR to confirm diagnosis. Testing asymptomatic persons should be avoided as it increases the likelihood of obtaining falsely-positive results. Asymptomatic close contacts of confirmed cases should not be tested and testing of contacts should not be used for post-exposure prophylaxis decisions."

—Pre-Covid statement from the CDC[9]

"As the positivity rate for SARS-CoV-2 decreases, the positive predictive value also decreases. This means that the probability that a person who has a positive result (SARS-CoV-2 detected) is truly infected with SARS-CoV-2 decreases as positivity rate decreases, irrespective of the assay specificity. Therefore, healthcare providers are encouraged to take into consideration testing results along with clinical signs and symptoms, confirmed status of any contacts, etc."

—Deleted but archived statement from the WHO[10]

As we can see, both the WHO and CDC acknowledged the obvious at one point. An important, additional question one might ask about, "asymptomatic carriers," however, is as follows: if SARS-CoV-2 is novel (meaning no one would inherently possess immunity to it), and is also the cause of the disease referred to as, "Covid," then how can anyone have been an asymptomatic carrier of it? The answer is that they obviously can't have been, and this implies one of two things:

1. SARS-CoV-2 is *not* novel and is therefore *not* the cause of the novel disease referred to as, "Covid"
2. SARS-CoV-2 *is* novel and *is* the cause of the novel disease called, "Covid." This, however, *must* imply that the PCR tests do not work to a dramatic extent, since the idea of asymptomatic infections with a novel virus is impossible if the germ theory is true.

The implications of either possibility are obvious and the damage caused by Public Health's ignorance of these logical determinations is extraordinary. Unfortunately however, the reality of the situation is even worse …

The Official PCR Test Calibration Used Worldwide was Riddled with Flaws

The conflict between disinterested scientists and the czars of public health has not died out today, despite Mullis' death—the torch has simply been taken up by a new, large swath of those who also practice the scientific method. And this brings us to our next issue as it relates to PCR in the Covid era.

On November 27, 2020, a group of 22 scientists submitted an extensive external peer review report to the Eurosurveillance editorial board.[11] These scientists came together with a broad range of expertise including pharmacology, genetics, engineering, molecular andrology, biochemistry, microbiology, cardiology, infectious disease, and immunology. In their report, they acknowledge that the methodology used to calibrate the PCR test came from a January 2020 report most famously attributed to Christian Drosten called, "Detection of 2019 Novel Coronavirus (2019-nCoV) by real-time RT-PCR."[12] The Corman-Drosten methodology was ultimately accepted by the WHO, and therefore (thanks to the centralization we've discussed before) became an accepted basis for testing globally. So the importance of this one publication cannot be overstated—it was directly responsible for the consequences of actions taken by societies worldwide.

The thesis of the external peer review report, however, is that there are a variety of major scientific flaws at the molecular and methodological level with the Corman-Drosten PCR calibration. According to the authors, these flaws lead to misdiagnosis and significant false-positive rates. As such, the recommendation of the scientists involved is a retraction of the Corman-Drosten paper by the Eurosurveillance board. The specific, egregious flaws they called out were as follows:

1. The scientists conclude that neither of the two stated aims (i.e. development and deployment of a robust diagnostic methodology) were possible, since the tests were developed **without any actual virus material**
   a. From external peer review report: *"The novel coronavirus is based on in silico (theoretical) sequences, supplied by a laboratory in China, because at the time neither control material of infectious ("live") or inactivated SARS-CoV-2 nor isolated*

genomic RNA of the virus was available to the authors. To date no validation has been performed by the authorship based on isolated SARS-CoV-2 viruses or full length RNA thereof."

b. A quote cited from the Corman-Drosten report: *"We aimed to develop and deploy robust diagnostic methodology for use in public health laboratory setting without having virus material available."*

Before we continue to the remainder of the flaws, I'd like to just reiterate how astonishing this point really is. In the words of the calibrators themselves, the PCR test for SARS-CoV-2 was developed, "without having virus material available." Please remember: *this test was considered the, "gold standard," during the two primary years of the Covid era.* Without virus material available it is obviously impossible for the test to have been accurate.

However, another extremely important point is when the external peer reviewers mention, "no validation has been performed by the authorship based on isolated SARS-CoV-2 or full length RNA thereof." If SARS-CoV-2 has been isolated and its entire genome sequenced (which is up for debate as we will come to discuss), it would seem a very logical next step to scrap and/or revise the Corman-Drosten report based on this new information. The fact that this never happened is unfathomable to the point of warranting criminal investigation. As someone with computer modeling experience myself, I can attest that it is impossible—not unlikely ... *impossible*—for an actually-identified sequence to exactly match a sequence generated theoretically (using computer modeling). An exact match would be a miracle of indescribable proportions, and that miracle is what would've needed to have happened for the tests developed on the Corman-Drosten standards to have been accurate.

2. The number of amplification cycles originally recommended by the WHO via the Corman-Drosten report and used by most laboratories in the US and Europe were set far too high, **leading to false positive rates of at least 97%.** They should have been set no higher than 25-30 cycles.

a. From external peer review: *"In the case of virus detection, >35 cycles only detects signals which do not correlate with infectious virus as determined by isolation in cell culture"*

b. *"If someone is tested by PCR as positive when a threshold of 35 cycles or higher is used (as is the case in most laboratories in Europe & the US),* **the probability that said person is actually infected is less than 3%, the probability that said result is false positive is 97%** (my emphasis)"*

This point is further supported by a 2020 study by Jaafar et al. in *Clinical Infectious Diseases* titled, "Correlation between 3790 qPCR positive samples & positive cell cultures including 1941 SARS-CoV-2," which found that *more than* 97% of PCR positives were not actually infectious in a cell culture at 35 cycles, and more than 80% at 30 cycles.[13] This study showed it took lowering the CT-rate to 25 cycles in order to get even 70% of PCR positives to be infectious in a cell culture (still a 30% false positive rate). And those findings are not even disputed by Anthony Fauci either, who has admitted that, "If you get a cycle threshold of 35 or more … the chances of it being replication-competent are miniscule … you almost never can culture virus from a 37 threshold cycle … even 36 … it's just dead nucleoids, period."[14] If this is true, then how can Fauci not be completely furious and at odds with the FDA and CDC, which, in a document titled, "CDC 2019-Novel Coronavirus (2019-nCoV) Real-Time RT-PCR Diagnostic Panel," declare, "… a specimen is considered positive for 2019-nCoV [virus] if all 2019-nCoV marker (N1, N2) cycle threshold growth curves cross the threshold line within 40.00 cycles (< 40.00 Ct)."[15]

Again, we find ourselves at another astonishing point which needs to be addressed. Anthony Fauci, the figurehead of the Covid era, declared the cycle threshold rates mandated by the FDA and CDC meaningless, yet has not in any way called out those organizations for the obvious scientific fraud that implies. It must be wondered by any reasonable person why this is the case. And whether the answer is fraud or incompetence is irrelevant when it comes to the damage done by errors as egregious as the at least 97% false positive rates identified by the external peer reviewers.

But despite our gracious refrain from assuming it, the case for intentional fraud is bolstered by the subsequent actions of these organizations in 2021. One example is the WHO reducing its recommended cycle threshold rate on the US inauguration day, just as the Covid mass inoculation program it supported was beginning.[16] Another is the CDC's deleted-after-pushback spring 2021 notice to reduce PCR cycle threshold rates to 28 in a report about inoculation, "breakthrough cases."[17] The changing of the methodology used to determine Covid case rates in *any* way in 2021 without acknowledging the obvious impact this would have had on the 2020 rates (97% reduction) is a clear, undeniable fraud. For it to align with the mass inoculation campaign suggests it was intentional, but more on that later.

Even the *New York Times* acknowledged this cycle-threshold scandal in their article titled, "Your Coronavirus Test is Positive. Maybe it Shouldn't Be."[18] The article admits, "Most tests set the limit at 40 cycles. A few at 37." A judge in Portugal also officially ruled any PCR tests greater than 25 cycles to be, "totally unreliable," and therefore determined lockdowns to be unlawful.[19] And to further reveal the absurdity of these issues, one need look no further than Tanzania, where a goat and a pawpaw fruit tested positive for Covid-19.[20]

3. Additional issues which disqualify the test as a diagnostic tool
    a. Extremely high concentrations of primers leading to non-specific bindings
    b. Six unspecified wobbly positions leading to enormous variability in the real world laboratory implementations of the test
    c. Temperature setting issues
    d. Lack of product validation at the molecular level
    e. **Lack of positive control to evaluate SARS-CoV-2 specificity or negative control to exclude other coronaviruses** (my emphasis)
    f. Lack of standardization in test design
4. The test cannot discriminate between the whole virus and viral fragments

Points 3e and 4 are more crucial details about the PCR protocol that bear repeating: the Corman-Drosten PCR protocol accepted by the WHO and used to establish the pandemic *does not* test for the novel corona virus. It does not differentiate between specific SARS viruses and also does not test for whole virus at all, but rather for genetic material that is claimed to make up a fragment of the virus. This, however, is still not even a believable premise, considering the virus the Corman-Drosten report is based on was determined theoretically by a Chinese laboratory, as we've discussed previously.

5. The Corman-Drosten report was not otherwise peer-reviewed despite the magnitude of its importance and the fact that peer-review is a common, necessary practice. Version 1-0 of the protocol was published at the official WHO website on January 13, 2020, which was updated to version 2-1 on January 17, 2020. This version was then submitted to Eurosurveillance on January 21, 2020, accepted for publication on January 22, 2020, and published on January 23, 2020. In the opinion of the external peer reviewers, the Corman-Drosten report was therefore not, at the time, peer-reviewed, and would not have been considered worthy of publishing if it had been.

6. Significant conflicts of interest
   a. Two of the authors of the Corman-Drosten paper, Christian Drosten and Chantal Reusken, are also members of the editorial board of Eurosurveillance. This severe conflict of interest strengthens suspicions the paper was not peer reviewed and further compromises its scientific integrity.
   b. Both Victor Corman and Christian Drosten also failed to mention their additional affiliation with the commercial test laboratory, "Labor Berlin," where they are responsible for virus diagnostics related to real time PCR-testing. This is extremely troubling when considering Drosten's position on the editorial board of Eurosurveillance.
   c. Two separate contributors' conflicts of interest were added in July 2020 which were not included in the original published version of the report and include conflicts with TIB-Molbiol—"the first," company to produce PCR kits based on the protocol published in the Corman-Drosten report.

In summary, this is a scandal of epic proportions on which the entire alleged pandemic was based. While I focus on Fauci's words in this book because I am American, Christian Drosten of Germany should receive an equal amount of scrutiny for the way his dishonest behavior mirrors Fauci's. The following excerpt from a *Wirtschafts Woche* interview Drosten did in 2014 is particularly telling as far as his culpability goes[21]:

> *"Yes, but the method [PCR] is so sensitive that it can detect a single genetic molecule of this virus. For example, if such a pathogen scurries across the nasal mucosa of a nurse for a day without her becoming ill or noticing anything else, then she is suddenly an MERS case. Where previously terminally ill people were reported, mild cases and people who are actually perfectly healthy are now suddenly included in the reporting statistics. This could also explain the explosion in the number of cases in Saudi Arabia. On top of that, the local media made the matter unbelievably high.*
>
> *... There is hardly any other topic in the TV news or daily newspapers in the region. And doctors in hospitals are also consumers of this news. They then also consider that they should keep an eye on this disease, which has also been very rare in Saudi Arabia up to now. Medicine is not free of fads.*
>
> *... I fear that the current increase [in MERS cases/deaths] is more due to the increased attention. It's no different in this country. If 'Bild' or the evening news reports about an outbreak of a certain virus, the number of laboratory tests increases significantly. Simply because doctors are then also sensitized and look out specifically for the pathogens that are being reported on.*
>
> *... It would be very helpful if the authorities in Saudi Arabia would go back to using the previous definitions of the disease. Because what interests us first are the real cases. I think it is questionable whether hospital staff who are asymptomatic or mildly infected are really virus carriers. Even more questionable is whether they can pass the virus on to others. The advisory team of the new health minister should distinguish more clearly between medically necessary diagnostics and scientific interest."*

Christian Drosten knew in 2014 that PCR tests would be over-sensitive. Christian Drosten knew in 2014 that such testing would lead to the false diagnosis of asymptomatic people, who he knew would not be infectious. Christian Drosten knew that the explosion of testing would lead to a vicious cycle of media hype. Christian Drosten knew that doctors would follow the hype of the, "fad," and would be, "sensitized," enough by it to encourage testing. Christian Drosten knew none of this was helpful to public health.

In 2020 Christian Drosten developed a PCR test anyway based on a theoretical virus and set the cycle threshold rate such that it would be excessively sensitive. In the report in which he developed this test he failed to disclose a conflict of interest with a commercial test laboratory responsible for diagnostics. There is perhaps no one in the entire world outside of Anthony Fauci himself with the type of means, motive, and opportunity that Christian Drosten had as far as knowing how a pandemic could be manufactured and how to profit from it. We will cover much more on Drosten later, but the 180-degree heel-turn he made in the Covid era to hysterical endorsement of mass testing paints an ugly picture about who this man is.[22]

PCR Pseudo-Epidemic Historical Precedent: The Whooping Cough

The *New York Times* published a story in 2007 called, "Faith in Quick Test Leads to Epidemic That Wasn't."[23] The story featured Dr. Brooke Herndon of the Dartmouth-Hitchcock Medical Center, who at the time experienced a ceaseless cough. When some of Dr. Herndon's colleagues began coughing as well, an outbreak of whooping cough was theorized and panic ensued. Writer Gina Kolata explains:

> *"Nearly 1,000 health care workers at the hospital in Lebanon, N.H., were given a preliminary test and furloughed from work until their results were in; 142 people, including Dr. Herndon, were told they appeared to have the disease; and thousands were given antibiotics and a vaccine for protection. Hospital beds were taken out of commission, including some in intensive care.*
>
> *Then, about eight months later, health care workers were dumbfounded to receive an e-mail message from the hospital*

administration informing them that the whole thing was a false alarm.

Not a single case of whooping cough was confirmed with the definitive test, growing the bacterium, Bordetella pertussis, in the laboratory. Instead, it appears the health care workers probably were afflicted with ordinary respiratory diseases like the common cold (my emphasis). *"*

Is this beginning to sound familiar at all? If not, think: *quick test*. Yes, these quick tests (PCR tests) are acknowledged by scientists to have, "led them astray," in the curious case of the Dartmouth-Hitchcock Medical Center. In fact, it led them so far astray that 15% of the people in question (the 142 told they had the disease) were falsely diagnosed, mistreated, and even inoculated, all prior to the revelation that the entire thing was a mistake. This is the reality of PCR tests. This is our reality today. And unfortunately, according to Kolata, the infectious disease, "experts," responsible seem to admit they are fine with the outlandish risk this presents as these quick tests, "… may be the only way to get a quick answer in diagnosing diseases like whooping cough, Legionnaire's, bird flu, tuberculosis, and SARS, and deciding whether an epidemic is under way."

So we ask again: why is it more important to decide there's an epidemic quickly than to be certain the decision to do so is accurate at all, given the consequences of being wrong (misdiagnosis, mistreatment, unnecessary illness-causing stress/fear[24]). And what if, as in the case of the Dartmouth Medical Center, among others, the decision is 100% wrong? Well, so be it, I guess. In fact, according to Dr. Trish M. Perl, an epidemiologist at John's Hopkins and past president of the Society of Health Care Epidemiologists of America, "pseudo-epidemics happen all the time," because of such testing. "It's a problem," she admits. "We know it's a problem. **My guess is that what happened at Dartmouth is going to become common** (my emphasis). *"*

The article continues by explaining why it will become common, with the acknowledgement that these tests are considered, "quick but technically demanding." Kolata points out, in fact, there is so much variability in how laboratories may use them that they are referred to as, "home brews," are not commercially available, and there's no good estimates (until now, thanks to the external peer reviewers) on their error rates. Because of this, Dr. Perl admits, "at face value, obviously they shouldn't be doing it," but that they continue to because the other options take too long or are harder to carry out.

Astonishment does not begin to describe my feeling toward this idea that because the alternatives are harder, these people choose to do the thing that they know can lead them entirely astray. And even though they know it can lead them entirely astray, they have no idea how often it can do so and they assume *very often*. And even though they have no idea how often and they assume very often, they aren't spending the entirety of their time figuring out how often so that they can prevent potential disasters—potentially *global* disasters, perhaps where everyone in the entire world meets the same fate, or worse (as we will clearly show), as the Dartmouth Medical Center...

The CDC Withdraws its Request for its PCR Emergency Use Approval

In February of 2020, the CDC requested an Emergency Use Authorization (EUA) from the FDA to use the aforementioned RT-PCR testing methodology for diagnosing Covid-19. An EUA is a special type of approval which the FDA grants during an emergency for unapproved products. We've already seen the problem this lack of scrutiny presents in the aforementioned external peer review and Dartmouth Medical Center example. But to really bring the lack of accountability, intellectual rigor, and/or honesty full circle, the following is a July 21, 2021 release the CDC posted related to this EUA[25]:

> *"After December 31, 2021, CDC will withdraw the request to the U.S. Food and Drug Administration (FDA) for Emergency Use Authorization (EUA) of the CDC 2019-Novel Coronavirus (2019-nCoV) Real-Time RT-PCR Diagnostic Panel, the assay first introduced in February 2020 for detection of SARS-CoV-2 only."*

As you can see above, approval was not granted for this, "gold standard," methodology. In fact, two years later it's not even being sought out. Instead, the CDC is simply withdrawing the test it used the entire time and letting any potentially accurate testing be someone else's problem now that the deed is done and the inoculations (which, don't you worry, we will get to) are in the arms of hundreds of millions of people. And is the CDC going to do a post-mortem to determine how wrong it was in diagnosing a pandemic using an un-approvable test? Of course it isn't.

To make matters worse, after two years of using these tests, within *hours* of this withdrawal coming to fruition at the very end of 2021, Walensky admitted that, "what we do know is the PCR test after infection can be positive for up to 12 weeks."[26] To put that into context: Walensky is claiming you could've been sick, tested *3 months later*, and still been told you were sick and needed to quarantine yourself, if you chose to do that at all. And a brief quarantine was hardly the only consequence, as well. The CDC itself publicly acknowledged the potential for the harms they were causing on a tremendous scale via these false positives, in a December 2020 Fact Sheet for Healthcare Providers[27]:

> *"In the event of a false positive result, risks to patients could include the following: a recommendation for isolation of the patient, monitoring of household or other close contacts for symptoms, patient isolation that might limit contact with family or friends and may increase contact with other potentially COVID-19 patients, limits in the ability to work, delayed diagnosis and treatment for the true infection causing the symptoms, unnecessary prescription of a treatment or therapy, or other unintended adverse effects."*

The implications this 12 week window has on every action taken the entire time are astounding. The implications it has on case and death counts are even more astounding, but we will save that for next chapter. The bottom line is these insane, nonsensical results are not surprising at all to us, given what we now know about both PCR in general, and how it was developed specific to the Covid era. But two years and an unprecedented power grab including *the assumption of domain over leases* later, Walensky is still permitted to either feign or act out incompetence on this matter and every other matter with which she is involved.

Yet, this slinking away isn't even the best part of the withdrawal post in question. For those who lived during the alleged pandemic, an astute question many raised was, "but what happened to the flu?" This question (which, not to repeat myself but, we will get to) came as case rates for the same-symptom-causing flu, "mysteriously," dropped to near zero, just as Covid cases raised to pre-Covid-era flu case rates.[28] Well, the CDC provides the obvious answer for this mystery in their PCR EUA withdrawal post:

> *"CDC encourages laboratories to consider adoption of a multiplexed method that can facilitate detection and differentiation of SARS-CoV-2 and influenza virus* (my emphasis). *Such assays can facilitate continued testing for both influenza and SARS-CoV-2 and can save both time and resources as we head into influenza season."*

In the words of Porky Pig, "th-th-th-th-th-th-that's all, folks!" There it is. The money shot. The CDC recommends that on a go-forward basis laboratories differentiate between influenza and SARS-CoV-2. Now that we head into influenza season—after we ignored the last two influenza seasons (whoopsie!)—it's finally time to start differentiating, since we clearly weren't before and everyone knows it. Oh well. Another day, another fraud for the CDC.

But wait! What's that sound? It's a turd! It's a plane crashing to earth in a disastrous inferno! No, it's the, "fact-checkers!" As always the public relations teams sprang into action to sweep this disaster under the rug, claiming that the CDC (the narrative) actually meant that PCR tests themselves can't differentiate between the two (Covid/flu), but also that they could not *confuse* the two.[29] So the recommendation, they claim, was for someone out there to therefore develop tests which can test for both.

However, this implies what we already know and what Christian Drosten confirmed in his 2014 interview—namely, that the obsession the CDC helped foster with the new, "fad," disease led to a two year hiatus of testing for flu. So, according to the CDC's media PR team, the CDC is recommending that hiatus come to an end. Now, instead of strictly testing for a portion of the genetic material of a theoretical virus sequence which wasn't based on an isolated novel coronavirus at all, they recommend using a test which can also test for both whatever that is, as well as the flu. Unfortunately, this also fell apart within days of suggesting it, with the un-ironic, ever-convenient introduction of, "flurona."

"Flurona," which the Cleveland Clinic decided to acknowledge was a thing in January 2022, is when a person tests positive with both a flu test and a Covid test.[30] If a person can have both the flu and SARS-CoV-2, however, then the allegation that the CDC Covid PCR test couldn't mistake Covid for the flu is irrelevant. And even if said allegation was true, the Covid era still could have been a seasonal flu with the over-utilized PCR simply identifying some other genetic material that also happened to be present. In simpler terms, it just as easily could have been, "flurona," (the flu) the whole time.

A Summary of the PCR Testing Disaster

At this point we've covered and established the unreliability of the, "gold standard," test—the PCR. We've found the following about this method:

- It is not actually a test for viral infection and could be, at best, a supplemental tool when it comes to diagnosis
- It should not be used for the purposes of diagnosis at all
- When it is used it must follow very specific criteria related to cycle rates, primers, temperatures, etc., and should be limited in its scope
- The Covid PCR tests developed could not differentiate between SARS-CoV-2 and other coronaviruses. They also could not identify influenza viruses and their overuse led to a hiatus of flu testing.
- The criteria which needed to be followed were not followed when the protocol for PCR related to SARS-CoV-2 was developed. Instead, cycle rates were set at extremely high rates, which yielded results with at least 97% false positives, among many other issues.
- PCR has been incorrectly used in the recent past to falsely identify a, "pseudo-epidemic," related to whooping cough, and we've heard a leading epidemiologist's declaration at the time that such instances would become, "common," because of PCR
- Those behind this malfeasance have not assessed or admitted to the error of their ways, have demonstrated deceitful behavior, and many have glaring conflicts of interest

- The CDC has confirmed a scheduled December 31, 2021 withdrawal of the request it made to the FDA for the Emergency Use Authorization it has secured since February 2020 for its RT-PCR diagnostic panel, which will then make the test unapproved as a diagnostic for SARS-CoV-2 infection

All of this together presents a troubling picture, to say the least, when considering the implications of how ubiquitous the PCR test has been in the lives of billions of people during the Covid era. By 2022 the CDC even came out and admitted that, "there's a 10% chance," the PCR test a given person took, "ended up in a lab for genomic sequencing analysis," which raises a whole series of ethical questions about consent the CDC will be happy to never answer.[31] In the next chapter, we will also discuss the impact of false positives on case and death counts. For now though, we will round out this chapter by looking at the other tests used despite known and admitted faults – because as hard to believe as it might be that things got even sloppier than the Corman-Drosten PCR test, they absolutely did.

Antigen Tests

The use of the phrase, "gold standard," as it relates to PCR can give us some insight into just how careless the CDC was in allowing tests to be used which were not up to said standard. The first example of this is the antigen test. The antigen test is another Emergency Use Authorized test, which is meant to detect proteins related to SARS-CoV-2. In November 2020 the FDA released a letter to healthcare providers, specifically to call out the potential for false positives in these tests.[32] Per the FDA:

> "Remember that positive predictive value (PPV) varies with disease prevalence when interpreting results from diagnostic tests. PPV is the percent of positive results that are true positives. As disease prevalence decreases, the percent of tests results that are false positives increase ... At 0.1% prevalence, the PPV would only be 4%, meaning that 96 out of 100 positive results would be false positives."

Considering the already enormous rates of false positive rates we've touched on related to the PCR tests, and the extremely low prevalence in the vast majority of communities using these tests when the alleged pandemic began, this acknowledgement sets off some obvious alarm bells. Just how exaggerated must such a test be for it to demonstrate *worse* results than a test as poorly calibrated as the Covid PCR? It's hard to imagine but it didn't stop such tests from being used in reporting and telling people in news feeds how scared they should be.

In fact, the entire, "omicron variant," narrative of early 2022 was built on the back mass antigen testing. This came at the very time the CDC's PCR test was being withdrawn, during a, "variant," scare which had incredibly *low disease prevalence*. Despite this low disease prevalence, the hysteria reached an all-time high and testing went through the roof, thanks in large part to the Biden Regime's outrageous fear mongering and buying up 500 million of such tests at a cost of $4 billion, according to Fox News.[33] Almost half of those tests went unclaimed, but corruption seems a primary function of the government at this point and this was just one tiny drop in an ocean of it relatively.[34]

As the FDA outlined, the low disease prevalence led to a false-positivity rate that saw the biggest, "case," spike in the entire Covid era, yet the least actual disease and death. While people attributed this to the allegedly mild characteristics of the, "omicron variant," this assumption is a category of the mind. It is a narrative which has been fit to a predictable outcome—not predictable because of assumptions about the nature of sub-microscopic particles, but rather because of phenomena which can much more directly be attributed to the FDA-admitted faults of rapid antigen testing it associated PPV.

But people who were worried and tested anyway despite the lack of symptoms, mainly did so with the goal of knowing whether or not to quarantine themselves so as not to get those around them sick. The problem is, as antigen tests became the predominant test in use, even Anthony Fauci admitted they don't tell you if you're transmissible[35]:

> *"The only way you can tell if it's transmissible—if you can show that there is really live replication virus in you and the tests don't measure that. They measure the presence or absence of not—of the virus and the virus could be a dead inactive virus that doesn't transmit. So it's entirely understandable how people can get confused over that."*

You don't say... Again, considering how many people have accepted this lie and pointless exercise of, "asymptomatic infection," if the testing doesn't end, this irrational behavior will never end. Every cold/flu season there would be an increasing wave of people getting tested and a subsequent wave of positive tests. Whether it's, "flurona," or the fact that the same test can show positive for all the different, "variants," without any recalibration, the results are equally meaningless and tell you nothing. But pretending otherwise is a lifestyle choice many people have made for themselves. We will have to see if in the future their submission to this testing regimen and the irrational, self-inflicted harms which result from it continue.

Either way, the reason you would get screened for an illness is to inform a treatment decision. For example, if I found a lump on my body, I wouldn't want to get chemotherapy, surgery, and/or radiation if it ended up being a cyst. So I would need to find out whether or not it was cancerous. Covid tests were not used for this purpose at all. Instead, they were used to lock oneself inside, sick or not, and to avoid all human contact. And for those who were sick, early treatments were not even permitted by the public health organizations—but more on that to come.

The CDC Used Antibody Tests Used to Count Covid Cases

In May of 2020 *the Atlantic* published a story titled, "How Could the CDC Make That Mistake?"[36] On the one hand, what is most surprising about this article is that the writers at *the Atlantic* seem surprised the CDC would do something that doesn't make any scientific sense. On the other hand, they do acknowledge yet another scandal which took place during the height of the alleged pandemic's opening days. This scandal is related to antibody tests and how the CDC (and several states) did not differentiate between them when reporting infection numbers.

An antibody test, per the FDA, is used to identify the antibodies associated with a virus to determine if an individual has had a *past* infection.[37] Having antibodies does not in any way suggest you are infected with a virus. In fact, as it relates to Covid the FDA even admits, "Researchers do not know whether the presence of antibodies means that you are immune to Covid-19." Also, in their question and answer section on these tests, they further clarify that antibody tests may detect coronavirus antibodies other than SARS-

CoV-2, "such as those that cause the common cold." One should be able to easily then make the logical leap that antibody tests are:

1. Worthless as it relates to telling you anything about your potential past experience with the alleged novel coronavirus specifically
2. Worthless as it relates to measuring current allegedly novel coronavirus infection rates
3. Worthless as it relates to your potential immunity (the entire point)
4. Just plain worthless

Actually, to clarify, using antibody tests to measure current novel coronavirus infection rates is not just, "worthless," but rather it is fraudulent. Yet, as *the Atlantic* points out, this is exactly what the CDC admitted to doing through, at least, May 2020. And this is why when people call, "Covid," the common cold they are literally not wrong—not just because the common cold is from the same family of viruses as the alleged novel coronavirus, but also because the tests (as we've seen previously, even the gold-standard PCR) don't even differentiate between them.

Atlantic writers Alexis C. Madrigal and Robinson Meyer point out as well how, "debilitating," this mistake was as states had, "set quantitative guidelines for reopening their economies based on these flawed data points." To further illustrate the utter incompetence and negligence of the people taking actions as impactful as closing economies during this time, Vermont authorities responded to *the Atlantic* by claiming they, "didn't even know they were doing this." And as for the CDC's part, not only did they fail to prevent or call out this mistake, but they too confirmed it as their practice when asked. Ashish Jha, K.T. Li, Professor of Global Health at Harvard and the director of the Harvard Global Health Institute, was bewildered by this failure:

> *"You've got to be kidding me. How could the CDC make that mistake? This is a mess."*

Professor Jha poses a great question. Here are some more: To what extent did this conflation exaggerate already-exaggerated case and death counts? How much fear did it produce? How much unnecessary destruction did it cause, based on the foolish decision-making it inspired? Why did no one publicly correct it and apologize for it? These are questions that organizations like the CDC, WHO, FDA, and NIH never seem to have to answer for. They're questions which should be demanded of them and which should lead to firings and/or investigations, but are instead ignored no matter how many distinct times they arise.

Endnotes

1   James, David. 2020. "Dr. Fauci Admits The PCR Test For Coronavirus Is All But Useless As It Is Administered In The US". *Aletho News.* https://alethonews.com/2020/11/03/dr-fauci-admits-the-pcr-test-for-coronavirus-is-all-but-useless-as-it-is-administered-in-the-us/.

2   "PCR Test Inventor Kary Mullis Tells The Truth About The Flawed COVID-19 Test". 2020. *Stateofthenation.Co.* https://www.stateofthenation.co/?p=30880.

3   "The Mysterious Death Of Dr Fauci's Most Notable Critic, Just Before COVID-19: Dr. Kary Mullis, The Inventor Of The PCR Technique". 2021. *Humans Be Free.* https://www.humansarefree.com/2021/05/mysterious-death-of-kary-mullis.html.

4   James, David. 2020. "Dr. Fauci Admits The PCR Test For Coronavirus Is All But Useless As It Is Administered In The US". *Aletho News.* https://alethonews.com/2020/11/03/dr-fauci-admits-the-pcr-test-for-coronavirus-is-all-but-useless-as-it-is-administered-in-the-us/.

5   Herer, James. 2020. "Quotes From Dr. Kary Mullis Regarding The Baseless HIV-AIDS Hypothesis". *Weblyf.* https://www.weblyf.com/2020/08/quotes-from-dr-kary-mullis-regarding-the-baseless-hiv-aids-hypothesis/.

6   Arden, Katherine. 2020. "How Do Viruses Make Us Ill?". *BBC Science Focus Magazine.* https://www.sciencefocus.com/the-human-body/how-do-viruses-make-us-ill/.

7   Foulsham, George. 2011. "10 Million Viruses In One Drop Of Seawater - Futurity". *Futurity.* https://www.futurity.org/millions-of-marine-viruses-ebb-and-flow/.

8   Sones, Mordechai. 2020. "Anthony Fauci: Asymptomatic Transmission Never Drives Outbreaks". *Israelnationalnews.Com.* https://www.israelnationalnews.com/News/News.aspx/286920.

9   "Pertussis: Use Of PCR For Diagnosis | CDC". 2017. *Cdc.Gov.* https://www.cdc.gov/pertussis/clinical/diagnostic-testing/diagnosis-pcr-bestpractices.html.

10   Henderson, Emily. 2020. "World Health Organization Issues Notice For In Vitro Diagnostics Users". *News-Medical.Net.* https://www.news-

medical.net/news/20201214/World-Health-Organization-issues-notice-for-in-vitro-diagnostics-users.aspx.

11   Borger, Pieter, Bobby Rajesh Malhotra, Michael Yeadon, Clare Craig, Kevin McKernan, Klaus Steger, and Paul McSheehy et al. 2020. "External Peer Review Of The RTPCR Test To Detect SARS-Cov-2 Reveals 10 Major Scientific Flaws At The Molecular And Methodological Level: Consequences For False Positive Results.". AN INTERNATIONAL CONSORTIUM OF SCIENTISTS IN LIFE SCIENCES (ICSLS). https://www.cormandrostenreview.com/report/.

12   Corman, Victor M, Olfert Landt, Marco Kaiser, Richard Molenkamp, Adam Meijer, Daniel KW Chu, and Tobias Bleicker et al. 2020. "Detection Of 2019 Novel Coronavirus (2019-Ncov) By Real-Time RT-PCR". *Eurosurveillance* 25 (3). doi:10.2807/1560-7917.es.2020.25.3.2000045.

13   Jaafar, Rita, Sarah Aherfi, Nathalie Wurtz, Clio Grimaldier, Thuan Van Hoang, Philippe Colson, Didier Raoult, and Bernard La Scola. 2020. "Correlation Between 3790 Quantitative Polymerase Chain Reaction–Positives Samples And Positive Cell Cultures, Including 1941 Severe Acute Respiratory Syndrome Coronavirus 2 Isolates". *Clinical Infectious Diseases* 72 (11): e921-e921. doi:10.1093/cid/ciaa1491.

14   Rappoport, Jon. 2020. "Fauci Himself Admits Covid PCR Test At Over 35 Cycles Is Deceitful, Worse Than Useless". *Anti-Empire.Com*. https://www.anti-empire.com/fauci-himself-admits-covid-pcr-test-at-over-35-cycles-is-deceitful-worse-than-useless/.

15   "CDC 2019-Novel Coronavirus (2019-Ncov) Real-Time RT-PCR Diagnostic Panel". 2021. *Fda.Gov*. https://www.fda.gov/media/134922/download.

16   "WHO Lowers Cycle Thresholds For PCR Tests | Covid Call To Humanity". 2021. *Covid Call To Humanity | Evidence-Based Truth About The COVID Scamdemic*. https://covidcalltohumanity.org/2021/01/27/who-lowers-cycle-thresholds-for-pcr-tests/.

17   "CDC Quietly Deletes Guidance Virally Criticized As Double Standard Higher Test Threshold For Reporting 'Breakthrough' Cases - Newsrescue.Com". 2021. *Newsrescue.Com - 100% News 0% Junk*. https://www.newsrescue.com/cdc-quietly-deletes-guidance-virally-criticized-as-double-standard-for-reporting-breakthrough-cases/.

18   Mandavilli, Apoorva. 2020. "Your Coronavirus Test Is Positive. Maybe It Shouldn'T Be. (Published 2020)". *Nytimes.Com*. https://www.nytimes.com/2020/08/29/health/coronavirus-testing.html.

19   "Portuguese Court Rules PCR Tests "Unreliable" & Quarantines "Unlawful"". 2020. *Offguardian*. https://off-guardian.org/2020/11/20/portuguese-court-rules-pcr-tests-unreliable-quarantines-unlawful/.

20   "President Queries Tanzania Coronavirus Kits After Goat Test". 2020. *Reuters.Com*. https://www.reuters.com/article/us-health-

coronavirus-tanzania/president-queries-tanzania-coronavirus-kits-after-goat-test-idUSKBN22F0KF.

21   Kutter, Susanne. 2014. "Virologe Drosten Im Gespräch 2014: „Die WHO Kann Nur Empfehlungen Aussprechen""". *Wiwo.De*. https://www.wiwo.de/technologie/forschung/virologe-drosten-im-gespraech-2014-die-who-kann-nur-empfehlungen-aussprechen/9903228-2.html.

22   "Who Launched COVID Global Hysteria?". 2021. *Natural Health News*. https://www.naturalblaze.com/2021/10/who-launched-covid-global-hysteria.html.

23   "Faith In Quick Test Leads To Epidemic That Wasn't". 2007. *Health.Maryland.Gov*. https://health.maryland.gov/newsclippings/archives/2007/jan07/012207.htm#Faith_in_Quick_Test_Leads_to_Epidemic_That_Wasn%E2%80%99t.

24   "Chronic Stress Puts Your Health At Risk". 2021. *Mayo Clinic*. https://www.mayoclinic.org/healthy-lifestyle/stress-management/in-depth/stress/art-20046037.

25   "Lab Alert: Changes To CDC RT-PCR For SARS-Cov-2 Testing". 2021. *Cdc.Gov*. https://www.cdc.gov/csels/dls/locs/2021/07-21-2021-lab-alert-Changes_CDC_RT-PCR_SARS-CoV-2_Testing_1.html.

26   George, Liz. 2021. "CDC Reveals COVID Tests Can Show Positive For 12 Weeks After Infection". *American Military News*. https://americanmilitarynews.com/2021/12/cdc-reveals-covid-tests-can-show-positive-for-12-weeks-after-infection/.

27   "FACT SHEET FOR HEALTHCARE PROVIDERS: CDC 2019-Ncov Real-Time RT-PCR Diagnostic Panel". 2020. *Cdc.Gov*. https://www.cdc.gov/coronavirus/2019-ncov/downloads/factsheet-for-healthcare-providers-2019-nCoV.pdf.

28   Johnson, Carla K. 2021. "Flu Is Making A Comeback In US After An Unusual Year Off". *ABC News*. https://abcnews.go.com/Health/wireStory/flu-making-comeback-us-unusual-year-off-81961642.

29   Vercellone, Chiara. 2021. "Fact Check: CDC Is Withdrawing Its PCR COVID-19 Test, But Not Because It Confuses Viruses". *News.Yahoo.Com*. https://news.yahoo.com/fact-check-cdc-withdrawing-pcr-213145798.html.

30   "What Is Flurona?". 2022. *Cleveland Clinic*. https://health.clevelandclinic.org/what-is-flurona/.

31   Hancock, Seth. 2022. "CDC Admits It Has Collected DNA From PCR Tests". *The Liberty Loft*. https://thelibertyloft.com/2022/03/03/cdc-admits-it-has-collected-dna-from-pcr-tests/.

32   "Potential For False Positive Results With SARS-Cov-2 Antigen Tests". 2020. *U.S. Food And Drug Administration*. https://www.fda.gov/medical-devices/letters-health-care-providers/potential-false-positive-results-

antigen-tests-rapid-detection-sars-cov-2-letter-clinical-laboratory?utm_medium=email&utm_source=govdelivery.

33 Musto, Julia. 2022. "Federal Government's At-Home COVID Test Website Launches". *Fox News*. https://www.foxnews.com/health/how-to-get-at-home-covid-test.

34 "Nearly Half Of Biden's 500M Free COVID-19 Tests Unclaimed". 2022. *Fox News*. https://www.foxnews.com/health/nearly-half-biden-500-million-free-covid-tests-unclaimed.

35 Schwartz, Ian. 2021. "Fauci: Antigen Tests Not Helpful To Assess Transmissibility, Only For Infection". *Realclearpolitics.Com*. https://www.realclearpolitics.com/video/2021/12/30/fauci_antigen_tests_not_helpful_to_assess_transmissibility_only_for_infection.html#.

36 Meyer, Robinson, and Alexis C. Madrigal. 2020. "'How Could The CDC Make That Mistake?'". *The Atlantic*. https://www.theatlantic.com/health/archive/2020/05/cdc-and-states-are-misreporting-covid-19-test-data-pennsylvania-georgia-texas/611935/.

37 "Antibody (Serology) Testing For COVID-19". 2022. *U.S. Food And Drug Administration*. https://www.fda.gov/medical-devices/coronavirus-covid-19-and-medical-devices/antibody-serology-testing-covid-19-information-patients-and-consumers.

Chapter 7

Statistical Fraud

*"I think people have gotten used to the fact that wearing masks, **clearly if you look at the data it diminishes respiratory diseases** (my emphasis), we've had practically a non-existent flu season this year merely because people were doing the kinds of public health things that were directed predominately against Covid-19."*

—Anthony Fauci, May 2021[1]

One of the most incredible phenomena I personally experienced during the Covid era was not just the magical disappearance of the flu—but also the reaction of people to this disappearance. When CDC flu case estimates ranged from 36-45M per year from 2017-2019, and then case counts came in at 1,675 in 2020, while at the same time their Covid case count for 2020 was just below 21M, my first thoughts were along the lines of, "okay—finally.[2,3,4] Finally this is the thing that's not possible to miss. This is the thing that's gonna wake everyone up from their slumber because there's no possible way to spin this. Mass testing for this respiratory disease with the same types of symptoms as the flu made the flu go to zero as it rose to comparable case rates as previous flu *estimates* made without mass testing. Obviously it's the flu. Obviously everyone will see this now. At long last, they took things too far!"

Unfortunately, I got ahead of myself and forgot that, no matter how unbelievably dumb the answer is, salesman Anthony Fauci has an answer for everything. And in this case, as can be seen above, his answer was that the flu is a respiratory disease, and respiratory diseases spread via droplet, which masks, "clearly," prevent, so the flu is gone because people wore masks. No, that isn't a joke. That is the actual position of the director of NIAID and one which was somehow accepted by people with brains.

And I truly can't even begin to wrap my head around how one reasons that out. Is the influenza virus bigger than SARS-CoV-2, causing it to get blocked by masks more? No. Influenza is in the same range as SARS-CoV-2 (50-140 nanometers as previously discussed) at 80-120 nanometers.[5] So there's no reason at all to think the two would behave differently in the air. I guess the message is to just ignore that though. Because the only way to make it make sense is to ignore all logic and reasoning. Severe Acute **Respiratory** Syndrome is a respiratory disease from a virus which masks can apparently *not* prevent the pandemic spread of, while the flu is a respiratory disease from the same sized virus which masks *can* apparently cause to completely vanish. And if you have a problem with any of that, well too bad—because in Fauci's high opinion[6]:

> *"A lot of what you're seeing as attacks on me quite frankly are attacks on science because all of the things I have spoken about from the very beginning have been fundamentally based on science."*

No, this is not a comedy book or a dystopian fiction. These are things people in positions of authority actually said, which is why I find it so important to document. And even if one is to accept Fauci's premise here, it implies a career-long failure on his part. As you will recall, Fauci laughed off the idea of mask-wearing in 2019 and warned against it on several other occasions. So if we are to believe something so simple could have eliminated the flu this whole time, then what has Fauci been doing as the director of NIAID recommending against it for almost 40 years?

Now don't get me wrong here—I understand why people would think Covid is different from the flu, because what people endured in hospitals *was* very different, thanks to dramatic changes in treatment practices (more on this in the next chapters). The fullness of hospitals and ICUs alone, however, is not a remotely new occurrence despite the incessant media fear porn of the contrary. For example, an article from *the Guardian* described how UK hospitals were, "full to bursting," in 2012.[7] Oh, and then another explained how they faced the, "toughest ever," winter in 2013;[8] and then faced another, "winter crisis," in 2014;[9] and *then* hospital bed occupancy rates hit record highs, "risking care," in 2015;[10] and then in 2016 NHS hospitals faced their, "toughest winter yet," once again;[11] but not before hospitals got, "dangerously full," during the winter crisis in 2017;[12] which was nothing compared to the, "toughest ever," winter crisis of 2018;[13] nor did it hold a candle to 2019's, "breaking point," over lack of intensive care beds.[14]

For people outside of hospitals, the main symptom used to distinguish this allegedly new disease was the loss of taste and/or smell. Even this complication, however, is not uncommon during a case of the flu, nor is this new information. In fact, in February of 1988 the *Los Angeles Times* reported that, "Some patients complain that they are unable to smell things or to taste food after a bout of influenza."[15] They even mention the phenomena was a material enough concern to have been at the attention of the University Of Cincinnati College Of Medicine, among others.

While the flu-vanishing mental gymnastics are a big deal, we've only just begun to scratch the surface on the statistical and logical misdirection which took place over the course of the alleged pandemic by public health officials. As a health statistician it has been particularly devastating to see traditional methodologies and standards of practice abandoned at-will, without any push back from organizations which should have been perfectly positioned to call out the obvious fraud and madness. Instead, seemingly all individual resistance or outright whistleblowing was stamped out with censorship and/or credential-stripping, like those we've covered previously. Unfortunately for the censors, however, the truth lives on—so we will cover it, point-by-point.

Covid Mortality: A Complete Fraud

> *"In cases where a definite diagnosis of COVID-19 cannot be made, but it is suspected or likely (e.g., the circumstances are compelling within a reasonable degree of certainty), it is acceptable to report COVID-19 on a death certificate as 'probable' or 'presumed.'"*
> —CDC guidance for certifying Covid-19 deaths[16]

> *"If you were in hospice and had already been given a few weeks to live, and then you also were found to have COVID, that would be counted as a COVID death. It means technically even if you died of a clear alternate cause, but you had COVID at the same time, it's still listed as a COVID death. So, everyone who's listed as a COVID death doesn't mean that that was the cause of the death, but they had COVID at the time of death."*

It was hard for me to not emphasize the entirety of the previous quote. As someone whose job it is to determine and interpret health morbidity/mortality methodology, this one point is what broke the entire pandemic narrative for me in the spring of 2020. To my shock then and amusement now, the apparent will to, "trust experts," largely did not apply when it came to my own expertise on this topic, even with members of my own family. Still, none of the peers in my field could explain this egregious error away when questioned on it, nor could anyone who doubted my declaration that this methodology represents statistical fraud.

In many ways, I accept responsibility for their doubt—any *honest* scientist would readily admit that if they can't explain their opinions to you in a simple enough way for you to understand (and restate), then you certainly *should* doubt/disregard them. This is a standard of practice for most organizations, though hopefully this book does a decent job of demonstrating the extent to which it has been disregarded in favor of anti-scientific coercion. In my case though, I've tried to follow it by focusing on simplifying my message as best I can in normal conversation, while also writing this book for those who were interested enough to get the full background. I'd recommend anyone trying to convince others of any opinion to try their best to do the same (i.e. simplify—you don't have to write a book, though you should if you're passionate enough about the subject).

To get back to why this methodology constitutes statistical fraud though, we can first start explaining this in the context of cause and effect. So far we have touched on the fact that viruses fill the human body. Therefore, the presence of a virus at the time of death does not imply cause any more than the presence of a red shirt on the deceased person's body. The quotes above and methodologies of public health departments the world over reveal they ignored simple cause and effect when counting, "Covid deaths."

Simply put, this means that the 724K, "Covid deaths," to-date (as of October 20, 2021) *cannot* be assumed to have been caused by the alleged novel corona virus, *because* public health departments included deaths with, "clear alternate cause," and even deaths, "presumed," to be Covid-related with no evidence of the virus causing it.[18] States like NY were documented as having abused this, "presumed," caveat as well, as in April of 2020 New York City added 3,778 deaths to its 10,367 total (36.4%) where no test or confirmation was done at all but death certificates made the presumption and listed the death as, "Covid-19 **or an equivalent** (my emphasis)."[19]

The second problem with these counts is the bias introduced by adding frequent testing to the 28-60 day, post-test death threshold utilized in many places.[20] To explain this issue with an example, let's say I watch a scary movie which causes me to jump in my seat. If within 60 days of watching this movie that makes me jump (positive test) I have a heart attack, is it safe to assume based on that alone the movie caused the heart attack? Of course not. But if I watch one movie in the year and it does make me jump, under the public health methodology there will be 60 days of the year where anything I die from will be included as a scary movie death.

Now let's say I watch a scary movie every week day for an entire year because my job requires it. Under those circumstances, with a 60 day threshold each time, the number of days in the year in which I could be counted could be every single day, as long as a subsequent movie makes me jump within a 60 day period of the last time I jumped. Obviously this would increase the probability of my CDC-classified, "scary movie death," from the actual probability of a scary movie death in a year (0%).

And based on what we now know about the testing, jumping at a scary movie isn't much less reliable as a signal of heart attack than a PCR test is as a signal of the novel coronavirus. The PCR test doesn't test for or specifically identify the novel coronavirus at all, so this makes the number of days in a year attributable as a Covid death for each person even more ambiguous.

For a more specific, yet still simple, mathematical example of this, consider the CDC assertion that the average person gets a cold (coronavirus) 2 to 3 times per year.[21] If we were to test everyone for colds and counted every death within a threshold of 44 days (mid-point of the 28-60 day range), there would be about 110 days per year each person could be considered a, "cold death," assuming about 2.5 colds per year on average (2.5 * 44). This is about 30% of a 365-day year that you could be considered a, "cold death," no matter what you die from (110/365). So, considering there were about 3.4M total US

103

deaths in 2020, and that the frequent testing only occurred in 9 months of the year after the Covid era began in March of 2020, we would expect, "cold deaths," to come in at just shy of 765K (30% * 3.4M * 9/12).[22] However, not everyone gets tested (my family and I never did, for example), and many of the people who did get tested will not have tested every day or even every time they got a cold in 2020. If we assume this imperfect testing accounts for anywhere from a 25-75% reduction in tested colds, we would have an expected range of, "cold deaths," of between 191K and 575K. A 50% reduction would represent approximately 382K, "cold deaths." For context, the CDC attributes approximately 375K deaths to Covid in 2020.[23] So while this is a simple, imperfect math example, you can see how their new testing and mortality regimen could have easily led to these conclusions, no matter the cause of the 2019-2020 jump in total deaths from about 2.9M to 3.4M.

That this regimen was new to the Covid era is also an extremely relevant point to dive in on. A 2020 report by Ealy et al. in *Science, Public Health Policy, and the Law* titled, "COVID-19 Data Collection, Comorbidity & Federal Law: A Historical Retrospective," questioned the CDC on why they would, "decide against using a system of data collection & reporting they authored, and which has been in use nationwide for 17 years without incident, in favor of an untested & unproven system exclusively for COVID-19 without discussion and peer-review."[24] What they specifically reference toward this change is a 2003, "Medical Examiners' and Coroners' Handbook on Death Registration and Fetal Death Reporting and Physicians' Handbook on Medical Certification of Death," published by the CDC itself. This document's death criteria, "have been used successfully for 17 years without need of update," and, "remain in use today for all causes of death except where COVID-19 is suspected or confirmed," in which case, "the March 24th 2020 COVID-19 Alert No. 2 guidelines are used instead."[25] The authors go on to continue raising several other data integrity offenses by the CDC and their legal implications, before reaching a similar conclusion as we already have[26]:

> *"With the inclusion of probable fatalities and significant changes made to how certificates of death are recorded*

exclusively for COVID-19, scientific objectivity demands that we acknowledge the data presented is inaccurate.

Federal agencies have a legal obligation to provide the most accurate data to the public, fellow agencies, and policy makers they are advising, and they have a responsibility to abide by every federal law. This responsibility to collect, analyze, and publish data accurately, transparently, and with unquestionable integrity increases exponentially during a national crisis.

It is concerning that the CDC may have willfully failed to collect, analyze, and publish accurate data used by elected officials to develop public health policy for a nation in crisis."

The final issue that has caused biased Covid mortality data— and also case/morbidity data, for that matter—is the financial incentive structure public health departments and the governments they advise set up during the alleged pandemic. Per an announcement from the US DHHS in July of 2020, certain hospitals in, "high impact," areas would receive as much as $55,000 per Covid-19 admission, down from $77,000 per admission in earlier months.[27] These payments would also be based on how the hospital's Covid patient rate compared to national averages. What this creates is an obvious and disturbing incentive to diagnose in a potentially competitive ecosystem. Then-acting CDC director Robert Redfield even acknowledged this issue while reporting to the US Congress at the time[28]:

> *"In the HIV epidemic, somebody may have a heart attack but also have HIV. The hospital would prefer the DRG [death report] for HIV because there's greater reimbursement. So I do think there is some reality to that."*

And Adm. Brett Giroir, DHHS assistant secretary of health concurred:

> *"The CDC that gathers the statistics is completely dependent on the reports of the local coroners ... Yes, there appear to be some misincentives to over-code."*

Why then-director Redfield gets away with addressing this in such a casual manner is beyond me. The reporting these hospitals have provided, during both this pandemic and during AIDS, has been used to justify actions which have had enormous consequences on all manner of human health and rights. To have such dramatic potential for fraud built in to that reporting should warrant firings at minimum for the policy-setters responsible. And we saw this potential more than realized during the Covid era. For example, doctors Dan Erickson and Artin Massihi held a press conference (yet another ultimately censored by *YouTube*) as early as April 2020, where they acknowledged hospitals were pressuring physicians to add, "Covid," to death certificates and diagnostics.[29,30]

Each of the incomprehensible methodologies of public health together allow for only one certain conclusion: **the claim that 724K people (or whatever number is officially cited at the time) died with a cause *or even contribution* of death by the novel coronavirus is a falsehood**. The contribution piece is important as well because it is also false to claim, "The 724K might not have died *of* it, but if it wasn't for the virus they otherwise wouldn't have died." Given the faults of the testing, as well as the absurdity of pretending to know with any confidence they wouldn't have otherwise died with their known co-morbidities, this is a claim without evidence.

And don't get me wrong here, I'm not saying the approximately 17.7% increase in total US deaths in 2020 didn't happen.[31] In the absence of any other explanation, it might even make sense to attribute this increase to a mysterious new disease called, "Covid-19." However, even beyond the simple alternative explanations of unprecedented despair, increased poverty, unsanitary/unhealthy mandates, healthcare system breakdown, etc. caused by public health actions, there is significant evidence of far more directly-causative, alternative explanations as well. We will touch on those alternatives and the evidence supporting them in the chapters ahead.

In fact, one need only look north to our maple-syrup-loving brothers and sisters in Canada to completely rule out an indiscriminate pandemic as the cause of the US death toll. To this end, a statistical mortality analysis called, "Analysis of all-cause mortality by week in Canada 2010-2021, by province, age and sex," was published in August 2021 by doctors Denis Rancourt, Marine Baudin, and Jérémie Mercier.[32] The authors started by stating the two defining characteristics of a pandemic—namely, that it occurs everywhere

106

because there is no prior immunity and that it causes excess mortality far greater than occurs on a normal, seasonal basis.[33] Based on their analysis of the official government data, they found neither definition to be met—mortality was not uniform across jurisdictions and in Canada, at least, it was not abnormal in total as far as excess mortality.[34] These factors led to their conclusion that, "there was no pandemic in the COVID-period in Canada," and that the, "pandemic response was so aggressive and ill-advised as to have large negative health consequences."[35]

Dr. Rancourt and the same team did go on to investigate why, unlike Canada, the US *did* show excess mortality during the Covid era, in a subsequent report titled, "Nature of the COVID-Era public health disaster in the USA, from all-cause mortality and socio-geo-economic and climatic data."[36] The findings of this report are similar to the conclusions we have and will continue to draw here—namely, the response is what is most attributable to the disaster. But many of the factors within the response which allowed for such death to occur we have yet to touch on, so I will refrain from diving too deep on all the ways this second report aligns with my own thesis. For now, we can also see these conclusions we've drawn about false mortality rates play out in the world with several examples:

- As highlighted in a resignation letter by a Royal Canadian Mounted Police officer forced out of his position due to his refusal to take the mRNA inoculations, the world's death rate (the number claimed to have died as a percentage of the population) was the same in 2018, 2019, and 2020, at 0.76%[37]
- Colorado coroner Brenda Bock found two of the five deaths (40%) attributed to Covid-19 in her one county alone were people who actually died of gunshot wounds[38]
- On the other side of the world in Australia, the following came from local news station, 1 News, in Auckland[39]: *"Today the Ministry of Health added another death to its Covid-19 reporting, but also said it was a case subject to police investigation that's ongoing. Now, 1 News understands that this is in relation to Operation [name unclear], a homicide investigation launched after a man named Robert Hart sustained serious injuries outside of Newland Hotel last week, and he died despite first aid attempts. Now, health authorities*

*say he tested positive for Covid-19 and 1 News understands that several people are also isolating. **So then you have to ask how someone who sustained these types of injuries and dies ends up as part of our Covid-19 death tally. Now the Ministry of Health says that's because under the World Health Organization guidelines, anyone who dies while also having an acute Covid-19 infection** (my emphasis) is recorded as part of the nation's death tally, whatever the cause of death might be."*

- o A few side notes here, the first being the WHO should be charged with or considered guilty of criminal fraud and/or conspiracy for this guideline at a bare minimum, as should any public health organization with a similar guideline. This is such an egregiously misguided policy that malicious intent isn't even relevant, though it almost has to be assumed, given on how wildly off base and misrepresentative the guidance is.
- o This scenario clearly demonstrates that Colorado coroner Bock's experience was not only not a geographically isolated incident during a short period of time where unintentional guideline mistakes were made, but was actually standard practice for the majority (if not all) of the world during the entire alleged pandemic, under the WHO's auspices
- o I just have to point out again how incredibly hilarious the, "so then you have to ask," line is, as well as how dumb the corporate media must think/know its audience has been made thanks to its complete abolition of truth and logic from its broadcasts. It's truly a marvel of the modern world.
- The Orange County Department of Health was forced to correct a traffic fatality initially identified as a Covid-19 death[40]
- The US makes up 4.2% of the world's population, but 18.8% of the world's deaths allegedly caused by an indiscriminate, infectious virus spreading throughout the world
  - o 360K Covid deaths in the US in 2020 / 1.92M Covid deaths worldwide in 2020 = 18.8%[41,42]

- o 331M US population 2020 / 7.80B worldwide population 2020 = 4.2%[43,44]
- o This is an overrepresentation of more than 4 times and lends further support to causes of death specific to the US public health course of action, while reducing support for an indiscriminate, infectious virus
- o Only two conclusions can come from this astounding statistic:
  - US, "Covid," death counts are correct (we can say with 100% certainty that they aren't), which means the responses of the NIH, CDC, and FDA were a complete failure and all involved should be immediately removed from their positions for gross incompetence
  - US Covid death counts are dramatically incorrect, which means those organizations either intentionally committed fraud on an epic scale (likely, for reasons to be discussed) or simply demonstrated gross incompetence in their methodologies (possible, but less likely)

By January 2022, the DHHS removed its Covid death reporting requirement for US hospitals, with many hospitals ceasing to report by the middle of the month.[45] The reason for this cover up is ultimately the same as the reason for the 2020 changes in mortality methodology—namely, the scary data was needed in 2020 to justify the mass mRNA inoculation campaign of 2021. I will prove this beyond a shadow of a doubt very soon. For now, we continue with more on how to manufacture a pandemic.

A Case Study in Confirmation Bias: the Seattle Windshield Pitting Pseudo-Epidemic[46]

On March 23, 1954, press accounts reporting windshield damage began to appear in Seattle newspapers. The accounts of dime-sized pits stemmed initially from a town 80 miles north of Seattle, but by mid-April the cases moved south into the city and in some cases entire parking lots were reported to police as having been struck. Within days, reported cases dropped to zero. However, fear of future cases remained and theories started to spread including:

- Sandflea eggs had somehow been deposited in the glass and later hatched
- Atomic fallout from hydrogen bomb tests in the Pacific
- Acid rain

The concern eventually became so great that on April 15th the mayor of Seattle sought the help of then-President Dwight Eisenhower. A team was soon arranged to investigate, and the findings were surprising to residents and sociologists alike: the incidence of pits was the same as ever. Yes, the truth was there was no epidemic. The pits always existed and resulted from mundane, ordinary road-wear. The problem was that with the onset of increased news coverage and rumor, residents of Seattle began looking *at* their windshields from the outside, instead of *through* them from the inside as they'd always done previously.

In his retelling of this incident, author Robert Bartholomew acknowledges the following sociological findings of the Seattle investigators, Nahum Z. Medalia and Otto N. Larsen:

> *"The literature on mass or collective delusions indicates the pivotal role of several key factors. These include the presence of ambiguity, anxiety, the spread of rumors and false but plausible beliefs, and a redefinition of the potential threat from general and distant to specific and imminent. Exacerbating factors include human perceptual fallibility, mass media influence in spreading the fears, recent geo-political events, and a reinforcement of the false belief by authority figures and those in institutions of social control (for example, the police, military, a university lecturer or the head of the Washington Skeptics).*
>
> *In their conclusions, Medalia and Larsen note at least two other possible functions of the pitting delusion. Firstly, as the pitting reports coincided with the H-Bomb tests, the media publicity seems to have reduced tension about the inevitable dire consequences of the bomb tests – "something was bound to happen to us as a result of the H-bomb tests – windshields became pitted – it's happened – now that threat is over."*
>
> *Secondly, the very act of telephoning police and appeals by the Mayor to the Governor and even President of the United*

States, "served to give people the sense that they were 'doing something' about the danger that threatened."

Bartholomew goes on to cite other examples of mass delusions, but hopefully by now a picture is starting to form about how real such vast delusions are. And the comparisons to the alleged Covid pandemic are easy to make, with the biggest difference being the damage avoided by the more-honest conclusions reached during the Seattle pseudo-epidemic. These honest, simple conclusions, in spite of the hysteria created by manic media coverage, prevented the type of disastrous counter-action experienced during the Covid era. Unfortunately, the CDC, NIH, FDA, and WHO have not been honest or tempered in their actions, as we've already seen and will continue to see.

In an incredible mirroring of Bartholomew's analysis, the anxiety-causing, rumor-spreading threat started as general and distant (sick people in China) before becoming specific and imminent (pandemic outbreak has spread around the world). Mass media then, "blasted," (to cite Bill Gates' Event 201 recommendation language) the airwaves with the exact, "authoritative," sources from institutions of social control (public health, government, police) mentioned both by Bartholomew above and in Bill Gates' Event 201 recommendations. Finally, with each public health action—no matter how coercive, damaging, or illogical—the anxiousness is given relief, as the sense that someone is, "doing something," is more important to the subjects of delusion than what is actually being done.

Unfortunately however, in the case of the alleged pandemic, the relief is only ever temporary. The threat is constantly re-emerging as a new case-spike or virus-variant, which requires continuous anxiousness-relief actions as outlined in this book. The great irony is these relief actions always seem to cause more damage for everyone except the wallets of those responsible for taking/enforcing them (we will analyze those conflicts of interest in later chapters), resulting in a vicious cycle. And based on how closely this cycle seems to benefit from Bartholomew's psychological and sociological findings, it isn't a reach to at least question whether there is intent behind this phenomenon.

Garbage In, Garbage Out: Coronavirus Impact Projection Models

As we discussed in chapter 2, the idea to lockdown in response to a pandemic started as a young girl's science fair project. Despite how compelling this child's project might have been however, more support would be needed to take an action as drastic as locking down the entire world. So governments turned to lockdown-justifying forecasts published on March 16, 2020 by the epidemiology modeling team at Imperial College-London (ICL), led by physicist Neil Ferguson.[47] According to the *New York Times*, by March 17, 2020 they had already specifically credited those forecasts for their decision to take the actions Ferguson recommended.[48]

By now we've already covered that these draconian measures not only provided no benefit to the most coercive countries, but in reality largely ended in their experiencing the worst death per capita outcomes—so we know the forecasts which justified them must have been incorrect based on that alone. But just how wrong were they? Well, a 2020 study by Friedman et al. in *medRxiv* measuring the predictive performance of international Covid-19 mortality forecasting models found that of the seven models compared, the ICL model had the highest 12-week error rate (79.9%), highest 6-week error rate by 5-fold, and demonstrated an over-estimation bias of 47.7%, the highest by far of all the models.[49] And upon further review of ICL's forecasts, we can also see some pretty horrendous predictions such as the following[50]:

- 179,000 estimated deaths in Taiwan compared to 12 actual deaths as of May 5, 2021 (off by 1,789,000%)
- 17,461% mortality over-estimation in South Korea
- 11,670% mortality over-estimation in Japan
- 392% mortality over-estimation in Sweden

When asked why their models were so horrendously wrong, Neil Ferguson and the ICL have frequently attempted to turn their astounding over-estimations into wins which, they claim, "may have prevented 3.1M deaths," in Europe alone.[51] And this underscores the biggest problem with these models. Since we know that there was, at best, no correlation at all between lockdown measures and deaths and, in-reality, an observable pattern connecting the *most* strict countries with *more* death, it is clear the most fundamental assumptions the ICL makes are flat-out wrong. And if there's anything a modeler knows, it's that bad assumptions make for bad modeling—garbage in, garbage out.

And this is an issue all models face. In fact, the more assumptions a model has, the more likely it is to spit out meaningless results. In the case of the ICL model, assumptions seem to have been made about whether or not lockdowns and other measures would be useful, the extent to which they would be useful, the trajectory of alleged infection in each country, and the actions of each country, at least. If any one of these assumptions is wrong, the forecast accuracy will be impacted. Now imagine the impact if more than one are wrong. This was clearly the case with the ICL model. For example, the false assumption lockdowns were useful then leads to a false assumption about how useful they would be. This is what allows Ferguson and the ICL to fantasize in press releases about how many lives they saved. And if you can't take all this from me, someone who has made a career out of modeling and understanding its limitations, take it from Anthony Fauci[52]:

> *"I've looked at all the models. I've spent a lot of time on the models. They don't tell you anything. You can't really rely upon models."*

Fauci said this in April of 2020, a month after the model's release and subsequent influence on, "American officials," per the *New York Times*. Though we don't have a quote of Fauci directly supporting or citing it in March of 2020, it is curious that these unnamed officials would be so at odds only a month earlier with the apparent figurehead of the pandemic response. Given our exhaustive coverage on Fauci's speaking out of both sides of his mouth whenever convenient, and his support at the time for coercive measures such as lockdowns, it is hard to believe he wouldn't have signed on with its conclusions in March. It becomes even harder to believe when one accounts for the shocking conflicts of interest we will later find tie together Fauci and the ICL.

All of the above though is to say nothing of the fact that even if mortality counts were accurately projected by lockdown supporters, it would not support their conclusions on its own. For example, we saw my example where I modeled out, "Covid deaths," using common cold case rates and testing assumptions. So as we've already discussed, what is far more important is how death/case counts are collected, and during the Covid era they were collected with an either careless or intentional fraudulence. So even if I came up with the simplest, most accurate trend model of, "Covid," deaths, all I would be forecasting is the rate at which data was being misrepresented.

What Is a Covid Case?

In our section on Covid mortality methodology we discovered that the CDC permitted the counting of, "probable," or, "presumed," Covid cases among the dead. But how exactly do they determine what, "probable," means? Here's how[53]:

> ### "Probable
> - *Meets clinical criteria **AND** epidemiologic linkage with no confirmatory or presumptive laboratory evidence for SARS-CoV-2, **OR***
> - *Meets presumptive laboratory evidence, **OR***
> - *Meets vital records criteria with no confirmatory laboratory evidence for SARS-CoV-2."*

The second bullet refers to testing, while the third bullet refers to deaths being considered as cases despite have no confirmatory evidence at all. Each of these points we've discussed the faults of in great detail. The first point is what we will focus on now. Based these distinct, "or," definitions we can consider each in isolation, but for the first bullet there are a few more things we need to define. Specifically, we need to understand the CDC's definition of, "clinical," and, "epidemiological," evidence[54]:

> ### "Clinical Criteria
> *In the absence of a more likely diagnosis:*
> - *Acute onset or worsening of at least two of the following symptoms or signs:*
>   - *Fever (measured or subjected),*
>   - *Chills,*
>   - *Rigors,*
>   - *Myalgia,*
>   - *Headache,*

114

- o *Sore throat,*
- o *Nausea or vomiting,*
- o *Diarrhea,*
- o *Fatigue,*
- o *Congestion or runny nose.*

OR

- • *Acute onset or worsening of any one of the following symptoms or signs:*
  - o *Cough,*
  - o *Shortness of breath,*
  - o *Difficulty breathing,*
  - o *Olfactory disorder,*
  - o *Taste disorder,*
  - o *Confusion or change in mental status,*
  - o *Persistent pain or pressure in the chest,*
  - o *Pale, gray, or blue-colored skin, lips, or nail beds, depending on skin tone,*
  - o *Inability to wake or stay awake.*

OR

- • *Severe respiratory illness with at least one of the following:*
  - o *Clinical or radiographic evidence of pneumonia,*
  - o *Acute respiratory distress syndrome (ARDS)."*

The first bewildering point to be made about these clinical criteria is this: SARS stands for, "Severe Acute Respiratory Syndrome." Given this definition, it makes absolutely no sense for the third bullet to be an, "or," bullet. We've spoken about this before and the CDC confirms it in this same summary when they say, "it is assumed there is no pre-existing human immunity to the virus."[55] If this is true, how can anyone with a novel SARS-causing virus to which they are not immune, not literally have a severe acute respiratory syndrome? And if they don't have a severe acute respiratory syndrome, how can they possibly be diagnosed with a disease related to it?

The answer to this second question comes from the surprisingly long symptom list the CDC provides in the first two bullets. Apparently, every single symptom a human being can experience when sick is a symptom of, "Covid." And the best part we

115

can see in the second bullet is—Covid can be diagnosed with as little as a cough, and *only* a cough! In my own personal experience this absurd CDC clinical criteria is what caused me to be denied care from an urgent care facility, because along with my parasite-caused diarrhea I also happened to have a cough. The US Centers for **Disease Control and Prevention** is directly responsible for my denial of care for a *parasite*. Think about how ironic that is. And I am certainly not an isolated, "case," in my incident, as anyone with symptoms as common as a headache, runny nose, vomiting, or *confusion* are also apparently worrisome enough to warrant SARS suspicion. The social consequences the CDC has facilitated (if not outright created) around that suspicion have been comparable to psychological torture, but more on that to come.

To be fair, "epidemiological," evidence must also support the clinical conclusions we just discussed. So next we will take a look at the CDC definition for that[56]:

> ### *"Epidemiologic Linkage*
> *One or more of the following exposures in the prior 14 days:*
> - *Close contact[t] with a confirmed or probable case of COVID-19 disease; OR*
> - *Member of an exposed risk cohort as defined by public health authorities during an outbreak or during high community transmission.*
>
> [t] *Close contact is generally defined as being within 6 feet for at least 15 minutes (cumulative over a 24-hour period). However, it depends on the exposure level and setting; for example, in the setting of an aerosol-generating procedure in health settings without proper personal protective equipment (PPE), this may be defined as any duration."*

Considering the high likelihood of at some point encountering someone who tested positive with the tremendous false-positive-rate-producing tests we discussed, it is pretty clear that an interaction with a, "probable," case is very high for anyone who didn't remain in their home for the entire Covid era. In fact a, "probable," case can simply be someone with effectively any symptoms, who interacts with another, "probable," case (someone with effectively any symptoms).

116

This is a backwards methodology which has completely perverted diagnostics in 2020-2021, as my small parasite example demonstrates. It allowed anything to be turned into, "Covid," and with the news blaring the fad on high 24/7, mass confirmation bias was inevitable. For those of us who lived during this time, every cough or sneeze was assumed, "Covid," by scared people. The tremendous amount of evidence and whistleblowing which has accumulated out of hospitals as a result show my example was just one in an entire medical system worth of others. But by early 2022, after almost two years of pretending otherwise, at a time when they needed it to look like the inoculations weren't failing as they undeniably were for the children of whom they'd recently been authorized, Anthony Fauci was forced to admit the truth of the, "Covid case," situation[57]:

> *"If you look at the children that are hospitalized with Covid, many of them are hospitalized **with** Covid, as opposed to **because of** Covid."*

Many other faithful servants, including New York Governor Kathy Hochul, echoed this new talking point.[58] CDC Director Rochelle Walensky even went as far as to finally confess as many as 40% of, "Covid hospitalizations," were not actually admitted for any Covid-type illness (flu/respiratory), while more still came in with only mild cold/flu symptoms.[59] The number was, in fact, slightly higher than 40% in New York and if you acknowledge that many of the test results are useless there's no reason to think the other 60% are receiving a meaningful diagnosis either, but we've already covered that. Still, the implications we will demonstrate this to have had because of the lack of normal treatment for, "Covid," patients were enormous and put the 17.7% mortality increase which resulted into context. This was a complete failure of the hospital system caused by the centralizing influence of the public health organizations themselves. And though they might now pretend they couldn't have known, they did know, and they spent the entirety of the prior two years responding to anyone who pointed it out with, "fact-checks," and the slanderous claim of, "misinformation."

Has SARS-CoV-2 Ever Been Isolated?
There is a lot of debate on the topic of whether SARS-CoV-2 has ever even truly been isolated in a purified sample and also

demonstrated to cause the never-ending-symptom-list disease called, "Covid." Given the CDC's willingness to declare, "asymptomatic infection," possible—and thus admit it doesn't necessarily *cause disease*—this seems like a more than fair thing to investigate. We will touch on the points of that debate in a moment. The most important questions I have always had on this topic though, which in my opinion are far more important than the debate over whether or not a specific paper shows the actual virus, are the following:

1. As we remember from the previous chapter, the actual virus was admitted as not being available to the Corman-Drosten PCR testing protocol developers. Instead, they used a theoretical (in-silico) version of the virus in order to calibrate the tests. Given this, if the virus *was* newly-isolated at any point after the Corman-Drosten test was developed, as is claimed, how then can it be explained that this protocol was not completely scrapped by the WHO immediately following isolation?

2. Why wouldn't the tests at least require immediate re-calibration based on the newly-isolated virus, considering it could not have possibly matched the in-silico version?

3. If the CDC's test is different from the Corman-Drosten WHO-sponsored test, why is it different and how can there not be a comparison on accuracy to standardize the tests?

4. Why was an analysis not completed, documented, and explained for how different the in-silico and actual viruses were?

5. Is the claim that the theoretically-modeled virus is the *exact same* as the one which actually occurred in nature? If so, we've already touched on the inaccuracy of models and why this is not even remotely believable.

6. Why did it take until December 2020 for a team of disinterested, external scientists to peer review and demand rejection of this in-silico protocol?

7. Why even after this external peer review did the WHO never formally acknowledge the error of their ways?

These are questions which never get answered because those they seek to query refuse to dialogue with those who have the audacity to ask such reasonable, important questions.

Now, before we get into the subject of viral isolation, I must be fully transparent: I am obviously not a virologist or biologist. So speaking to the specifics of lab work, electron microscopy, and the meaningfulness of purification is not something I'm going to pretend I have the background to do. What I will say though is that especially on such a complicated topic, it is as important as ever to take nothing at face value. There is no claim, on any topic, made by any person, which should be beyond your comprehension enough to simply accept without some form of support or predictive ability. If there is something that doesn't make sense or is confusing, questions must be asked until any issues are resolved. As Hitchens's Razor dictates, the burden of proof regarding the truthfulness of a claim lies with the one who makes the claim.[60] In this case the burden of proof is on the public health organizations and proponents of the novel coronavirus theory, who in my opinion have failed miserably to provide satisfactory proof on any of the subjects which we have or will discuss.

At the same time, I've already laid out fundamental problems I see which inherently suggest that either the virus hasn't actually been isolated at all, or whatever is being seen under the microscope hasn't been demonstrated to cause disease if it has. What I will highlight beyond that will focus on the opinions of scientists who are better equipped than myself to go deeper than that on viral identification. And I find it particularly necessary to document them for four reasons which we will elaborate on:

1. The process of, "isolation," as the CDC describes it (and mainstream virology, apparently), seems to make no sense at all to me as far as what the assumed definition of, "isolation," should be

2. The predictive ability of these opposition scientists, as it relates to treatments, mitigation recommendations, etc., has been far superior to that of the public health organizations from whose opinions on this subject they differ. In fact, a better distinction would be: they treat people, and the public health organizations do not. Also, by stark contrast to public health, the prescriptions/solutions of the aforementioned

scientists have largely been humane and they have not been coercive.

3. Their primary question as it relates to the alleged novel coronavirus is the same question Kary Mullis was unable to find an answer to as it related to HIV—specifically, where is the paper which demonstrates SARS-CoV-2, isolated from a symptomatic person and then brought in contact with a healthy person or cell, causes the disease called Covid-19?

4. As stated in the author's note, one of the primary purposes of this book is to document the history which authoritarian censors have openly admitted (Event 201, Social Media, Media, etc.) to trying to erase from the consciousness of the masses. The scientists who give these opinions have universally been the subject of this censorship despite their sterling credentials. In a well-functioning society however, a public debate would have been had between both sides and featured by our largest institutions. Not only did the unelected public health authority figures demanding such dramatic societal changes not engage in such a debate, they actively attempted to and called for the suppression of the other side. Thanks to algorithms and the extreme centralization of the mainstream media, in many ways they succeeded. For the sake of human health, dignity, and intellectual advancement however, this cannot be permitted to go unanswered.

So without further caveat, I will focus mostly on a summary provided by Dr. Andrew Kaufman. Dr. Kaufman is not a man yelling at the wind alone in this regard, either. His opinion that modern virology itself is an extremely weak science is shared by many other medical experts including such names as Dr. Tom Cowan, Dr. Stefan Lanka, Dr. Robert Young, Dr. William P. Trebing, Dr. Tom Barnett, Torsten Engelbrecht, and Robert F. Kennedy Jr., to name a few. As explained by, Dr. Kaufman[61]:

"... We have a situation where if we're going to demonstrate that we've discovered a new organism—like they say that a virus would be—then we have to show that we can find that alleged organism in nature, you know, so that we can study it—we take a specimen of it and look at it in a laboratory—

you know, like you [interviewer] *do on a daily basis. And then we can dissect it and see what it's made of, take out the genetic material and sequence that if there is any.*

And I just assumed that would be how they discover viruses. But what has happened is, since the 1950's they have this procedure that they call, 'isolation,' but it's actually a complete inversion of the meaning of that word. What they do is they have the possible or the putative source of an alleged virus or a possible virus in nature that they might have a theory is causing a disease, but they can't actually find it.

So what they do is they take the diseased tissue from whatever organism and they mix it in a foreign cell culture—often using cells of monkeys. But they do some further things to make the cell culture not grow well—they're not nice to it—they add poisonous chemicals and they remove critical nutrients and they create what I call a starvation diet. And then when they show there's damage to those cells in the culture they say that that's evidence of a virus.

And then they show electron microscope pictures of particles, but as we've seen even the scientists in that field knew about this problem for a long time that the particles they see are just what happens when cells break down in the process of dying. And they can't be distinguished from each other in any way based on appearance because they've never been actually shown to exist separately in nature and they've never been purified in any form that could be used for further study—like as a reference material that you mentioned.

*They do have what they might call reference material available but what it is, is they just take the fluid from the cell culture and filter it and put it in a vial. **And interestingly— and I think this is actually the purpose of why they use this experiment—that's the same exact procedure to manufacture a vaccine** (my emphasis). Because that very same fluid from that cell culture is essentially the vaccine material, minus the adjuvants.*"

Dr. Kaufman's claims sound shocking for a variety of reasons. First, can it really be that the process of so-called, "virus isolation," really just involves mixing a diseased person's snot sample with poisons and monkey cells, and then claiming the mess that results is somehow an isolated virus? The answer, straight from the CDC, is that's exactly what they do.[62]

First, they use, "Vero CCL-81 cells," which are monkey kidney cells.[63] If one had already isolated a virus, one would think it could be an appropriate experiment to see how healthy monkey cells (I would imagine, similar to humans/mammals) react to the introduction of the isolated virus. This however, is not what the CDC uses the Vero cells for. Instead, they culture them with, "heat-activated fetal bovine serum (5% or 10%) and antibiotics/antimycotics," as well as the, "NP (nasopharyngeal) and OP (oropharyngeal) swab specimens," from the sick patient who they *believe* has the new virus. To summarize, exactly as Dr. Kaufman says, the process the CDC and modern virology follows is *not* to first isolate the virus from the NP and OP specimens and *then* to see if it can infect a cell, such as a Vero cell. Instead, it is to combine the Vero cell, antibiotics, antimycotics (anti-fungal), fetal bovine serum (liquid remaining after blood drained from bovine fetus), and sick person's sputum into a soup.[64]

The cultures are then observed under certain conditions, as the cells are inevitably damaged by the nutrient-draining antibiotics (which literally means "anti-life" from the Greek word "bios") and antimycotics. In fact, from a 2017 study by Ryu et al. in *Scientific Reports*, we can see various studies have demonstrated changes in gene expression and regulation *in vitro* can even be induced by antibiotics.[65] According to another such study drawing exactly this conclusion, "data from studies in which antibiotics are used for cell cultures should be examined with caution."[66] Noted!

What is also simple to understand about this synopsis is that viruses are considered dead organisms. It would therefore make sense that the excretions which might occur during cell death (brought on by environmental toxins, malnutrition, and/or stress factors—as introduced to the Vero cell in the culture) could be confused for, "replication," of a virus (dead cell tissue), when in reality it is decay/excretions of the dying cell.

What is also somewhat easy to understand, but perhaps less easy to stomach, is how this process could then be used to make vaccines. Typically, a traditional vaccine (of which the Covid inoculations are not) is understood to contain a, "killed," virus.

Considering viruses are, "isolated," in the way described above however, it's hard to say with any confidence this is actually the case or that what is called a, "killed virus," is actually something you'd want inside of you. But traditional vaccines are a topic for another book that I probably will not have any desire to write.

To continue, a reinforcing summary by Dr. Tom Cowan[67]:

"When you come to do—uh—the alignment, from my understanding—the way I explain it to people is when you're talking about finding the genome of a virus, you're talking about finding the pieces or components of a bigger thing, right? So the virus is the bigger thing and the genome is one of the pieces of this virus, supposedly. And so the question is, how does a human-being find out the components of anything? So you could take a book and you could say, 'what are the letters that make up the book?' And as long as you have the book, if you want to you can go through the painstaking process of writing out the letters that make up that page or that chapter or whatever ... But that's how human beings understand what something is made of—they start with the whole thing and then they take it apart piece by piece trying to remember which piece lined up with which one, and that's how we do it.

Virologists have somehow turned it around and done it the other way. So, in other words, they start with a million or so letters ... and then they say to you, 'okay, make the book.' Most people would say, 'which book?' And then they say, 'I'm not telling you which book. This is unbiased de novo genome sequencing, so you can't be biased...'"

As mentioned, the aforementioned issues around the lack of purification have gone unanswered with no one from the public health organizations willing to have a debate.[68] In the absence of such a debate, the only way to get closer to the truth is to continue asking for proof from those organizations which use this methodology to justify tyranny. To this end, at least 177 Freedom of Information Act requests have been made to governments around the world asking for said proof of SARS-CoV-2, as documented by a Canadian watchdog group.[69] According to the group, all 177 have either confirmed the process Dr. Cowan and Dr. Kaufman claim does not represent isolation or have outright declined to respond with no proof provided at all.

For full disclosure, I will conclude this topic by clarifying that several alternative and public-health-exiled doctors *do* find the public health method of isolation satisfactory, including Dr. Robert Malone and Dr. Joseph Mercola.[70] They too admit that the ability for the alleged virus to create disease is dependent on the person's health conditions, among other factors, and do not support the coercive public health endeavors. But they still believe there is adequate support for the existence and relevance-to-disease of the virus, due to whole genome sequencing (the process Dr. Cowan describes as backwards). They also cite studies which they claim matched the proposed genome of the alleged virus.

This is fine. In fact, this is more than fine—it's fantastic. It is fantastic to see real scientists with seemingly honest, disinterested intentions disagree and debate about the nature of things. That *is* science. It is for everyone else to decide for themselves, based on this breadth of opinions, which side they think is more predictive of the situation and should guide their actions toward the best outcome.

While I continue to have questions I feel are unanswered from the novel virus proponents and do not believe that paradigm to be a helpful one in my own personal experience, I have no interest in convincing you, dear reader, to decide either way. This is because whether the virus exists or not is irrelevant to the damage done by public health officials in every way we've covered to this point. Lockdowns, masks, censorship, isolation, the tests used, and methodologies used were all still destructive no matter which side is correct. That said, I am not a medical professional, and this book is not about providing any kind of advice about your unique health situation. My only goal here was to present both sides in the interest that you might know a debate exists on this topic at all. Especially as the ideology of the Covid collaborators continues to fall apart and this decade-long culture of censorship continues to plague our society, it is and will continue to be an incredibly relevant debate in the future.

Endnotes

1   Macias, Amanda. 2021. "Fauci Says Face Masks Could Become Seasonal After Covid Pandemic". *Cnbc.Com.*

https://www.cnbc.com/2021/05/09/fauci-says-masks-could-become-seasonal-after-covid-pandemic.html.

2   "Past Seasons Estimated Influenza Disease Burden | CDC".
    2020. *Cdc.Gov.* https://www.cdc.gov/flu/about/burden/past-seasons.html.

3   "2020-2021 Flu Season Summary". 2021. *Cdc.Gov.*
    https://www.cdc.gov/flu/season/faq-flu-season-2020-2021.htm.

4   Ibid.

5   Vajda, Judith, Dennis Weber, Dominik Brekel, Boris Hundt, and Egbert
    Müller. 2016. "Size Distribution Analysis Of Influenza Virus Particles
    Using Size Exclusion Chromatography". *Journal Of Chromatography
    A* 1465: 117-125. doi:10.1016/j.chroma.2016.08.056.

6   Dougherty, Michael Brendan. 2021. "Fauci: Criticizing Me Is Criticizing
    Science | National Review". *Nationalreview.Com.*
    https://www.nationalreview.com/corner/fauci-criticizing-me-is-
    criticizing-science/.

7   Campbell, Denis. 2012. "Hospitals 'Full To Bursting' As Bed Shortage
    Hits Danger Level". *The Guardian.*
    https://www.theguardian.com/society/2012/dec/02/hospitals-full-
    bursting-nhs-report.

8   Campbell, Denis. 2013. "Hospitals Scramble To Prevent Crisis In NHS's
    'Toughest Ever' Winter". *The Guardian.*
    https://www.theguardian.com/society/2013/nov/24/nhs-hospitals-
    toughest-winter-flu-weather-vomiting.

9   Taylor, Diane. 2014. "Fears Of NHS Winter Crisis After Major Incident
    At Colchester Hospital". *The Guardian.*
    https://www.theguardian.com/society/2014/nov/14/colchester-hospital-
    sedation-restraint-cqc-nhs-crisis.

10 Siddique, Haroon. 2015. "Hospital Bed Occupancy Rates Hit Record
    High Risking Care". *The Guardian.*
    https://www.theguardian.com/society/2015/mar/27/nhs-hospital-bed-
    occupancy-rates-hit-record-figures-risking-care.

11 Campbell, Denis. 2016. "NHS Hospitals Facing Toughest Winter Yet,
    Say Health Experts". *The Guardian.*
    https://www.theguardian.com/society/2016/dec/21/nhs-hospitals-facing-
    toughest-winter-yet-say-health-experts.

12 Campbell, Denis. 2017. "Hospitals 'Dangerously Full' During Winter
    Crisis, Says Thinktank". *The Guardian.*
    https://www.theguardian.com/society/2017/jan/28/hospitals-dangerously-
    full-during-winter-crisis-says-thinktank.

13 Campbell, Denis. 2018. "Hospitals In Race To Combat 'Toughest Ever'
    Winter Crisis For NHS". *The Guardian.*
    https://www.theguardian.com/society/2018/dec/08/nhs-hospitals-
    emergency-measures-winter-crisis.

14 Campbell, Denis. 2019. "'Breaking Point': Fears Over Lack Of Intensive
    Care Beds For Children". *The Guardian.*

https://www.theguardian.com/society/2019/dec/29/nhs-picu-shortage-intensive-care-beds-critically-ill-children.

15   Nolan, John. 1988. "Sense Of Smell Can Be Victim Of Bout With Flu". *Los Angeles Times*. https://www.latimes.com/archives/la-xpm-1988-02-21-mn-44059-story.html.

16   The Department of Health and Human Services. 2020. "Guidance For Certifying Deaths Due To Coronavirus Disease 2019 (COVID–19)". DHHS, CDC, NCHS, and NVSS.

17   "IDPH Director Explains How Covid Deaths Are Classified". 2020. *Homesteadingtoday.Com*. https://www.homesteadingtoday.com/threads/idph-director-explains-how-covid-deaths-are-classified.607908/.

18   "US COVID-19 Cases And Deaths By State". 2020. *Usafacts.Org*. https://www.usafacts.org/visualizations/coronavirus-covid-19-spread-map/.

19   Marsh, Julia. 2020. "NYC's Coronavirus Death Toll Surpasses 10K With New Tally Of Home Deaths". *Nypost.Com*. https://www.nypost.com/2020/04/14/nycs-coronavirus-death-toll-surpasses-10k-with-new-tally-of-home-deaths/.

20   UK Office of National Statistics. 2022. "COVID-19 Deaths In 2020 And 2021 Within 28 And 60 Days Of A Positive Test". UK ONS.

21   "Common Colds". 2021. *Centers For Disease Control And Prevention*. https://www.cdc.gov/features/rhinoviruses/index.html.

22   "United States Death Statistics Per Year". 2022. *Dead Or Kicking*. Accessed March 6. https://deadorkicking.com/death-statistics/us/per-year/.

23   "Provisional Mortality Data — United States, 2020". 2021. *The Centers For Disease Control And Prevention*. https://www.cdc.gov/mmwr/volumes/70/wr/mm7014e1.htm.

24   Ealy, Henry, Michael McEvoy, Daniel Chong, John Nowicki, Monica Sava, Sandeep Gupta, David White, James Jordan, Daniel Simon, and Paul Anderson. 2020. "COVID-19 Data Collection, Comorbidity & Federal Law: A Historical Retrospective". *Science, Public Health Policy, And The Law* 2 (4-22): 1. https://standforhealthfreedom.com/wp-content/uploads/2021/09/2-2020-COVID-Data-A-Historical-Retrospective-IPAK-v24.pdf.

25   Ibid, 3.

26   Ibid, 21.

27   Daly, Rich. 2020. "Hospitals In COVID-19 Hotspots To Receive $10 Billion More In Federal Aid". *Hfma*. https://www.hfma.org/topics/news/2020/07/the-new-round-will-pay--50-000-per-covid-19-admission--compared-.html. .

28   Fussell, Blake. 2020. "CDC Director Agrees Hospitals Have Monetary Incentive To Inflate COVID-19 Data". *The Christian Post*. https://www.christianpost.com/news/cdc-director-agrees-that-hospitals-have-monetary-incentive-to-inflate-covid-19-data.html.

29   Miltimore, Jon. 2020. "Physicians Say Hospitals Are Pressuring ER Docs To List COVID-19 On Death Certificates. Here's Why". *Fee.Org*. https://www.fee.org/articles/physicians-say-hospitals-are-pressuring-er-docs-to-list-covid-19-on-death-certificates-here-s-why/.

30   Dreher, Rod. 2020. "Why Did Youtube Remove The Doctors' Briefing? - The American Conservative". *The American Conservative*. https://www.theamericanconservative.com/why-did-youtube-remove-the-doctors-briefing/.

31   Ahmad, Farida B., and Robert N. Anderson. 2021. "The Leading Causes Of Death In The US For 2020". *JAMA* 325 (18): 1829. doi:10.1001/jama.2021.5469.

32   Rancourt, Denis, Marine Baudin, and Jérémie Mercier. 2021. "Analysis Of All-Cause Mortality By Week In Canada 2010-2021, By Province, Age And Sex: There Was No COVID-19 Pandemic, And There Is Strong Evidence Of Response-Caused Deaths In The Most Elderly And In Young Males". Denis Rancourt. https://denisrancourt.ca/entries.php?id=104&name=2021_08_06_analysis_of_all_cause_mortality_by_week_in_canada_2010_2021_by_province_age_and_sex_there_was_no_covid_19_pandemic_and_there_is_strong_evidence_of_response_caused_deaths_in_the_most_elderly_and_in_young_males.

33   Ibid, 4.

34   Ibid, 18.

35   Ibid, 47.

36   Rancourt, Denis, Marine Baudin, and Jérémie Mercier. 2021. "Nature of the COVID-Era public health disaster in the USA, from all-cause mortality and socio-geo-economic and climatic data". Denis Rancourt. https://denisrancourt.ca/entries.php?id=107&name=2021_10_25_nature_of_the_covid_era_public_health_disaster_in_the_usa_from_all_cause_mortality_and_socio_geo_economic_and_climatic_data.

37   Kirsch, Steve. 2022. "Very Clear Thinking From An RCMP Officer Who Is Now On Unpaid Leave". *Stevekirsch.Substack.Com*. https://stevekirsch.substack.com/p/very-clear-thinking-from-an-rcmp?s=r.

38   Pavlich, Katie. 2020. "In Colorado, They're Counting Gun Shot Fatalities As COVID Deaths". *Townhall*. https://www.townhall.com/tipsheet/katiepavlich/2020/12/17/in-colorado-theyre-counting-gun-shot-fatalities-as-covid-deaths-n2581730.

39   Shea, Sydney. 2021. "New Zealand Man Who Died Of Gunshot Wound To Be Recorded As COVID-19 Death: Report". *Washington Examiner*. https://www.washingtonexaminer.com/policy/healthcare/new-zealand-man-who-died-of-gunshot-wound-to-be-recorded-as-covid-19-death-report.

40   Zimmer, Beau. 2020. "Governor Questions Traffic Fatality Initially Classified As COVID-19 Death". *Wtsp*. https://www.wtsp.com/article/news/health/coronavirus/governor-

questions-traffic-fatality-classified-covid-19-death/67-f77eeb4b-b002-40d3-bda8-675c1796df40.

41   "United States COVID - Coronavirus Statistics - Worldometer". 2020. *Worldometers.Info*. https://www.worldometers.info/coronavirus/country/us/.

42   "COVID Live - Coronavirus Statistics - Worldometer". 2020. *Worldometers.Info*. https://www.worldometers.info/coronavirus/.

43   "United States Population (2022) - Worldometer". 2022. *Worldometers.Info*. Accessed March 5. https://www.worldometers.info/world-population/us-population.

44   "World Population Clock: 7.9 Billion People (2022) - Worldometer". 2022. *Worldometers.Info*. Accessed March 5. https://www.worldometers.info/world-population/.

45   Mahoney, Wendy Strauch. 2022. "HHS Drops Reporting Of Daily COVID-19 Deaths And Adds Pediatric Reporting Guidelines - Uncoverdc". *Uncoverdc*. https://uncoverdc.com/2022/01/17/hhs-drops-reporting-of-daily-covid-19-deaths-and-adds-pediatric-reporting-guidelines/.

46   Bartholomew, Robert. 1998. "The Seattle Windshield Pitting Epidemic: A Famous Mass Delusion Of The Twentieth Century". *Rr0.Org*. https://rr0.org/time/1/9/9/8/Bartholomew_TheSeattleWindshieldPittingEpidemic/index.html.

47   Neil M Ferguson, Daniel Laydon, Gemma Nedjati-Gilani et al. 2020. "Impact of non-pharmaceutical interventions (NPIs) to reduce COVID-19 mortality and healthcare demand." *Imperial College London*. https://doi.org/10.25561/77482.

48   Landler, Mark, and Stephen Castle. 2020. "Behind The Virus Report That Jarred The U.S. And The U.K. To Action (Published 2020)". *Nytimes.Com*. https://www.nytimes.com/2020/03/17/world/europe/coronavirus-imperial-college-johnson.html.

49   Friedman, Joseph, Patrick Liu, Emmanuela Gakidou, Christopher E. Troeger, Austin Carter, Robert C. Reiner Jr., and Ryan M. Barber et al. 2020. "Predictive Performance Of International COVID-19 Mortality Forecasting Models". doi:10.1101/2020.07.13.20151233.

50   Magness, Phillip W. 2021. "Imperial College Predicted Catastrophe In Every Country On Earth...". *AIER*. https://www.aier.org/article/imperial-college-predicted-catastrophe-in-every-country-on-earth-then-the-models-failed/.

51   Wighton, Kate. 2020. "Lockdown And School Closures In Europe May Have Prevented 3.1M Deaths | Imperial News | Imperial College London". *Imperial News*. https://www.imperial.ac.uk/news/198074/lockdown-school-closures-europe-have-prevented-/?fbclid=IwAR3X6xqqXEyemthHFrAdGNa_d7T6VgBZaQS-ncbz8b_9mlHeZyt0mQqZlmw.

52   Morse, Brandon. 2020. "Fauci: We Can't Really Rely On Coronavirus Models". *Redstate.Com.* https://www.redstate.com/brandon_morse/2020/04/03/fauci-we-cant-really-rely-on-models-n133329.

53   "Coronavirus Disease 2019 (COVID-19) 2021 Case Definition". 2021. *Cdc,Gov.* https://ndc.services.cdc.gov/case-definitions/coronavirus-disease-2019-2021/.

54   Ibid.

55   Ibid.

56   Ibid.

57   Barkoukis, Leah. 2021. "Fauci Finally Admits Something About Covid-19 Others Have Been Censored For Saying". *Townhall.* https://townhall.com/tipsheet/leahbarkoukis/2021/12/31/fauci-kids-hospitalizations-n2601257.

58   Colarossi, Natalie. 2022. "42 Percent Of New York's Hospitalized COVID Patients Admitted For Other Reasons". *Newsweek.* https://www.newsweek.com/42-new-yorks-hospitalized-covid-patients-admitted-other-reasons-1667220.

59   Cole, Brendan. 2022. "Jake Tapper Rails Against "Misleading" CDC COVID Hospitalization Numbers". *Newsweek.* https://www.newsweek.com/jake-tapper-cnn-cdc-rochelle-walensky-covid-gupta-1667833.

60   "Hitchens's Razor". 2022. *The Spiritual Life.* Accessed March 5. https://www.slife.org/hitchenss-razor/.

61   "Drs. Thomas Cowan And Andrew Kaufman Interviewed By Mike Adams: Why The "Virus" Pandemic Is A FARCE - Freedom Of Speech". 2021. *Freedom Of Speech.* https://www.fos-sa.org/2021/08/30/drs-thomas-cowan-and-andrew-kaufman-interviewed-by-mike-adams-why-the-virus-pandemic-is-a-farce/.

62   Harcourt J, Tamin A, Lu X, Kamili S, Sakthivel SK, Murray J, et al. 2020. "Severe Acute Respiratory Syndrome Coronavirus 2 from Patient with Coronavirus Disease". *Emerging Infectious Diseases,* 26(6), 1266-1273. https://doi.org/10.3201/eid2606.200516.

63   "Vero Cells: Green Kidneys To Produce Vaccines". 2022. *Blog.Genofab.Com.* Accessed March 5. https://blog.genofab.com/vero-cells.

64   "What Is Fetal Bovine Serum | Thermo Fisher Scientific - UK". 2022. *Thermofisher.Com.* Accessed March 5. https://www.thermofisher.com/us/en/home/references/gibco-cell-culture-basics/cell-culture-environment/culture-media/fbs-basics/what-is-fetal-bovine-serum.html.

65   Ryu, Ann H., Walter L. Eckalbar, Anat Kreimer, Nir Yosef, and Nadav Ahituv. 2017. "Use Antibiotics In Cell Culture With Caution: Genome-Wide Identification Of Antibiotic-Induced Changes In Gene Expression And Regulation". *Scientific Reports* 7 (1). doi:10.1038/s41598-017-07757-w.

66   Stone, Mike. 2021. "The Effects Of Antibiotics On Cell Cultures". *Viroliegy*. https://www.viroliegy.com/2021/08/25/the-effects-of-antibiotics-on-cell-cultures/.

67   "Freedom Talk 3". 2021. *Odysee*. https://odysee.com/@DeansDanes:1/Freedom-Talk-3-2:b.

68   "Has SARS-COV-2 Been Isolated And Purified To Show Existence?". 2021. *Algora Blog*. https://www.algora.com/Algora_blog/2021/08/21/has-sars-cov-2-been-isolated-and-purified-to-show-existence.

69   "Fois Reveal That Health/Science Institutions Around The World (177 And Counting!) Have No Record Of SARS-COV-2 Isolation/Purification, Anywhere, Ever – Fluoride Free Peel". 2022. *Fluoridefreepeel.Ca*. Accessed March 5. https://www.fluoridefreepeel.ca/fois-reveal-that-health-science-institutions-around-the-world-have-no-record-of-sars-cov-2-isolation-purification/.

70   Toupos, Josh. 2022. "Mercola: Yes, SARS-Cov-2 Is Real Virus | Amos37". *Amos37.Com*. Accessed March 6. https://amos37.com/mercola-yes-sars-cov-2-is-real-virus/.

Chapter 8

Treatments Pt. 1: The Lack Thereof

"There's been a global oblivion to the idea of treating patients with Covid-19. And that's everything that—that's what Americans want to know. They want to know, 'doctor, when I get Covid how do I avoid two bad outcomes: hospitalization and death?'

*...Patients get sick—they get sick for two weeks at home until they can't breathe anymore, **and then they become hospitalized and almost everybody dies in the hospital** (my emphasis)."*

—Dr. Peter McCullough[1]

In the previous two chapters we outlined a variety of ways in which the healthcare system, following the orders of centralized public health departments, misdiagnosed a viral pandemic using false tests and nonsensical methodologies. This, however, is not to say that there was not worse sickness and/or more death in 2020 (and beyond). In the United States there certainly was, which is unsurprising when considering the destructiveness of the public health actions we've described to this point including the consequences of lockdowns, an onslaught of unnecessary stress/fear, the recommendation/mandate of unhygienic practices such as mask-wearing, and the impact on health of anti-social behavior. But these things alone only scratch the surface on the cause of the devastation experienced in hospitals and nursing homes. In this chapter, we will explain the rest and answer the question: what *is* the disease Covid-19?

As Dr. Peter McCullough points out in the video from which the above quote is sourced, the focus from the beginning of the alleged pandemic was inoculations.[2] In a later chapter we will go very deep on demonstrating that—by their own admission—selling the public on these inoculations was the basis of the entire fraud, and we will explore the reasons why that was the case. However, the point McCullough drives home here is that there was no effort given by national or international public health organizations to provide, suggest, or recommend treatments outside of hospitals. In the context of the goal being universal inoculations, the reason for this should be obvious—if there's a cure, there's no incentive to inoculate.

Once in a hospital, a person's fate was effectively sealed, as he also mentions. This is because the, "treatments," recommended by public health officials, including but not limited to Anthony Fauci, were not treatments at all. Like the inoculations, these drugs had horrendous risk profiles—*a fact which would have been known* by Fauci himself, among others. However, no one questioned the horrendous outcomes in hospitals—places meant to *prevent* death and *treat* disease—because of the assumed novel nature of what was being faced.

But what was truly novel in this case was the drugs/strategies recommended to and utilized by these hospitals. And the devastation which resulted served only to further the panic of both the public and the hospital care-givers themselves. Thanks to this panic, as well as the financial incentives to diagnose, "Covid," patients, many of these hospitals happily followed the misguided orders of those providing the incentives.

At the same time, outpatient and early treatments *were* being effectively administered in the thousands by physicians including Dr. McCullough, Dr. Vladimir Zelenko, and Dr. Pierre Kory, to name a prominent few. Unlike the public health organizations, these physicians were actually providing care to patients throughout 2020 and beyond. They used known, repurposed drugs with infinitely lesser risk-profiles, and they did so to great success. For their efforts, they were censored, slandered, and threatened, many times with the support of the public health organizations whose actions they opposed. We will cover more on these physicians and their treatments in the next chapter, Treatments Pt. 2.

For now, I understand these are big claims. What I am hypothesizing here is that the novel misguidance of public health organizations, as followed by hospitals, caused the very sickness and death people attributed to a viral pandemic—in my opinion without evidence, based on all previous support. But there is a landslide of evidence for this hypothesis which I will provide here, and with all the hysteria of the past two years it should not be all that difficult for someone who lived through it to imagine this at least being a possibility.

What I am not alleging here is bad intent on the part of hospital systems as a whole, nor am I accusing your doctor/nurse cousin of any wrongdoing. In my professional career I have personal experience with hospital systems lying for financial gain and being caught/punished for it. Given that, I know there would have been corruption during such a time as this when financial incentives were so dramatically misaligned. And one need only recall former CDC director Redfield's remarks we highlighted previously on this very point to see that I'm not alone in this understanding.

But I also do not think hospitals and their staffs would have needed to be, "in on," anything sinister intentionally in order for such a result to have occurred. Many of these people faced extraordinary pressure, which was exacerbated by a type of war-time propaganda which was so on-the-nose it literally saw them referred to as, "front line," heroes. Many of them *are* heroic for their efforts, in the same way a soldier is heroic for theirs. The problem in my opinion, however, is that these heroes were sent to the, "front line," with bad information, provided by people who did not deserve the trust they were given. And just like in war, this is a losing strategy.

Fauci's "Standard of Care" Drug and the Fraud on Which It Was Supported

> *"This drug* [remdesivir] *happens to be blocking a enzyme that the virus uses, and that's an RNA polymerase, but there's a lot of other enzymes that the virus uses that are now gonna be targets for this.* **This will be the standard of care** (my emphasis). *"*
> —Anthony Fauci from the White House, April 29, 2020[3]

Though most will not realize it, April 29, 2020 would turn out to be a monumental day in the history of the Covid era. Specifically, three things happened simultaneously on that same day:

1. Anthony Fauci declared remdesivir the, "standard of care," for treatment of the pneumonia-like symptoms of, "Covid," based on a NIAID-sponsored study (his own organization)
2. A couple hours prior to Fauci's announcement, Gilead Sciences, the maker of remdesivir, released a statement on, "positive data from National Institute of Allergy and

133

Infectious Diseases' Study of investigational antiviral remdesivir for COVID-19"[4]

3. The *Lancet* published a randomized, double-blind, placebo-controlled, multicenter trial on remdesivir use in adults with severe COVID-19 symptoms, which found, "remdesivir was not associated with statistically significant clinical benefits," and, "more patients in the remdesivir group (12%) than the placebo group (5%) discontinued the study drug because of adverse events or severe adverse events"[5]

These events occurring together is fascinating for a variety of reasons—especially considering, as acknowledged by the Alliance for Human Research Protection (AHRP), that it was based on the aforementioned, "positive data," from the NIAID-sponsored study (and Fauci's White House promotion of it) alone that the FDA ultimately approved remdesivir for emergency use against, "Covid," as soon as *two days later* on May 1, 2020.[6] And per a *Science* magazine expose, "[the] FDA never consulted a group of outside experts that it has at the ready to weigh in on complicated antiviral drug issues," prior to the approval, which is typically a commonplace best-practice.[7]

To be clear: this was a drug which in Gilead's own statement they admitted was, "not yet licensed or approved anywhere globally," for *any* purpose and had, "not yet been demonstrated to be safe or effective for the treatment of COVID-19."[8] Given this caveat by the drug's manufacturer and the negative findings of the *Lancet* study, one would think the NIAID-sponsored study would have to have had airtight execution with downright impressive results to have led to such a swift FDA action. Unfortunately, this could not have been further from what happened.

First of all, as described by Olivia Goldhill of the publication *Quartz*, the data of the NIAID study was not peer-reviewed prior to its use for EUA approval, nor was it even made available to researchers for this purpose.[9] While, "there's definitely a space to announce things ahead of peer review," says James Heathers, a research scientist at Northeastern University, this does not justify Fauci's, "gold standard," claim or the FDA's EUA without necessary peer-review. And in the words of Holly Fernandez Lynch, a medical ethics professor at the University of Pennsylvania, "even Tony Fauci needs peer-review."

Second, when asked about the *Lancet*'s randomized, double-blind, placebo-controlled study (considered the, "gold standard," of trials generally) Fauci dismissed it as, "not adequate," apparently due to its smaller size. This is an interesting take considering that despite the NIAID study's larger size, *Reuters News* reported that prominent leaders in the medical community were not impressed with the outcomes of the NIAID study's primary endpoints (goal posts used to measure success), which were *revised mid-study* from a reduction in death to improvement in, "date of recovery."[10,11] One of those leaders was Dr. Eric Topol, director and founder of the Scripps Research Translational Institute, who actually referred to the *Lancet* trial as, "the only thing I'll hang my hat on," and called the results, "negative. It was expected to be a whopping effect. It clearly does not have that." This quote from a *Reuters*-acknowledged prominent doctor also completely contradicts Fauci's claim about the *Lancet* study that it was, "not an adequate study and everybody in the field feels that."[12] *Clearly* not the case. *Clearly* a lie.

And this is to say nothing of how, "dubious and suspicious," it is to have changed primary endpoints in the middle of a study, as the AHRP acknowledges. In the simplest terms, imagine you are trying to demonstrate to a friend that your dog has super powers. To prove this, you set up a trial where your primary endpoint is that your dog can jump 10 feet higher in the air than the average dog (placebo). This is a very specific, extraordinary thing for a dog to do as not only must he jump 10 feet in the air, he must jump an *additional* 10 feet over the average dog's jump. So if he can accomplish this, the claim of your dog having super powers might actually be warranted.

The problem is, as you begin logging jump heights you start to realize, "oh, crap ... Baxter isn't jumping 10 feet ... he's not even close to ten feet." Determined to prove how great your dog is, you refuse to admit failure toward the primary endpoint. Instead, you simply adjust it mid-study to be that the dog can simply jump *higher* than the average dog. The results then come in and he is higher—by about a half an inch. Do you claim victory still or do you admit the truth—namely, that you shifted the goal posts and your dog doesn't actually have super powers? As much as I wish my dog had super powers, I would admit the truth. Unfortunately for everyone who

135

depends on his judgement though, Anthony Fauci did not do that (and he's also a documented dog murderer, but more on that later...).

Silly example aside, the following is a quote from Dr. Steve Nissen to the *Washington Post*, in an article where they cover this scandal and Dr. Nissen expands on the red flags it presents[13]:

> *"I think that they thought they weren't going to win, and they wanted to change it to something they could win on. I prefer the original outcome. It's harder. It's a more meaningful endpoint. Getting out of the hospital early is useful, but it's not a game-changer."*

As Dr. Nissen's questioning makes clear, the primary endpoint change resulted in a conclusion which otherwise would have been negative. This leads to his accurate phrasing of the study's outcome in a, "win/loss," context. Fauci and NIAID's sponsorship of this study for *this* drug represents a vested interest in its outcome leading to a, "win," at a time when a, "win," was desperately needed. And this was not only the case for a, "pandemic response leader," in the opening days of a declared pandemic, but also for the relationship of the NIH, the federal government and Gilead, whose antiviral drug to this point had been an abject failure.

You see, the recommendation of remdesivir to treat, "Covid," came from the NIH Panel on COVID-19 Treatment Guidelines.[14] This panel included seven people with financial ties to Gilead, including Daniel Campbell, who is on Gilead's advisory board, as well as David Glidden and Eric Darr, who are consultants for the company. In addition to these members of the panel, a petition had been filed requesting Fauci himself (the highest paid government employee at over $410K annual salary) disclose any financial ties he might have to the company, since he had not yet done so related to *any* pharmaceutical company financial conflicts.[15,16] But besides their distinct conflicts with the company, the federal government and NIH were also heavily invested in the drug itself. According to a *Public Citizen* report, public financial support for remdesivir's development (initially for Ebola) totaled *at least* $70 million (likely higher), through federal grants and clinical trials.[17] Patent rights group Knowledge Ecology International (KEI) also discovered via Freedom of Information Act request that the US Army, the CDC, and the

NIH/NIAID all either conducted or funded much of the preclinical and clinical development of remdesivir.[18] They were initially blocked in this FOIA pursuit by the NIH, but received the disclosure after subsequently suing the organization for failure to respond.

And this is relevant especially because remdesivir is a particularly expensive drug. As a result of Fauci's promotion, the Trump administration bought up 500,000 treatment courses at around $3,200 per course.[19] For context, developed countries outside the US still pay around $2,340 per course, with generics manufacturers in India selling a copied design for $320 per course. Trump was not alone in buying up massive stocks of remdesivir however, as the European Commission also bought up 500,000 treatment courses in 2020.[20]

Just to summarize this entire deal in the simplest of terms, a taxpayer funded study was carried out by the organization of the highest-paid taxpayer funded government employee. This poorly-conducted study was used to measure the utility of a to-this-point failed drug, which was developed largely using taxpayer dollars. The study results were at odds with those of another study held in higher regard by prominent doctors/scientists, but was recommended and approved anyway by government panels with documented conflicts of interest and a direct development-funding arrangement with the manufacturing organization. The EUA then granted two days later gave sole treatment status to an extremely expensive drug with negligible benefits, no history of prior use, and a bad risk profile, bought up in droves with taxpayer money, by the same government that used taxpayer money to fund its development. And all of this occurred without as much as a peer review of the study's results, in an environment where censorship ran rampant and was encouraged by those spending the taxpayer money.

To put a few astonishing bows on this trove of corruption, KEI also reported in March of 2020 that the FDA had given Gilead a patent monopoly on remdesivir for seven years, despite extensive US government funding of the drug.[21] This means the FDA would not be allowed to register a generic version of the drug for use for, "Covid," for seven years. The FDA informed KEI that the decision about the patent application (including, curiously, the date of submission) was, "confidential," which KEI blasted[22]:

"... allowing Gilead an incredible monopoly on a potential treatment for a global pandemic, and giving them the power to charge incredibly high, national-budget-breaking prices for remdesivir. It is appalling that the FDA would hand over such a powerful monopoly in such an unprecedented time, and insist that the date of submission is confidential information when a corporation is seemingly manipulating statutes in order to ensure market superiority that was intended to help stimulate innovation in the treatment of truly rare diseases."

This is especially troubling because of the timing only one month before Fauci's sketchy study pronouncement and the subsequent EUA approval, but also because of how intensely the FDA in particular would act to suppress all other possible treatments (more on that in the next chapter) for the symptoms attributed to, "Covid." And to be fair, the act of granting EUAs to drugs with some unknowns during a declared, "emergency," is not particularly shocking or unethical on the face of it. But the way in which the FDA—in coordination with the NIH and CDC—failed to grant this same status to drugs with *better* demonstrated success and risk profiles, makes no sense whatsoever outside of some other motive.

Months after the EUA approval, on October 23, 2020 the FDA would grant full approval to remdesivir. To make matters even more absurd, this approval came one week after the WHO reported their own trial on the drug, titled, "Solidarity."[23] The Solidarity trial found remdesivir had little to no effect on a, "Covid," patient's chance of survival. Reporting on the FDA's full approval despite the negative outcome of this trial (among others), *USA Today* noted the strange situation, pointing out, "The U.S. Food and Drug Administration late Friday allowed the drug remdesivir to be used on all patients hospitalized with COVID-19, although no published research supports such widespread use."[24] They also got the opinion of Dr. Eric Topol on the matter, who said he was appalled by the expanded approval:

"It seems to be a pattern of approval without science, without data, without evidence. There are no data to support wide use of remdesivir. This is extraordinary."

138

Senators Bernie Sanders and Elizabeth Warren rightly questioned then-president Trump for the unethical deal to buy up remdesivir and the, "windfall," it would provide Gilead.[25] What they and many others seemingly failed to question in their game of politics however, is who was actually responsible (Fauci, the FDA, etc.) and whether or not remdesivir was even worth spending *any* taxpayer money on at all. In a press conference, US representative Lloyd Doggett got a little closer to making this point, acknowledging that, "Gilead is overcharging on a drug that was saved from the scrap heap of failed drugs only because of taxpayer-funded research."[26] And that's exactly what remdesivir was: a scrap heap drug—not only for its lack of effectiveness at its stated purpose, but also for its horrendous risk profile—a risk profile Fauci would have known damn well about, thanks to trials conducted only two years earlier for the treatment of Ebola.

An Evident, Unacknowledged Cause of Severe, "Covid-19," in Hospitals: Remdesivir Side Effects

So far we've established the corrupt, anti-scientific actions of Anthony Fauci and the FDA, which led to the unsupported, sole-treatment status of remdesivir for, "Covid," hospitalized patients throughout 2020 and much of 2021. But what's the big deal, right? According to the studies the drug maybe reduced hospitalization time by a day or two, or if not had no benefit at all—so basically it was at least better than *nothing*, no? The answer is no. Remdesivir has literally been demonstrated to be worse than nothing, even outside of the people pulled out of the *Lancet* study due to severe adverse reactions from the drug. And as stated previously, Fauci would have known this perfectly well.

In late 2018, NIAID sponsored a study called, "Investigational Therapeutics for the Treatment of People With Ebola Virus Disease."[27] They also published a review of the study as recently as December 2019, called, "Two drugs reduce the risk of death from Ebola."[28] The review explained the four drugs tested in the study were ZMapp, Mab114, REGN-EB3, and remdesivir. All but remdesivir, an antiviral, were monoclonal antibody treatments. Of particularly interesting note, the primary endpoint of *this* NIAID-sponsored study was the drug's impact on mortality. Also ironically fascinating, was the point the NIH made to point out the importance of early treatment,

139

considering their position not a few months later to refrain from treating, "Covid," patients outside of hospitals.

Returning to the study itself, the two drugs found to reduce mortality risk were Mab114 and REGN-EB3. The trial's safety monitors recommended that ZMapp (considered the control treatment) and remdesivir be removed from the trial following the results of the first 499 participants involved, due to safety concerns. These drugs were also much less effective in reducing death (~50% of participants died versus ~35% with the other two), with remdesivir being the *least* effective of the four (53%), even worse than the control treatment.

That remdesivir would become the first choice for a NIAID-sponsored study on the treatment of, "Covid," in February of 2020 despite these results (summarized only *two months* prior) is mind-boggling. First of all, why would the first choice not have been a monoclonal antibody treatment, since each of the three in the Ebola trial were demonstrated superior in reducing mortality? Wouldn't the immediacy of the alleged pandemic demand a better use of resources and time? Surely Fauci would have had these trials front of mind too, since he is literally quoted opining on the results in the aforementioned December 2019 NIH summary. If Fauci was at all concerned with finding an effective treatment, why not start with what he would've known from recent experience works better (i.e. monoclonal antibodies)?

And this brings us to the flip side of that question: why would remdesivir have been considered at all, given both its lack of effectiveness *and* the findings of the trial's safety monitors? The drug was pulled early, not only because it was worse than the baseline treatment at the primary endpoint of mortality reduction, but also because of serious side-effects, one of which is acknowledged as having *caused* a death by hypotension.

The case also cannot be made that the Ebola study's increased deaths and side effects would somehow be different than they would when used for, "Covid." Those side effects were actually *confirmed*— not just in the *Lancet* study in the spring of 2020—but also by the WHO in late August of 2020.[29] Specifically, the WHO noted a disproportionately high number of reports of liver and kidney problems in patients receiving remdesivir, compared with those receiving other drugs for the treatment of, "Covid." From their report:

"Regarding remdesivir, a major increase in reports was seen in this review.

... The new reports for remdesivir in a suspect or interacting role in this review comprise 76% of the cumulative total of reports; adding the updated reports since the last review, this number increases to 91%.

... A vast majority of reports which included hepatic [liver-related] terms mentioned above were coded as serious. Except for reports on cases reported with a fatal outcome, most of these hepatic terms were fatal only in a minority (<10%) of reported cases. Notable exceptions are hepatic failure and acute hepatic failure where 37% and 67% of cases respectively were fatal.

... The majority of the reports of the renal terms were coded as serious and a smaller proportion of the reports were coded as having a fatal outcome."

It doesn't even stop with the WHO/Ebola trials, either. The following are additional support for the findings of severe toxicity in remdesivir:

- A 2015 review in *Clinical Pharmacology & Therapeutics* found a link between remdesivir and acute renal (kidney) failure[30]
- A late 2020 safety review was launched by the European Medicines Agency after patients report acute kidney injury after taking the drug[31]
- A 2021 review by Touafchia et al. in *Clinical Microbiology and Infection* connected remdesivir to cardiac events, finding the following[32]: *"In recent clinical trials some cardiac arrhythmias were reported with use of remdesivir for COVID-19. We found 302 cardiac effects including 94 bradycardia (31%) among the 2,603 reports with remdesivir prescribed in COVID-19 patients. Most of the 94 reports were serious (75, 80%), and in 16 reports (17%) evolution was fatal. The use of remdesivir was associated with an increased risk of reporting bradycardia."*
- The previously mentioned review also identified similar outcomes in the aforementioned *Lancet* study (cardiac arrest

following remdesivir use) and even in Fauci's own NIAID-sponsored study, in which, "more cardiac arrhythmias occurred with the use of remdesivir than with placebo (8% versus 2%)"

- September 2021 phase 3 clinical trial by Ader et al. published in the *Lancet* concluded[33]: *"No clinical benefit was observed from the use of remdesivir in patients who were admitted to hospital for COVID-19, were symptomatic for more than 7 days, and required oxygen support ...* **Three deaths (acute respiratory distress syndrome, bacterial infection, and hepatorenal syndrome) were considered related to remdesivir by the investigators** *(my emphasis)."*

It bears repeating at this point: the FDA gave full approval to remdesivir only a month or two after it was demonstrated by the WHO to have *the* worst risk profile of any of the drugs used over the past year and a half, as well as only five months after the NIH summarized that it was worse than baseline for treating Ebola and had been pulled early from that trial. The WHO would even go on to reaffirm its opposition to remdesivir in November of 2020, citing, "No important effect on mortality, need for mechanical ventilation, time to clinical improvement, and other patient-important outcomes."[34] Severe adverse reactions from the drug in the various trials mentioned include hypotension, acute respiratory distress syndrome, bacterial infection, a variety of kidney issues including kidney failure, a variety of liver issues including liver failure, and even cardiac events such as bradycardia.

Despite all of this, according to *News Medical Life Sciences*, remdesivir is used in as much as 50% of hospitalized, "Covid," patients in the US, at least.[35] It was used from the very beginning too, as the first confirmed patient (35 years old) determined to have, "Covid," in the US was for some inexplicable reason treated using it—a drug never before approved for any use.[36] So now we can clearly see how significant Fauci's, "standard of care," declaration proved to be and the implications it would have, given the drug's risk profile, as we move on to reviewing the societal outcomes of these calamitous actions.

We begin at the epicenters of the alleged, "Covid outbreaks," China, Italy, and New York. In the first days of the alleged pandemic,

John's Hopkins captured the shock of doctors the world over as they stewed over how a respiratory disease like, "Covid," could be causing patients to experience heart and kidney problems.[37] In fact, according to John's Hopkins, up to 30% of hospitalized patients in China and New York developed moderate or severe kidney injury. While various theories were floated for why, "Covid," was causing this, they admitted the answer was not, "yet clear."

I would contend they were most likely asking the wrong question by assuming the cause without evidence. And while we have made the case for this by citing trial outcomes and use of the drug in the US so far, we can also see China had experience of its own with remdesivir in the opening days of the Covid era[38]:

- **Case 1** – *"A 31-year-old man from Wuhan, China, started on the drug on illness Day 11. It was stopped four days later because of liver alterations and a maculopapular rash. The liver abnormalities improved after discontinuing the treatment."*
- **Case 2** – *"An 80-year-old man from China was given remdesivir for two days. It was discontinued when his kidneys failed. The gentleman received the drug again as the disease severity persisted and progressed. He died nine days later."*
- **Case 3** – *"A 39-year-old man with obesity and obstructive sleep apnea received eight doses of remdesivir, which was stopped because of liver enzyme alterations and the same kind of rash as was seen in Case 1. This resolved after the drug was discontinued. The gentleman was discharged on day 20."*
- **Case 4** – *"A 76-year-old man from France with a history of chronic kidney injury received remdesivir for nine days without side effects. He was discharged on illness day 23."*
- **Case 5** – *"A 70-year-old man with a history of chronic obstructive bronchopneumopathy was admitted with acute respiratory distress syndrome. Remdesivir was given for two days and discontinued because he suffered acute kidney injury, requiring a kidney transplant. His disease progressed and he died."*

The connection of the side effects of the primary treatment for, "Covid," with the alleged complications of it cannot be ignored. This is especially true considering the ambiguity of, "Covid case," identification and the seemingly endless list of, "Covid's," symptoms and complications. The following are among those complications, and they will look eerily familiar:

- Acute kidney injury[39]
- Multiple organ failure[40]
- Hypotension[41]
- Septic shock[42]
- Bradycardia[43]
- Cardiac Arrhythmia[44]

To wrap this section up, we recall the complete lack of support for the claim that there exists any evidence of a novel-virus-caused pandemic. From erroneous death attribution methodology, to extraordinarily high false-positive PCR tests which don't even test for the alleged novel virus itself, to all other statistical/epidemiological slights of hand mentioned—we have made the case that there *must* be some better explanation with *real* evidence for abnormal hospital morbidity/mortality in specific areas. The observed severe side effects of remdesivir having been the same as the severe, unexplainable, "complications of Covid," is a better explanation with real, documented evidence. This is especially the case when considering experimental remdesivir was the only authorized and most widely used treatment for the aforementioned, "novel respiratory disease."

And from our reviews of how easy it would be to mistake (and/or intentionally mischaracterize) ordinary flu/pneumonia hospitalizations as something new, it is a logical conclusion to determine this mischaracterization and resulting dangerous treatment recommendation was one of the true causes of the most severe symptoms called, "Covid-19," in 2020 and beyond. When this many cases of illness are being mischaracterized using nonsensical methodology, misdiagnoses will lead to mistreatment. In the Covid era, with the exceptional amount of misdiagnosis under one scary umbrella disease title, that mistreatment was remdesivir. At the same time though, it wasn't the only one…

The Finisher of Lungs: The Abuse of Ventilators
In April of 2020, the height of the Covid panic, New York City physician Cameron Kyle-Sidell posted two videos on *YouTube*.[45] As

New York was the US epicenter for the disaster taking place in hospitals, Dr. Kyle-Sidell was in a desperate situation and felt based on what he'd personally seen to that point that the entire approach to treating, "Covid," by hospitals was incorrect. In fact, he too didn't believe the disease he was seeing made sense in the context of a viral pneumonia at all:

> *"In treating these patients, I have witnessed medical phenomena that just don't make sense in the context of treating a disease that is supposed to be a viral pneumonia.*
>
> *... the patients I'm seeing in front of me, the lungs I'm trying to improve, have led me to believe that COVID-19 is not this disease, and that we are operating under a medical paradigm that is untrue.*
>
> *... In short, I believe we are treating the wrong disease, and I fear that this misguided treatment will lead to a tremendous amount of harm to a great number of people in a very short time. I feel compelled to give this information out.*
>
> *... COVID-19 lung disease, as far as I can see, is not a pneumonia and should not be treated as one.*
>
> *... These patients are slowly being starved of oxygen."*

Since the propagandists of this entire situation saw it fit to use wartime language, let's consider a similar scenario... Let's say instead of being a doctor, Cameron Kyle-Sidell was a soldier in a war. And let's say while he's out on the frontline executing the strategy of his superior officers, he notices something is off—the enemy is not following their expected attack patterns on which his army's plans were based and his fellow soldiers are heading into a massacre. As things are looking dire, Kyle-Sidell finds a radio and blasts out his message on all frequencies in the hopes enough people will listen so the plan can be changed and potentially countless lives saved. Unfortunately however, what starts as a shocking message to many is ultimately turned to static, as his radio has been jammed—by his own army's technicians.

The outcome of this scenario is a massacre and, if justice were to be done, a punishment of treason for any involved in jamming the radio. This is exactly what Dr. Kyle-Sidell described happening in real life, short of justice being done (so far). You see, like many doctors who were directly involved in caring for patients—the very *last* people you'd want censored during a pandemic—Dr. Kyle-Sidell's video pleas were taken down from *YouTube* and their sharing prevented on social media.[46] And while this common Covid-era practice remains just as vile now as it was when we covered it at length previously, the biggest problem as it related to this particular message was in the doctor's determination—that ventilators were being overused and were themselves causing the very lung damage which was ravaging the hospital systems at the height of the phenomenon:

> *"When we treat people with ARDS* [Acute Respiratory Distress Syndrome], ***we typically use ventilators to treat respiratory failure. But these patients' muscles work fine*** *(my emphasis). I fear that if we are using a false paradigm to treat a new disease, then the method that we program [into] the ventilator, one based on respiratory failure as opposed to oxygen failure, that this method being widely adopted ... aims to increase pressure on the lungs in order to open them up, is actually doing more harm than good. And that the pressure we are providing to lungs, we may be providing to lungs that cannot take it.* ***And that the ARDS that we are seeing may be nothing more than lung injury caused by the ventilator*** *(my emphasis)."*

And again in his second video:

> *"We are putting breathing tubes in people and putting them on ventilators and dialing up the pressure to open their lungs. I've talked to doctors all around the country and it is becoming increasingly clear that the pressure we are providing may be hurting their lungs."*

Plenty of other doctors would come to agree with Dr. Kyle-Sidell, as pointed out by *Reuters* in April of 2020.[47] However, in the same special report, the authors also mention that ventilators had become a, "major weapon for medics fighting COVID-19," and that when the alleged pandemic began, "governments around the world raced to build or buy ventilators." At the time, the US had spent $2.9 billion for nearly 190,000 ventilators, according to the authors.

146

President Trump would even declare the US was the, "king of ventilators."

The outcome of this would have been predictable and avoidable if the approach was the free back-and-forth spread of information during a time when it was most needed. As *Business Insider* reported, however, at least 80% of NYC's, "Covid," patients who were put on ventilators ultimately died.[48] This is yet another case of the horrific failure of the very, "authoritative," voices people like Bill Gates and Jen Psaki openly claim should be the sole sources of information.

And when combined with the policy of remdesivir as the only treatment in the very hospitals people eventually ended up on these ventilators in, the outcomes become even more troubling. For one example, consider the aforementioned remdesivir-tied kidney failures. Per doctors on *HealthTap*, kidney failure leads to toxic fluid buildup, which backs up into the lungs.[49] During the alleged pandemic medical professionals puzzled over and theorized about how, "Covid," was causing fluid buildup in the lungs.[50] One wonders what the additional impact on these fluid-filled lungs would be of excessive ventilation.

For another example, recall the findings of the aforementioned *Clinical Microbiology and Infection* study that, "the use of remdesivir was associated with an increased risk of reporting bradycardia." Per Mayo Clinic, bradycardia is, "A slower than normal heart rate," which can, "prevent the brain and other organs from getting enough oxygen."[51] Taking the two things together, along with the fact that remdesivir was being used since literally the first US patient as we found, Dr. Kyle-Sidell's findings of patients being, "starved of oxygen," can be explained without having to resort to complex theories of animal-human transmissions or lab leaks (both of which we will expand upon in future chapters).

And whether one agrees with my assessment on there being no evidence of a novel coronavirus or not, it cannot be disputed that this overall hospital strategy to combat illness in the spring of 2020 was an absolute disaster of, "pandemic," proportions. As Dr. Kyle-Sidell and the others who have been cited clearly demonstrate, this is not even a controversial opinion amongst the very people doing the combatting in those hospitals. If they were right, as history and science seem to have validated they were, it would be downright false to fail to attribute much of the death during this time to medical malpractice and/or the mistakes they *admitted* to making. This is not to say they can't be forgiven for these mistakes. But it is without question that those who gave the orders, mischaracterized the damages the orders caused, and then deemed their own, "authority," significant enough to censor (or encourage censoring) the mere questioning of their actions, should not go unpunished.

The New York Nursing Home Scandal of 2020 (That Didn't Just Occur in New York)

Of all the points made in this chapter, the Nursing Home Scandal of 2020 is probably the most well-known. At this point it is well-documented that various politicians and public health officials around the world—perhaps most notably, Andrew Cuomo of New York—redirected, "overflow Covid patients," from hospitals to nursing homes in the spring of 2020.[52]

It is pointless to beat this obviously catastrophic mistake into the ground, so I won't linger here long. However, it is part of the history of this entire disaster, and my purpose with this book is to account for each of the criminal/negligent actions taken. This is certainly one of those actions. And it is so whether you are of the mind there is a novel corona virus or that there is no evidence of one because:

- **If you think there is a novel corona virus**, these people locked down the young and violated basic human rights in the name of, "protecting the old and vulnerable," while at the same time sending people known to be sick people straight to the old and vulnerable
- **If you see no evidence of a novel corona virus**, these actions still overextend nursing homes, thus reducing the standard of care for people who are already old and vulnerable, which obviously increases their risk of getting sick and going without care, in general

It goes without saying that these hospital overflow patients were also largely not going to receive the type of care they'd need from a nursing home. This combination of factors would make worsened mortality a certainty for all involved. And again, given the fraud of the tests and the absurd case methodologies, these deaths cannot accurately be attributed to anything but the negligence of those who pulled these strings.

The final thing that makes this scandal so necessary to call out is the disgusting efforts by its perpetrators to bury it. The *American Spectator* article cited above provides one example of this. Author Paul Kengor points out how the Pennsylvania secretary of health had the nerve to play victim when being, "misgendered," during a hard question by a radio host on this very topic. This type of feigned emotional wounding turned out to be so convenient for Secretary Levine, that causing the deaths of thousands apparently paled in comparison. Levine's actions were, in fact, so repugnant that during a press conference it was admitted Levine's own 95-year-old mother was removed from her nursing home, just as the secretary was condemning others to them. And Levine (who, unsurprisingly at this point, has previously endorsed puberty blockers for minors) not only got away with this, but was actually promoted in short order to the federal government *twice*, most recently to a four-star admiral position without any military experience.[53]

While that whole paragraph may or may not sound shocking and dystopian to future generations, such absurdities by America's major/mainstream institutions are now expected by the average, common American. For many, like myself, it's become as humorous as it is just downright pathetic. But not much straddled the line between hilarity and vulgarity during the Covid era as effectively as the actions of New York governor Andrew Cuomo.

Having been the most public of the nursing-home offenders from the beginning, Cuomo would do everything he could to cover his deadly scandal up. He'd have a lot of help from the downright creepy corporate propaganda machine as well (more on that later). But Cuomo's book, *American Crisis: Leadership Lessons from the Covid-19 Pandemic*, truly must have been one of the most ironic written since OJ Simpson's, *If I Did It*.[54] This appalling attempt to re-write history by one of the lead criminals in the Covid crimes against humanity is so on-the-nose that again, it cannot be permitted without pushback.

Today Cuomo has resigned from office, having been charged with a sex crime, and is under investigation for covering up the death toll his nursing home directive created.[55,56] Unfortunately, "Covid," is still wrongly considered the cause of these deaths by his accusers, so

149

he will likely escape without the full extent of blame that justice demands. However, the lack of recognition of the underlying crime by broken institutions doesn't negate it—these deaths are attributable directly to Cuomo, as they are to Levine and any other official who gave similar directives.

"A Good Death": Death Penalty Drugs and the English Midazolam Euthanasia Scandal

"Luke Evans: *A good death* (my emphasis) *needs three things: it needs equipment, it need medication, and it needs the staff to administer it. So in terms of equipment, a few quick questions. Do you have enough syringe drivers in the NHS to deliver medications to keep people comfortable when they're passing away?*

Matt Hancock: *Yes, we do. There was a challenge raised about this about eight days ago and we resolved—actually it was as big a challenge as was made public and we resolved that so yes, right now we do.*

Evans: *And the second one is, with that—the syringe drivers deliver medication, particularly things like* **midazolam** (my emphasis) *and morphine. Do you have any precautions put in place to make sure we have enough of those medications to be delivered?*

Hancock: *Yes, and we've got a big project to make sure that those medications as well as the ITU medications I spoke about earlier—that the supply chains—local supply chains that support those medicines are clear. They are, in fact, those medicines are made in a relatively small number of factories around the world. So it is a delicate supply chain and we are in contact with the whole supply chain.*

Evans: *In line with that,* **morphine is currently prescribed per patient. The reason for that is to stop it being abused** (my emphasis). *I would have to prescribe it for Mr. Hancock, for example. In this situation, however, if you are going into a healthcare home, you may not want to waste precious things such as morphine.* **Have you considered relaxing the laws on doctors and healthcare professionals prescribing morphine, so that there is no waste** (my emphasis)?

150

Hancock: *This is something we keep under review. I have looked at that particular point, to reduce wastage of key medicines. It is something that the supply and clinical teams in the Department talk about all the time.*"
—Video conferenced discussion between UK Health Secretary Matt Hancock and MP Dr. Luke Evans, early 2020[57]

*"Euthanasia (from Greek: εὐθανασία **'good death'** (my emphasis): εὖ, eu 'well, good' + θάνατος, thanatos 'death') is the practice of **intentionally ending life** (my emphasis) to relieve pain and suffering.*"
—"Euthanasia," Greek origin as identified in definition[58]

In UK MP Dr. Luke Evans' own words, the UK government adopted a policy of euthanizing, "Covid," patients in 2020 using midazolam. That's not a provocative statement or a theory or anything other than their publicly-stated plan of action. And if I was less thorough, I could end this section right here and let you stew on the moral implications of that without any more elaboration. The concept of euthanasia in general is one which is part of an extremely difficult, intense moral debate, specifically when considering whether or not a person being euthanized has given or has the capacity to give informed consent. As a side note, the most interesting, nuanced course I took in college included this very topic, among other difficult life and death decisions. For more on that I would highly recommend the book *Life and Death Decisions* by my professor in that class, Sheldon Ekland-Olson.[59]

However, the practice of euthanizing patients during an alleged respiratory pandemic, and the manner in which the UK government (among others) did so, raises extremely troubling questions to which attention must be drawn. So we will start by reviewing the drug used to this end itself—midazolam.

As covered by *NPR* in their September 2020 (of all times) article, "Gasping For Air: Autopsies Reveal Troubling Effects Of Lethal Injection," midazolam is a sedative used in executions—and a controversial one even for that purpose.[60] In death penalty autopsies reviewed by *NPR*, they found that of 32 inmates executed using midazolam, 87% had developed pulmonary edema—a condition when the lungs *fill with fluids* such as blood and plasma. One inmate on

151

death row is described as having, "wheezed and gasped for air," as he was executed with the drug. Anatomical pathologist Mark Edgar presented these types of findings on the drug during a federal court hearing in the Southern District of Ohio in December 2018.[61] He informed the court that inmates executed using midazolam specifically:

> *"Would experience **severe respiratory distress** (my emphasis) with associated sensations of drowning, asphyxiation, panic, and terror."*

And the magistrate judge acknowledged his findings, writing in his decision:

> *"All medical witnesses to describe pulmonary edema agreed it was painful, both physically and emotionally, inducing a sense of drowning and the attendant panic and terror, much as would occur with the torture tactic known as waterboarding."*

Doctors who spoke to *NPR* informed them that, "extremely high doses of drugs, given quickly, directly damage the delicate architecture of the lungs." They describe these high doses as the 500 milligrams given to an inmate, versus the 1 to 2 milligrams given to sedated hospital patients.

This is a key place to take a step back and break our analysis into two parts:

1. Midazolam for the purposes of administering, "a good death," as MP Dr. Evans describes it, and
2. Midazolam in low doses (1 to 2 mg) as a hospital sedative

The reason this needs to be broken out is first because it cannot be assumed that the prescription amount is the same in both instances—especially with Dr. Evans openly requesting (without pushback) that health secretary Matt Hancock relax the laws on prescribing amounts. If one were to want to give someone a, "good death," using midazolam (as Dr. Evans claims to along with wanting to, "reduce waste") then a higher dose would surely be required the same way it is in an attempt to give a death penalty inmate a, "good death." Only, as we saw with the *NPR* article, midazolam not only doesn't provide a good death, it actually contributes to a drowning-like suffering from the lungs filling with fluid. Perhaps ironically—or perhaps intentionally—I will make no claims about intent—the lungs filling with fluid also happens to be a, "complication of Covid," as we've covered previously.

Subsequent whistleblower allegations of misuse of the drug in the UK came from a variety of sources.[62,63] And support for these claims is readily available, as in an official guidance document titled, "COVID-19 and Palliative and End of Life in Secondary Care," the Association for Palliative Medicine of Great Britain and Ireland (APM) confirms our aforementioned suspicions on how the drug was used for end of life care.[64] In a section titled, "Management of agitation at the end of life in COVID-19," the APM recommends as much as 60 milligrams of midazolam, a *far* cry from the 1 to 2 milligrams used in normal hospital circumstances.

And use of midazolam was no less abusive for patients who weren't at the end of their life either, as we mentioned in the second point. In a section titled, "Management of breathlessness and anxiety in COVID-19," the APM still recommends as much as 20mg of midazolam for severe cases—more than 10 times the average hospital use amount. For the purposes of respiratory illness, sedatives such as midazolam are meant to reduce stress caused by struggling lungs. And this is fine at a normal dosage, but these were clearly not normal dosages. In fact, the media even publicly acknowledged that, "nurses were sedating patients more to manage workload," in response to hospital ICU strain during this time, apparently as opposed to limited sedation as a means of meaningful treatment.[65] The picture becomes even darker when considering the side effects, which *drugs.com* reports as respiratory depression and respiratory arrest.[66] Again, both of these also happen to be considered, "symptoms of Covid."

Whether or not we're talking about end of life use or in-hospital care use too, the sheer emphasis placed on a sedative at this time is very strange on its face, even ignoring the side effect profile. First of all, the *Pharmaceutical Journal (PJ)* reported in May 2020 that the NHS had been buying up extraordinary amounts of the drug from French distributors, and was doing so at 4 different strengths.[67] Now, I'm all for stress reduction as a means of care since stress is tied to basically all disease. However, there doesn't seem to be any good reason why it would be necessary to purchase abnormal volumes of such sedatives at abnormal strength levels, and then to also make recommendations to use them at up to 10 times the dosage of average hospital use, in order to treat a respiratory illness.

Adding midazolam's side effect profile of respiratory depression to the equation, it again becomes easier to explain previously mentioned, ventilator-questioning New York doctor Cameron Kyle-Sidell's concern, that many, "Covid," patients suffered from reduced oxygen. And we can corroborate this was the case in the US, where Dr. Kyle-Sidell obviously operated, too. Bill Galluccio, for example, reported in April 2020 a 73% increased demand in death penalty drugs for, "Covid," use, including midazolam and fentanyl.[68] According to the doctors Galluccio cited, these drugs were used on ventilator patients—patients we've already discussed were subsequently dying at a rate greater than 80%.

The midazolam scandal is a recognized one in the UK, as reported on by *the Sun*.[69] One reason why this might be the case there and not in the US is because the UK has public experience with the problem of institutionalized euthanasia. As documented by the Discovery Institute in 2013, the UK's NHS created a protocol called Liverpool Care Pathway (LCP) in order to respond to family member complaints of patients dying in agony in NHS hospitals.[70] While intentions might have started good, the protocol soon shifted from one of palliative care (pain-controlling treatment) to one of terminal sedation (slow-motion euthanasia/killing). This problem got so bad that, "an alarming 16.5% of patients who died in 2007-2008," died while under, "continuous deep sedation." An open letter signed by palliative physicians and other pain-control experts blowing the whistle on this scandal tied it in a scary way to the Covid era:

> *"Just as, in the financial world, so-called algorithmic banking has caused problems by blindly following a computer model, so a similar tick-box approach to the management of death is causing a national crisis in care. The government is rolling out a new treatment pattern of palliative care into hospitals, nursing homes, and residential homes. It is based on experience in a Liverpool hospice. If you tick all the right boxes in the Liverpool Care Pathway, the inevitable outcome of the consequent treatment is death.*

... As a result, a nationwide wave of discontent is building up, as family and friends witness the denial of fluids and food to patients. Syringe drivers are being used to give continuous terminal sedation, without regard to the fact that the diagnosis could be wrong.

... Experienced doctors know that sometimes, when all but essential drugs are stopped, 'dying,' patients get better."

This proved to be an incredibly prophetic statement for a variety of reasons. The first is that the public-health-centralized, tick-box approach to healthcare has largely become the only permitted approach. We've seen the damage of this throughout this book. Another interesting note by these physicians is how family and friends were at least able to speak up for their loved ones after witnessing the LCP in action. Imagine what the consequences could be if hospital patients' family and friends were routinely denied the visiting rights necessary to identify this malpractice. Unfortunately, anyone who lived through the Covid era knows this to have been a common policy of far too many hospitals. And finally, we've already gone into great length about all the non-essential, downright dangerous drugs used during the alleged pandemic, and the physicians make a good point in the final sentence above about the cost of this deadly policy.

What makes euthanasia such a difficult question morally is that a person can't be truly informed on the consequences of death. This presents a blurry line for a doctor to have to cross once consent is given. However, looking past this, it seems many people would be willing to grant a person in excruciating pain a merciful death. And this is not necessarily a repugnant stance to take, so long as the person doing the dying does consent.

The problem is that such a scenario is not what Matt Hancock and Dr. Luke Evans discussed. A respiratory illness is not the same as having a mortal wound or terminal cancer. One not only cannot predict with certainty that a respiratory death is both imminent and unpreventable, but a respiratory illness is also one the average person faces with the expectation they will *survive* it. As such, it is impossible to imagine a scenario where it is:

1. Not worth it to continue attempting to treat the patient,
2. Certain the patient will die, and

3. Possible to get the patient's consent

Perhaps no example illustrates this better than the account of comedian Jim Brewer during an appearance on the Joe Rogan Experience.[71] Brewer recounted a story about his obese friend, who ultimately went to the hospital, "with Covid." The friend was soon on a ventilator and got stroke-induced brain damage. Originally he was told this stroke was a, "Covid complication," but it soon became clear it was actually due to a lack of his regular blood-pressure-and-similar-maintenance medications while in the hospital. As the series of unfortunate events at the hospital continued (fun fact: he was denied access to hydroxychloroquine), the friend soon became *brain dead*. Due to insane, evil hospital protocols, his wife and child were told he was going to die and they wouldn't be able to say their goodbyes in person. Fortunately for this man, one last desperate effort by friends secured a visit by an outside specialist, who found that the man *wasn't* braindead—he was *dehydrated*. Within months of being treated for dehydration, he was fully recovered.

So my question is this: how many people didn't have the luxury of such passionate friends and an honest outside specialist in 2020-2021? How many families were too scared, compliant, or trusting to push back against hospitals following the orders of those like Matt Hancock and Dr. Luke Evans? Without the resistance of his friends/family this man would have been dead and he'd have been so without any informed consent. And I wonder, what drugs was he given when he was senselessly brought to the point of a coma? At this point I know where I'd put my money and it'd be as safe a bet as any. An additional dimension to this scandal was also predominantly called out in the UK, where reports came of blanket Do Not Attempt Resuscitation orders coerced upon patients without proper consent like Brewer's friend.[72] Such orders reframe the midazolam scandal as a midazolam *cover-up*. Lastly, is it still difficult to see why I use quotes when referring to, "Covid," patients? To think this man's story was an isolated incident when we know what we do about the testing/methodology is not only not likely, it's absurd.

What really sets the midazolam scandal apart from the rest of the crimes/misdoings identified in this book is how unmistakably cold-blooded it is. Death penalty drugs were used as alleged treatments, they were so with extraordinary frequency and in abnormally high dosages, and the horrendous death rates which occurred during their usage wasn't even hidden. In fact, these deaths and the side effects of these drugs were verifiably used to establish the pandemic itself, most predominantly through the destructive, "first wave."

More Empty Profit in the Pipeline

As 2022 rolled around and the Ukraine story replaced the Covid story for what the mainstream media wanted the world talking about 24/7, the official public health recommendations for Covid treatment remained insane. In-hospital patients continued to receive remdesivir while the NIH and CDC for the first time in two years decided the ever-suppressed benefits of early treatment were not, "misinformation," as they'd previously claimed.

> *"If you test positive for COVID-19 and have one or more health conditions that increase your risk of becoming very sick, treatment may be available. Contact a health professional right away after a positive test to determine if you may be eligible, even if your symptoms are mild right now. Don't delay: Treatment must be started within the first few days to be effective."*
>
> —CDC February 2022 updated guidance[73]

> *"In order of preference, clinicians should use the oral antiviral nirmatrelvir-ritonavir (Paxlovid), the monoclonal antibody sotrovimab, the IV antiviral remdesivir (Veklury) and finally, the oral antiviral molnupiravir, said Alice Pau, PharmD, of the NIH COVID-19 Treatment Guidelines panel."*
>
> —NIH January 2022 recommendation for outpatient (out of hospital) care[74]

We've already covered the horrendous safety profile and real world outcomes of remdesivir. As for the other three mentioned by the NIH, we can start with Paxlovid, Pfizer's Covid drug which apparently needs to exist despite the company also producing an inoculation meant to provide immunity. In the FDA Fact Sheet on the drug, the listed adverse effects are allergic reactions, liver problems, resistance to HIV medicines, altered sense of taste (apparently drugs cause this too), diarrhea, high blood pressure, and muscle aches.[75]

Now I don't mention these things to disqualify the drug. Though they might be enough for me not to take it, drug fact sheets surely all include lists of potential side effects. However, consider the following caveat the FDA makes right after listing these side effects:

> *"These are not all the possible side effects of PAXLOVID. Not many people have taken PAXLOVID. Serious and unexpected side effects may happen. PAXLOVID is still being studied, so it is possible that all of the risks are not known at this time."*

You will recall: this is somehow the *first* recommended treatment the NIH says people should take in the outpatient setting if they test positive. And the reason why they would recommend a brand new drug shouldn't be surprising at this point. If you didn't already guess, the US government inexplicably (other than the explanation of corruption) bought up $5.3 billion worth of Paxlovid in November 2021, a month *before* the FDA authorized it for emergency use.[76,77]

Another interesting note comes from the FDA's December 2021 post-authorization press release, in which they claim, "Paxlovid is not a substitute for vaccination in individuals for whom COVID-19 vaccination and a booster dose are recommended."[78] The first thing to note here is there is a very specific reason this, "not a substitute," language is used, which we will get to in our chapters on inoculations. Beyond that though, this statement seems to imply Paxlovid is *not* specifically intended for those who did *not* receive the inoculation, in which case it would seem Pfizer both didn't protect the inoculated from the disease(s) in question and is also now set to profit *again* off that fact. However, Paxlovid, two inoculation doses, and a booster are not all you need to subject your body to in less than a year to be protected. According to the NIH, Paxlovid should also be, "boosted," with the HIV drug ritonavir.[79] To any who opt into all of the above experimentation I would say: please, on behalf of your body, at least ask for sponsorship money from Pfizer. You've earned at least that.

Moving on, monoclonal antibodies seem to have worked for people and improved mortality outcomes in the aforementioned Ebola study, but supply has been increasingly short at a time of increased demand.[80] Since the federal government controls the supply and was all-in on an obsessive inoculation-only campaign, many questions were raised about this by both states such as Texas and observers alike.[81,82]

As for Merck's molnupiravir, doctors such as Rajesh Ghandi of Boston's Mass General Hospital have been reluctant to prescribe it for its ineffectiveness.[83] Still, as covered by *TrialSiteNews*, the US government has also bought up $2.2 billion of it after providing Merck $365 million in taxpayer funding for its development, so the conflict of interest to encourage its use remains.[84] But the safety profile remains in question for this drug as well, as documented by the FDA in its Fact Sheet.[85] One extremely troubling warning, of the several included, reads as follows:

> *"Advise individuals of childbearing potential to use effective contraception correctly and consistently while taking molnupiravir and for 4 days after the last dose.*
> *While the risk is regarded as low, nonclinical studies to fully assess the potential for molnupiravir to affect offspring of treated males have not been completed. Advise sexually active individuals with partners of childbearing potential to use a reliable method of contraception consistently and correctly while taking molnupiravir and for at least 3 months after the last dose of molnupiravir. The risk beyond 3 months after the last dose of molnupiravir is unknown."*

The FDA, NIH, WHO, and CDC have taken an experimental-drug-only approach to the Covid era. This strategy has come with glaring conflicts of interest and without the least bit of success. In fact, the outcomes point to a resoundingly negative impact overall, in many cases causing the very problems which were attributed to a viral pandemic. At the same time, it was not the case that there were not better, cheaper, more-available alternatives. There absolutely were in spades and those alternatives were actively suppressed despite observably positive results. We will cover them in detail in the next chapter.

Endnotes

1   "Dr. Peter Mccullough On Tucker Carlson: Not An Error Of Omission!". 2021. *Rumble*. https://www.rumble.com/vguakb-dr.-peter-mccullough-on-tucker-carlson-not-an-error-of-omission.html.

2   Ibid.

3   Hughes, Sue. 2020. "Remdesivir Now 'Standard Of Care' For COVID-19, Fauci Says". *The Hospitalist*. https://www.the-hospitalist.org/hospitalist/article/221518/coronavirus-updates/remdesivir-now-standard-care-covid-19-fauci-says.

4   Gilead Sciences. 2020. "Gilead Sciences Statement On Positive Data Emerging From National Institute Of Allergy And Infectious Diseases' Study Of Investigational Antiviral Remdesivir For COVID-19". https://www.gilead.com/news-and-press/press-room/press-releases/2020/4/gilead-sciences-statement-on-positive-data-emerging-from-national-institute-of-allergy-and-infectious-diseases-study-of-investigational-antiviral-rem.

5   Wang, Yeming, Dingyu Zhang, Guanhua Du, Ronghui Du, Jianping Zhao, Yang Jin, and Shouzhi Fu et al. 2020. "Remdesivir In Adults With Severe COVID-19: A Randomised, Double-Blind, Placebo-Controlled, Multicentre Trial". *The Lancet* 395 (10236): 1569-1578. doi:10.1016/s0140-6736(20)31022-9.

6   "Fauci's Promotional Hype Catapults Gilead's Remdesivir – Alliance For Human Research Protection". 2020. *Ahrp.Org*. https://www.ahrp.org/faucis-promotional-hype-catapults-gileads-remdesivir/.

7   Cohen, Jon, and Kai Kupferschmidt. 2020. "'A Very, Very Bad Look' For Remdesivir". *Science* 370 (6517): 642-643. doi:10.1126/science.370.6517.642.

8   Gilead Sciences. 2020. "Gilead Sciences Statement On Positive Data Emerging From National Institute Of Allergy And Infectious Diseases' Study Of Investigational Antiviral Remdesivir For COVID-19". https://www.gilead.com/news-and-press/press-room/press-releases/2020/4/gilead-sciences-statement-on-positive-data-emerging-from-national-institute-of-allergy-and-infectious-diseases-study-of-investigational-antiviral-rem.

9   Goldhill, Olivia. 2020. "Scientists Want To See The Evidence That Shows Remdesivir Works For Covid-19". *Quartz*. https://www.qz.com/1849113/scientists-demand-data-to-show-remdesivir-works-for-covid-19/.

10   Steenhuysen, Julie. 2020. "Fauci Says Leak Concerns Fueled His White House Revelation Of Gilead Drug Results". *Reuters*. https://www.reuters.com/article/us-health-coronavirus-gilead-fauci/fauci-says-leak-concerns-fueled-his-white-house-revelation-of-gilead-drug-results-idUSKBN22C0KX.

11   "History Of Changes For Study: NCT04280705". 2020. *Clinicaltrials.Gov*. https://www.clinicaltrials.gov/ct2/history/NCT04280705?A=10&B=16&C=Side-by-Side#StudyPageTop.

12   Nelson, Steven. 2020. "Fauci Praises Remdesivir After Breakthrough In Coronavirus Treatment". *Nypost.Com*.

https://www.nypost.com/2020/04/29/fauci-praises-remdesivir-after-breakthrough-in-coronavirus-treatment/.

13   Rowland, Christopher. 2020. "Government Researchers Changed Metric To Measure Coronavirus Drug Remdesivir During Clinical Trial". *The Washington Post.* https://www.washingtonpost.com/business/2020/05/01/government-researchers-changed-metric-measure-coronavirus-drug-remdesivir-during-clinical-trial/.

14   "Appendix A, Table 2. COVID-19 Treatment Guidelines Panel Financial Disclosure For Companies Related To COVID-19 Treatment Or Diagnostics". 2020. *NIH.Gov.* https://www.covid19treatmentguidelines.nih.gov/about-the-guidelines/panel-financial-disclosure/.

15   Tunney, Jacob. 2020. "Sign The Petition". *Change.Org.* https://www.change.org/p/national-institute-of-health-nih-require-dr-anthony-fauci-disclose-financial-relationship-with-gilead-sciences.

16   Andrzejewski, Adam. 2021. "Dr. Anthony Fauci: The Highest Paid Employee In The Entire U.S. Federal Government". *Forbes.* https://www.forbes.com/sites/adamandrzejewski/2021/01/25/dr-anthony-fauci-the-highest-paid-employee-in-the-entire-us-federal-government/amp/.

17   "The Real Story Of Remdesivir". 2020. *Public Citizen.* https://www.citizen.org/article/the-real-story-of-remdesivir/.

18   Love, James. 2020. "KEI FOIA Lawsuit With The NIH To Obtain Documents Related To COVID-19 Contracts And Collaborations - Knowledge Ecology International". *Knowledge Ecology International.* https://www.keionline.org/34197.

19   Boseley, Sarah. 2020. "US Secures World Stock Of Key Covid-19 Drug Remdesivir". *The Guardian.* https://www.theguardian.com/us-news/2020/jun/30/us-buys-up-world-stock-of-key-covid-19-drug.

20   "Coronavirus: Commission Signs A Joint Procurement Contract With Gilead For The Supply Of Remdesivir - Newsroom - European Commission". 2020. *Newsroom - European Commission.* https://europa.eu/newsroom/content/coronavirus-commission-signs-joint-procurement-contract-gilead-supply-remdesivir_en.

21   Love, James. 2020. "FDA Gives Gilead A Seven Year Regulatory Monopoly For Remdesivir To Treat COVID-19, On Grounds It Is An "Orphan" Treating A Rare Disease - Knowledge Ecology International". *Knowledge Ecology International.* https://www.keionline.org/32546.

22   Cassedy, Claire. 2020. "FDA States Submission Date Of Gilead's Coronavirus Treatment Orphan Status Application Is 'Confidential' - Knowledge Ecology International". *Knowledge Ecology International.* https://www.keionline.org/32581.

23   "Covid: Remdesivir 'Has Little Or No Effect' On Survival, Says WHO". 2020. *BBC News.* https://www.bbc.com/news/world-54566730.

24   Weintraub, Karen. 2020. "'Without Evidence': Once Again, FDA Expands Use Of COVID-19 Treatment Without Research To Back It Up". *Usatoday*. https://www.usatoday.com/story/news/2020/08/28/fda-ignores-science-expanding-remdesivir-treat-covid-19/5662305002/.

25   Lovelace Jr., Berkeley. 2020. "Sens. Elizabeth Warren And Bernie Sanders Slam Trump For Giving Gilead 'Windfall' Deal For Coronavirus Drug". *CNBC*. https://www.cnbc.com/2020/07/16/sens-elizabeth-warren-and-bernie-sanders-slam-trump-for-giving-gilead-windfall-deal-for-coronavirus-drug.html.

26   Tribble, Sarah. 2021. "Remdesivir, Given To Half Of Hospitalized Covid Patients In U.S., Is Big Win For Gilead — Boosted By Taxpayers". *Kaiser Health News*. https://khn.org/news/article/remdesivir-given-to-half-of-hospitalized-covid-patients-in-u-s-is-big-win-for-gilead-boosted-by-taxpayers/.

27   National Institute of Allergy and Infectious Diseases (NIAID). 2018. "Investigational Therapeutics For The Treatment Of People With Ebola Virus Disease". ClinicalTrials.gov.

28   National Institutes of Health. 2019. "Two Drugs Reduce Risk Of Death From Ebola". NIH.

29   WHO Collaborating Centre for International Drug Monitoring. 2020. "Descriptive Analysis Of COVID Descriptive Analysis Of COVID Escriptive Analysis Of COVID-19-Related Spontaneous Related Spontaneous Reports From Vigibase: Interim Results". World Health Organization. https://www.who.int/medicines/regulation/medicines-safety/COVID19-PV-update11.pdf.

30   "Issue Information - TOC". 2015. *Clinical Pharmacology & Therapeutics* 99 (1): 3-4. doi:10.1002/cpt.214.

31   "EU Regulator Starts Safety Review Of Coronavirus Drug". 2020. *ABC News*. https://abcnews.go.com/Health/wireStory/eu-regulator-starts-safety-review-coronavirus-drug-73391738.

32   Touafchia, Anthony, Haleh Bagheri, Didier Carrié, Geneviève Durrieu, Agnès Sommet, Laurent Chouchana, and François Montastruc. 2021. "Serious Bradycardia And Remdesivir For Coronavirus 2019 (COVID-19): A New Safety Concerns". *Clinical Microbiology And Infection* 27 (5): 791.e5-791.e8. doi:10.1016/j.cmi.2021.02.013.

33   Ader, Florence, Maude Bouscambert-Duchamp, Maya Hites, Nathan Peiffer-Smadja, Julien Poissy, Drifa Belhadi, and Alpha Diallo et al. 2022. "Remdesivir Plus Standard Of Care Versus Standard Of Care Alone For The Treatment Of Patients Admitted To Hospital With COVID-19 (Discovery): A Phase 3, Randomised, Controlled, Open-Label Trial". *The Lancet Infectious Diseases* 22 (2): 209-221. doi:10.1016/s1473-3099(21)00485-0.

34   "WHO Recommends Against The Use Of Remdesivir In COVID-19 Patients". 2020. *Who.Int*. https://www.who.int/news-room/feature-stories/detail/who-recommends-against-the-use-of-remdesivir-in-covid-19-patients.

35   "Remdesivir, Given To Half Of Hospitalized Covid Patients In U.S., Is Big Win For Gilead — Boosted By Taxpayers". 2021. *News-Medical.Net*. https://www.news-medical.net/amp/news/20210127/Remdesivir-given-to-half-of-hospitalized-covid-patients-in-US-is-big-win-for-Gilead-e28094-boosted-by-taxpayers.aspx.

36   Holshue, Michelle L., Chas DeBolt, Scott Lindquist, Kathy H. Lofy, John Wiesman, Hollianne Bruce, and Christopher Spitters et al. 2020. "First Case Of 2019 Novel Coronavirus In The United States". *New England Journal Of Medicine* 382 (10): 929-936. doi:10.1056/nejmoa2001191.

37   Sperati, C. John. 2022. "Coronavirus: Kidney Damage Caused By COVID-19". *Hopkinsmedicine.Org*. https://www.hopkinsmedicine.org/health/conditions-and-diseases/coronavirus/coronavirus-kidney-damage-caused-by-covid19.

38   Jones, Stephen. 2020. "Remdesivir Stopped After Kidney Failures Occur In Covid Drug Trials". *Godskingdom.Org*. https://godskingdom.org/blog/2020/07/remdesivir-stopped-after-kidney-failures-occur-in-covid-drug-trials.

39   Nadim, Mitra K., Lui G. Forni, Ravindra L. Mehta, Michael J. Connor, Kathleen D. Liu, Marlies Ostermann, and Thomas Rimmelé et al. 2020. "COVID-19-Associated Acute Kidney Injury: Consensus Report Of The 25Th Acute Disease Quality Initiative (ADQI) Workgroup". *Nature Reviews Nephrology* 16 (12): 747-764. doi:10.1038/s41581-020-00356-5.

40   Mokhtari, Tahmineh, Fatemeh Hassani, Neda Ghaffari, Babak Ebrahimi, Atousa Yarahmadi, and Ghomareza Hassanzadeh. 2020. "COVID-19 And Multiorgan Failure: A Narrative Review On Potential Mechanisms". *Journal Of Molecular Histology* 51 (6): 613-628. doi:10.1007/s10735-020-09915-3.

41   Hanidziar, Dusan, and Edward A. Bittner. 2020. "Hypotension, Systemic Inflammatory Response Syndrome, And COVID-19: A Clinical Conundrum". *Anesthesia & Analgesia* 131 (3): e175-e176. doi:10.1213/ane.0000000000005062.

42   Zick, Marvin. 2020. "Update: Can COVID-19 Cause Sepsis? Explaining The Relationship Between The Coronavirus Disease And Sepsis — Global Sepsis Alliance". *Global Sepsis Alliance*. https://www.global-sepsis-alliance.org/news/2020/4/7/update-can-covid-19-cause-sepsis-explaining-the-relationship-between-the-coronavirus-disease-and-sepsis-cvd-novel-coronavirus.

43   Douedi, Steven, Anton Mararenko, Abbas Alshami, Mohammed Al-Azzawi, Firas Ajam, Swapnil Patel, Hani Douedi, and Dawn Calderon. 2021. "COVID-19 Induced Bradyarrhythmia And Relative Bradycardia: An Overview". *Journal Of Arrhythmia* 37 (4): 888-892. doi:10.1002/joa3.12578.

44   Bhatla, Anjali, Michael M. Mayer, Srinath Adusumalli, Matthew C. Hyman, Eric Oh, Ann Tierney, and Juwann Moss et al. 2020. "COVID-19 And Cardiac Arrhythmias". *Heart Rhythm* 17 (9): 1439-1444. doi:10.1016/j.hrthm.2020.06.016.

45   Adams, Mike. 2020. "Bombshell Plea From NYC ICU Doctor: COVID-19 A Condition Of Oxygen Deprivation, Not Pneumonia". *Newswars*. https://www.newswars.com/bombshell-plea-from-nyc-icu-doctor-covid-19-a-condition-of-oxygen-deprivation-not-pneumonia.

46   Hollander, Buzz. 2021. "Commentary: The Problems With Censoring Doctors Over Their COVID-19 Stances - The Georgia Star News". *The Georgia Star News*. https://www.georgiastarnews.com/2021/10/13/commentary-the-problems-with-censoring-doctors-over-their-covid-19-stances/.

47   Aloisi, Silvia, Deena Beasley, Gabriella Borter, Kate Kelland, and Thomas Escritt. 2020. "Special Report: As Virus Advances, Doctors Rethink Rush To Ventilate". *Reuters*. https://www.reuters.com/article/us-health-coronavirus-ventilators-specia/special-report-as-virus-advances-doctors-rethink-rush-to-ventilate-idUSKCN2251PE.

48   Baker, Sinead. 2020. "80% Of NYC's Coronavirus Patients Who Are Put On Ventilators Ultimately Die, And Some Doctors Are Trying To Stop Using Them". *Business Insider*. https://www.businessinsider.com/coronavirus-ventilators-some-doctors-try-reduce-use-new-york-death-rate-2020-4?op=1.

49   "Why Does Kidney Failure Cause You To Get Fluid In Your Lungs?". 2022. *Healthtap*. Accessed March 8. https://www.healthtap.com/questions/37089-why-does-kidney-failure-cause-you-to-get-fluid-in-your-lungs/.

50   "Why Does COVID-19 Cause Excess Fluid In The Lungs?". 2020. *Medium*. https://medium.com/health-and-disease/why-does-covid-19-cause-excess-fluid-in-the-lungs-abe0f016760b.

51   "Bradycardia - Symptoms And Causes". 2021. *Mayo Clinic*. https://www.mayoclinic.org/diseases-conditions/bradycardia/symptoms-causes/syc-20355474.

52   Kengor, Paul, George Neumayr, Wesley Smith, Scott McKay, and James Delmont. 2020. "Pennsylvania's Nursing Home COVID-19 Scandal - The American Spectator | USA News And Politicsthe American Spectator | USA News And Politics". *The American Spectator | USA News And Politics*. https://www.spectator.org/pennsylvanias-nursing-home-covid-19-scandal-rachel-levine/.

53   Freiburger, Calvin. 2021. "Biden Promotes 'Transgender' Rachel Levine To Four-Star Admiral In Health Service Corps - Lifesite". *Lifesite*. https://www.lifesitenews.com/news/biden-promotes-transgender-health-official-rachel-levine-to-four-star-admiral/.

54   Gregorian, Dareh, and Adam Reiss. 2021. "N.Y. Gov. Andrew Cuomo's Covid Book Deal Worth More Than $5.1 Million". *NBC News*. https://www.nbcnews.com/politics/politics-news/n-y-gov-andrew-cuomo-s-covid-book-deal-worth-n1267679.

55   McKinley, Jesse, and Luis Ferré-Sadurní. 2021. "New Allegations Of Cover-Up By Cuomo Over Nursing Home Virus Toll (Published 2021)". *Nytimes.Com*.

https://www.nytimes.com/2021/02/12/nyregion/new-york-nursing-homes-cuomo.html.

56   Mangan, Dan. 2021. "Former NY Gov. Cuomo Charged With Sex Crime, Months After Resigning Amid Harassment Probe". *CNBC*. https://www.cnbc.com/2021/10/28/former-ny-gov-cuomo-charged-with-sex-crime-months-after-resigning-amid-harassment-probe-nbc-news.html.

57   "HANCOCK HOUSE OF COMMONS CONVERSATION WITH TORY MP DR LUKE EVANS PURCHASE OF MIDAZOLAM.". 2021. *Bitchute*. https://www.bitchute.com/video/SYcbbDqb2BG0/.

58   "Euthanasia - Wikipedia". 2022. *En.Wikipedia.Org*. Accessed March 8. https://en.wikipedia.org/wiki/Euthanasia.

59   Ekland-Olson, Sheldon. 2014. "Life And Death Decisions: The Quest For Morality And Justice In Human Societies". *Amazon.Com*. https://www.amazon.com/Life-Death-Decisions-Societies-Sociology/dp/1138808881.

60   Chang, Ailsa. 2020. "Gasping For Air: Autopsies Reveal Troubling Effects Of Lethal Injection". *Npr.Org*. https://www.npr.org/2020/09/21/793177589/gasping-for-air-autopsies-reveal-troubling-effects-of-lethal-injection.

61   Ibid.

62   "High Levels Of Midazolam Prescriptions". 2021. *Health Advisory And Recovery Team*. https://www.hartgroup.org/midazolam-prescriptions/.

63   Icke, David. 2021. "The Midazolam Virus - How Psychopath Hancock Killed Thousands And Called It The 'First Wave'". *Bitchute*. https://www.bitchute.com/video/Fo3xwHY09zeJ/.

64   Lawrie, Iain, and Sarah Cox. 2021. "COVID-19 And Palliative And End Of Life In Secondary Care". Association for Palliative Medicine of Great Britain.

65   Visontay, Elias. 2021. "Sydney ICU Nurses Sedating Patients More To Manage Workload As Covid Outbreak Strains Hospitals". *The Guardian*. https://www.theguardian.com/australia-news/2021/aug/30/sydney-icu-nurses-sedating-patientsmore-to-manage-workload-as-covid-outbreak-strains-hospitals.

66   "Midazolam Side Effects". 2022. *Drugs.Com*. https://www.drugs.com/sfx/midazolam-side-effects.html.

67   Wickware, Carolyn. 2020. "Supplies Of Sedative Used For COVID-19 Patients Diverted From France To Avoid Potential Shortages - The Pharmaceutical Journal". *The Pharmaceutical Journal*. https://www.pharmaceutical-journal.com/article/news/supplies-of-sedative-used-for-covid-19-patients-diverted-from-france-to-avoid-potential-shortages.

68   Galluccio, Bill. 2020. "Doctors Say Death Penalty Drugs Could Help COVID-19 Patients On Ventilators". *Iheart.Com*. https://www.iheart.com/content/2020-04-23-doctors-say-death-penalty-drugs-could-help-covid-19-patients-on-ventilators.

69   Fuller, Alice. 2020. "Care Homes Accused Of Using Powerful Sedatives To Kill Corona Victims Quickly". *The Sun*. https://www.thesun.co.uk/news/12100515/care-homes-accused-sedatives-coronavirus-die-quickly/.

70   Smith, Wesley J. 2013. "Liverpool Care Pathway: The Road To Backdoor Euthanasia". *Discovery Institute*. https://www.discovery.org/a/21001/.

71   "Jim Breuer's Coronavirus Questions". 2021. *Youtube*. https://youtu.be/3FHRe3ISh5M.

72   "34% Of NHS Staff Say They Were Pressured To Place 'Do Not Resuscitate' Orders On Disabled Covid Patients". 2021. *The Exposé*. https://dailyexpose.uk/2021/02/14/34-of-nhs-staff-say-they-were-pressured-to-place-do-not-resuscitate-orders-on-disabled-covid-patients/.

73   "If You Are Sick Or Caring For Someone". 2022. *Centers For Disease Control And Prevention*. https://www.cdc.gov/coronavirus/2019-ncov/if-you-are-sick/index.html.

74   Walker, Molly. 2022. "Which COVID Outpatient Therapy Should Clinicians Reach For?". *Medpagetoday.Com*. https://www.medpagetoday.com/infectiousdisease/covid19/96655.

75   The Food and Drug Administration. 2022. "FACT SHEET FOR PATIENTS, PARENTS, AND CAREGIVERS: EMERGENCY USE AUTHORIZATION (EUA) OF PAXLOVID FOR CORONAVIRUS DISEASE 2019 (COVID-19)". FDA.

76   Phillips, Jack. 2021. "FDA Authorizes Pfizer's COVID-19 Pill Weeks After Landing $5 Billion Deal With Biden Administration". *Www.Theepochtimes.Com*. https://www.theepochtimes.com/fda-authorizes-pfizers-covid-19-pill-after-securing-5-billion-deal-with-federal-government_4172758.html.

77   U.S. Department of Health and Human Services. 2021. "Biden Administration Secures 10 Million Courses Of Pfizer's COVID-19 Oral Antiviral Medicine As Additional Tool To Reduce Hospitalizations And Save Lives". https://www.hhs.gov/about/news/2021/11/18/biden-administration-secures-10-million-courses-pfizers-covid-19-oral-antiviral-medicine-as-additional-tool-reduce-hospitalizations-save-lives.html.

78   The U.S. Food and Drug Administration. 2021. "Coronavirus (COVID-19) Update: FDA Authorizes First Oral Antiviral For Treatment Of COVID-19". https://www.fda.gov/news-events/press-announcements/coronavirus-covid-19-update-fda-authorizes-first-oral-antiviral-treatment-covid-19.

79   "Ritonavir-Boosted Nirmatrelvir (Paxlovid)". 2022. *Nih.Gov*. https://www.covid19treatmentguidelines.nih.gov/therapies/antiviral-therapy/ritonavir-boosted-nirmatrelvir--paxlovid-/.

80   "Sotrovimab Monoclonal Antibody Remains In Short-Supply". 2022. *Precisionvaccinations.Com*. https://www.precisionvaccinations.com/2022/01/18/sotrovimab-monoclonal-antibody-remains-short-supply.

81   Texas Department of State and Health Services. 2022. "Statement On
        Monoclonal Antibody Availability".
        https://dshs.texas.gov/news/releases/2021/20211227.aspx.

82   "Biden Administration Usurpation Of Monoclonal Antibody Supply
        Chain Endangering COVID-19 Patients". 2021. *Trialsitenews*.
        https://trialsitenews.com/biden-administration-usurpation-of-monoclonal-
        antibody-supply-chain-endangering-covid-19-patients/.

83   Huang, Pien. 2022. "Doctors Find Limited Use For Less Effective
        COVID Pill". *Npr.Org*. https://www.npr.org/sections/health-
        shots/2022/02/22/1081898013/doctors-find-limited-use-for-less-effective-
        covid-pill.

84   "Merck's Molnupiravir A Last Choice? Reports Of Glut Of Authorized
        Product Despite Omicron Crisis". 2022. *Trialsitenews*.
        https://trialsitenews.com/mercks-molnupiravir-a-last-choice-reports-of-
        glut-of-authorized-product-despite-omicron-crisis/.

85   The U.S. Food and Drug Administration. 2021. "FACT SHEET FOR
        HEALTHCARE PROVIDERS: EMERGENCY USE
        AUTHORIZATION FOR MOLNUPIRAVIR". The FDA.

Chapter 9

Treatments Pt. 2: Early Treatment, Compassionate Care

We have now covered the dangerous, expensive medications and treatment procedures which made up the public health strategy during the Covid era. We've touched on how these practices, in many cases, *caused* the very death and side effects those responsible attributed without satisfactory evidence to a novel coronavirus. But this is not to imply the people who were given those bad treatments were not ill in some fashion beforehand. They obviously were, in my opinion with a variety of illnesses—as we saw with comedian Jim Brewer's not-Covid-patient friend.

At the same time, my intention with this book is not to be doom and gloom. The events/actions described *are* extremely dark and *do* warrant some form of justice be done. But I've found that simply having the historical and situational background can help arm you against the lies enough to resist them, with or without the criminals being put before an earthly court. And maybe one day that background might even be shared with the right person in the right position of authority to act. This is why many alternative media outlets described this time as a choice everyone had to make: "The Great Reset," or, "The Great Awakening."

Electing the path of awakening myself, I find myself ironically *grateful for* the irrational, hardline stance public health departments took toward pushing those bad treatments. Their having been so obvious about it is what made information on alternatives so thirsted for, and ultimately attained, during the Covid era. This chapter highlights those more effective, safer, more natural treatment and prevention alternatives, as well as the over the top efforts to suppress them.

The Documented Benefits of Early Treatment

As we touched on in the previous chapter, early treatment and prevention outside of hospitals was not a priority for public health departments for the first and most crucial two years of the Covid era, with only a half-hearted, dishonest effort pivoted to in 2022. Given our understanding that many diseases/ailments were mischaracterized as, "Covid," during this time period, it should be obvious why this would lead to disaster. Again, we can review the case of Jim Brewer's friend for direct evidence of this problem. We can also validate them via studies which have showed the difference between life and death in effectively all cases came down to whether or not the person received treatment, as if studies would be needed for such an idea.[1]

Common sense alone should tell any honest person that the primary encouragements by public health departments should have been healthy behavior, clean eating, exercise, vitamin supplementation, and a sense of calm. Instead, they unfathomably opted for gym closures, masks, anti-social isolation, silence on diet/nutrition, and mass panic. And to underline just how incomprehensible this was, we need simply return our attention to the aforementioned NIH Ebola study, in which the benefits of early treatment are explicitly called out.

Not only that, but even as it relates to coronavirus and/or influenza-based illnesses, a 2010 study published by Baric et al. in *PLOS Pathogens* found that, "Increasing the intracellular Zn^{2+} concentration with zinc-ionophores like pyrithione (PT) can efficiently impair the replication of a variety of RNA viruses."[2] Among the viruses they claimed zinc-ionophores inhibited were arterivirus, poliovirus, influenza virus, and—you guessed it—coronavirus. It will come as little surprise then that the early treatments we will cover in this chapter such as ivermectin, hydroxychloroquine, and quercetin all satisfy the criteria of zinc-ionophores, which are any chemicals that facilitate the passage of zinc ions through the cell membrane, something elemental zinc cannot do on its own.[3,4,5] Several subsequent studies have continued to support the benefits of zinc specifically for the purposes of the disease(s) referred to as, "Covid," as well.[6,7]

Despite these findings, we can see it inexplicably took Fauci and NIAID until November of 2020 to even acknowledge and recommend research into early treatments—research which had clearly already been done![8] And even if we pretend it hadn't, how could this not have been the very first priority at the beginning of 2020? Why did it take until a month before the inoculation rollout for this recommendation to be made? That question has a known answer, and it's coming in the next chapter. For now, are we to assume this man simply forgot every single thing he once knew about diseases and treatments? Of course not. It is as impossible to assume that as it is impossible for him to have forgotten.

Additionally, despite Fauci's public ass-covering plea for early treatment research in November 2020, he had already ignored plenty of demonstrations of effective early treatment options by prominent physicians. One example, as published in *Pulmonary Pharmacology & Therapeutics* by Blanco et al., came out of a nursing home in Spain as early as March 2020.[9] The mean age of residents at the home was 85, with 48% over 80 years old—surely a place where, "Covid," would wreak havoc. Within a few months 100% of the residents had tested positive, meaning they were all goners—only, they weren't goners. *Not one* resident died or was hospitalized, and all seroconverted (showed signs of antibodies).

So how did they do it? The answer is early treatment—regardless of symptom severity. And this included simple, common treatments like antihistamines, antibiotics, nasal washing, and pain/headache medications. Why hasn't this study been acknowledged to date by the major public health organizations, considering the extraordinary implications? Is it because it's an observational study? The CDC, NIH, and FDA have never shied away from citing observational studies before in the name of supporting their determinations and subsequent actions.[10,11,12] Ignoring for a second that these nursing home patients both tested positive for an allegedly novel disease and clearly didn't have one, why wouldn't the NIH recommendations for non-hospitalized patients include these clearly effective, common, low-risk-profile treatments as potential options?[13] Is it because the FDA hasn't approved them for the use of treating, "Covid?" If so, why hasn't it, when it's granted allegedly, "emergency-justified," use authorizations to dangerous risk-profile, unproven, novel drugs? Why wouldn't *all* common treatments for similar ailments (i.e. the common cold, flu) be granted emergency use authorization for this purpose? One would think in an emergency you'd want *more* options on the table for treating sick people, not less, especially options known to be safe for similar uses.

These are questions which cannot be answered without a response of, "corruption." But to return to the topic at hand for now, this was not nearly the only example of early treatment benefits to draw from. Another frontline example comes from Dr. Brian Tyson, a California physician who has treated, "more than 6,000 Covid patients."[14] Decrying the inhibition of early treatment by public health authorities, Dr. Tyson explains how he simply did what a doctor always does—namely, treating inflammation with anti-inflammatories, treating blood clots with anti-coagulants, and treating breathing issues with asthma medications.

Dr. Vladimir Zelenko, a prominent New York physician, is another who was on the, "frontline," having treated, "thousands of COVID-19 patients," as well as having been, "cited in over 10 COVID-19 research studies," and, "conducting several of his own studies."[15] Dr. Zelenko primarily seems to recommend hydroxychloroquine as a treatment (more on that later), having had a role in the treatment of President Donald Trump.[16] He also stresses the benefits of prevention with his ZStack protocol however, with emphasis placed on quercetin, zinc, vitamin C, and vitamin D. The benefits of quercetin and vitamin D, in particular, are supported in an increasing number of peer-reviewed studies related to the diseases called, "Covid."[17,18,19]

Another example of successful early treatment protocols comes from the Front Line COVID-19 Critical Care Alliance (FLCCC), which developed the I-MASK+ prevention and early treatment protocol.[20] The FLCCC points out that all medications are FDA-approved (though not for, "Covid"), inexpensive, readily available, and have been used for decades with well-established safety profiles. The protocol includes antivirals, mouthwashes, nasal sprays, nutritional recommendations, and vitamin recommendations, such as vitamin D3, vitamin C, quercetin, zinc, and melatonin. One would think the FDA, CDC, WHO, or NIH would have similar documentation for simple things a person can do to treat and/or prevent similar illness, but they do not, nor do they endorse the FLCCC protocol.

In fact, according to the CDC, "Those at highest risk for severe disease and death include … those with underlying conditions, including but not limited to obesity, hypertension, diabetes, cardiovascular disease, chronic respiratory or kidney disease, immunosuppression from solid organ transplant, and sickle cell disease."[21] Also, they acknowledge that, "for only 6% of deaths, Covid is the only cause mentioned," and, "for deaths with conditions or causes in addition to Covid-19, on average, there were 2.9 additional conditions or causes per death."[22]

Given these conclusions, it seems obvious that if one wanted to avoid a serious case of the cold/flu (aka, "Covid," to anyone who still insists on referring to all illnesses as that), one should maybe do the general nutritional maintenance type things mentioned in the I-MASK+ protocol. Up until this tragic point, this included things like maintaining a healthy, natural diet and supplementing vitamins/nutrients, if necessary. Unfortunately however, along with such basic healthy activities as working out and *breathing*, the benefits of these things too were considered exaggerated and certainly insufficient by both public health organizations and their propagandist media PR teams, as it related to, "Covid." This was because the only thing worth focusing on—the thing everyone would have to take in order to save the day—was gene therapy inoculations. And there was no substitute which would suffice.

The antivirals the I-MASK+ protocol recommends are ivermectin (more on that shortly) and nitazoxanide. This also made me reflect on the situation I mentioned earlier, when I was denied care at an urgent care clinic, despite ultimately having been found to have had a parasite. Once accurately diagnosed, I was prescribed nitazoxanide. Like ivermectin, nitazoxanide is considered an anti-parasitic, which apparently also has anti-viral properties. The reason I'd been denied care at the urgent clinic is because along with not being tested for, "Covid," I had a mild cough alongside my ongoing diarrhea symptoms.

So my problem with this situation, beyond my having been discriminated against, is this: I knew not to get a, "Covid," test because I knew they were nonsense. If I had gotten one though, which I now in hindsight almost wish I had just to conduct this experiment, I almost certainly would have tested positive, as some of my friends who got tested at that time did. And I would have tested positive despite the fact that my ailment was actually related to a parasite. So, given the inclusion of something like diarrhea as a symptom of, "Covid," the fact that doctors can diagnose a, "Covid case," based on these symptoms per the CDC, and the fact that parasite treatments can also be used for viral infections, this serves as just another example of how incredibly *likely* misdiagnosis was made, thanks to the intervention of these organizations in the doctor-patient relationship.

173

I also wonder what would have happened to me—what *has* happened to many unfortunate others—if I'd have been ignorant enough of the situation to have originally gotten the test as the urgent care recommended, gone to a hospital thinking I had a scary new disease that wouldn't go away, and had been treated with the recommended treatments in the prior chapter. I shudder to think…

I am grateful to the doctors out there who helped prevent that outcome, many of whom have done everything they can to share their findings. Alongside Dr. Kory, Dr. George Fareed, Dr. Steven Hatfill, and Dr. Peter McCullough each presented on the issue of early treatment and its suppression to the Italian Senate in the fall of 2021.[23] This is just one example, as many others have spoken out too from the beginning in various avenues. Despite their calls for adoption of early treatment as an official policy going unanswered in favor of experimental drugs and gene therapy inoculations, the impact they had in sharing what they know about providing care—as a doctor is meant to—undoubtedly saved many lives.

The Slander of Ivermectin and the Assault on the Doctor-Patient Relationship

On October 5th, 2015, just 4 years prior to the outbreak of the alleged pandemic, NBC reported on three scientists having won the Nobel Prize of Medicine.[24] Their names were William C. Campbell, Satoshi Omura, and Youyou Tu, and their award-winning accomplishment was discovering natural-based remedies against parasites that cause malaria and river blindness. The compounds they discovered were called artemisinin and ivermectin, which NBC claimed have been, "used by millions of people around the world and have saved countless lives." They went on to highlight that ivermectin specifically, "now is used to fight pests from bed bugs and lice to serious diseases such as lymphatic filariasis," and, "was derived from naturally occurring bacteria in soil." NBC also acknowledged the Nobel committee's lauding of the discovery as well, saying:

> *"These two discoveries have provided* **humankind** *(my emphasis) with powerful new means to combat these debilitating diseases that affect hundreds of millions of* **people** *(my emphasis) annually. The consequences in terms of*

174

*improved **human** (my emphasis) health and reduced suffering are immeasurable."*

Fast forward to August 2021, when the same NBC characterized the same ivermectin[25]:

*"...ivermectin, a drug **primarily** (my emphasis) used to deworm animals..."*

This despite the fact that not one time in the 2015 article did NBC mention ivermectin's use in animals (they did connect artemisinin to use in animals). In fact, I took the time to count and they referenced the, "immeasurable," benefits specifically for, "humans," "humankind," "people," and, "children," 9 times in 15 total paragraphs. This is not to say ivermectin is not used in animals—it is and clearly has an exceptional variety of benefits. The primary issue here though is this is just another example of the exceptional dishonesty and passive-aggressive unprofessionalism with which the US propagandist media and public health institutions carry themselves. And that's just the tip of the iceberg. Also in August of 2021, the US FDA's *Twitter* page went as far as to post the following in reference to ivermectin[26]:

"You are not a horse. You are not a cow. Seriously, y'all. Stop it."

Well, gee willikers, y'all! The FDA sure is hip and totally not at all speaking down to millions of people. Just take it from acting FDA commissioner Janet Woodcock, speaking on the post[27]:

"That was great! Even I saw it!"

Did you hear that!? Even the FDA director saw what is said on the FDA's official social media page! Another senior FDA official also concurred with Woodcock on how, "great," it was, calling it a, "unique viral moment … in a time of incredible misinformation."[28] There's that word again—that lazy, un-scientific word. And unsurprisingly, it was not said without a heaping smack of hubris to follow.

You see, the data this tweet used as its justification came from a Mississippi health department poison control alert.[29] According to Mary Beth Pfeiffer and Linda Bonvie, publishing for *Rescue with*

175

Michael Capuzzo, Freedom of Information Act emails would reveal this data was not only not vetted by the FDA, but was even still viewed as, "an opportunity to remind the public of our warnings for ivermectin." As much as I hate the word, this is misinformation by its very definition. It is also a gross—though at this point, expected—failure of duty and demonstration of incompetence.

The same incompetence ravages the mainstream media, which also jumped all over the story. As they did, in lock-step narrative consistency as with every story ever, music-magazine-turned-propaganda-rag *Rolling Stone* wrote of Oklahoma hospitals so jammed with ivermectin overdoses that gunshot victims had to wait for care.[30] As if the story was even remotely believable to begin with, even the *Washington Post* admitted that it was simply false as they acknowledged for *Rolling Stone* it must have been, "too good to check."[31] But don't mistakenly think *WaPo* is innocent either. Along with the *Associated Press*, *New York Times*, and *the Guardian*, *WaPo* also had to correct their own reporting on the Mississippi story.[32,33,34,35] As for the *New York Times*, they outright lied, referring in their own piece to a, "staggering number of calls," before printing corrections, which have become a staple for them. And before we continue, let me just re-iterate that these are the same organizations which constantly use the word, "misinformation," and declare it a problem which can apparently only be corrected by listening to them. Staggering.

So what actually happened in Mississippi which led to this dumpster fire? A now-corrected health alert did go out which before read, "At least 70% of the recent calls have been related to ingestion of livestock or animal formulations of ivermectin purchased at livestock supply centers."[36] What the media failed to ask, however, is 70% *of what*? The alert now clarifies, "of ivermectin-related calls," as opposed to of all poison control calls, as the FDA/media insinuated without checking. The total of, "ivermectin-related calls," was also only 14. In fact, the other 30% of the 14 were strictly informational calls, and of the 70% who called about ingesting the horse de-wormer *version* of ivermectin, only one had worse than mild symptoms.

Examples like these of childish mainstream media and public health slander related to ivermectin abounded in the Covid era. Another prominent one which seemed to go viral was the experience of podcaster and comedian Joe Rogan, who took the *human* version

176

of ivermectin when sick.[37] Rogan recovered shortly after, but was slandered by CNN and countless other outlets as having taken horse de-wormer anyway. CNN is even accused of having gone as far as to alter a video of a post-ivermectin Rogan, to make him look pale and sickly.[38] Rogan later had the chance to question leading CNN medical personality Sanjay Gupta, who did not seem to have an answer for why his network lied about Rogan's medication, which he claimed was prescribed to him by a doctor.

While it is and has been a huge problem that the US mainstream media lies seemingly all the time, there is an equally troubling problem presented here, which has become more prominent in the Covid era. The problem this case study demonstrates is that none of these people—not the FDA, nor the mainstream media— actually treat patients, yet they have the audacity to slander natural, potentially life-saving treatments which *are* being prescribed by doctors for people with the symptoms related to, "Covid." Though it seems to have been forgotten thanks to their hellish propaganda, this is a role reserved for the discretion of a medical doctor, in relationship with that doctor's patient.

And the sabotage of the basic doctor-patient relationship during this Covid era has not gone unnoticed by the doctors themselves. One unfathomable example is Dr. Robert Karas of Arkansas, who was reportedly being investigated by the Arkansas State Medical Board for his use of ivermectin to treat his patients.[39] And as far as what's reported is concerned, it seems the only apparent justification for this investigation was the CDC and FDA's absurd propaganda related to ivermectin's alternative use as horse medication. According to Dr. Karas:

> *"In my medical judgment, weighing the known risks and side effect profile of ivermectin against the potential benefits supports the administration of ivermectin. I do not have the luxury of conducting my own clinical trial or study and am not attempting to do so. I am on the front line of trying to prevent death and serious illness.*
> *I am proud of our track record in both of my clinics and at the jail in particular, where not one single patient of the five hundred plus who have followed our plan of care has been hospitalized, intubated, or died."*

177

Another example of the same issue came out of Alberta, Canada, where Dr. Daniel Nagase reportedly received a warning by Alberta Health Services for treating patients with ivermectin.[40] Dr. Nagase claimed these health officials were, "withholding a life-saving medication from an entire province." Predictably, the warning he apparently received cited both the slanderous, hollow term, "misinformation," as well as the slanderous talking-point of ivermectin as a, "veterinary medication."

The frustrations of Drs. Karas and Nagase were also echoed at a Global Covid Summit held in Rome, Italy, where a, "Physician's Declaration," was announced by the International Alliance of Physicians and Medical Scientists.[41] The Declaration, which as of October 22, 2021 had been signed by more than 12,700 doctors & scientists, both recognizes the, "assault on our ability to care for our patients," as well as reaffirming the commitment to the Hippocratic Oath. The Declaration reads as follows:

> *"We the physicians of the world, united and loyal to the Hippocratic Oath, recognizing the profession of medicine as we know it is at a crossroad, are compelled to declare the following;*
>
> ***WHEREAS***, *it is our utmost responsibility and duty to uphold and restore the dignity, integrity, art and science of medicine;*
>
> ***WHEREAS***, *there is an unprecedented assault on our ability to care for our patients;*
>
> ***WHEREAS***, *public policy makers have chosen to force a 'one size fits all' treatment strategy, resulting in needless illness and death, rather than upholding fundamental concepts of the individualized, personalized approach to patient care which is proven to be safe and more effective;*
>
> ***WHEREAS***, *physicians and other health care providers working on the front lines, utilizing their knowledge of epidemiology, pathophysiology and pharmacology, are often first to identify new, potentially life saving treatments;*
>
> ***WHEREAS***, *physicians are increasingly being discouraged from engaging in open professional discourse and the exchange of ideas about new and emerging diseases, not only endangering the essence of the medical profession, but more importantly, more tragically, the lives of our patients;*

WHEREAS, thousands of physicians are being prevented from providing treatment to their patients, as a result of barriers put up by pharmacies, hospitals, and public health agencies, rendering the vast majority of healthcare providers helpless to protect their patients in the face of disease. Physicians are now advising their patients to simply go home (allowing the virus to replicate) and return when their disease worsens, resulting in hundreds of thousands of unnecessary patient deaths, due to failure-to-treat;

*WHEREAS, this is not medicine. This is not care. **These policies may actually constitute crimes against humanity** (my* emphasis).

NOW THEREFORE, IT IS:

RESOLVED, that the physician-patient relationship must be restored. The very heart of medicine is this relationship, which allows physicians to best understand their patients and their illnesses, to formulate treatments that give the best chance for success, while the patient is an active participant in their care.

RESOLVED, that the political intrusion into the practice of medicine and the physician/patient relationship must end. Physicians, and all health care providers, must be free to practice the art and science of medicine without fear of retribution, censorship, slander, or disciplinary action, including possible loss of licensure and hospital privileges, loss of insurance contracts and interference from government entities and organizations – which further prevent us from caring for patients in need. More than ever, the right and ability to exchange objective scientific findings, which further our understanding of disease, must be protected.

RESOLVED, that physicians must defend their right to prescribe treatment, observing the tenet FIRST, DO NO HARM. Physicians shall not be restricted from prescribing safe and effective treatments. These restrictions continue to cause unnecessary sickness and death. The rights of patients, after being fully informed about the risks and benefits of each option, must be restored to receive those treatments.

RESOLVED, that we invite physicians of the world and all health care providers to join us in this noble cause as we endeavor to restore trust, integrity and professionalism to the practice of medicine.

***RESOLVED**, that we invite the scientists of the world, who are skilled in biomedical research and uphold the highest ethical and moral standards, to insist on their ability to conduct and publish objective, empirical research without fear of reprisal upon their careers, reputations and livelihoods.*

***RESOLVED**, that we invite patients, who believe in the importance of the physician-patient relationship and the ability to be active participants in their care, to demand access to science-based medical care."*

The Truth about Ivermectin

*"Don't do it [take ivermectin]. There's no evidence whatsoever that that works and it could potentially have toxicity, as you just mentioned, with people who have gone to poison control centers because they've taken the drug at a ridiculous dose and wind up getting sick. **There's no clinical evidence that indicates that this works** (my emphasis)."*
—Anthony Fauci on CNN, August 29, 2021[42]

The above quote by Anthony Fauci in August of 2021 is particularly ironic considering his own organization, the NIH, changed its stance on ivermectin as a treatment for, "Covid," in January of 2021, from, "against," to, "neutral."[43] It was also made in response to the CNN anchor prompting it, by specifically referencing the Mississippi poison control center story we already determined to have been a gross exaggeration. This means Fauci is either lying or totally incompetent in this case, a familiar story to be sure. Either way, it is this type of incessant slander and suppression of real information on ivermectin, a potentially life-saving treatment, by Fauci and people in positions like his, that constitutes a crime against humanity—one of the many we've listed to this point. And despite the claims Fauci admits through his actions are false, the vast majority of doctors and studies seem to point to ivermectin as an effective treatment for these types of flu-like symptoms.

Before we address the litany of studies mentioned, let's look at the potential toxicity risks of ivermectin, of which Fauci, the FDA, and the media seem so obnoxiously concerned. A quick search of, "ivermectin," in VigiAccess, the WHO's adverse events drug monitoring database, renders 5,697 **total** reported adverse events from 1992 through October 2021.[44] For context on how incredibly low this total is, a search of, "Advil," (aka generic name: "ibuprofen") tallied over the same time period, renders 157,320 total reported adverse events. Does Fauci think Advil should be taken off the counters? And what about if we compare ivermectin to the drugs public health *did* sanction and say were, "safe and effective?" A search of, "remdesivir," yields 7,663 reported results **in the less than two years** since it was EUA approved, with the, "Covid-19 vaccine," at an astounding 2,403,506 reported results in the same less-than two year period (way more on that to come). Where's the FDA's snarky tweet about how *y'all* shouldn't take those never-before-approved-for-human-use drugs because you're not a guinea pig?

So ivermectin's risk profile is clearly one of the least significant of any drug ever. In fact, there seems to be almost no risk at all if one simply refrains from taking more than the prescribed amount, which should be obvious. The next question though is: does it work to treat the symptoms of, "Covid?" And the answer from countless studies and doctors' experiences seems to be a resounding, "yes."

First, we have a 2021, "Systemic Review, Meta-Analysis, and Trial Sequential Analysis to Inform Clinical Guidelines," on, "Ivermectin for Prevention and Treatment of Covid-19 Infection," by Bryant et al. in the *American Journal of Therapeutics*.[45] In this report the authors reviewed twenty-four randomized, controlled trials involving 3,406 participants. Their conclusions were as follows:

> *"Moderate-certainty evidence finds that large reductions in COVID-19 deaths are possible using ivermectin. Using ivermectin early in the clinical course may reduce numbers progressing to severe disease. The apparent safety and low cost suggest that ivermectin is likely to have a significant impact on the SARS-CoV-2 pandemic globally."*

This analysis obviously provides a dark context to Fauci's quote of, "no clinical evidence," supporting ivermectin. But the story behind this paper gets much more disturbing. On the heels of its release, one of its authors, Dr. Tess Lawrie, reached out to fellow researcher Dr. Andrew Hill about joining a team to do an additional systematic review.[46] According to Lawrie, Hill agreed and was all in on ivermectin, having testified to an NIH panel about the benefits of the drug on January 6, 2021.[47] In fact, Hill was so enthusiastic about ivermectin he went as far as to publicly say the following[48]:

> *"I'll give you an example, my brother—he's 58, he's a smoker, and if he was hospitalized with COVID-19 I don't know that there isn't a way to get supplies of ivermectin into the UK. If I could, and I knew it was good quality, I would want my brother to be taking it."*

Before Hill could join Lawrie's team and less than two weeks after his NIH hearing however, on January 18, 2021 he published a pre-print of a paper titled, "Meta-analysis of Randomized Trials of Ivermectin to Treat SARS-CoV-2 Infection."[49,50] This pre-print found ivermectin to have several benefits, ultimately recommending larger trials be done. Lawrie reached out to Hill, who she acknowledges is not a treating doctor, requesting a retraction of this new paper for its lack of endorsement of ivermectin despite these findings.[51] She then met with him on Zoom the next day. On the call, Lawrie called Hill out on an independent communication specialist's confirmation that Hill's paper included, "multiple instances of interference (additional text added to the paper)," from what the specialist termed a, "shadow author."[52] And while this might seem speculative, it was confirmed by Hill himself on the Zoom call:

> *"Lawrie: Who's conclusions are those on the review that you've done? Who's not listed as an author who's actually contributed?*
> *Hill: Well, I mean, I don't really want to get into it. I mean, Unitaid—*
> *Lawrie: I think it needs to be—it needs to be clear. I would like to know who—who are these other voices that are in your paper that are not acknowledged? Does Unitaid have a say? Do they influence what you write?*
> *Hill: Unitaid has a say in the conclusions of the paper, yeah.*
> *Lawrie: Okay, um ... so who is it in Unitaid then, who is sharing—who is giving you opinion on your evidence?*

Hill: *Well it's just the people there, I don't—*
Lawrie: *I thought Unitaid was just a charity. Is it not a charity that—so they have a say in your conclusions?*
Hill: *... yeah."*

Unitaid is an affiliate of the WHO, which describes itself as a, "global health agency engaged in finding innovative solutions to prevent, diagnose, and treat diseases more quickly, cheaply and effectively, in low- and middle-income countries."[53] Like the WHO, it is funded by both governments and large grants, such as a $50 million contribution from the Bill & Melinda Gates Foundation.[54] We will cover the massive conflicts of interest these large grants can lead to in a later chapter. But for now we can clearly see the result of those conflicts in their admitted influence over Hill, whose study was funded by Unitaid to provide research for the WHO.[55] On January 12, 2021, sandwiched in between Hill's NIH testimony and pre-print reversal, Unitaid also happened to award $40 million to the University of Liverpool, where Hill is a senior visiting Research Fellow in the Pharmacology Department.[56,57]

Hill's paper *was* ultimately retracted, not for the scientific fraud he openly admits to having committed, but instead citing concerns claimed to exist with some of the studies the paper reviewed.[58] Still, Hill lists no conflicts of interest of his own in this retraction, despite confessing to his conclusions being dictated by Unitaid. This is the sorry state of the same, "infallible," science which is used as a justification to enact some of the most all-encompassing tyrannies the world has ever seen. It is proof that without a full commitment to morality, actual science and reasonable conclusions are impossible. Andrew Hill's submission is a vile example of the type of void-of-ethics science which has plagued the Covid era and the practice of the scientific method in general.

One of the people who called Hill out for his actions was Dr. Pierre Kory, who both testified with Hill at the January 2021 NIH panel and also on December 8, 2020 before the Senate Homeland Security Committee Hearing on Medical Response to COVID-19 in favor of what he called a, "miracle," repurposed drug[59]:

"... I want to start out by saying that I'm not speaking as an individual. I'm speaking on behalf of the organization that I

am a part of. We are a group of some of the most highly published physicians in the world. We have near 2,000 peer reviewed publications among us.

... You just mentioned that I was here in May and I touted—I wouldn't say, 'touted'—I recommended that it was critical that we use corticosteroids in this disease when all of the national and international health care organizations said we cannot use those. That turned out to be a life-saving recommendation.

... We have now come to the conclusion, after nine months— and I have to point out, I am severely troubled by the fact that the NIH, the FDA, and the CDC, I do not know of any task force that was assigned or compiled to review repurposed drugs in an attempt to treat this disease. Everything has been about novel and/or expensive pharmaceutically engineered drugs, things like tocilizumab and remdesivir and monoclonal antibodies and vaccines.

... We have a solution to this crisis. There is a drug that is proving to be of miraculous impact. And when I say miracle, I do not use that term lightly. And I don't want to be sensationalized when I say that. That is a scientific recommendation based on mountains of data that has emerged in the last three months.

When I am told, and I just heard this in the opening sentence, that we are touting things that are not FDA or NIH recommended, let me be clear: the NIH, their recommendation on ivermectin, which is to not use it outside of controlled trials, is from August 27th. We are now in December. This is three to four months later. Mountains of data have emerged from many centers and countries around the world showing the miraculous effectiveness of ivermectin. It basically obliterates transmission of this virus. If you take it you will not get sick."

Those are big claims, but they are also supported claims. In a summary document titled, "Review of the Emerging Evidence Demonstrating the Efficacy of Ivermectin in the Prophylaxis and Treatment of Covid-19," Dr. Kory and the team he referenced in his speech to the senate, the Front Line Covid-19 Critical Care Alliance, provide the, "mountain of evidence," he referred to.[60] This mountain includes the following summary of studies/conclusions, among others:

- Since 2012, many in vitro studies have demonstrated that Ivermectin inhibits the replication of many viruses, including influenza, Zika, Dengue and others[61,62,63,64,65,66,67,68]
- Ivermectin inhibits SARS-CoV-2 replication and binding to host tissue via several observed and proposed mechanisms[69]
- Ivermectin has potent anti-inflammatory properties with in vitro data demonstrating profound inhibition of both cytokine production and transcription of nuclear factor-κB (NF-κB), the most potent mediator of inflammation[70,71,72]
- Ivermectin significantly diminishes viral load and protects against organ damage in multiple animal models when infected with SARS-CoV-2 or similar coronaviruses[73,74]
- Ivermectin prevents transmission and development of COVID-19 disease in those exposed to infected patients[75,76,77,78,79]
- Ivermectin hastens recovery and prevents deterioration in patients with mild to moderate disease treated early after symptoms[80,81,82,83,84,85,86,87,88]
- Ivermectin hastens recovery and avoidance of ICU admission and death in hospitalized patients[89,90,91,92,93,94,95]
- Ivermectin reduces mortality in critically ill patients with COVID-19[96,97,98]
- Ivermectin leads to striking reductions in case-fatality rates in regions with widespread use[99,100,101]
- The safety, availability, and cost of ivermectin is nearly unparalleled given its near zero drug interactions along with only mild and rare side effects observed in almost 40 years of use and billions of doses administered[102]
- The WHO has long included ivermectin on its "List of Essential Medicines"[103]

It cannot be said that this evidence went unnoticed by the congress to which Dr. Kory presented it, either. In what can only be described as yet another horrendous scandal if true, the same congress which seems to have turned a blind eye to Dr. Kory's testimony allegedly followed his advice on ivermectin for their own treatments.

185

In a post by Dr. Kory on his *Twitter* account, dated October 7, 2021, he alleged[104]:

> *"Fun fact: Between 100-200 United States Congress Members (plus many of their staffers & family members) with COVID.. were treated by a colleague over the past 15 months with ivermectin & the I-MASK+ protocol at flccc.net. None have gone to the hospital. Just sayin'"*

Another similar story comes from a *Reuters*, "fact-check," (aka: a *Reuters* lie) about an Australian news channel's coverage of the Queen of England's bout with, "Covid."[105] The coverage featured a doctor who touted two new, "tablets and infusions," which, "could make a dramatic difference," to the, "welfare and health," of sick, elderly people. While saying this, the network aired pictures of sotrovimab (monoclonal antibody infusion, as covered) and Stromectol (ivermectin tablet). *Reuters*, along with other obedient propagandist networks, was quick to mention the Australian network in question later claimed it made an editing mistake.[106,107] It apparently didn't mean to show ivermectin, so the, "fact-checkers," claimed there was no proof the Queen took the drug.

The problem with this is several-fold. First, the doctor *did himself* mention a, "tablet," whether or not the footage was an error. None of the dishonest, "fact-checkers," felt it necessary to mention this or identify which tablet he was talking about, if not ivermectin. Second, I thought sotrovimab wasn't a substitute for inoculation according to the FDA. In its blind focus on painting a specific picture, *Reuters* makes no attempt to dispute the infusion could save the life of an at-risk elderly person. If that's the case, what could possibly be the need to inoculate, especially assuming the Queen is inoculated? And third, if *Reuters*, a global media conglomerate, wanted to confirm what the Queen did take, it almost certainly could. The fact that it doesn't in what is already blatantly dishonest coverage seems to tell us everything we need to know as far as what the Queen took.

So where are the calls for investigations into the FDA, NIH, and CDC from these congressmen, congresswomen, and the Queen? The same question is asked by Dr. Tess Lawrie.[108] Upon seeing Dr. Kory's testimony to the US senate, Dr. Lawrie compiled a report of her own in January 2021, in which she took the time to assess the 27 studies cited by Dr. Kory and the FLCCC and to validate their findings.[109] Upon validation, via her own rapid-review and meta-analysis, she ultimately submitted her report as well to the UK and WHO.

The issue of why such a breadth of evidence is ignored and/or so viciously discredited by those with conflicts of interest was also not limited to single scientists like Andrew Bryant—at times it infected the thinking of entire journals. In a February 2017 article entitled, "Ivermectin: enigmatic multifaceted 'wonder' drug continues to surprise and exceed expectations," for example, *Nature Magazine* hailed ivermectin's, "unexpected potential as an antibacterial, antiviral, and anti-cancer agent."[110] Fast forward five years and *Nature* had a new mission: discrediting ivermectin while making no attempt to follow up on their own 2017 article which specifically acknowledged, "antiviral," properties, among other benefits.[111] The problem with this sudden heel-turn is that *Nature* shows its hand when it, in the same article questioning a single flawed ivermectin study, admits, "scientists worry that it will also be seen as an alternative to vaccines, which are highly effective." My questions for *Nature* based on this absurd line are as follows:

- Who exactly are these unnamed, "scientists," of which you speak?
- What are their affiliations?
- Why is it not a problem that these scientists are so fixed on one possible solution, which is experimental and to-date clearly demonstrates an absolutely absurd risk profile?
- What evidence do you have for this, "highly effective," claim?
- Why do these scientists find it okay to have called brand new, "vaccines," never before used in humans, "highly effective," when the same the types of trials you're demanding of the proven drug ivermectin (controlled, randomized trials) haven't and can't have been completed for those, "vaccines?"
- Why is the agenda of these scientists, whether a good thing or bad, more important—or important at all—relative to the experience and treatment decisions of medical doctors and scientists who disagree?

Scientific studies get questioned and critiqued all the time, and that's a good thing. The problem in the Covid era is this has solely been a one-way street as far as policy implementation and enforcement. The agenda of the media's mostly unnamed, "scientists," as well as of named figures like Andrew Bryant, has been clearly demonstrated in this book to have been considered a worthy excuse to justify lies, slander, and empty rhetoric during the past two years. Still, the amount of evidence for ivermectin's benefits has simply been too numerous for those agenda setters to keep up with. It is beyond doubt and they know this. Beyond all the studies previously cited, there are also several anecdotal and epidemiological examples of countries/people apparently benefiting from the adoption of ivermectin as a primary treatment strategy. They are as follows:

- India's largest state, Uttar Pradesh, eradicated its, "Covid," case spike with adoption of universal ivermectin use strategy.[112] This also contrasts starkly with the Indian state of Kerala, which instead adopted a mass inoculation strategy in 2021 and despite only accounting for 3% of India's population, represented more than 65% of its, "Covid," cases in September 2021.[113]
- Per *LifeSiteNews*, a December 2020 initiative in Mexico City to prescribe ivermectin and azithromycin to COVID-19 positive patients has resulted in a 52-76% reduction in hospitalizations in the city.[114] A home-treatment-kit was created and used even in patients with no symptoms. Dr. Juan J. Chamie-Quintero, a senior data analyst at private Colombian university EAFIT, followed the trends as within two weeks of the regimen's introduction hospitalizations and deaths began to plummet. In fact, by February Dr. Chamie-Quintero noted a staggering 3,000 person decrease in weekly excess deaths.
- A 2020 study by Guerrero et al. in *Colombia Médica* compared data from 19 African countries which participated in the African Programme for Onchocerciases Control (APOC), from 1995 until 2015, to African countries which did not.[115] A regression analysis, which controlled for different factors, found significantly lower mortality and case rates in APOC countries compared to non-APOC countries. As the APOC campaign included mass use of ivermectin, the authors

hypothesized a role could have been played by the drug which should be studied further.

- *Buffalo News* reported in January 2021 on an 80-year-old woman who was, "on a ventilator, literally on her deathbed," prior to her family convincing her doctors to try ivermectin.[116] Her doctors previously gave her a 20% chance to live and told her family she'd likely be on a ventilator in the ICU for at least a month. With pressure from the family, her first doctor started her on the drug, but another doctor prevented further use. Thanks to this public-health-fed dogma, the family was then forced to get a court order for the hospital to continue ivermectin treatment. The judge ultimately did provide the order and with resumed treatment the woman's health was soon restored, which her family attributed to what they called the, "miracle drug." While this is an anecdotal example, both the article and doctors in the story demonstrate the absurdity of their aforementioned dogma, by referring to ivermectin as, "experimental." This is a term never applied to their public-health-authorized drugs (i.e. remdesivir and gene therapy inoculations), which by any reasonable/honest standard are far more appropriately classifiable as, "experimental," both as treatments for this alleged novel disease, and in general.

So, given this bounty of support for positive treatment outcomes, *why* all the ivermectin slander? At worst (ignoring all the evidence to the contrary for a moment) ivermectin doesn't treat the flu-like symptoms in question, but is a natural, cheap drug with noted benefits beyond those symptoms, and has an abnormally negligible risk profile. So why the need for the extra effort in discrediting it? Well, the answer is threefold:

1. The financial conflicts of interest public health organizations have with the makers of the mRNA inoculations and of Gilead's remdesivir. We will summarize these in detail in a later chapter.
2. How those conflicts of interest contrast with the extremely low price of ivermectin

Unlike the mRNA inoculations and remdesivir, ivermectin was FDA approved prior to the alleged pandemic and has been since

1987.[117] Israeli professor Eli Schwartz, founder of the Center for Travel Medicine and Tropical Disease at Sheba, conducted a randomized, controlled double-blinded study of his own on the, "Covid," usefulness of the drug, from May 2020 through January 2021. What his study found was that ivermectin did have an, "almost 100% chance that a person will be noninfectious in four to six days." These findings were exciting to Schwartz, when he considered the drug was as cheap as $1 a day in some places. However, despite his study, a lack of *any* evident side effects, the exceptional affordability, and sole prior-approved status, Schwartz was disheartened by what he found to be senseless opposition and the lack of WHO support for even conducting their own trial. He voiced his discontent bluntly: "We tried to publish it, and it was kicked away by three journals. No one even wanted to hear about it. You have to ask how come when the world is suffering ... This drug will not bring any economic profits," and so Big Pharma doesn't want to deal with it, he said.

3. The fact that ivermectin is (or... was?) considered solely an anti-parasitic by the FDA

This third point might be the most important for their need to discredit the benefits of ivermectin. The FDA even unwittingly acknowledges this in their update, "Why You Should Not Use Ivermectin to Treat or Prevent Covid-19."[118] Thanks to the *Way Back Machine*, we can see an August 2021 screenshot of this same update included the line, "Ivermectin is not an anti-viral (a drug for treating viruses)."[119] The removal of this line in the current version reveals the profound implications that it presents. What the FDA surely by now knows, thanks to countless study demonstrations, is that ivermectin *can be* and *is* used as a treatment for the flu-like symptoms called, "Covid," and would therefore be considered an antiviral. So this change needed to happen because they were faced with an impossible dilemma:

1. If August 2021 FDA claim was true—that ivermectin *cannot* be used successfully against Covid because it's not an antiviral and Covid is caused by a virus—then its proven use and success implies Covid is not caused by a virus
2. With the October 2021 deletion, the FDA unburdened itself from the previous issue. Such a deletion would also be easy

190

enough to memory-hole. Being aware of this deletion however (as we now are), makes it clear there's no good reason for them to not have completed studies in 2020 on ivermectin (which their deletion itself implies they know *can* treat the flu-like symptoms called, "Covid"). The fact that even WebMD was acknowledging ivermectin's potential, "Covid," benefits as early as April of 2020, makes the FDA's actions with regard to this drug all the more embarrassing/criminal.[120]

And this is where we close on our summary of ivermectin. The criminally corrupt FDA still, in October 2021, a year and a half after WebMD was acknowledging the potential benefits of ivermectin, admits, "Clinical trials assessing ivermectin tablets for the prevention or treatment of COVID-19 in people are ongoing." They use the claim these mysterious trials are ongoing to make the demonstrably false claim, "Current available data do not show ivermectin is effective against COVID-19." And they make this demonstrably false claim as they sanction via Emergency Use Authorizations expensive drugs and inoculations *in as little as two days* following the *announcement* (not even the publication) of NIH-sponsored, non-peer reviewed studies, like we saw with remdesivir in the previous chapter. They sanction these drugs which somehow—despite never being used in humans and not having prior FDA approval for *any* use—managed to allegedly complete, "safety," trails before an available, cheap, approved, proven, natural alternative. This is not believable, it is unethical, and it is a dereliction of duty which is either criminal or should be.

Hydroxychloroquine Bad Because Orange Man Bad

At the beginning of the alleged pandemic, hydroxychloroquine (HCQ) was considered by the majority of polled physicians to be *the* most promising, effective candidate for both preventive and treatment purposes.[121] And unsurprisingly so, considering its affordability, biological support, historical safety profile, previous use cases, and early use experiences of those very physicians. As the months wore on, randomized controlled trials were eventually conducted which seemed to show HCQ didn't provide much benefit for hospitalized, severe-conditioned patients.[122,123] Still, debate continued, as proponents claimed the purpose was intended primarily for early treatment to keep people out of hospitals, and to be administered alongside a specific regimen not used in those trials. We will cover this debate shortly.

While ivermectin's benefits are somewhat more clearly documented, what HCQ did have in common with that drug was the rabid, irrational vitriol it received from public health and its mainstream media attack dogs. And this early irrationality is the most important thing we will analyze in this section. Because while the unprecedented debate on HCQ effectiveness rages on to this day in the medical community, the immediate, reflexive response to its initially suggested benefits created a controversy which—like for ivermectin—previously did not exist for this drug once widely considered to be one of the most ethical in existence.

To demonstrate this irrational controversy, and as an early introduction to our upcoming chapter on political, "science," let us review an example of how utterly captured the CDC really is, which would be comical if it did not have life or death consequences.

> *"Now, a drug called chloroquine, and some people would add to it, hydroxy—hydroxychloroquine—so chloroquine or hydroxycholorquine ... it is known as a malaria drug and it's been around for a long time and it's very powerful. But the nice part is it's been around for a long time, so we know that if it—if things don't go as planned, it's not going to kill anybody. When you go with a brand new drug, you don't know that that's going to happen."*
> —President Donald Trump, March 19, 2020[124]

An astute point by the president, with a certainly reasonable, cautious optimism about a drug being used by 6,200 surveyed physicians at the time. This assessment was not without some form of support either, as it seems to have come directly from a 100% treatment success rate reported at the time by Dr. Vladimir Zelenko.[125] Zelenko's strategy was to use HCQ *specifically alongside* zinc and azithromycin (AZ). HCQ was used because it helps zinc enter the cell, as covered, which will then allow zinc to exercise its viral-replication-slowing properties. AZ was also used to prevent secondary bacterial infections. Dr. Zelenko's team treated all of their approximately 350 patients using this strategy.

To be fair, Trump was almost certainly never clear about this important distinction that HCQ was to be used in sequence with AZ and zinc. There will also be additional blustery quotes an immature charlatan could/will find by Trump so they can cheer, "told-you-so," like they love to do so much. The Trump-obsessed simply can't help themselves in this regard, and since blustery/absurd is what Trump has always been, letting this devolve to their level is pointless. But simply contrast this quote with Fauci's, "standard of care," comment on remdesivir—clearly a bigger story with bigger consequences given the unjustified FDA action two days later. Predictably though, as was always the case with Trump, the vulture mainstream media responded by losing its collective mind, and HCQ became the mean orange man's drug from that point on.

> *"The U.S. Centers for Disease Control and Prevention has removed from its website highly unusual guidance informing doctors on how to prescribe hydroxychloroquine and chloroquine, drugs recommended by President Donald Trump to treat coronavirus. **The move comes three days after Reuters reported that the CDC published key dosing information involving the two antimalarial drugs based on unattributed anecdotes rather than peer-reviewed science** (my emphasis)."*
>
> —*Reuters* article, April 7, 2020[126]

In the above quote, *Reuters* proudly admits they shamed the CDC into altering its website language. I'm truly not sure what's more corrupt here—that *Reuters* tells the CDC what is, "highly unusual," about what they publish during an alleged once-in-a-century pandemic, or that the CDC actually considers *Reuters* its website's editor and makes the recommended change. At the same time, there's nothing surprising about either, given the actions of each organization throughout this time. What is confusing is why it would be a problem for the CDC to simply acknowledge what dosages real doctors (who are meant to have autonomy in the relationship between themselves and their patients) are using to treat their patient's conditions. The truth of the matter is it wouldn't be. And as always with the corporate media, things get even more ridiculous.

"Throughout the coronavirus pandemic, President Trump has embraced unproven treatments for coronavirus, especially anti-malaria drug hydroxychloroquine, which a new study found is linked to an increased risk of death in patients."

—Andrew Solender via *Forbes*, May 22, 2020[127]

Knowing what we know about remdesivir and the refusal to investigate early treatments, I wonder what drug, if any, Solender considered, "proven," in May 2020. Far more embarrassing than this politicking though, is the failure of *Forbes*/Solender more than a year later to retract their note on the study they claimed linked HCQ to an increased risk of death in patients. Simply following the link they provide to this study, one would see that it was retracted.[128] And the circumstances/implications of this retraction are incredible.

Only two weeks after the *Forbes* article, on June 4, 2020, *the Guardian* published a report on the retraction, in which they identified inconsistencies in data and, "research misconduct."[129] Specifically, the company that provided the data actually refused to cooperate with an independent audit. And unfortunately the damage was already done, as the WHO's randomized controlled trials had already been stopped based on the publishing of this report alone.

Still, several doctors recommend HCQ as part of their protocols and use it to treat. Their justification in doing so only seems to increase over time too. For example, one November 2021 international, multicenter, randomized trial in *Cureus* by Ried et al., found a combination of HCQ, azithromycin, and zinc to be, "safe and effective in the treatment of COVID-19, with IV vitamin C contributing to a significantly quicker recovery."[130] A running list has also been kept at the website *C19early* of 298 other peer-reviewed studies as of March 2022, including the note that HCQ and/or chloroquine have been adopted for early treatment by 36 countries (53 including non-governmental medical organizations).[131]

Now please understand, I'm not a treating physician recommending any medication. I don't take and currently have no intention of taking HCQ or any of the drugs mentioned in this book, other than daily vitamin D3, quercetin, and zinc supplements. To re-iterate, the point of this section and of this entire book is simply to illustrate the corruption involved in the conflict which took place between those doing the authoritarian censoring/slandering and the damage it led to. And the story in this regard for HCQ is the same as it was for ivermectin (both previously approved and patent-expired, so affordable), as well as anything else which didn't align with the goal of inoculations ultimately being the only, universal solution.

So with that out of the way, the following are public-health-ignored studies and findings supporting the use of HCQ. There's no *good* reason why this support and ongoing prescription activity by doctors wouldn't have warranted the same type of public health, "Covid," use endorsement/availability received by an unapproved, worse risk profile, less evidence supported drug like remdesivir, at least in the outpatient setting and until randomized controlled trials could be done in that setting:

- Yale M.D. Ph.D. Harvey A. Risch May 2020 report in *American Journal of Epidemiology* finds the following[132]:
    - HCQ + AZ + zinc combination widely misrepresented in both clinical reports and public media
    - Five studies at the time (again, this is in May 2020), including 2 controlled clinical trials, had demonstrated significant major outpatient treatment efficacy
    - Relatively low risk profile
    - Recommendation: these medications need to be made widely available and promoted immediately for physicians to prescribe
- A 2020 study by Su et al. published in *Bioscience Trends* measured the efficacy of HCQ at different stages of disease.[133] It found use at an early stage, "decreased improvement time and duration," of illness.
- A 2020 study by Ayerbe et al. published in *Internal and Emergency Medicine* found, "significant," association between treatment with HCQ and lower mortality.[134] You will recall, mortality was the original primary endpoint of NIAID's remdesivir study, which was revised once it became clear there was no association between remdesivir and reduced mortality. This provides more support that HCQ suppression costed lives.
- A 2021 multicenter observational study by Ip et al. in *BMC Infectious Diseases* found an association between HCQ and a decreased rate of subsequent hospitalization[135]

195

- CDC scientists in 2005 published findings in *Virology Journal* that chloroquine (of which hydroxychloroquine is a slightly milder derivative) is a, "potent inhibitor of SARS coronavirus"[136]

Consider this final note. The scientific community knew as early as 2005 that chloroquine was a, "potent," inhibitor of the so-called SARS-CoV-1 virus (for which there is also little evidence of its existence, but this nonetheless supports the drug as a treatment for the associated symptoms). Given this, alongside the downright disastrous failure of remdesivir in the recent Ebola trials, corruption is the only possible explanation for why Anthony Fauci would fail to study HCQ as a primary candidate. Instead, he focused on remdesivir and then also slandered HCQ once it gained traction—something he did on CNN in May 2020, citing nothing but the promptly-retracted *Lancet* study[137]:

> *"The scientific data is really quite evident now about the lack of efficacy."*

Only a lack of efficacy wasn't evident at all at this time as it related to *normal doses* of HCQ—at least, not nearly as evident as it had been with regular doses of remdesivir. Another excuse to call this common, approved drug dangerous was a small study in which high doses of *chloroquine* (again, the more potent derivative of HCQ) were found to be linked to heart issues.[138] This seemed a common theme too, as even in the randomized controlled trial mentioned at the beginning of this section, which found lack of benefit in the hospital setting, the starting dosage was 800mg, almost double the daily maximum dosage recommendation in most nations of 500mg. Yet another particularly dramatic case of this was the UK Recovery trial, which also found HCQ to have no benefit in *hospitalized* patients.[139] This trial was itself also strangely found to have used *almost five times* the UK's own maximum daily dosage (500mg) in the trial, giving patients a whopping 2,400mg on the first day. And the only excuse given for this overuse was as follows:

> *"There's no recommended dosage **for Covid-19** (my emphasis) because it's a new disease."*

196

Again, this is an excuse which is so absurd that it *has* to be viewed as intentionally corrupt for a person to not instead conclude the medical community is utterly inept. Also, I'm not even shilling for HCQ here. In fact, this Recovery trial makes it clear patients were inexplicably being given far more than the recommended *maximum* dosage of the drug. Therefore, I'd say it's very likely these experimental, hospital-patient-prescribed dosages also bore responsibility for some of the heart symptoms we've touched on being misattributed to, "Covid," previously. And in an email, Yale epidemiologist Harvey Risch concurred[140]:

> *"I agree about hydroxychloroquine overdosing, both from a reduced function point of view and toxicity."*

Before we conclude this section on HCQ, there is one more example I must share which perfectly captures the type of bold, flagrant, unprofessional behavior which characterized the overconfident public health officials of this time. In this instance, I am talking about Rick Bright, who was director of the Biomedical Advanced Research and Development Authority (BARDA) until April 20, 2020. Bright is relatively lesser known but plays an extremely prominent role in the Covid conspiracy, which we will highlight in the next chapter. For now it must be pointed out that he was demoted from his role in April 2020, which he claimed was a retaliation due to President Trump not taking the pandemic as seriously as Bright thought it should be taken. Whatever the truth of that dispute was, Bright eventually told of how HCQ would factor into the equation in an interview during the anti-Trump propaganda film *Totally Under Control*.[141]

The narrator starts by absurdly claiming Donald Trump was, "reading from the Fox script," in March 2020 when he discussed HCQ—literally *the* most popular drug in use among *physicians* at the time. So to be clear, my calling this film which was released right before the election, "propaganda," was not hyperbole. That said, shortly before the narrator's reference to Fox News' coverage of the drug, Rick Bright was featured answering a question about how it came into the picture:

> *"You know—*[smug chuckle]*—I wish I never heard of chloroquine, hydroxychloroquine, honestly."*

197

Again, this is the director of the Department of Health and Human Services' BARDA, saying he, "wished he'd never heard of," a *drug*—a drug which was tied in the past *by CDC scientists* to viral inhibition *of the alleged SARS-CoV-1 virus*. Bright says this in a documentary which is meant to criticize the response of an administration which acknowledged the potential of this drug he wishes he'd never heard of, in the earliest months of an alleged pandemic for which there were obviously no drugs known to be effective. Somehow, despite this incompetent, childish response, Bright is meant to be presented here as the adult in the room, who was dismissed for simply being too, "honest," and, "scientific." The absurdity gets worse, however, when Bright describes just how little sense his opposition to the drug made:

> "I believe it was March 23rd. I got a call from secretary Azar's chief counsel—the White House wanted us to move quickly on making this drug available. I called my scientific team at BARDA, and they said, 'no way.' There was no data to support that they had any benefit against the coronavirus. They pushed back, but doctor [unknown name] reiterated that directive to us, and said, 'get on it, get it done.'"

By all possible accounting of historical events, the above claim about there being, "no data to support," is an outright lie. In fact, as of March 23rd, the *only* available data supporting the use of *any* drug for this purpose was on chloroquine from the 2005 study, HCQ from the observational testimonies of actually-treating physicians, and the observational testimonies of other early treatment medications *also* from actually-treating physicians. As we covered previously, even Fauci's corrupt claims about remdesivir wouldn't come until the end of April. And as if this unprofessional liar could dig himself any deeper of a hole, he manages to when he admits the, "compromise," he made:

> "We came up with the option of an Emergency Use Authorization. We could put boundaries in it—restrict the drug to only be used in people who are hospitalized ... And I was proud of our team for coming up with that compromise that we thought would protect Americans."

Ladies and gentlemen, I give you: hubris. First of all, if Bright was so concerned that HCQ was dangerous to Americans, why the hell would he sign off *at all* on its use in the very setting where the most vulnerable Americans lay sick and dying? The man gets awfully emotional as he recalls his, "bravery," for whistleblowing—so why didn't he just take his stand by refusing to sign off on *any* use of this drug he, "wishes he'd never heard of?" Most importantly though, recall the randomized, controlled trials which would ultimately (but hadn't even at that time in March) demonstrate HCQ was *not* effective in hospitalized, severe patients. *Especially* considering the results of these trials, this compromise Bright was, "proud," of proved to actually be a tremendous blunder. And it resulted only from his clearly-political, immediate dismissal of HCQ as an outpatient treatment—which is what doctors were using it for with some evidence of clinical success at keeping people out of hospitals, at a time when there was no apparent alternatives. Instead, thanks to Bright's efforts, it would be restricted to hospitals, where it would be used at more than double the maximum dosage and even more than that beyond the dosage doctors had been using in the outpatient setting. And still, this HCQ debacle is only our introduction to Rick Bright, whose story of corruption gets *way* worse and makes his motivation for taking such an irrational stance on this issue very clear.

In summary, I will again restate that I do not recommend, nor do I intend to use HCQ or any other medication mentioned in these chapters. I'm not a medical professional and am in no way providing medical advice. Still, it seems possible to likely that there could be some anti-inflammatory benefits to this drug, and it seems to have a much better risk profile than remdesivir when used in the proper dosage (the only way any drug should ever be used). The story of HCQ remains: doctors continue to endorse it as a way to keep people out of the hospital, while corrupt liars obsessively oppose it. The latter also did so from the start despite there being more prior evidence of its use for this very purpose than any alternative. So could HCQ have helped reduced hospitalizations if used correctly? The studies, physician testimonies, and reflexive reaction of corrupt public health departments suggest this could have been the case and could have saved lives had the corruption not been a factor.

Endnotes

1   Crawford, Mathew. 2022. "The First Tyson/Fareed Study Text". *Roundingtheearth.Substack.Com.* https://roundingtheearth.substack.com/p/the-first-tysonfareed-study-text?s=r.

2   te Velthuis, Aartjan J. W., Sjoerd H. E. van den Worm, Amy C. Sims, Ralph S. Baric, Eric J. Snijder, and Martijn J. van Hemert. 2010. "Zn2+ Inhibits Coronavirus And Arterivirus RNA Polymerase Activity In Vitro And Zinc Ionophores Block The Replication Of These Viruses In Cell Culture". *Plos Pathogens* 6 (11): e1001176. doi:10.1371/journal.ppat.1001176.

3   Rizzo, Emanuele. 2020. "Ivermectin, Antiviral Properties And COVID-19: A Possible New Mechanism Of Action". *Naunyn-Schmiedeberg's Archives Of Pharmacology* 393 (7): 1153-1156. doi:10.1007/s00210-020-01902-5.

4   Reisewitz, Shauna, and Benjamin Vazsonyi. 2020. "Hydroxychloroquine (And Other Zinc Ionophores), In Combination With Zinc For The Treatment Of COVID-19". *Learn Your Way.* https://learnyourwayacademy.com/2020/08/27/hydroxychloroquine-and-other-zinc-ionophores-in-combination-with-zinc-for-the-treatment-of-covid-19/.

5   Dabbagh-Bazarbachi, Husam, Gael Clergeaud, Isabel M. Quesada, Mayreli Ortiz, Ciara K. O'Sullivan, and Juan B. Fernández-Larrea. 2014. "Zinc Ionophore Activity Of Quercetin And Epigallocatechin-Gallate: From Hepa 1-6 Cells To A Liposome Model". *Journal Of Agricultural And Food Chemistry* 62 (32): 8085-8093. doi:10.1021/jf5014633.

6   Vogel-González, Marina, Marc Talló-Parra, Víctor Herrera-Fernández, Gemma Pérez-Vilaró, Miguel Chillón, Xavier Nogués, and Silvia Gómez-Zorrilla et al. 2021. "Low Zinc Levels At Admission Associates With Poor Clinical Outcomes In SARS-Cov-2 Infection". *Nutrients* 13 (2): 562. doi:10.3390/nu13020562.

7   Al Sulaiman, Khalid, Ohoud Aljuhani, Abdulrahman I. Al Shaya, Abdullah Kharbosh, Raed Kensara, Alhomaidi Al Guwairy, and Aisha Alharbi et al. 2021. "Evaluation Of Zinc Sulfate As An Adjunctive Therapy In COVID-19 Critically Ill Patients: A Two Center Propensity-Score Matched Study". *Critical Care* 25 (1). doi:10.1186/s13054-021-03785-1.

8   National Institute of Allergy and Infectious Diseases (NIAID). 2020. "Treatments For People With Early COVID-19 Infection Is An Urgent Research Focus". https://www.nih.gov/news-events/news-releases/treatments-people-early-covid-19-infection-urgent-research-focus.

9   Morán Blanco, Juan Ignacio, Judith A. Alvarenga Bonilla, Sakae Homma, Kazuo Suzuki, Philip Fremont-Smith, and Karina Villar Gómez de las Heras. 2021. "Antihistamines And Azithromycin As A Treatment For COVID-19 On Primary Health Care – A Retrospective Observational

Study In Elderly Patients". *Pulmonary Pharmacology & Therapeutics* 67: 101989. doi:10.1016/j.pupt.2021.101989.

10   Janssen, Nico A.F. et al. 2021. "Multinational Observational Cohort Study Of COVID-19–Associated Pulmonary Aspergillosis". *Cdc.Gov*. https://wwwnc.cdc.gov/eid/article/27/11/21-1174_article.

11   National Institute of Allergy and Infectious Disease (NIAID). 2020. "NIH Observational Study Of Coronavirus Infection And Multisystem Inflammatory Syndrome In Children Begins". https://www.niaid.nih.gov/news-events/nih-observational-study-coronavirus-infection-and-multisystem-inflammatory-syndrome.

12   "Real-World Evidence". 2022. *U.S. Food And Drug Administration*. Accessed March 9. https://www.fda.gov/science-research/science-and-research-special-topics/real-world-evidence.

13   The National Institutes of Health (NIH). 2021. "General Management Of Nonhospitalized Patients With Acute COVID-19". NIH.

14   "Doctor Cites Early Treatment As Reason For Success With 6,000 Covid Patients". 2021. *Global Covid Summit*. https://globalcovidsummit.org/news/doctor-cites-early-treatment-success-with-6000-covid-patients.

15   Zelenko, Vladimir. 2022. "About Vladimir Zelenko MD". *Vladimir Zelenko MD*. Accessed March 9. https://www.zstacklife.com/pages/about-vladimir-zelenko-md.

16   Sidman, David. 2020. "Trump's 'Hydroxy' Doctor Driven Out Of Town By Cuomo-Affiliated Politician". *Israel365 News | Latest News. Biblical Perspective.*. https://www.israel365news.com/150707/shock-dr-zelenko-chased-out-of-hometown-by-cuomo-affiliated-politician/.

17   Gorter, Robert. 2021. "Better Than Hydroxychloroquine? Two New Studies Show Quercetin Improves COVID Outcomes". *Robert Gorter, MD, Phd*. https://robert-gorter.info/better-hydroxychloroquine-two-new-studies-show-quercetin-improves-covid-outcomes/.

18   Borsche, Lorenz, Bernd Glauner, and Julian von Mendel. 2021. "COVID-19 Mortality Risk Correlates Inversely With Vitamin D3 Status, And A Mortality Rate Close To Zero Could Theoretically Be Achieved At 50 Ng/Ml 25(OH)D3: Results Of A Systematic Review And Meta-Analysis". *Nutrients* 13 (10): 3596. doi:10.3390/nu13103596.

19   Dror, Amiel A., Nicole Morozov, Amani Daoud, Yoav Namir, Orly Yakir, Yair Shachar, and Mark Lifshitz et al. 2022. "Pre-Infection 25-Hydroxyvitamin D3 Levels And Association With Severity Of COVID-19 Illness". *PLOS ONE* 17 (2): e0263069. doi:10.1371/journal.pone.0263069.

20   Frontline COVID-19 Critical Care Alliance (FLCCC). 2020. "I-MASK+ Prevention & Early Outpatient Treatment Protocol For COVID-19". https://covid19criticalcare.com/covid-19-protocols/i-mask-plus-protocol/.

21   "Coronavirus Disease 2019 (COVID-19) 2021 Case Definition". 2021. *Cdc.Gov*. https://ndc.services.cdc.gov/case-definitions/coronavirus-disease-2019-2021/.

22   National Center for Health Statistics. 2020. "Conditions Contributing To Deaths Involving COVID-19, By Age Group, United States. Week Ending 2/1/2020 To 12/5/2020". CDC.

23   "Doctors Testify About Early Treatment For COVID-19 In Italian Senate Hearing - We The Pundit". 2021. *We The Pundit*. https://wethepundit.com/doctors-testify-about-early-treatment-for-covid-19-in-italian-senate-hearing/.

24   Fox, Maggie. 2015. "Nobel Prize Goes To Pioneers Of Natural-Based Medicines". *NBC News*. https://www.nbcnews.com/health/health-news/new-jersey-based-william-campbell-shares-nobel-prize-medicine-n438511.

25   Collins, Ben, and Brandy Zadrozny. 2021. "Clamoring For Ivermectin, Some Turn To A Pro-Trump Telemedicine Website". *NBC News*. https://www.nbcnews.com/tech/tech-news/ivermectin-demand-drives-trump-telemedicine-website-rcna1791.

26   Pfeiffer, Mary Beth, and Linda Bonvie. 2021. "Horse-Bleep: How 4 Calls On Animal Ivermectin Launched A False FDA-Media Attack On A Life-Saving Human Medicine". *Rescue.Substack.Com*. https://rescue.substack.com/p/a2520b80-bcd1-4905-a913-68f6f6809779.

27   Ibid.

28   Ibid.

29   Ibid.

30   Wade, Peter. 2021. "Gunshot Victims Left Waiting As Horse Dewormer Overdoses Overwhelm Oklahoma Hospitals, Doctor Says". *Rolling Stone*. https://web.archive.org/web/20210903231939/https:/www.rollingstone.com/politics/politics-news/gunshot-victims-horse-dewormer-ivermectin-oklahoma-hospitals-covid-1220608/.

31   Wemple, Erik. 2021. "Opinion: Bogus Oklahoma Ivermectin Story Was Just Too Good To Check". *The Washington Post*. https://www.washingtonpost.com/opinions/2021/09/09/bogus-oklahoma-ivermectin-story-was-just-too-good-check/.

32   "Correction: Virus Outbreak-Mississippi Story". 2021. *US News*. https://www.usnews.com/news/best-states/mississippi/articles/2021-08-23/health-dept-stop-taking-livestock-medicine-to-treat-covid.

33   Goldberg, Emma. 2021. "Demand Surges For Deworming Drug For Covid, Despite Scant Evidence It Works". *Nytimes.Com*. https://www.nytimes.com/2021/08/30/health/covid-ivermectin-prescriptions.html.

34   "Corrections And Clarifications". 2021. *The Guardian*. https://www.theguardian.com/news/2021/sep/15/corrections-and-clarifications.

35   Bella, Timothy. 2021. "As Covid-19 Surges In Mississippi, Some People Are Ingesting An Unproven Livestock Dewormer". *The Washington Post*. https://www.washingtonpost.com/nation/2021/08/21/mississippi-ivermectin-covid-surge-livestock/.

36   The Mississippi Poison Control Center. 2021. "Increased Poison Control Calls Due To Ivermectin Ingestion And Potential Toxicity". Jackson, MS: Mississippi Department of Health.

37   Pavlich, Katie. 2021. "Watch Joe Rogan Make CNN's Dr. Gupta Squirm For Lying About Ivermectin". *Townhall*. https://www.townhall.com/tipsheet/katiepavlich/2021/10/14/joe-rogan-calling-out-cnn-and-gupta-n2597425.

38   Sharma, Puneet. 2022. "Joe Rogan Accuses CNN Of Altering Video Color To Make Him Look Sick". *Sportskeeda.Com*. https://www.sportskeeda.com/mma/news-joe-rogan-accuses-cnn-altering-video-color-make-look-sick.

39   Burke, Minyvonne. 2021. "Doctor Investigated By Medical Board For Using Ivermectin To Treat Patients, Inmates". *NBC News*. https://www.nbcnews.com/news/us-news/doctor-who-used-ivermectin-treat-covid-patients-inmates-under-investigation-n1277826.

40   Snowdon, Wallis. 2021. "Doctor Who Says He Gave Ivermectin To Rural Alberta COVID-19 Patients Prompts Warning From AHS | CBC News". *CBC*. https://www.cbc.ca/news/canada/edmonton/ivermectin-covid-alberta-nagase-1.6205075.

41   "Physicians Declaration – Updated Global Covid Summit". 2021. *Global Covid Summit*. https://www.doctorsandscientistsdeclaration.org/.

42   "'Don't Do It': Dr. Fauci Warns Against Taking Ivermectin To Fight Covid-19 - CNN Video". 2021. *CNN*. https://www.cnn.com/videos/health/2021/08/29/dr-anthony-fauci-ivermectin-covid-19-sotu-vpx.cnn.

43   State of Nebraska Office of the Attorney General. 2021. "Prescription Of Ivermectin Or Hydroxychloroquine As Off-Label Medicines For The Prevention Or Treatment Of Covid-19". Lincoln, Nebraska: Attorney General of Nebraska.

44   "WHO Collaborating Center For International Drug Monitoring". 2021. *Vigiaccess*. Accessed October. https://vigiaccess.org/.

45   Bryant, Andrew, Theresa A. Lawrie, Therese Dowswell, Edmund J. Fordham, Scott Mitchell, Sarah R. Hill, and Tony C. Tham. 2021. "Ivermectin For Prevention And Treatment Of COVID-19 Infection". *American Journal Of Therapeutics* Publish Ahead of Print. doi:10.1097/mjt.0000000000001402.

46   "Ivermectin Cover-Up!! Dr Tess Lawrie's Asks Dr Andrew Hill - Who Is Influencing You ?". 2022. *Bitchute*. https://www.bitchute.com/video/aDVPtTTgE2O2/.

47   "Front Line COVID-19 Critical Care Alliance (FLCCC) Invited To The National Institutes Of Health (NIH) COVID-19 Treatment Guidelines Panel To Present Latest Data On Ivermectin". 2021. *Newswise.Com*. https://www.newswise.com/coronavirus/front-line-covid-19-critical-care-alliance-flccc-invited-to-the-national-institutes-of-health-nih-covid-19-treatment-guidelines-panel-to-present-latest-data-on-ivermectin.

48   "Ivermectin Cover-Up!! Dr Tess Lawrie's Asks Dr Andrew Hill - Who Is Influencing You ?". 2022. *Bitchute*. https://www.bitchute.com/video/aDVPtTTgE2O2/.

49   "A Letter To Andrew Hill". 2022. *Oracle Films*. https://www.oraclefilms.com/alettertoandrewhill.

50   Hill, Andrew, Anna Garratt, Jacob Levi, Jonathan Falconer, Leah Ellis, Kaitlyn McCann, Victoria Pilkington, Ambar Qavi, Junzheng Wang, and Hannah Wentzel. 2021. "Retracted: Meta-Analysis Of Randomized Trials Of Ivermectin To Treat SARS-Cov-2 Infection". *Open Forum Infectious Diseases* 8 (11). doi:10.1093/ofid/ofab358.

51   "Ivermectin Cover-Up!! Dr Tess Lawrie's Asks Dr Andrew Hill - Who Is Influencing You ?". 2022. *Bitchute*. https://www.bitchute.com/video/aDVPtTTgE2O2/.

52   Ibid.

53   "About Us - Unitaid". 2022. *Unitaid*. Accessed March 10. https://unitaid.org/about-us/#en.

54   Unitaid. 2017. "Unitaid Hails New US$ 50 Million Contribution From The Bill & Melinda Gates Foundation". https://unitaid.org/news-blog/unitaid-hails-new-us-50-million-contribution-bill-melinda-gates-foundation/#en.

55   "The Case Of Dr. Andrew Hill: Was Their Unethical Activity Associated With His Ivermectin Meta-Analysis Or Just Another Drug Dev Day? | Covid Strategies". 2021. *Covidstrategies.Org*. https://www.covidstrategies.org/the-case-of-dr-andrew-hill-was-their-unethical-activity-associated-with-his-ivermectin-meta-analysis-or-just-another-drug-dev-day/.

56   Unitaid. 2021. "Unitaid Funding Sees Launch Of World's First Long-Acting Medicines Centre At University Of Liverpool". https://unitaid.org/news-blog/unitaid-funding-sees-launch-of-worlds-first-long-acting-medicines-centre-at-university-of-liverpool/#en.

57   "Andrew Hill, MD Biography | AME". 2022. *Academicmedicaleducation.Com*. Accessed March 10. https://academicmedicaleducation.com/andrew-hill-md.

58   Hill, Andrew, Manya Mirchandani, and Victoria Pilkington. 2022. "Ivermectin For COVID-19: Addressing Potential Bias And Medical Fraud". *Open Forum Infectious Diseases* 9 (2). doi:10.1093/ofid/ofab645.

59   "Dr Pierre Kory In Senate Homeland Security Hearing On Medical Response To COVID-19, 12-08-20". 2020. *Ratical.Org*. https://ratical.org/PandemicParallaxView/MedRespToCovid19-120820.html.

60   Front Line COVID-19 Critical Care Alliance. 2021. "Review Of The Emerging Evidence Demonstrating The Efficacy Of Ivermectin In The Prophylaxis And Treatment Of COVID-19". FLCCC. https://covid19criticalcare.com/wp-content/uploads/2020/11/FLCCC-Ivermectin-in-the-prophylaxis-and-treatment-of-COVID-19.pdf.

61   Mastrangelo, E., M. Pezzullo, T. De Burghgraeve, S. Kaptein, B.
Pastorino, K. Dallmeier, and X. de Lamballerie et al. 2012. "Ivermectin Is
A Potent Inhibitor Of Flavivirus Replication Specifically Targeting NS3
Helicase Activity: New Prospects For An Old Drug". *Journal Of
Antimicrobial Chemotherapy* 67 (8): 1884-1894. doi:10.1093/jac/dks147.

62   Wagstaff, Kylie M., Haran Sivakumaran, Steven M. Heaton, David
Harrich, and David A. Jans. 2012. "Ivermectin Is A Specific Inhibitor Of
Importin A/B-Mediated Nuclear Import Able To Inhibit Replication Of
HIV-1 And Dengue Virus". *Biochemical Journal* 443 (3): 851-856.
doi:10.1042/bj20120150.

63   Tay, M.Y.F., J.E. Fraser, W.K.K. Chan, N.J. Moreland, A.P. Rathore, C.
Wang, S.G. Vasudevan, and D.A. Jans. 2013. "Nuclear Localization Of
Dengue Virus (DENV) 1–4 Non-Structural Protein 5; Protection Against
All 4 DENV Serotypes By The Inhibitor Ivermectin". *Antiviral
Research* 99 (3): 301-306. doi:10.1016/j.antiviral.2013.06.002.

64   Götz, Veronika, Linda Magar, Dominik Dornfeld, Sebastian Giese, Anne
Pohlmann, Dirk Höper, and Byung-Whi Kong et al. 2016. "Erratum:
Corrigendum: Influenza A Viruses Escape From Mxa Restriction At The
Expense Of Efficient Nuclear Vrnp Import". *Scientific Reports* 6 (1).
doi:10.1038/srep25428.

65   Varghese, Finny S., Pasi Kaukinen, Sabine Gläsker, Maxim Bespalov,
Leena Hanski, Krister Wennerberg, Beate M. Kümmerer, and Tero
Ahola. 2016. "Discovery Of Berberine, Abamectin And Ivermectin As
Antivirals Against Chikungunya And Other Alphaviruses". *Antiviral
Research* 126: 117-124. doi:10.1016/j.antiviral.2015.12.012.

66   Lv, Changjie, Wenkai Liu, Bin Wang, Ruyi Dang, Li Qiu, Juan Ren,
Chuanqi Yan, Zengqi Yang, and Xinglong Wang. 2018. "Ivermectin
Inhibits DNA Polymerase UL42 Of Pseudorabies Virus Entrance Into
The Nucleus And Proliferation Of The Virus In Vitro And
Vivo". *Antiviral Research* 159: 55-62.
doi:10.1016/j.antiviral.2018.09.010.

67   King, Cason R., Tanner M. Tessier, Mackenzie J. Dodge, Jason B.
Weinberg, and Joe S. Mymryk. 2020. "Inhibition Of Human Adenovirus
Replication By The Importin A/B1 Nuclear Import Inhibitor
Ivermectin". *Journal Of Virology* 94 (18). doi:10.1128/jvi.00710-20.

68   Yang, Sundy N.Y., Sarah C. Atkinson, Chunxiao Wang, Alexander Lee,
Marie A. Bogoyevitch, Natalie A. Borg, and David A. Jans. 2020. "The
Broad Spectrum Antiviral Ivermectin Targets The Host Nuclear
Transport Importin A/B1 Heterodimer". Antiviral Research 177: 104760.
doi:10.1016/j.antiviral.2020.104760.

69   Caly, Leon, Julian D. Druce, Mike G. Catton, David A. Jans, and Kylie
M. Wagstaff. 2020. "The FDA-Approved Drug Ivermectin Inhibits The
Replication Of SARS-Cov-2 In Vitro". *Antiviral Research* 178: 104787.
doi:10.1016/j.antiviral.2020.104787.

70   Zhang, X., Y. Song, X. Ci, N. An, Y. Ju, H. Li, X. Wang, C. Han, J. Cui,
and X. Deng. 2008. "Ivermectin Inhibits LPS-Induced Production Of

Inflammatory Cytokines And Improves LPS-Induced Survival In Mice". *Inflammation Research* 57 (11): 524-529. doi:10.1007/s00011-008-8007-8.

71   Ci, Xinxin, Hongyu Li, Qinlei Yu, Xuemei Zhang, Lu Yu, Na Chen, Yu Song, and Xuming Deng. 2009. "Avermectin Exerts Anti-Inflammatory Effect By Downregulating The Nuclear Transcription Factor Kappa-B And Mitogen-Activated Protein Kinase Activation Pathway". *Fundamental & Clinical Pharmacology* 23 (4): 449-455. doi:10.1111/j.1472-8206.2009.00684.x.

72   Zhang, Xuemei, Yu Song, Huanzhang Xiong, Xinxin Ci, Hongyu Li, Lu Yu, Lei Zhang, and Xuming Deng. 2009. "Inhibitory Effects Of Ivermectin On Nitric Oxide And Prostaglandin E2 Production In LPS-Stimulated RAW 264.7 Macrophages". *International Immunopharmacology* 9 (3): 354-359. doi:10.1016/j.intimp.2008.12.016.

73   Arévalo, A. P., R. Pagotto, J. L. Pórfido, H. Daghero, M. Segovia, K. Yamasaki, and B. Varela et al. 2021. "Ivermectin Reduces In Vivo Coronavirus Infection In A Mouse Experimental Model". *Scientific Reports* 11 (1). doi:10.1038/s41598-021-86679-0.

74   Melo, Guilherme Dias, Françoise Lazarini, Florence Larrous, Lena Feige, Etienne Kornobis, Sylvain Levallois, and Agnès Marchio et al. 2021. "Attenuation Of Clinical And Immunological Outcomes During SARS-Cov-2 Infection By Ivermectin". *EMBO Molecular Medicine* 13 (8). doi:10.15252/emmm.202114122.

75   Behera, Priyamadhaba, Binod Kumar Patro, Arvind Kumar Singh, Pradnya Dilip Chandanshive, Ravikumar S. R., Somen Kumar Pradhan, and Siva Santosh Kumar Pentapati et al. 2021. "Role Of Ivermectin In The Prevention Of SARS-Cov-2 Infection Among Healthcare Workers In India: A Matched Case-Control Study". *PLOS ONE* 16 (2): e0247163. doi:10.1371/journal.pone.0247163.

76   Chosidow, Olivier, Charlotte Bernigaud, Didier Guillemot, Bruno Giraudeau, Anne Lespine, Jean-Pierre Changeux, Hervé Bourhy, Marc Lecuit, and Zahir Amoura. 2021. "Ivermectin As A Potential Treatment For COVID-19?". *PLOS Neglected Tropical Diseases* 15 (6): e0009446. doi:10.1371/journal.pntd.0009446.

77   Héctor, Carvallo, Hirsch Roberto, and Farinella María Eugenia. 2020. "Safety And Efficacy Of The Combined Use Of Ivermectin, Dexamethasone, Enoxaparin And Aspirin Against COVID 19". doi:10.1101/2020.09.10.20191619.

78   Hellwig, Martin D., and Anabela Maia. 2021. "A COVID-19 Prophylaxis? Lower Incidence Associated With Prophylactic Administration Of Ivermectin". *International Journal Of Antimicrobial Agents* 57 (1): 106248. doi:10.1016/j.ijantimicag.2020.106248.

79   Shouman, Waheed. 2020. "Prophylactic Ivermectin In COVID-19 Contacts". Sharkia, Egypt: National Library of Medicine.

80   Héctor, Carvallo, Hirsch Roberto, and Farinella María Eugenia. 2020. "Safety And Efficacy Of The Combined Use Of Ivermectin,

Dexamethasone, Enoxaparin And Aspirin Against COVID 19". doi:10.1101/2020.09.10.20191619.

81   Gorial, Faiq I, Sabeeh Mashhadani, Hend M Sayaly, Basim Dhawi Dakhil, Marwan M. AlMashhadani, Adnan M Aljabory, Hassan M Abbas, Mohammed Ghanim, and Jawad I Rasheed. 2020. "Effectiveness Of Ivermectin As Add-On Therapy In COVID-19 Management (Pilot Trial)". doi:10.1101/2020.07.07.20145979.

82   Khan, Md. Saiful Islam, Md. Sakirul Islam Khan, Chitto Ranjan Debnath, Progga Nanda Nath, Mamun Al Mahtab, Hiroaki Nabeka, Seiji Matsuda, and Sheikh Mohammad Fazle Akbar. 2020. "Ivermectin Treatment May Improve The Prognosis Of Patients With COVID-19". *Archivos De Bronconeumología* 56 (12): 828-830. doi:10.1016/j.arbres.2020.08.007.

83   Reaz, Mahmud et al. 2021. "Ivermectin In Combination With Doxycycline For Treating COVID-19 Symptoms: A Randomized Trial". *Dryad*. doi:10.5061/dryad.qjq2bvqf6.

84   Morgenstern, Jose, Jose N Redondo, Alvaro Olavarria, Isis Rondon, Santiago Roca, Albida De Leon, and Juan Canela et al. 2021. "Ivermectin As A SARS-Cov-2 Pre-Exposure Prophylaxis Method In Healthcare Workers: A Propensity Score-Matched Retrospective Cohort Study". *Cureus*. doi:10.7759/cureus.17455.

85   Alam, Mohammed Tarek, Rubaiul Murshed, Elias Bhiuyan, Sadia Saber, Rafa Faaria Alam, and Rishad Choudhury Robin. 2020. "A Case Series Of 100 COVID-19 Positive Patients Treated With Combination Of Ivermectin And Doxycycline". *Journal Of Bangladesh College Of Physicians And Surgeons*, 10-15. doi:10.3329/jbcps.v38i0.47512.

86   Chaccour, Carlos, Aina Casellas, Andrés Blanco-Di Matteo, Iñigo Pineda, Alejandro Fernandez-Montero, Paula Ruiz-Castillo, and Mary-Ann Richardson et al. 2021. "The Effect Of Early Treatment With Ivermectin On Viral Load, Symptoms And Humoral Response In Patients With Non-Severe COVID-19: A Pilot, Double-Blind, Placebo-Controlled, Randomized Clinical Trial". *Eclinicalmedicine* 32: 100720. doi:10.1016/j.eclinm.2020.100720.

87   Babalola, O E, C O Bode, A A Ajayi, F M Alakaloko, I E Akase, E Otrofanowei, O B Salu, W L Adeyemo, A O Ademuyiwa, and S Omilabu. 2021. "Ivermectin Shows Clinical Benefits In Mild To Moderate COVID19: A Randomized Controlled Double-Blind, Dose-Response Study In Lagos". *QJM: An International Journal Of Medicine* 114 (11): 780-788. doi:10.1093/qjmed/hcab035.

88   Ravikirti, Ranjini Roy, Chandrima Pattadar, Rishav Raj, Neeraj Agarwal, Bijit Biswas, and Pramod Kumar Manjhi et al. 2021. "Evaluation Of Ivermectin As A Potential Treatment For Mild To Moderate COVID-19: A Double-Blind Randomized Placebo Controlled Trial In Eastern India". *Journal Of Pharmacy & Pharmaceutical Sciences* 24: 343-350. doi:10.18433/jpps32105.

89   Hashim, Hashim A., Mohammed F. Maulood, Anwar M. Rasheed, Dhurgham F. Fatak, Khulood K. Kabah, and Ahmed S. Abdulamir. 2020.

207

"Controlled Randomized Clinical Trial On Using Ivermectin With Doxycycline For Treating COVID-19 Patients In Baghdad, Iraq". doi:10.1101/2020.10.26.20219345.

90   Khan, Md. Saiful Islam, Md. Sakirul Islam Khan, Chitto Ranjan Debnath, Progga Nanda Nath, Mamun Al Mahtab, Hiroaki Nabeka, Seiji Matsuda, and Sheikh Mohammad Fazle Akbar. 2020. "Ivermectin Treatment May Improve The Prognosis Of Patients With COVID-19". *Archivos De Bronconeumología* 56 (12): 828-830. doi:10.1016/j.arbres.2020.08.007.

91   Gheibi, Nematollah, Morteza Shakhsi Niaee, Peyman Namdar, Abbas Allami, Leila Zolghadr, Amir Javadi, and Amin Karampour et al. 2021. "Ivermectin As An Adjunct Treatment For Hospitalized Adult COVID-19 Patients: A Randomized Multi-Center Clinical Trial". *Asian Pacific Journal Of Tropical Medicine* 14 (6): 266. doi:10.4103/1995-7645.318304.

92   Portmann-Baracco, Arianna, Mayte Bryce-Alberti, and Roberto Alfonso Accinelli. 2020. "Propiedades Antivirales Y Antiinflamatorias De Ivermectina Y Su Potencial Uso En COVID-19". *Archivos De Bronconeumología* 56 (12): 831. doi:10.1016/j.arbres.2020.06.011.

93   Rajter, Juliana Cepelowicz, Michael S. Sherman, Naaz Fatteh, Fabio Vogel, Jamie Sacks, and Jean-Jacques Rajter. 2021. "Use Of Ivermectin Is Associated With Lower Mortality In Hospitalized Patients With Coronavirus Disease 2019". *Chest* 159 (1): 85-92. doi:10.1016/j.chest.2020.10.009.

94   Spoorthi, Veerapaneni, and Surapaneni Sasank. 2020. "Utility Of Ivermectin And Doxycycline Combination For The Treatment Of Sarscov-2". *International Archives Of Integrated Medicine* 7 (10).

95   Lima-Morales, René, Pablo Méndez-Hernández, Yvonne N. Flores, Patricia Osorno-Romero, Christian Ronal Sancho-Hernández, Elizabeth Cuecuecha-Rugerio, Adrián Nava-Zamora, Diego Rolando Hernández-Galdamez, Daniela Karola Romo-Dueñas, and Jorge Salmerón. 2021. "Effectiveness Of A Multidrug Therapy Consisting Of Ivermectin, Azithromycin, Montelukast, And Acetylsalicylic Acid To Prevent Hospitalization And Death Among Ambulatory COVID-19 Cases In Tlaxcala, Mexico". *International Journal Of Infectious Diseases* 105: 598-605. doi:10.1016/j.ijid.2021.02.014.

96   Hashim, Hashim A., Mohammed F. Mauood, Anwar M. Rasheed, Dhurgham F. Fatak, Khulood K. Kabah, and Ahmed S. Abdulamir. 2020. "Controlled Randomized Clinical Trial On Using Ivermectin With Doxycycline For Treating COVID-19 Patients In Baghdad, Iraq". doi:10.1101/2020.10.26.20219345.

97   Rajter, Juliana Cepelowicz, Michael S. Sherman, Naaz Fatteh, Fabio Vogel, Jamie Sacks, and Jean-Jacques Rajter. 2021. "Use Of Ivermectin Is Associated With Lower Mortality In Hospitalized Patients With Coronavirus Disease 2019". *Chest* 159 (1): 85-92. doi:10.1016/j.chest.2020.10.009.

98 Okumuş, Nurullah, Neşe Demirtürk, Rıza Aytaç Çetinkaya, Rahmet Güner, İsmail Yaşar Avcı, Semiha Orhan, and Petek Konya et al. 2021. "Evaluation Of The Effectiveness And Safety Of Adding Ivermectin To Treatment In Severe COVID-19 Patients". *BMC Infectious Diseases* 21 (1). doi:10.1186/s12879-021-06104-9.

99 "An Old Drug Tackles New Tricks: Ivermectin Treatment In Three Brazilian Towns". 2020. *Trialsitenews*. https://trialsitenews.com/an-old-drug-tackles-new-tricks-ivermectin-treatment-in-three-brazilian-towns/.

100 Kerr, Lucy, Flavio A Cadegiani, Fernando Baldi, Raysildo B Lobo, Washington Luiz O Assagra, Fernando Carlos Proença, Pierre Kory, Jennifer A Hibberd, and Juan J Chamie-Quintero. 2022. "Ivermectin Prophylaxis Used For COVID-19: A Citywide, Prospective, Observational Study Of 223,128 Subjects Using Propensity Score Matching". *Cureus*. doi:10.7759/cureus.21272.

101 Kerr, Lucy, Flavio A Cadegiani, Fernando Baldi, Raysildo B Lobo, Washington Luiz O Assagra, Fernando Carlos Proença, Pierre Kory, Jennifer A Hibberd, and Juan J Chamie-Quintero. 2022. " Strictly regular use of ivermectin as prophylaxis for COVID-19 leads to a 90% reduction in COVID-19 mortality rate, in a dose-response manner: definitive results of a prospective observational study of a strictly controlled 223,128 population from a city-wide program in Southern Brazil". *Cureus*. https://www.researchgate.net/publication/358386329_Strictly_regular_us e_of_ivermectin_as_prophylaxis_for_COVID-19_leads_to_a_90_reduction_in_COVID-19_mortality_rate_in_a_dose-response_manner_definitive_results_of_a_prospective_observational_stu dy_of_a.

102 Kircik, L. H., Del Rosso, J. Q., Layton, A. M., & Schauber, J. (2016). "Over 25 Years of Clinical Experience With Ivermectin: An Overview of Safety for an Increasing Number of Indications". *Journal of drugs in dermatology : JDD*, 15(3), 325–332.

103 "WHO Model List Of Essential Medicines For Children - 7Th List, 2019". 2019. *Who.Int*. https://www.who.int/publications/i/item/WHOMVPEMPIAU201907.

104 Kory, Pierre. 2021. "Tweet By Pierre Kory, October 7, 2021". *Twitter.Com*. https://www.twitter.com/PierreKory/status/1446312291302055940.

105 "Fact Check-News Channel Says Ivermectin Images Included In Queen COVID-19 Report In Error". 2022. *Reuters*. https://www.reuters.com/article/factcheck-queen-ivermectin-idUSL1N2UX0S1.

106 Serna-Diez, Isaac. 2022. "False Rumor That Queen Elizabeth II Is Taking Ivermectin To Treat COVID-19 Spreads After 'Error' In News Report". *Yourtango*. https://www.yourtango.com/news/is-queen-elizabeth-ii-taking-ivermectin-covid-19.

107 Evon, Dan. 2022. "Is The Queen Taking Ivermectin?". *Snopes*. https://www.snopes.com/fact-check/is-the-queen-taking-ivermectin/.

108   Lawrie, Tess. 2021. "Dr Tess Lawrie: Why Are We Not Using Ivermectin For Covid? 7 May 2021". *Ratical.Org*. https://www.ratical.org/PandemicParallaxView/DrTessLawrie-IVM-for-Covid-050721.html.

109   Lawrie, Theresa A. 2021. "Ivermectin Reduces The Risk Of Death From COVID-19 -A Rapid Review And Meta-Analysis In Support Of The Recommendation Of The Front Line COVID-19 Critical Care Alliance. (Latest Version V1.2 - 6 Jan 2021)". ResearchGate. https://www.researchgate.net/publication/348297284_Ivermectin_reduces_the_risk_of_death_from_COVID-19_-a_rapid_review_and_meta-analysis_in_support_of_the_recommendation_of_the_Front_Line_COVID-19_Critical_Care_Alliance_Latest_version_v12_-_6_Jan_2021.

110   Crump, Andy. 2017. "Ivermectin: Enigmatic Multifaceted 'Wonder' Drug Continues To Surprise And Exceed Expectations". *The Journal Of Antibiotics* 70 (5): 495-505. doi:10.1038/ja.2017.11.

111   Reardon, Sarah. 2021. "Flawed Ivermectin Preprint Highlights Challenges Of COVID Drug Studies". *Nature.Com*. https://www.nature.com/articles/d41586-021-02081-w.

112   Horowitz, Daniel. 2021. "Horowitz: The Unmistakable Ivermectin Miracle In The Indian State Of Uttar Pradesh". *Theblaze*. https://www.theblaze.com/op-ed/horowitz-the-unmistakable-ivermectin-miracle-in-the-indian-state-of-uttar-pradesh.

113   Horowitz, Daniel. 2021. "Horowitz: Heavily Vaccinated State Accounts For 65% Of India's COVID Cases After Rejecting Ivermectin". *Theblaze*. https://www.theblaze.com/op-ed/horowitz-heavily-vaccinated-state-accounts-for-65-of-indias-covid-cases-after-rejecting-ivermectin.

114   McLoone, David. 2021. "After Mexico City Introduced Ivermectin Plan, COVID Hospitalizations And Deaths Disappeared - Lifesite". *Lifesite*. https://www.lifesitenews.com/news/after-mexico-city-introduced-ivermectin-plan-covid-hospitalizations-and-deaths-disappeared/.

115   Guerrero, Rodrigo, Luis Eduardo Bravo, Edgar Muñoz, Elvia Karina Grillo Ardila, and Esteban Guerrero. 2020. "COVID-19: The Ivermectin African Enigma". *Colombia Médica*. doi:10.25100/cm.v51i4.4613.

116   Herbeck, Dan. 2021. "After Judge Orders Hospital To Use Experimental Covid-19 Treatment, Woman Recovers". *Buffalo News*. https://www.buffalonews.com/news/local/after-judge-orders-hospital-to-use-experimental-covid-19-treatment-woman-recovers/article_a9eb315c-5694-11eb-aac5-53b541448755.html.

117   JAFFE-HOFFMAN, MAAYAN. 2021. "Israeli Scientist Says COVID-19 Could Be Treated For Under $1/Day". *The Jerusalem Post*. https://www.jpost.com/health-science/israeli-scientist-says-covid-19-could-be-treated-for-under-1day-675612.

118   "Why You Should Not Use Ivermectin To Treat Or Prevent COVID-19". 2021. *U.S. Food And Drug Administration*. https://www.fda.gov/consumers/consumer-updates/why-you-should-not-use-ivermectin-treat-or-prevent-covid-19.

119   "Why You Should Not Use Ivermectin To Treat Or Prevent COVID-19".
        2021. *U.S. Food And Drug Administration*.
        https://web.archive.org/web/20210812051524/https:/www.fda.gov/consu
        mers/consumer-updates/why-you-should-not-use-ivermectin-treat-or-
        prevent-covid-19.

120   Doheny, Kathleen. 2022. "Parasite Drug Shows Early Promise Against
        COVID-19". *Webmd*.
        https://www.webmd.com/lung/news/20200407/parasite-drug-shows-
        early-promise-against-covid-19.

121   "Sermo Doctors Reveal Global COVID Treatment Patterns".
        2020. *Sermo*. https://www.sermo.com/press-releases/largest-statistically-
        significant-study-by-6200-multi-country-physicians-on-covid-19-
        uncovers-treatment-patterns-and-puts-pandemic-in-context/.

122   Queen's Medical Centre. 2020. "A Randomized Controlled Clinical Trial:
        Hydroxychloroquine For The Treatment Of COVID-19 In Hospitalized
        Patients (OAHU-COVID19)". Honolulu, Hawaii: ClinicalTrials.gov.
        https://www.clinicaltrials.gov/ct2/show/NCT04345692.

123   Réa-Neto, Álvaro, Rafaella Stradiotto Bernardelli, Bruna Martins
        Dzivielevski Câmara, Fernanda Baeumle Reese, Marcos Vinicius
        Oliveira Queiroga, and Mirella Cristine Oliveira. 2021. "An Open-Label
        Randomized Controlled Trial Evaluating The Efficacy Of
        Chloroquine/Hydroxychloroquine In Severe COVID-19
        Patients". *Scientific Reports* 11 (1). doi:10.1038/s41598-021-88509-9.

124   Taylor, Ryan. 2020. "Donald Trump Coronavirus Task Force Briefing
        Transcript March 19: Trump Takes Shots At The Media". *Rev*.
        https://www.rev.com/blog/transcripts/donald-trump-coronavirus-task-
        force-briefing-transcript-march-19-trump-takes-shots-at-the-media.

125   Zelenko, Vladimir. 2020. "A Report On Successful Treatment Of
        Coronavirus - Global Research". *Global Research*.
        https://www.globalresearch.ca/report-successful-treatment-
        coronavirus/5708056.

126   Roston, Aram, and Marisa Taylor. 2020. "CDC Removes Unusual
        Guidance To Doctors About Drug Favored By Trump". *Reuters*.
        https://www.reuters.com/article/us-health-coronavirus-usa-
        cdcguidance/cdc-removes-unusual-guidance-to-doctors-about-drug-
        favored-by-trump-idUSKBN21P39R.

127   Solender, Andrew. 2020. "All The Times Trump Has Promoted
        Hydroxychloroquine". *Forbes*.
        https://www.forbes.com/sites/andrewsolender/2020/05/22/all-the-times-
        trump-promoted-hydroxychloroquine/amp/.

128   Mehra, Mandeep R, Sapan S Desai, Frank Ruschitzka, and Amit N Patel.
        2020. "RETRACTED: Hydroxychloroquine Or Chloroquine With Or
        Without A Macrolide For Treatment Of COVID-19: A Multinational
        Registry Analysis". *The Lancet*. doi:10.1016/s0140-6736(20)31180-6.

129   Boseley, Sarah, and Melissa Davey. 2020. "Covid-19: Lancet Retracts
        Paper That Halted Hydroxychloroquine Trials". *The Guardian*.

https://www.theguardian.com/world/2020/jun/04/covid-19-lancet-retracts-paper-that-halted-hydroxychloroquine-trials.

130   Ried, Karin, Taufiq BinJemain, and Avni Sali. 2021. "Therapies To Prevent Progression Of COVID-19, Including Hydroxychloroquine, Azithromycin, Zinc, And Vitamin D3 With Or Without Intravenous Vitamin C: An International, Multicenter, Randomized Trial". *Cureus*. doi:10.7759/cureus.19902.

131   "HCQ For COVID-19: Real-Time Analysis Of All 395 Studies". 2022. *C19hcq.Com*. Accessed March 10. https://c19hcq.com/.

132   Risch, Harvey A. 2020. "Early Outpatient Treatment Of Symptomatic, High-Risk COVID-19 Patients That Should Be Ramped Up Immediately As Key To The Pandemic Crisis". *American Journal Of Epidemiology* 189 (11): 1218-1226. doi:10.1093/aje/kwaa093.

133   Su, Yi, Yun Ling, Yuyan Ma, Lili Tao, Qing Miao, Qingfeng Shi, Jue Pan, Hongzhou Lu, and Bijie Hu. 2020. "Efficacy Of Early Hydroxychloroquine Treatment In Preventing COVID-19 Pneumonia Aggravation, The Experience From Shanghai, China". *Bioscience Trends* 14 (6): 408-414. doi:10.5582/bst.2020.03340.

134   Ayerbe, Luis, Carlos Risco-Risco, and Salma Ayis. 2020. "The Association Of Treatment With Hydroxychloroquine And Hospital Mortality In COVID-19 Patients". *Internal And Emergency Medicine* 15 (8): 1501-1506. doi:10.1007/s11739-020-02505-x.

135   Ip, Andrew, Jaeil Ahn, Yizhao Zhou, Andre H. Goy, Eric Hansen, Andrew L. Pecora, and Brittany A. Sinclaire et al. 2021. "Hydroxychloroquine In The Treatment Of Outpatients With Mildly Symptomatic COVID-19: A Multi-Center Observational Study". *BMC Infectious Diseases* 21 (1). doi:10.1186/s12879-021-05773-w.

136   Vincent, Martin J, Eric Bergeron, Suzanne Benjannet, Bobbie R Erickson, Pierre E Rollin, Thomas G Ksiazek, Nabil G Seidah, and Stuart T Nichol. 2005. "Chloroquine Is A Potent Inhibitor Of SARS Coronavirus Infection And Spread". *Virology Journal* 2 (1). doi:10.1186/1743-422x-2-69.

137   Cole, Devan. 2020. "Fauci: Science Shows Hydroxychloroquine Is Not Effective As A Coronavirus Treatment". *CNN*. https://www.cnn.com/2020/05/27/politics/anthony-fauci-hydroxychloroquine-trump-cnntv/index.html.

138   THOMAS, KATIE, and KNVUL SHEIKH. 2020. "Small Chloroquine Study Halted Over Risk Of Fatal Heart Complications". *Chicago Tribune*. https://www.chicagotribune.com/coronavirus/sns-nyt-chloroquine-study-halted-over-fatal-risk-20200413-kchjndg655e6doekx5emoivor4-story.html.

139   "Recovery Trial: Brexit And Overdose". 2020. *Francesoir*. https://www.francesoir.fr/politique-monde/recovery-trial-brexit-and-overdose.

140   Engelbrecht, Torsten, and Konstantin Demeter. 2020. "Anthony Fauci: 40 Years Of Lies From AZT To Remdesivir". *Offguardian*. https://off-

guardian.org/2020/10/27/anthony-fauci-40-years-of-lies-from-azt-to-remdesivir/#9.

141   "Death Sentence - Special Thanks To Dr. Rick Bright".
        2021. *Ourfreedomtube.Com.*
        https://www.ourfreedomtube.com/watch/death-sentence-special-thanks-to-dr-rick-bright_JBxj4jHmbRUhiE2.html.

Chapter 10

Inoculations Pt. 1: The Motive

False mortality/morbidity attribution, authorizations of dangerous drugs/treatments, and suppression of safe, effective, early treatments. With these things we should now have a clear picture of the means and opportunity which can be attributed to the public health criminals responsible for the Covid crimes against humanity. But *why* did they do this?

The answer, as I will go on to explain in the following chapters, is several-fold. The truth is that many people benefited from this orchestrated disaster, and those who did had a variety of things to gain from it. As far as public health departments go however, there is one clear, overarching motive. It is the one which is least subject to conjecture—they confessed to it openly beforehand. It is also at least tangentially related to pretty much all the others, so I would consider it the most relevant. The motive I'm talking about is, of course: the inoculations.

The Milken Institute Confession

> *"To act in harmony toward a common end."*
> —The definition of, "conspire," per Merriam-Webster[1]

By the very definition of the word, there *did* exist an open conspiracy to sell the world on mRNA, "vaccines," which had never before been used in humans. This conspiracy was made public during an October 29, 2019 meeting at the Milken Institute—mere weeks before the alleged outbreak was meant to have begun.[2] The meeting was streamed on C-SPAN and featured government health officials such as Anthony Fauci and Rick Bright. The topic: a "universal flu vaccine." The first speaker to highlight is Michael Specter, who was identified as a staff writer for *the New Yorker*:

> *"Why don't we blow the system up? **I mean obviously we can't just turn off the spigot on the system we have and then say, 'hey, everyone in the world should get this new vaccine we haven't given to anyone yet.' But there must be some way***

215

(my emphasis) *that—we grow vaccines mostly in eggs the way we did in 1947."*

In Specter's own words, the goal this Milken Institute conspiracy he was a part of hoped to achieve was to, "blow up," the traditional system of vaccines in favor of, "this new vaccine." As we will see, the new vaccine technology he is referring to is mRNA.

While Specter is not a public health official, it would be extremely reasonable, if not necessary, to question the possibility of his objectivity in subsequent pieces on the matter. Such objectivity would be extraordinarily important during a time when people are being presented with information on whether or not to inject themselves with a substance never before used widely in humans. However, not only did *the New Yorker* not question this glaring conflict in one of its primary science-related contributors, it published Specter's subsequent promotion pieces on the mRNA inoculations, once, "some way," to, "blow up the system," came. One example is his November 16, 2020 piece titled, "Trump Is Right: Andrew Cuomo Should Accept F.D.A. Approval of a Coronavirus Vaccine," which is without question an article for which Specter would have an exceptional conflict of interest.[3] And perhaps nothing illustrates the significance of this better than the simple fact that *the New Yorker*, a magazine so opposed to Trump that it still considers the man's presidency an, "Active Crime Scene," on this one issue claimed Trump was, "right."[4]

In all seriousness though, Specter is the perfect example of how rife these conflicts are between the media presenting the information and the public health officials with which they openly collaborate. Anthony Fauci is, of course, one of those officials, and his comments at the Milken Institute alongside Specter were predictably corrupt:

> *"In order to make the transition from getting out of the tried-and-true egg growing, which we know gives results which can be beneficial—I mean, we've done well with that—to something that has to be much better. Uh, **you have to prove that this works** (my emphasis), and then you have to go through all of the clinical trials: phase 1's, phase 2's, phase 3's—and then show that the particular product is gonna be*

*good over a period of years. **That alone, if it works perfectly, is gonna take a decade.***

*... **So we really do have a problem with how the world perceives influenza and it's gonna be very difficult to change that, unless you do it from within and say, 'I don't care what your perception is, we're gonna address the problem in a disruptive way and in an iterative way*** (my emphasis).' *Because you do need both."*

Pretend for a second there was no Covid era and the above wasn't the direct confession it is, given this man executed exactly what he described only 5 or so months later. Anthony Fauci, in his own words, does not believe he is obligated to prove that what he is trying to sell people *works*. When considering the life and death implications of this comment alone and his blatant disregard for those implications, it is without question that this man exhibits the behavior of a psychopath.

Fauci doesn't even stop at whether or not it works though. Despite the fact that these mRNA shots have never been used widely in humans, he somehow believes it's acceptable to not only try to convince everyone in, "the world," to take them (without any caveat), he also calls for the historical process of completing safety trials to simply be skipped. Could there possibly be a time where safety trials would be more necessary? Of course not. And this recklessness was contrasted very well by long-time vaccine developer and Australian university Professor Nikolai Petrovsky, during a speech he gave in late 2021[5]:

"And we have a situation where we have some very new technologies, in their infancy—and that is the mRNA vaccines and the adenoviral vector vaccines—which are the only ones which you're being forced to have—or certainly, some of us are being forced to have—to remain in employment. And the question around what level of confidence do we have that they have been through the usual process—which is usually ten to fifteen years of rigorous testing in, you know, just thousands of people.

Now, those thousands of people accept the risk, because they're in a clinical trial, they're given a very extensive

217

warning, 'this could kill you, this could maim you,' and they still sign up and agree to that process, and then they're followed for five, ten, fifteen years. And if they survive and there are no terrible occurrences, then regulators will look at all of that data and approve the product.

Now, that hasn't happened in this situation, which is really a first. And so, you know, we all have to sit back and say, 'well, you know, should then everyone who gets these vaccines be signing an informed consent form, as if they're in a clinical trial?' Now my personal perspective is, first, no harm, and two, the principles of informed consent. You know, we have the Nuremberg Code—I mean, **the Nazis didn't take informed consent, and as a consequence a number of them were executed after the war for war crimes** (my emphasis).

And so where you have a situation—yes, you may accelerate things and develop a vaccine very rapidly and it's still, you know, there's uncertainties—**but then you have to tell people the honest truth. I can't tell you whether in ten years there will be a side effect of an mRNA vaccine or there won't be. No one can—maybe God can, if you believe in him. But in truth, no scientist can. And so if they can't, how can they mandate something which has that level of uncertainty around it? You have to get informed consent** (my emphasis)."

But Fauci isn't concerned about informed consent or safety. And the only reason he gives for skipping this process which ensures a genocide isn't committed is that it will, "take a decade," otherwise. Consider now the common phrase: "the path to hell is paved with good intentions." Some might argue Fauci's sped-up timeline to hell might come with good intentions. There is no support for this at all, however. Since he doesn't think it necessary to even demonstrate the usefulness of this product, it cannot be said that he's concerned about the potential lives lost in the absence of it. Is the idea that he just *believes* it will work? Okay, then what is that belief based on and why should anyone be required to trust in it?

Status quo mortality deaths are unavoidable, and obviously don't justify the informed consent violations—aka, crimes against humanity—Fauci openly advocates for here. That said, the only possible reason this timeline would be a problem to Fauci is his age and assumed proximity to retirement. To make matters worse, these Covid mRNA inoculations have had by-far the worst outcomes of seemingly any inoculations ever. And this paints a much darker picture about the intention behind these comments, which we will touch on in a bit.

To finish with how this quote ties to the alleged Covid pandemic though, Fauci flat-out declares, "how the world perceives influenza," to be a, "problem," and says he doesn't, "care what your perception is," because he's, "gonna address the problem in a disruptive way and an iterative way." The concept of, "flurona," and the data manipulation previously discussed point strongly to, "Covid," being the, "disruptive," solution created to solve this, "problem." Further support for this hypothesis has been provided in January 2022, as the idea of an annual flu/Covid mRNA shot combo have been floated by both Fauci and the media as a way to increase flu shot uptake—the exact goal of the Milken Institute conspiracy.[6,7]

Fauci's Milken quote also demonstrates a historically unprecedented, tyrannical narcissism in the name of an un-scientific, "science," which is as wicked as it is absurd. Not only does no human being on earth have the type of authority Fauci is saying he's simply going to commandeer, the idea it should be given to someone on a global scale for the first time in history *without any proof of concept* is both evil and silly. It's not as silly, however, as the idea Fauci would be capable of, "saving," the human race from symptoms as regular and necessary to a healthy body as the cold/influenza, if only every single person did what he said. And all of this might be surprising if it did not come from a man unashamed to advertise a home office filled with several pictures, and even a bobble-head, of himself.[8]

But this is what Fauci is: a silly little megalomaniac and a salesman who has taken one too many deals with the devil. Fauci was far too public with this plot and he executed it so in line with his pre Covid comments that pre-meditation is indisputable. As the head of NIAID for the past 40 or so years, Fauci had the means; thanks to his conflicts of interest with both the Moderna vaccine itself and billionaire medical tycoon Bill Gates (more on both in a bit), he had the motive; and with the arrival of mRNA technology, he had the opportunity—an opportunity that now-familiar liar and BARDA

219

director Rick Bright seemed practically giddy to announce at the same Milken Institute meeting alongside him:

> *"There might be a need, or even an urgent call, for **an entity of excitement out there that's completely disruptive, that's not beholden to bureaucratic strings and processes.***
> ***... But it is not too crazy to think that an outbreak of a novel avian virus could occur in China somewhere. We could get the RNA sequence from that** (my emphasis), beam it to a number of regional centers—if not local, if not in your home at some point—and print those vaccines on a patch and self-administer."*

Unfortunately for Rick Bright, what actually happened here *is*, "too crazy to think," for a mind not clouded by narcissism. This is because what happened is that a powerful figure theorized a disruptive justification to sell a new, unprecedented drug. This figure, who happens to now be in a prominent position at the Rockefeller Foundation (more on why that's extremely relevant later), would then see his theory come true in the form of an alleged once-in-a-century pandemic *within a month* of his theorizing it amongst other powerful figures.[9] And as if it wasn't already completely impossible for this pandemic to have occurred in nature, given the timing of all this theorizing (which it *is* impossible), this figure's theory would occur within a month, *in the very country he predicted it would*. He would then go on to aggressively, and in his official capacity, slander alternative treatments to the mRNA inoculations he set out to sell from before the alleged, "outbreak," he theorized, as we saw him do with HCQ.

The organizations of which Bright was both a part of and ran tangentially alongside also just so happened to act the following year in unprecedented ways. Take, for one example, the CDC's assertion of jurisdiction over private residential leases. The, "bureaucratic strings and processes," which make this type of economic upheaval illegal for the worse-than-useless CDC are the very same Bright cheered for them to disrupt only months prior. This hysterical, illegal action even ultimately empowered the CDC to theorize, "Green Zones," with which to, "relocate," vaguely-defined, "high-risk individuals," in settings which they claimed would necessitate, "strict adherence to protocol."[10] The organization actually admits, in the same document they present the idea, that the concentration of high risk individuals in this prison-like setting could actually present a *greater* danger to this population. But again, thanks to Bright, we know their goal was, "disruption," as opposed to logic, human rights, or respecting the bounds of their authority.

Bright also elaborates on the mRNA technology itself, highlighting future (and current) application goals including inoculations in the form of a patch and the ability to, "beam," mRNA sequences to those patches in one's own home. And don't get me wrong here, there's nothing inherently wrong with futuristic health technology. The problem, again, is the way in which these authority figures schemed to make these things universal/mandatory, and then executed on that scheme. Also, given their complete disregard for privacy and human rights, the technology itself *does* actually present serious issues related to those topics. We will touch on those later as well.

What we can observe here though, is a group of public health officials who devised a plan. Within a month of their planning, the exact circumstances arose with which they could execute this plan. Each possessed the means, motive, and opportunity to have been responsible for those circumstances. Acting in concert, as they clearly were both before and after, allowed them to amplify their already-significant authority and capabilities. Actions they were responsible for during 2020—including false testing, counting, treatment suppression, lockdowns, mask measures, etc.—would then directly frame the very narrative they needed to achieve the goal of their conspiracy. Their culpability seems pretty cut and dry at this point to me thanks to this confession, but there is also plenty more evidence to support it.

Event 201

We touched briefly on the Event 201 pandemic simulation held on October 18, 2019 in our chapter on censorship. In that chapter we saw how the Bill & Melinda Gates Foundation explicitly called for censorship in its Event 201 concluding recommendations, as well as for a, "flood," of the airwaves with what public health officials deem, "factual," information. As we've seen with almost every single directive public health officials gave during the Covid era, their grasp on what is, "factual," was not even respected by scientists and physicians in many cases, of whom tens of thousands personally signed their names to multiple opposition declarations.

But the simple fact that Event 201's pandemic simulation even occurred in October 2019, immediately prior to the once-in-a-century event it simulated a coordinated government/media response to, is a truly unbelievable thing—and by that I mean it's literally *not believable*, even less so when considering its happening alongside the Milken Institute meeting. So what was Event 201 and who was involved?

In the words of its own organizers, Event 201 was a, "3.5 hour pandemic tabletop exercise that simulated a series of dramatic, scenario-based facilitated discussions, confronting difficult, true-to-life dilemmas associated with response to a hypothetical, but scientifically plausible, pandemic."[11] The cited purpose of this simulation was a, "growing number of epidemic events." According to these organizers, unnamed, "experts," agreed that, "it is only a matter of time before one of these epidemics becomes global—a pandemic with potentially catastrophic consequences." The simulation was sponsored, organized, and recommendations were given jointly by the John's Hopkins Center for Health Security, the World Economic Forum (WEF), and the Bill & Melinda Gates Foundation. The following is a transcript of simulated news coverage describing Event 201's coronavirus pandemic scenario[12]:

> "Narrator: *A new coronavirus. Infected people got a respiratory illness with symptoms ranging from mild, flu-like signs, to severe pneumonia.*
> Broadcaster: *In related news, a significant demand for personal protective equipment, like N-95 masks and gloves, are on the rise ... Patients are overwhelming healthcare facilities ... People are avoiding public spaces out of fear of infection and in compliance with public health recommendations ...* **Our U.S. affiliate has just released polling results on public expectations for a vaccine and 65% of those polled are eager to take the vaccine, even if it's experimental** (my emphasis).
> Doctor: *I'm not optimistic on having the vaccine in time to be relevant during this pandemic.*

Public health official (presumably): *With enough money and political will, anything is possible.*

Government official: *Penalties have been put in place for spreading harmful falsehoods, including arrests.*

Pundit: *If the solution means controlling and reducing access to information, I think it's the right choice.*

News Contributor: *What exactly are the risks and benefits of staying home from work? Absolutely, we need to save lives. But we literally cannot afford a heavy-handed response that suffocates our economy.*

Narrator: *The world saw large scale protests and in some places riots. This led to violent crackdowns in some countries and even martial law. The public lost trust in their respective administrations.* ***Economists say the economic turmoil caused by such a pandemic will last for years. The societal impacts—the loss of faith in government, the distrust of news, and the breakdown of social cohesion—could last even longer*** (my emphasis)."

If you feel that you could vomit from this psychological warfare predictive programming, you are not alone. With introspection, I realize that this entire book is fulfilling the prophesy set forth in the final lines of this dystopian propaganda. I not only do not trust these institutions, but I believe there to be ample evidence they are guilty of crimes against humanity. The solace I get despite this comes from the following:

1. Faith in God
2. I know I am searching for the truth in this pursuit, which is all that matters
3. The apparent solutions of the Event 201 conspirators on this matter are the opposite of my own

On this third point, it would seem most likely based on the words and history of Event 201's conspirators that they believe the only solution for this type of thing is global coordination. Perhaps it is possible they *wanted* to sabotage trust in national organizations like the FDA, NIH, and CDC, in the hopes that people would come running to the, "more reasonable," WHO. I don't have any definitive proof of that beyond the fact that they anticipated the outcome however, so I will not focus on it here. I also would find it laughable if this actually was a goal, considering the equal-if-not-more-significant culpability of the WHO, relative to the others. But as I stated previously, there are many players with many motives and this may or may not be one of them, based on the repeated focus on globalism.

What's more important to our purposes in this chapter though, is the clearly-intentional seed planted about, "experimental vaccines," and the predictive programming study about the, "eagerness," of people to take it. As told by Michael Specter at the Milken Institute, the traditional method of vaccine production has been around since 1947. Therefore, for Event 201 to call the anticipated vaccines, "experimental," implies a foreknowledge that the focus during such an event would be on the experimental mRNA inoculations, as opposed to traditional vaccine development. And whether or not they would even admit they were referencing mRNA shots specifically, this coverage and the event itself also demonstrates that they completely dismissed the possibility of any sufficient treatment beyond inoculations.

No mention is made of any treatment at all in the skit above. One would think this would be a focus during such a scenario, but it wasn't—not in the simulation, *or* in the actual, alleged pandemic. This alignment of the Event 201 response with the actual response suggests a relationship which *does* exist between Gates, the WHO, the WEF, and the various players on the national level like Fauci and Bright. These conflicts of interest will be discussed soon. But again, for Event 201 to have taken place when it did, with the content it featured, and for it to have done so right alongside the Milken Institute meeting, it continues to rule out the possibility of the alleged pandemic being a natural occurrence, whether or not a novel coronavirus is actually part of the equation.

Tying the Two Together: Gates, Fauci, and the "Decade of Vaccines"

"Twenty years ago when we created these new multilateral organizations—GAVI for the vaccines, Global Fund for HIV, TB, and malaria—we didn't know they'd be successful. We've gone through lots of challenges about making sure the money

gets there, making sure the efficiency is right. But as we look at upcoming replenishments for those—and we've got so much distractions politically that the international needs like this could get eclipsed if we're not careful—you know, we see a phenomenal track record. **It's been $100 billion overall that the world's put in. Our foundation is a bit more than $10 billion. But we feel that there's been over a 20-to-1 return. So if you just look at the economic benefits, that's a pretty strong number compared to anything else** (my emphasis). *"*
—Bill Gates[13]

In January of 2010, Bill and Melinda Gates used the World Economic Forum at Davos to announce a $10 billion commitment to research and develop vaccines, kicking off what he called the, "Decade of Vaccines," per researcher James Corbett.[14] The WHO corroborates this story in their, "Review and Lessons Learned," document on the program, in which they also refer to it specifically as a, "collaboration," between the Bill & Melinda Gates Foundation, the WHO, and Anthony Fauci's NIAID.[15] In this document they repeatedly make clear and track progress toward the goal of a, "global immunization strategy," namely, "A world in which all individuals and communities enjoy lives free from vaccine-preventable disease."

While one might find this an innocent enough goal, the primary point here is the clear-cut connection it establishes between all the major players of both Event 201 and the Milken Institute meeting—namely, Gates, Fauci, the WEF, the WHO, and NIAID. In fact, Fauci is even listed as being on the Leadership Council of the Decade of Vaccines Collaboration on the official Bill & Melinda Gates Foundation announcement of the program.[16] Even without all the context we now have on Fauci's plethora of conflicts, the very nature of this simultaneously-held position on a global collaboration is curious when considering his status as the director of a US national health organization. For example, one of the high-level recommendations in the aforementioned WHO review is, "a key focus on countries," where vaccine uptake is low. How exactly is it within the purview or authority of the director of NIAID to be leading such an effort? Whatever the case, this relationship between Gates and Fauci has clearly blossomed over the years, as CNBC now reports the two, "talk regularly."[17] Gates even mentions in the quote above the same type of, "distractions," from inoculations which Fauci loathed and announced his desire to, "address," with or without popular support.

The Decade of Vaccines also reinforces the major players' stated goal of inoculating the entire world which, as we can see from Gates's quote above, is not simply an innocent, philanthropic pursuit. In fact, the goal if met would effectively serve as a perpetual, worldwide tax for the magnate and the pharmaceutical companies he supports in these efforts. The more vaccines are introduced into national immunization programs around the world—as James Corbett points out is the Gates-founded global vaccine alliance GAVI's mission statement—the higher the tax pocketed by Gates and his partners. And the benefit of the service received for the tax is also highly debatable, as for one example even ABC acknowledged in 2019 that more polio cases are now vaccine-caused than otherwise.[18] The debate on vaccines in general is, of course, not a debate to be had in this book, as it would take us off the primary topic of the Covid era and perhaps double (or more) the length. However, there does exist plenty of precedent for the idea this is about more than health for Gates and his, "collaborators." The following are several examples which occurred during the Decade of Vaccines, as reported by James Corbett[19]:

- The Decade of Vaccines kicked off with an HPV vaccine study in India which, according to a government investigation, violated the human rights of the study participants with, "gross violations," of consent, and failed to properly report adverse events
    o After the deaths of seven girls involved were reported, a parliamentary investigation concluded that the Gates-funded Program for Appropriate Technology in Health (PATH), which ran the study, had been engaged in a scheme to help ensure, "healthy markets," for pharmaceutical companies GlaxoSmithKline and Merck, the manufacturers of the vaccines in the trial
    o To quote the investigation findings: *"Had PATH been successful in getting the HPV vaccine included in the universal immunization program of the concerned countries, this would have generated windfall profit*

for the manufacturer(s) by way of automatic sale, year after year, without any promotional or marketing expenses. It is well known that once introduced into the immunization program it becomes politically impossible to stop any vaccination."

- o Samiran Nundy, editor emeritus of the National Medical Journal of India is quoted as saying, "This is an obvious case where Indians were used as guinea pigs."

- In 2016, the steering group of India's National Health Mission blasted the Indian government for allowing the country's National Technical Advisory Group on Immunization (NTAGI)—the primary government vaccine advisory group—to be effectively purchased by the Bill & Melinda Gates Foundation

  - o One steerage group member commented: *"The NTAGI secretariat has been moved out of the* [government's health] *ministry to the office of Public Health Foundation of India and the 32 staff members in that secretariat draw their salaries from the BMGF* [Bill & Melinda Gates Foundation]. *There is a clear conflict of interest—on one hand, the BMGF funds the secretariat that is the highest decision making body in vaccines and, on the other, it partners with the pharma industry in GAVI. This is unacceptable."*

  - o In 2017, the government responded by cutting all financial ties between the advisory group and the Foundation

- The Gates-founded and funded Meningitis Vaccine Project led to between 40 and 500 children suffering from seizures and convulsions and eventually becoming paralyzed

- Internal memo by WHO malaria chief, Dr. Arata Kochi, complaining that Gates' influence meant that the world's leading malaria scientists are now, "locked up in a 'cartel' with their own research funding being linked to those of others within the group," and that the Foundation, "was stifling debate on the best ways to treat and combat malaria, prioritizing only those methods that relied on new technology or developing new drugs"[20]

- o Several conflicts between the government policy-pushing Bill & Melinda Gates Foundation and the pharmaceutical industry have existed over the course of its existence as well, Corbett points out
- o One last interesting note on Corbett's coverage of these issues, is that the majority of linked sources lead to broken webpages, which must be searched for in website archiving platforms. This is yet another interesting note on Gates' determination to control the narrative behind his operations and his influence over the media, to whom Mintpress reports he's funded to the tune of at least $300 million.[21]

To demonstrate how this reckless philosophy translated into the Covid era, take the following Fox interview from Gates on April 5, 2020[22]:

"I was very glad that those models are out there. Dr. Fauci is doing a very good job of saying the numbers are what count here and the various models that we, Imperial University do show that without this dramatic behavior change you could even get worse than that. But I do think that if we get the testing fixed, if we get all 50 states involved, we'll be below that [mortality projection]—of course, we'll pay a huge economic price to achieve that.

*... **It is fair to say things won't go back to truly normal until we have a vaccine that we've gotten out to basically the entire world** (my emphasis). And so, the best people at the [Bill & Melinda Gates] Foundation, we're all about high-volume vaccines..."*

In early April of 2020 it was not remotely, "fair to say," that the only way back to, "normal," was a vaccine. At that point in time in the alleged pandemic, only a person with an agenda would exclude the possibilities of either a repurposed treatment proving effective, natural immunity being achieved, the illness otherwise receding as SARS1 is claimed to have, or the models being wildly inaccurate. Gates' having done so implicates him for his role in the suppression that did happen of those possible outcomes. As we've already covered there *were* effective repurposed treatments, as we will cover soon there *is* evidence of post-illness immunity, and we also already touched on how wildly inaccurate the very model Gates cites here by Imperial College London—which his foundation has provided tens of millions in funding to—has proved to be, along with its prescriptions.[23] His mentioning Fauci in relation to supporting those garbage-in, garbage-out models, is also particularly fitting. These two figures jointly used their tremendous influence to push for the most damaging of policies across the board—policies which accepted only one possible outcome in favor of their objective, and at the direct, documented expense of public health.

The History of SARS Inoculations and mRNA Gene Therapies
 Since SARS-CoV-1 was initially alleged to have broken out in the early 2000's, there have been several attempts to develop SARS inoculations. These attempts sought to create a neutralizing antibody response by introducing the spike protein of the virus. One example was in 2004, when a Modified Vaccinia Virus Ankara-Based Recombinant (rMVA) vaccine expressing the spike protein was tested on ferrets.[24] This experiment found that, "vaccination with rMVA expressing SARS-CoV spike protein," actually caused enhanced hepatitis. A similarly poor result came from a 2012 experiment, in which various SARS inoculations were tested in mice including a virus-like-particle vaccine, an inactivated whole virus vaccine, and an rDNA-produced spike protein inoculation.[25] *All* inoculations led to the, "occurrence of Th2-type immunopathology, suggesting hypersensitivity to SARS-CoV components was induced." The conclusion was that, "Caution in proceeding to application of a SARS-CoV vaccine in humans is indicated."

 Let me repeat that with emphasis: *"hypersensitivity to SARS-CoV components was induced," and, "caution in proceeding to application of a SARS-CoV vaccine in humans," was indicated.*

 Again, this second study was published in 2012 and there do not appear to be any published studies attempting SARS inoculations since. While past studies did not test mRNA gene therapy inoculations specifically, they *did* attempt to induce immunity by introducing the spike protein meant to be a component of the coronavirus. The claimed objective of the *new* inoculations is to introduce synthetic messenger RNA (mRNA) to the body, which then, "teaches," the cells to make copies of the spike protein.[26] Seeing as this is obviously the same type of strategy only with a different spike protein delivery method, there's no reason the past studies wouldn't be an extremely relevant precedent on the capability of neutralizing the alleged SARS virus through that route. Therefore, for the, "caution in proceeding to application of a SARS-CoV vaccine in humans," recommendation to have gone unheeded given this background is criminal.

And even without this relevant SARS inoculation background, I would repeat as many times as I can that mRNA is a new, experimental technology. Per *Nature Magazine*, its history of development is long and complex, starting with the discovery of its potential use case in 1987 by Dr. Robert Malone.[27] But for the two decades following this discovery there were many struggles and doubts about a possible, affordable use case. Things came to a head in the 2010's however, which was a decade that saw increased investment including from the US Defense Advanced Research Projects Agency (DARPA) in 2012. It was during this decade that lipid nanoparticles were determined to be a potential mRNA delivery system. Delivery to the cells was previously one of the biggest road blocks, since the immune system would otherwise reject the package containing the synthetic mRNA.

This sequence of events—the decades-long ramp up and eventual breakthrough of a technology—would be a fascinating history if not for the ominous way in which it was built up directly into the perfect storm of demand—a demand which otherwise wouldn't have existed. And it is in this lack of demand that we can find the real reason Fauci viewed the world's perception of influenza as a problem—namely, because it hindered his stated goal of, "universal," mRNA flu inoculations. This previous lack of and need for demand is also admitted by the pharmaceutical industry itself, perhaps no better than in a speech by Bayer executive Stefan Oelrich at the World Health Summit in the fall of 2021[28]:

> *"We are really taking that leap* [to drive innovation]*—us as a company, Bayer—in cell and gene therapies ... ultimately the mRNA vaccines are an example for that cell and gene therapy. I always like to say:* **if we had surveyed two years ago in the public—'would you be willing to take a gene or cell therapy**

230

and inject it into your body?'—we probably would have had a 95% refusal rate (my emphasis)."

As a demonstration of just how coordinated media, pharmaceutical, and public health interests have become, this extraordinary truth drop was actually removed from *YouTube*.[29] This removal came despite the fact that it took place at a conference with the very, "authoritative," public health voices (Tedros Ghebreyesus of the WHO and Rick Bright, for example) who fancied themselves the arbiters of, "accurate information."[30] At the same time it's not surprising at all why evidence of this statement would demand erasure, considering what it reveals.

The first thing, which we have been discussing, is that Oelrich admits the overwhelming majority of the demand—billions of people worth—would not have existed without the alleged pandemic. The Covid era presented a too-perfect problem-reaction-solution scenario, as presented famously in the Hegelian Dialectic, with which the world could be sold on this product that had just a few years earlier became possible to sell.[31] As *Nature* highlighted in, "The tangled history of mRNA vaccines," this propaganda trick worked with resounding success, with global sales of these products expected to top $50 billion in 2021 alone.[32]

But in this quote Oelrich reveals something else perhaps even more troubling to the cause of the medical/economic oligarchs— namely, the mRNA, "vaccines," are not vaccines at all, but are better described as gene therapies. And this is why, as you might have noticed, I do not refer to them as vaccines in this book. To explain, we need simply refer to the Merriam-Webster dictionary definition of, "vaccine," as of 2019[33]:

> *"A preparation of killed microorganisms, living attenuated organisms, or living fully virulent organisms that is administered to produce or artificially increase immunity to a particular disease."*

We can contrast this with the Merriam-Webster dictionary definition of, "vaccine," in 2022, which is significantly different[34]:

"A preparation that is administered (as by injection) to stimulate the body's immune response against a specific infectious agent or disease."

The entire idea of a vaccine is that the virus itself, in a killed or whole form, is presented to the immune system so that it may be recognized upon future presentation and handled without the onset of illness. This is not the case with mRNA shots, which do not contain the virus itself and are said to fundamentally reprogram the cell to do a process it otherwise wouldn't do—namely, to create copies of the spike protein allegedly specific to the virus. While both focus on creating an immune response, to equate the two is false and is nothing more than a marketing ploy, as Oerlich effectively admits.

And even when, "fact-checked," the truth that mRNA inoculations are more accurately described as gene-related therapies cannot be avoided. In an article by *Reuters* titled, "Fact Check-mRNA vaccines are distinct from gene therapy, which alters recipient's genes," one of the first things said by the primary virologist source *Reuters* cites is the following[35]:

*"As mRNA is genetic material, mRNA vaccines **can be looked at as a genetic-based therapy** (my emphasis)."*

They go on to say that these inoculations are not actually, "gene therapies," though, because they do not literally alter a person's genetic code, as, "gene therapies," do. Science is ever evolving however, so despite *Reuters'* propagandist objective to establish a narrative, the very-real concern that mRNA could impact a person's DNA has since been confirmed by a February 2022 study by Aldén et al. in *Current Issues in Molecular Biology.*[36] This study found that Pfizer's inoculation, "can be reverse-transcribed to DNA … and this may give rise the concern if [inoculation]-derived DNA may be integrated into the host genome and affect the integrity of genomic DNA, **which may potentially mediate genotoxic side effects** (my emphasis)." Images in a separate study submitted by Pfizer itself to the Australian government have also supported this gene alteration according to some scientists, as they seemed to show the spike protein entering the nucleus.[37,38]

But *Reuters* also ignores one simpler point here, which is the *fact* that the very argument it makes can be used the same way against it. For example, let's say I was either deranged or corrupt and wanted to make a, "fact-check," blog. If that were the case, I could make an article titled, "Fact Check-mRNA inoculations are distinct from vaccines, which contain attenuated or whole viruses," and it would be just as true. But, of course, there's a reason these, "fact checks," only go out of their way to play semantics in one slanted direction every single time—and it's because there isn't as much money in opposing a $50 billion per year industry as there is in shilling for it.

Again though, if it can be said that mRNA inoculations are not, "gene therapies," because they do not alter genes, it can also be said that they are not, "vaccines," because they do not contain the virus in question. And this might seem like a pointless debate to attempt. However, it *is* relevant, because of the very specific reason the medical oligarchs refuse to adjust the definition of, "gene therapy," to include the very-similar, "genetic-based therapy," but are willing to reach further in adjusting the definition of, "vaccine," to include what is described *by their own sources* as a, "genetic-based therapy."

This game of changing definitions to suit agendas gets *way* worse as it relates to the public health organization definitions too, but we will get to that later. Another issue with the use of the term, "vaccine," as a definition is that these shots are now widely accepted to not prevent infection or transmission—another thing we will go into in tons of detail on in the next chapter. What's important for now though is that the history of both SARS inoculations and mRNA inoculations pointed to a need for caution as it related to any use in humans. Not only was the opposite of caution practiced when the time came to bring the two together, those in positions of authority pre-emptively plotted what would need to happen to excuse their complete lack of any caution at all. Then, a month later, it happened.

The NIH Claims Ownership of the Moderna Inoculation

Yes, you read that correctly. In October of 2019 Anthony Fauci, the face of US infectious disease response for decades and the director of NIAID, a division of the NIH, theorized at the Milken Institute a way in which mRNA inoculations could both skip safety and efficacy trials, and also garner *universal* demand. But not only did this incredible situation occur without questions raised by the media on the astounding conflicts of interest this implies Fauci had—the answers to those questions were *provided by* the media as, "matter-of-fact," despite confirming the worst fears any honest observer would have had—namely, the NIH, and by-extension Fauci, had a direct, substantial financial stake in one of the primary mRNA inoculation candidates Fauci was so intent on selling to the public.

Unknown to most, the scandal-of-the-century, which was presented as a milk-toast morning read, was reported by *Axios* as early on as June of 2020.[39] The should-have-been-earth-shattering headline on the unmitigated corruption of US public health read: "The NIH claims joint ownership of Moderna's coronavirus vaccine." Instead of focusing on the underlying conflicts however, *Axios* predictably shilled, *telling* readers, "why it matters," as:

> *"Because the federal government has an actual stake in this vaccine, it could try to make the vaccine a free or low-cost public good with wide distribution, if the product turns out to be safe and effective."*

This propagandist's description completely perverts the real nature of the situation, however. First of all, the federal government's massive stake in the vaccine incentivizes its sale to the public *rather than* its safety or its efficacy in the ending of the pandemic, if there actually was one. This is as evident in Fauci's pre-alleged-pandemic rhetoric, as it is in the relentless efforts to both get everyone inoculated and to suppress alternative, superior treatments during the alleged pandemic. In fact, things got so absurd and on-the-nose in this regard that the US *treasury deputy secretary*, obviously not a health official at all, admitted in October 2021, "The reality is that the only way we're going to get to a place where we work through this [supply chain issues] transition is if everyone in America and everyone around the world gets vaccinated."[40] We will go way more in depth on the macroeconomic forces behind the Covid era in a later chapter. But the treasury deputy secretary's sentiments were echoed by Joe Biden as well, who infamously said his, "patience is wearing thin," with un-inoculated Americans.[41]

The issue isn't just with the impact on the health of Americans though, either. The government invested massive amounts of taxpayer funding in the deal to be a part owner of these inoculations. That taxpayer funding means the inoculations are not then, "free," once they are received by the public, but are rather the payout of an investment the public itself made, willingly or not. The obvious problem with this is that in order for the government to make, "its," (the tax payer's) money back on its investment, it now has a perverse incentive to push the inoculation whether it's good for (or, wanted by) people or not. And since the inoculation is falsely, and intentionally, referred to as a, "vaccine," the government can attempt to justify coercing it. This is thanks to the implication of, "herd immunity," which is assumed to result from vaccines. "Herd immunity," can be exploited whether or not there's any evidence it can be achieved, in the name of the, "public good," just like the production of the shots were justified the same way, whether it was to end up being true or not. Lost in this incredible scheme is the rights of the individual, who had no say in either the initial investment or the informed consent violations that came from the false scenario created to justify them. Criminals like Fauci, the highest paid government official for a reason, profit at the expense of those individuals.

As hard to believe as it must be that there could be more—or at this point, perhaps it's expected—it gets even worse. *Axios* goes on to point out that while the NIH and Moderna have done joint research in the past, it was *only in December of 2019* that the NIH signed a contract with Moderna stating the following[42]:

> *"mRNA coronavirus vaccine candidates [are] developed and **jointly owned** (my emphasis)."*

Again, despite the fact that *Axios* acknowledges this contract, "was signed before the new virus had been sequenced," they fail to mention a far more important point. According to ABC News, the official timeline of events says the WHO only claimed to have first been *informed* of the first cases of a mysterious pneumonia in Wuhan *on December 31, 2019.*[43] Indeed, the WHO confirms this timeline of events, and claims that Chinese authorities didn't determine that the outbreak was caused by a novel coronavirus until January 9th of 2020.[44] This means the NIH/Moderna part-ownership contract for coronavirus mRNA inoculations came *a few weeks before* the alleged pandemic was even first identified. As if pre-meditation could be more of a certainty at this point, NIAID and Moderna also shared this mRNA coronavirus inoculation in a Material Transfer Agreement

(MTA) with the University of North Carolina at Chapel Hill's Ralph Baric on December 12th 2019.[45] And this was a particularly telling deal, considering allegations of Fauci's NIAID funding Baric's own gain-of-function research, yet another troubling detail we will cover later.

Axios goes on to point out that four NIH scientists had filed for a provisional patent application entitled, "2019-nCoV vaccine," according to disclosures in a pending scientific paper.[46] And the kicker? While Moderna scientists co-authored the paper, *none were listed as vaccine co-inventors*. *Axios* also quotes health and law policy researcher Zain Rizvi as confirming, "The vaccine would not exist without the intellectual contributions of federal scientists." This presents incredible conflicts of interest also due to well-documented policies which allow those NIH scientists to collect up to $150,000 per year in royalties on their work, per Janice Hopkins Tanne in the *BMJ*.[47] Tanne documented how exploiting such policies had been a common practice of the NIH for decades. Meanwhile, *Axios* ends its article by suggesting that, "developers aren't likely to seek big profits from," the shots. While this report was from June 2020, prior to the distribution of the shots, one still has to laugh and wonder whether this was either incredible naiveté, or just more shilling, given the histories of both the pharmaceutical industry and the regulatory agencies it's captured, including the NIH.

What the NIH specifically takes credit for creating is the, "stabilized coronavirus spike proteins for the development of vaccines against **coronaviruses, including SARS-CoV-2** (my emphasis)." This stunning admission came in an official NIH statement made to *Axios* on the subject.[48] What it makes clear, yet *again*, is that the spike proteins being produced by the shot are *not* specific to the alleged SARS-CoV-2. This admission also implies the alleged discovery of the novel coronavirus was immaterial to the development of the inoculations, which is just another detail beyond the litany I've already covered that, in my opinion, brings into question the claim that there is a SARS-CoV-2 at all. It also follows that this indistinct spike protein must be what's produced by all the different inoculation companies as well, unless they would like to admit they're all producing something different in the body.

Additional proof of the inoculations' lack of specificity to the allegedly novel virus comes from the timeline of events related to

Christian Drosten's PCR protocol. The paper on that protocol was published on January 25, 2020 and included a theoretical virus sequence provided by the Chinese, as we've covered. You will recall, they used this in-silico sequence because they admitted they had no isolate available at this time. Understanding the situation as it was at that time, consider the following timeline of events Fauci provided in a March 19, 2020 interview with *Facebook*'s Mark Zuckerberg[49]:

> *"So what happened is that as soon as we got the sequence of the virus from the Chinese, we pulled it out from the public database and stuck the gene into a vaccine platform and worked on it literally within a day of when it came out. Sixty-five days later, namely two days ago, we gave the first injection to a normal volunteer for a phase one trial to see if it's safe."*

Let's take stock of these dates Fauci provides. Two days before this interview would have been March 17, 2020, and sixty-five days before that would have been January 12, 2020. So Fauci is claiming that the shots were developed based on a January 12, 2020 sequence, shared by the Chinese. However, this sequence *had to* have been the same one being used by Drosten in his PCR report, considering the timing. This makes it clear that the inoculations *must have* also been developed based on a theoretical virus sequence, as opposed to the alleged novel coronavirus. So *even if* the alleged novel coronavirus was later isolated and proven to exist at all, that virus *cannot have been* what was used to develop the inoculations, given Fauci's timeline and the impossibility of the theoretical matching the actual.

Again, this lends further support to the idea that the inoculations were simply developed beforehand and the allegation of a novel virus was just a narrative to justify their mass use. The only possible explanation otherwise is if the theoretical virus had matched the actual thing 100%. Since such a match is impossible by chance, the only possible explanation would have been the Chinese having had access to the virus beforehand. This would prove the gain of function theory correct and would implicate both the Chinese and US governments in their having collaborated on this project. However, I tend to doubt this possibility because I've never heard anyone, even the non-mainstream scientists who *do* believe the novel virus theory, suggest that the theoretical was an 100% match with what they believe to be the actual, now-sequenced genome. So this is one reason I tend to doubt the novel virus theory myself, but I will provide significant coverage on the gain-of-function theory and its support in a later chapter.

Back to the NIH-Moderna deal, at this point it's hard to see the US government as being one distinct from, "private," industry at all. And one only has to understand a few things about the company Moderna's history to understand just how indistinct from the government it really is. In September 2016, the national biotech reporter for the medical media company *STAT* wrote a lengthy exposé on the, "ego, ambition, and turmoil," plaguing Moderna, referred to as "one of biotech's most secretive startups."[50] The story goes on to explain how Moderna CEO Stéphane Bancel created an environment which was, "loath to publish its work in *Science* or *Nature*, but enthusiastic to herald its potential on CNBC or CNN."

Former employees—of which there were many the company hemorrhaged, allegedly due to Bancel's ego and lack of any medical or scientific background—charged that Bancel was actually, "running an investment firm," and, "then hoping it also develops a drug that's successful." The company lost all manner of employees too at the time of the *STAT* article, including executives, two heads of chemistry, its chief scientific officer, its head of manufacturing, its head of cancer research, it head of research and development (a significant loss as far as a pharma company's future outlook is concerned), and its head of rare disease research. Several of these departures came after periods of less than 18 months on the job. This because prior to 2020, the company never developed a successful drug and was one of the least transparent of any in the industry in sharing any kind of data or trial information.

And the story as it related to the Covid era gets even more troubling too. As recently now as January 2017, *STAT* again reported on Moderna, highlighting a serious problem with the same mRNA delivery system used in the, "Covid," inoculations of today.[51] This problem would present such an issue that a former employee explained solving it would require, "a miraculous, Hail Mary sort of save." The problem with this lipid nanoparticle delivery system was that with too small a dose, there wouldn't be enough protein produced to make a difference. With too high a dose however, the drug would be too toxic for patients. Because of this, Moderna poured over medical literature for diseases that might be treated with very small amounts of additional protein. Unfortunately for them, the list of such diseases was, "very, very short." One project in the works by the company for such a disease called, "Crigler-Najjar," still proved to fail too, with whistleblowers ultimately decrying safety issues.

Despite this, "Hail Mary," dilemma and a company history that *STAT* aptly points out rivals the corruption of infamous pharma-fraud Theranos, Moderna is now claimed to have developed an inoculation which does somehow solve this toxicity problem. Not only that though, it's meant to have done so for a disease as historically challenging to immunize against as SARS. Thanks to Anthony Fauci and the strategy of Emergency Use Authorizations however, no solution to this very recent problem need be demonstrated at all. In fact, Fauci and Bancel seem to make a great team at the head of this company/government abomination, as Fauci too clearly prefers media appearances over scientific demonstration and evidence.

But are we really to believe this toxicity problem was actually solved? We will soon demonstrate pretty thoroughly that it must not have been. But even before we get to the damage we now know has been done upon inoculating the population, we can simply observe that the Moderna mRNA inoculations inject 40 trillion packages of mRNA per dose, each of which instructing cells to produce a multiple of spike protein.[52] Now, obviously I do not have a reference for how to quantify, "too high," a dose of lipid-nanoparticle-delivered mRNA-instructed protein production, as it relates to the *STAT* article highlighting Moderna's dilemma. But are we to believe 40 trillion packages times the production per package is to be considered a, "moderate," amount somewhere between too little (no effect) and too much (toxic)? Of course not, at least not without the type of demonstration Fauci isn't willing to provide and the FDA has requested courts allow it 50-100 years before being required to share.[53]

Also, besides the quantity issue in general, what about the spike protein itself? Is it a good thing to have the body producing in such massive quantities, which it naturally would not do? Well it sure doesn't seem like it to me at least, considering the role scientists claim it plays in people who do get sick. According to *News Medical Life Sciences*, for example, a 2021 paper by Lei et al. published in *Circulation Research* shows conclusively that the spike protein damages vascular endothelial cells, *in the absence of the alleged virus*, by binding to ACE2 and disrupting its molecular signal to the mitochondria, causing it to become damaged.[54,55] *News Medical* points out that the dangers of the spike protein itself had been shown in previous studies as well. So, given the damage the spike protein causes on its own, and the seemingly tremendous, unnatural production of this spike protein by the inoculations, alongside the historical problems with both lipid nanoparticle delivered mRNA quantities *and* with SARS inoculations in general, how can these inoculations possibly not have come with tremendous risk warnings? Corruption is the only valid response. And corruption there most certainly was…

The Perfect Storm of Corruption: EUA's and Liability Protection

On March 17, 2020 the US DHHS issued a declaration to provide, "liability immunity for activities related to medical countermeasures against COVID-19."[56] This declaration was authorized under the Public Readiness and Emergency Preparedness Act (PREP Act), an authorization which is meant to prevent a stifling of innovation. The obvious problem with this policy is that it has accompanied the following:

1. The Moderna shot is a joint creation of the liability-immunized company and the government granting that liability immunity
2. The shots have also been granted EUA authorizations by the FDA, allowing them to skip the standard, decade-long efficacy and safety trials, for an indefinite period of time thanks to the PREP Act[57]
3. The illegal economic, social, and physical coercions which have occurred related to these liability-immunized products (more on this to come)
4. The blatant lack of informed consent related to these EUA-granted inoculations
5. The Occupational Safety and Health Administration's (OSHA) sudden, inexplicable suspension of its vaccine

workplace-injury reporting requirement once inoculations
were in distribution (more on this to come)

To summarize where we've come at this point: In October
2019 Anthony Fauci, among others, publicly planned a scheme,
alongside a coordinated pandemic wargame, to sell the world on a
universal mRNA inoculation without having to prove it works. This
mRNA vaccine was a product of the labor of scientists in his
organization within the federal government, funded for years by
taxpayer dollars, and supported by a demand which didn't exist.
Despite this, the product was falsely marketed to the public as the
private innovation of a failing company, supported in the heat-of-the-
moment by Donald Trump's, "Operation Warp Speed," to sudden,
impossible success. Little did the public know, however, the
groundwork for this operation Trump takes credit for initiating in
response to the alleged Covid pandemic was actually signed by Trump
himself via executive order in *September 2019*, just before the Milken
Institute gathering.[58] Take a look and see if the language of EO 13887
sounds familiar:

> *"Vaccination is the most effective defense against influenza.*
> *Despite recommendations by the Centers for Disease Control*
> *and Prevention (CDC) that nearly every American should*
> *receive the influenza vaccine annually, however, seasonal*
> *influenza vaccination levels in the United States have*
> *currently reached only about 45 percent of CDC goals.*
> *... Most influenza vaccines are made in chicken eggs, using a*
> *70-year-old process that requires months-long production*
> *timelines, limiting their utility for pandemic control...*
> *... Because the market does not sufficiently reward speed, and*
> *because a pandemic has the potential to overwhelm or*
> *compromise essential government functions, including*
> *defense and homeland security, the Government must take*
> *action to promote faster and more scalable manufacturing*
> *platforms.*
> *... This order directs actions to ... support the promotion of*
> *increased influenza vaccine immunization across*
> *recommended populations.*

... innovative, faster, and more scalable technologies, including cell-based and recombinant vaccine manufacturing...

... evaluate incentives for the development and production of vaccines by private manufacturers and public-private partnerships, including, in emergency situations, the transfer of technology to public-private partnerships... "

Complaints about low inoculation rates, replacing the egg model, speed as the first priority over safety, cell-based inoculation technology and disruptive public-private cooperation. It's simply uncanny. Donald Trump must have had as serious a passion on the subject as Fauci himself to have written this! Whether the man who now gets booed for selling out to pharma interests knew what he was signing here or not, Trump's Warp-Speed-pre-planning executive order and its timing undoubtedly implicates him in the conspiracy.[59] Perhaps he was convinced to sign it and his having done so was ultimately held over him as leverage by those he should have opposed; on the other hand, maybe he was fully aware of what was to come and had his role to play in it. Either way, the shameless hawking of the inoculations by, "Grandpa Moderna," makes a lot more sense in this context.

The truth of the Executive Order, Warp Speed, and the inoculations themselves is that the military's fingerprints seemed to be everywhere, as we saw with the heavy investment of DARPA in mRNA technology. DARPA itself is the research & development wing of the US Department of Defense (DOD). As covered by Nicholas Florko of *STAT News* in September 2020, the DOD also just happened to have a majority role in, "Trump's," $10 billion Operation Warp Speed.[60] In fact, according to Florko, roughly 60 of the 90 leaders on the Warp Speed organizational chart were military officials, including at least four generals. The remainder were from DHHS, which you will recall is the organization responsible for authorizing inoculation-injury liability protection. It is worth wondering why there were twice as many military officials as civilian scientists involved in such a group.

And this provides additional context to the true nature of the NIH-Moderna relationship. This company (Moderna) the federal government hid behind to paint a picture of private, spur-of-the-moment innovation had never brought a product to market previously, due to toxicity issues. Still, in a demonstration of Fauci's willingness to be transparent in his corruption, he publicly talked up Moderna anyway, as early as January of 2020.[61] Once the product was released, Fauci and the government he serves as a salesman for then went on to illegally coerce it without informed consent via economic and psychological control. They did this despite its emergency use status and extraordinary risks, and as they did it they shielded the front companies (aka: themselves) from liability to any damages.

There are no claims or theories in the above. It is all documented history. Anthony Fauci is a criminal in his own words, as are those tangential to him who support his directives. At the same time, Fauci is not the devil himself—he is but a slave to his appetites. There are other players in this game who know this about Fauci, so he serves as an ideal, controllable figurehead for them. We will cover the other legs of this spider in a future chapter. For now though, we have demonstrated the means, motive, and opportunity associated with the most observable objective and overall scheme of the Covid crimes against humanity: inoculations. In the following chapters, we will discuss the outcomes and impacts of that objective.

Endnotes

1   "Conspire Definition & Meaning". 2022. *Merriam-Webster*. Accessed March 11. https://www.merriam-webster.com/dictionary/conspire.

2   "Fauci, HHS Officials Discuss Using New Virus From China To Enforce Universal Vaccines In Footage From Oct. 2019". 2021. *Oann.Com*. https://www.oann.com/fauci-hhs-officials-discuss-using-new-virus-from-china-to-enforce-universal-vaccines-in-footage-from-oct-2019/.

3   Specter, Michael. 2020. "Trump Is Right: Andrew Cuomo Should Accept F.D.A. Approval Of A Coronavirus Vaccine". *The New Yorker*. https://www.newyorker.com/news/daily-comment/trump-is-right-andrew-cuomo-should-accept-fda-approval-of-a-coronavirus-vaccine.

4   Glasser, Susan B. 2021. "The Trump Presidency Is Still An Active Crime Scene". *The New Yorker*. https://www.newyorker.com/news/letter-from-bidens-washington/the-trump-presidency-is-still-an-active-crime-scene.

5   "Vaccine Developer Nikolai Petrovsky Says He Is Not Comfortable". 2021. *Rumble*. https://www.rumble.com/vouqa1-vaccine-developer-nikolai-petrovsky-says-he-is-not-comfortable.html.

6   Morens, David M., Jeffery K. Taubenberger, and Anthony S. Fauci. 2022. "Universal Coronavirus Vaccines — An Urgent Need". *New England Journal Of Medicine* 386 (4): 297-299. doi:10.1056/nejmp2118468.

7   Lajeunesse, Sara. 2022. "Can A Flu And COVID Shot Combo Increase Vaccination? - Futurity". *Futurity*. https://www.futurity.org/covid-flu-vaccine-combination-2683352-2/.

8   Crane, Emily. 2022. "Fauci's Home Office Features Photos Of Self, Bobblehead". *Nypost.Com*. https://nypost.com/2022/01/20/faucis-home-office-features-photos-of-self-bobblehead/.

9   The Rockefeller Foundation. 2021. "Dr. Rick Bright Joins The Rockefeller Foundation To Lead Pandemic Prevention Institute Development". https://www.rockefellerfoundation.org/news/dr-rick-bright-joins-the-rockefeller-foundation-to-lead-pandemic-prevention-institute-development/.

10   The Centers for Disease Control and Prevention. 2020. "Interim Operational Considerations For Implementing The Shielding Approach To Prevent COVID-19 Infections In Humanitarian Settings". CDC.

11   "About Event 201, A High-Level Pandemic Exercise On October 18, 2019". 2019. *Event 201*. https://www.centerforhealthsecurity.org/event201/about.

12   "Event 201: Coronavirus Pandemic Simulation 2019". 2021. *Vimeo*. https://www.vimeo.com/641345320.

13   Belvedere, Matthew J. 2019. "Bill Gates: My 'Best Investment' Turned $10 Billion Into $200 Billion Worth Of Economic Benefit". *CNBC*. https://www.cnbc.com/2019/01/23/bill-gates-turns-10-billion-into-200-billion-worth-of-economic-benefit.html.

14   Corbett, James. 2020. "Bill Gates' Decade Of Vaccines". *Howestreet*. https://www.howestreet.com/2020/05/bill-gates-decade-of-vaccines/.

15   "The Global Vaccine Action Plan And The Decade Of Vaccines Review And Lessons Learned". 2019. *Who.Int*. https://www.who.int/immunization/sage/meetings/2019/october/1_GVAP_review_YB.PDF.

16   Bill & Melinda Gates Foundation. 2010. "Global Health Leaders Launch Decade Of Vaccines Collaboration | Bill & Melinda Gates Foundation". https://www.gatesfoundation.org/Ideas/Media-Center/Press-Releases/2010/12/Global-Health-Leaders-Launch-Decade-of-Vaccines-Collaboration.

17   Stieg, Cory. 2021. "Bill Gates And Dr. Fauci Talk Regularly — Here's What They'Re Discussing Now". *CNBC*. https://www.cnbc.com/2021/02/11/bill-gates-and-dr-anthony-fauci-talk-regularly-about-covid-pandemic.html.

18   "More Polio Cases Now Caused By Vaccine Than By Wild Virus". 2019. *ABC News*. https://abcnews.go.com/Health/wireStory/polio-cases-now-caused-vaccine-wild-virus-67287290.

19   Corbett, James. 2020. "Bill Gates' Decade Of Vaccines". *Howestreet*. https://www.howestreet.com/2020/05/bill-gates-decade-of-vaccines/.

20   McNeil Jr., Donald G. 2008. "Gates Foundation's Influence Criticized". *The New York Times*. https://archive.md/vVJFo.

21   MacLeod, Alan. 2021. "Revealed: Documents Show Bill Gates Has Given $319 Million To Media Outlets". *Mintpress News*. https://www.mintpressnews.com/documents-show-bill-gates-has-given-319-million-to-media-outlets/278943/.

22   Hains, Tim. 2020. "Bill Gates: "Things Won't Get Back To Normal Until We Have Gotten A Vaccine Out To The Entire World"". *Realclearpolitics*. https://www.realclearpolitics.com/video/2020/04/05/bill_gates_things_wont_get_back_to_normal_until_we_have_got_a_vaccine.html.

23   Imperial College London. 2018. "$14.5M Gates Foundation Grant To Help Improve Global Healthcare". https://www.imperial.ac.uk/news/189502/145m-gates-foundation-grant-help-improve/.

24   Weingartl, Hana, Markus Czub, Stefanie Czub, James Neufeld, Peter Marszal, Jason Gren, and Greg Smith et al. 2004. "Immunization With Modified Vaccinia Virus Ankara-Based Recombinant Vaccine Against Severe Acute Respiratory Syndrome Is Associated With Enhanced Hepatitis In Ferrets". *Journal Of Virology* 78 (22): 12672-12676. doi:10.1128/jvi.78.22.12672-12676.2004.

25   Tseng, Chien-Te, Elena Sbrana, Naoko Iwata-Yoshikawa, Patrick C. Newman, Tania Garron, Robert L. Atmar, Clarence J. Peters, and Robert B. Couch. 2012. "Immunization With SARS Coronavirus Vaccines Leads To Pulmonary Immunopathology On Challenge With The SARS Virus". *Plos ONE* 7 (4): e35421. doi:10.1371/journal.pone.0035421.

26   The Centers for Disease Control and Prevention. n.d. "How Mrna COVID-19 Vaccines Work."

27   Dolgin, Elie. 2021. "The Tangled History Of Mrna Vaccines". *Nature.Com*. https://www.nature.com/articles/d41586-021-02483-w.

28   Bingham, Jack. 2021. "Bayer Executive: Mrna Shots Are 'Gene Therapy' Marketed As 'Vaccines' To Gain Public Trust - Lifesite". *Lifesite*. https://www.lifesitenews.com/news/bayer-executive-mrna-shots-are-gene-therapy-marketed-as-vaccines-to-gain-public-trust/.

29   "This Video Isn't Available Anymore". 2022. *Youtube.Com*. Accessed March 11. https://www.youtube.com/watch?v=MqK58Bb2GU.

30   "World Health Summit". 2022. *Worldhealthsummit.Org*. https://www.worldhealthsummit.org/.

31   Rearden, Kyle. 2011. "Problem-Reaction-Solution (The Hegelian Dialectic)". *The Last Bastille*. https://thelastbastille.wordpress.com/2011/12/31/problem-reaction-solution-hegelian-dialectic/.

32   Dolgin, Elie. 2021. "The Tangled History Of Mrna Vaccines". *Nature.Com*. https://www.nature.com/articles/d41586-021-02483-w.

33   "Definition Of VACCINE". 2019. *Merriam-Webster*. https://web.archive.org/web/20190123105554/https:/www.merriam-webster.com/dictionary/vaccine.

34   "Vaccine Definition & Meaning". 2022. *Merriam-Webster*. https://www.merriam-webster.com/dictionary/vaccine.

35   "Fact Check-Mrna Vaccines Are Distinct From Gene Therapy, Which Alters Recipient's Genes". 2021. *Reuters*. https://www.reuters.com/article/factcheck-covid-mrna-gene-idUSL1N2PH16N.

36   Aldén, Markus, Francisko Olofsson Falla, Daowei Yang, Mohammad Barghouth, Cheng Luan, Magnus Rasmussen, and Yang De Marinis. 2022. "Intracellular Reverse Transcription Of Pfizer Biontech COVID-19 Mrna Vaccine Bnt162b2 In Vitro In Human Liver Cell Line". *Current Issues In Molecular Biology* 44 (3): 1115-1126. doi:10.3390/cimb44030073.

37   Australian Department of Health Therapeutic Goods Administration. 2021. "Nonclinical Evaluation Report Bnt162b2 [Mrna] COVID-19 Vaccine (COMIRNATY™)". Pfizer Australia Pty Ltd.

38   "Pfizer Study: "Vaxx Spike Protein Can Enter Cell Nucleus & Possibly Alter Genes"". 2022. Rumble. https://rumble.com/vw5psb-pfizer-study-vaxx-spike-protein-can-enter-cell-nucleus.html.

39   Herman, Bob. 2020. "The NIH Claims Joint Ownership Of Moderna's Coronavirus Vaccine". *Axios*. https://www.axios.com/moderna-nih-coronavirus-vaccine-ownership-agreements-22051c42-2dee-4b19-938d-099afd71f6a0.html.

40   Shaw, Adam. 2021. "Treasury Official Claims Inflation Part Of 'Economy In Transition,' Only Way Out Is 100% Global Vaccination". *FOX Business*. https://www.foxbusiness.com/politics/treasury-official-inflation-part-economy-transition-global-vaccination.

41   Chumley, Cheryl K. 2021. "Biden Is Pathetic, And Americans' 'Patience Is Wearing Thin'". *The Washington Times*. https://www.washingtontimes.com/news/2021/sep/13/joe-biden-pathetic-and-americans-patience-wearing-/.

42   National Institute of Allergy and Infectious Disease (NIAID). 2019. "Confidential Disclosure Agreement: Material Transfer Agreement". NIH. https://www.documentcloud.org/documents/6935295-NIH-Moderna-Confidential-Agreements.html#document/p105/a568569.

43   Schumaker, Erin. 2020. "Mysterious Pneumonia Outbreak Sickens Dozens In China". *ABC News*. https://abcnews.go.com/Health/mystery-pneumonia-outbreak-sickens-dozens-china/story?id=68094861.

44   World Health Organization. 2020. "Listings Of WHO's Response To COVID-19". https://www.who.int/news/item/29-06-2020-covidtimeline.

45   National Institute of Allergy and Infectious Disease (NIAID). 2019. "Confidential Disclosure Agreement: Material Transfer Agreement".

NIH. https://www.documentcloud.org/documents/6935295-NIH-Moderna-Confidential-Agreements.html#document/p105/a568569.

46   Corbett, Kizzmekia S., Darin Edwards, Sarah R. Leist, Olubukola M. Abiona, Seyhan Boyoglu-Barnum, Rebecca A. Gillespie, and Sunny Himansu et al. 2020. "SARS-Cov-2 Mrna Vaccine Development Enabled By Prototype Pathogen Preparedness". doi:10.1101/2020.06.11.145920.

47   Tanne, Janice Hopkins. 2005. "Royalty Payments To Staff Researchers Cause New NIH Troubles". *BMJ* 330 (7484): 162.2. doi:10.1136/bmj.330.7484.162-a.

48   "National Institutes Of Health Statement To Axios". 2022. *Documentcloud.Org.* Accessed March 11. https://www.documentcloud.org/documents/6956323-NIH-Statement-to-Axios.html.

49   O'Rourke, Ciara. 2021. "Politifact - Old Fauci Comments About Vaccine Safety Are Being Taken Out Of Context". *@Politifact.* https://api.politifact.com/factchecks/2021/dec/17/viral-image/old-fauci-comments-about-vaccine-safety-are-being-/.

50   Garde, Damian. 2016. "Ego, Ambition, And Turmoil: Inside One Of Biotech's Most Secretive Startups". *STAT.* https://www.statnews.com/2016/09/13/moderna-therapeutics-biotech-mrna/.

51   Garde, Damian. 2017. "Lavishly Funded Moderna Hits Safety Problems In Bold Bid To Revolutionize Medicine". *STAT.* https://www.statnews.com/2017/01/10/moderna-trouble-mrna/.

52   Sardi, Bill. 2021. "Jab Remorse - Lewrockwell". *Lewrockwell.* https://www.lewrockwell.com/2021/07/bill-sardi/jab-remorse/.

53   Greene, Jenna. 2021. "Wait What? FDA Wants 55 Years To Process FOIA Request Over Vaccine Data". *Reuters.* https://www.reuters.com/legal/government/wait-what-fda-wants-55-years-process-foia-request-over-vaccine-data-2021-11-18/https://www.reuters.com/legal/government/wait-what-fda-wants-55-years-process-foia-request-over-vaccine-data-2021-11-18/.

54   Henderson, Emily. 2021. "SARS-Cov-2's Distinctive "Spike" Protein Plays A Key Role In The Disease Itself, Shows Study". *News-Medical.Net.* https://www.news-medical.net/news/20210503/SARS-CoV-2e28099s-distinctive-spike-protein-plays-a-key-role-in-the-disease-itself-shows-study.aspx.

55   Lei, Yuyang, Jiao Zhang, Cara R. Schiavon, Ming He, Lili Chen, Hui Shen, and Yichi Zhang et al. 2021. "SARS-Cov-2 Spike Protein Impairs Endothelial Function Via Downregulation Of ACE 2". *Circulation Research* 128 (9): 1323-1326. doi:10.1161/circresaha.121.318902.

56   U.S. Federal Register. 2020. "Declaration Under The Public Readiness And Emergency Preparedness Act For Medical Countermeasures Against COVID-19". Health and Human Services Department.

57   The U.S. Food and Drug Administration. 2021. "Emergency Use Authorization For Vaccines To Prevent COVID-19". FDA.

58   *Executive Order 13887: Modernizing Influenza Vaccines In The United States To Promote National Security And Public Health.* 2019. Executive Office of the President.

59   Smith, Allan. 2021. "Trump Booed At Alabama Rally After Telling Supporters To Get Vaccinated". *NBC News.* https://www.nbcnews.com/politics/donald-trump/trump-booed-alabama-rally-after-telling-supporters-get-vaccinated-n1277404.

60   Florko, Nicholas. 2020. "New Document Reveals Scope And Structure Of Operation Warp Speed And Underscores Vast Military Involvement". *STAT.* https://www.statnews.com/2020/09/28/operation-warp-speed-vast-military-involvement/.

61   Nathan-Kazis, Josh. 2020. "'No Glitches' In Early Effort For Coronavirus Vaccine, NIH Says. Moderna Stock Is Flying.". *Barrons.Com.* https://www.barrons.com/articles/moderna-gilead-stock-coronavirus-vaccine-51581109485.

Chapter 11

Inoculations Pt. 2: The Emperor Has No Immunity

"When we decide whether something—whether the risk is worth it, we do a risk versus benefit analysis. And in the case of these vaccines you have to look at three separate components to do that. One is medical necessity, meaning, 'is it medically necessary?'
... Number two is efficacy—you have to make sure the stuff actually works—and number three is safety. And if we analyze each separate component, the answer to your question [whether to take Covid inoculations] will be very obvious."
—Dr. Vladimir Zelenko, November 2021[1]

In the previous chapter, we established that there existed a premeditated plot to sell the world on experimental mRNA gene therapy inoculations without having to provide proof of their safety or efficacy. The tactics used to accomplish this goal included psychological-warfare-induced fear, censorship, and economic coercion. These things constitute evil, criminal behavior, and they would whether the mRNA gene therapies proved to be deadly or if no one who took those therapies ever got sick again. Still, as stated by Dr. Zelenko, there are three questions we must answer to truly address the severity of these crimes, namely:

1. Is there medical necessity?
2. Does the product work?
3. Is the product safe?

In our chapters on treatments and testing, we established that the answer to number 1 is a resounding, "no." The alleged disease, "Covid," is, at best, dramatically over-diagnosed by at least 97%, thanks to tests that don't test for the alleged virus itself; it has a CDC-acknowledged case fatality rate of greater than 99.5% for anyone beneath the average age of death in America, based on death counts that are somewhere between incredibly and completely exaggerated;[2] and finally, it also has a variety of highly safe, highly effective, proven treatment options, which one can readily have access to as long as one has a doctor not beholden to the corrupted will of public health. At worst, "Covid," is a misdiagnosis entirely.

Either way, there is no medical necessity for these inoculations. Still, if they could be proven effective and safe, it wouldn't hurt for people who want them to get them. So in this chapter we will review the effectiveness—and in later chapters, the safety—of the mRNA gene therapy inoculations which were wrongly coerced on the world.

Ever-Moving Goal Posts, Also Known as Outright Lies

"Excited to share that updated analysis from our Phase 3 study with BioNTech also showed that our COVID-19 vaccine was 100% effective in preventing #COVID19 cases in South Africa. 100%!"
—Pfizer CEO Albert Bourla, April 1, 2021[3]

"And we know that two doses of the vaccine offer very limited protection, if any."
—Albert Bourla, January 2022[4]

"If you are fully vaccinated, you no longer need to wear a mask ... the rule is very simple: get vaccinated or wear a mask until you do. It's vaxx-ed or masked."
—Joe Biden, May 13, 2021 (inoculation uptake ~47%)[5,6]

"You're okay, you're not gonna get Covid if you have these vaccinations ... If you're vaccinated, you're not gonna be hospitalized, you're not gonna be in an ICU unit, and you're not gonna die."
—Joe Biden, July 22, 2021 (uptake ~57%)[7,8]

"That [inoculated not needing masks] *was true at the time."*
—Joe Biden, July 29, 2021 (uptake ~58%)[9,10]

"These vaccines are highly, highly effective ... they're really, really good against variants ... when people get vaccinated they can feel safe that they are not gonna get infected."
—Anthony Fauci, May 2021[11]

"The level of virus in the nasal pharynx of a person whose vaccinated and infected, is the same level of the level of virus in the nasal pharynx of an unvaccinated person."
                                                    —Anthony Fauci, July 2021[12]

"And if you look at Israel, which has always been a month to a month and a half ahead of us, they are seeing a waning of immunity not only against infection, but against hospitalizations and to some extent death."
                                          —Anthony Fauci, November 2021[13]

"One thing that vaccinated people can feel comfortable with, for example — let's take the holiday setting, you're with your family, you have grandparents and parents and children, when you get vaccinated and you have a vaccinated group and you are in an indoor setting, you can enjoy, as we have traditionally over the years, dinners and gatherings within the home with people who are vaccinated.
That's the reason why people should, if they invite people over their home, essentially ask and maybe require that people show evidence that they are vaccinated."
                                          —Anthony Fauci, December 2021[14]

"Vaccinated people do not carry the virus, don't get sick."
    —Rochelle Walensky, March 30, 2021 (uptake ~29%)[15,16]

"Anyone who is fully vaccinated can participate in indoor and outdoor activities, large or small, without wearing a mask or physical distancing."
    —Rochelle Walensky, May 14, 2021 (uptake ~47%)[17,18]

"Our vaccines are working exceptionally well. They continue to work well for delta with regard to severe illness and death— they prevent it. But what they can't do anymore is prevent transmission."
    —Rochelle Walensky, August 6, 2021 (uptake ~59%)[19,20]

"Reports from our international colleagues, including Israel, suggest increased risk of severe disease amongst those vaccinated early."
    —Rochelle Walensky, August 18, 2021 (uptake ~61%)[21,22]

"Everyone who takes the vaccine is not just protecting themselves, but reducing their transmission to other people and allowing society to get back to normal."

—Bill Gates[23]

"A key goal is to stop the transmission—to get the immunity levels up so you get almost no—almost no infection going on whatsoever."

—Bill Gates[24]

"You know, we didn't have vaccines that block transmission. We got vaccines that help you with your health, but they only slightly reduce the transmissions. We need a new—a new way of doing the vaccine."

—Bill Gates[25]

What the above quotes reveal is that the purveyors of, "authoritative information," *at best* did not know if the inoculations would work or not. At worst, they did know, which is the more likely scenario based on their documented habits of deception and abuse, as well as the history of these inoculations. But even if they hadn't known, they clearly pretended as if they did in order to get people to take the shots. And they did so at a time when these mRNA inoculations were not only strictly emergency use authorized—which they should have never been, given there *were* proven alternatives—but also at a time when the fact that they were entirely experimental was being actively suppressed in every sphere from the media to the medical industry itself.

The perfect place to confirm this is another hubris-ridden, "fact-check," this time by the *Associated Press (AP)*. Ever-focused on, "debunking," valid concerns, the *AP*, "fact-check," had to do with a *true* claim that the package insert for the Johnson & Johnson inoculation was left blank.[26] The, "missing context," the *AP* provides for this is that these package inserts (which for drugs are usually filled with disclaimers) are *intentionally* left blank so that consumers refer to the most up-to-date information on the FDA's website itself. While it is all well and good to refer to up-to-date information on something where the information is constantly changing, this is a blatant admission that the drug is experimental with consequences that are unknown and continuously evolving with new information.

At the same time, the above statements do not urge caution or present anywhere near an adequate disclaimer of the massive risk involved. Instead, they are declarative and certain, which makes them lies, because there could be no certain safety or efficacy related to any of the inoculations. Getting as close as possible to certainty typically requires a 15-year process for vaccines, as mentioned previously by Professor Nikolai Petrovsky. We've already established these people were actively seeking to skip that process though, so that they would be lying about the situation is hardly surprising.

As for the corporate media, they carried the water of the public health liars with slavish obedience. One ridiculous example is *Fortune*'s article titled, "It's official: Vaccinated people don't transmit COVID-19."[27] This article was appropriately published on April Fool's Day of 2021, less than three months into mass inoculating people with an unproven technology and only 17% of the population, "fully vaccinated." As is tradition on April Fool's Day, *Fortune* provided an update the next day which clarified there were many scientists who disagreed with the CDC's assessment on the protection of the, "vaccinated." It really is a shame they didn't simply update it with the quip, "April Fools!"

Another point to be made based on the subsequent admissions of the aforementioned authorities is that these inoculations *do not* prevent transmission or provide immunization, which serves as more support for the assertion they are not vaccines. And even if they did reduce hospitalization and death—a notion we will completely dismantle shortly—this would much more clearly satisfy the definition of a *therapy*, since there is no vaccine ever that wasn't intended to immunize against infection. For example, you don't get a chicken pox vaccine to, "avoid hospitalization and death," but rather to not get chicken pox.

What this lack of preventing transmission also means is that there's no basis whatsoever for even attempting to justify a mass inoculation campaign. While we will dissect the concept of, "herd immunity," at the end of this book, even if that premise is accepted there is no possible way to suggest that the inoculated, "herd," can be immune, while the inoculated individual both *isn't* immune and *is* able to transmit the disease. The only justification at all to take the shot then is theoretically to protect oneself from hospitalization or death, which does not impact anyone else. If your body is being instructed

253

unnaturally to produce spike proteins, for example, and that is meant to keep you out of the hospital somehow, mine neither benefits from that process, nor impairs it. It doesn't make any sense why this wouldn't be the case for traditional vaccines either. For example, if your body has the attenuated virus in it meant to train your immune system to identify and handle the virus, it makes no sense that mine not having it would impair your body's ability to recognize the virus in the future when it comes into contact with it. But again, that's a bigger topic for later.

For now, the lies continue. And Rochelle Walensky is an offender who at times seems to rival Fauci himself. Take for example her July 16, 2021 press briefing, where she claimed 97% of people entering hospitals for, "Covid," were unvaccinated, as well as the following[28]:

> *"This is becoming a pandemic of the unvaccinated. We are seeing outbreaks of cases in parts of the country that have low vaccination coverage because unvaccinated people are at risk. ... The good news is that if you're fully vaccinated, you are protected against severe COVID hospitalization and death and are even protected against the known variants, including the delta variant."*

As we already know from her previous quotes at later dates, Walensky would eventually acknowledge the blatant lie that is the entire second paragraph. However, she would also reveal the following about the data used to support the 97% claim itself during an August 5, 2021 briefing[29]:

> *"... data were from analyses in several states from January through June and didn't reflect the data that we have now from the delta variant."*

To understand just how dishonest this is, one need only observe that from January 2021 to June 2021 cases sloped progressively down, while inoculation uptake moved progressively upward. We've already discussed the reason cases were ticking down at that time was the WHO's Inauguration Day recommendation to reduce the recommended PCR cycle threshold rates. This is the only thing which can be attributed to the sudden January 2021 drop of an approximately 225K 7-day case average, to a 75K 7-day case average by mid-February.[30]

The propagandist media was quick to attribute this drop to the inoculations, while the alternative media claimed it was due to, "herd immunity," being attained, but neither of those explanations make sense. First of all, the percentage of the population with two doses at the beginning of February was less than 2%, while the percentage with one dose was below 8%. So even if the inoculations were *perfectly* effective, they still could not have possibly caused a 67% drop in cases at this time. The, "herd immunity," theory is equally unlikely in my opinion as well though, not only because we have an explanation that makes more sense, but also because I find it hard to believe the effect of herd immunity could be so precipitous.

Either way though, the dishonesty of the 97%, "unvaccinated," hospitalization number can be demonstrated using simple math. For example, consider that, per *USAFacts*, on January 15, 2021 0.5% of the US population was fully vaccinated, with 99.5%, "unvaccinated." Obviously the overwhelming number of people hospitalized are going to be, "unvaccinated," in such a month, when the overwhelming number of people in general are, "unvaccinated." Since that month also had by-far the highest case rates relative to the rest of the time period (67% greater than February on average and 96% greater than June), it is also going to significantly overweight the impact of this least-descriptive month. So to include the month of January and February in a demonstration of the effectiveness of the inoculations is downright fraudulent.

Of course, Walensky knows this very well. In fact, it might even be in her best interest to admit she was completely incompetent, because if not for that it could only be assumed she was purposefully dishonest. And it seems she opted for the former, because by 2022 when the inoculation campaign had already clearly failed, she made the following astonishing admission[31]:

> *"Where could we have improved? Um ... well ... I think ... **I can tell you where I was when the CNN feed came that it was 95% effective—the vaccine** (my emphasis). So many of us wanted it to be helpful. So many of us wanted to say, 'okay, this is our ticket out. Right? Now we're done. Um, so I think we had, perhaps, **too little caution and too much optimism**

(my emphasis) *for some good things that came our way, I really do. I think all of us wanted this to be done.*

Nobody said, 'waning,' when, you know—'this vaccine's gonna work'—'oh, maybe it'll wear off' [laughing]—nobody said it, 'well what if the next variant doesn't—it doesn't—it's not as potent against the next variant.

And then maybe the other thing I'll say is this area of, 'gray.' Um I have frequently said, you know, we're gonna lead with the science, science is gonna be the foundation of everything we do—that is entirely true. I think the public heard that as science is foolproof—science is black and white—science is immediate and we get the answer and we make the decision based on the answer—and the truth is, science is gray, and science is not always immediate, and sometimes it takes months and years to find out the answer. But you have to make decisions in a pandemic before you have that answer."

You read that right: the director of the CDC admitted to reacting to and acting on information from CNN, a network so rife with degenerates and so void of truth that to say you'd get more accurate information about geopolitics from a circus would not even be slightly hyperbolic.[32,33,34,35] In response to this CNN claim, which was presented in the first months of 2021 before it could have possibly been certain, Walensky claims to have had, "too little caution and too much optimism," opting to move ahead with a mass, experimental inoculation campaign in its name. She then justifies the failure of this campaign in the most gaslighting of ways possible—namely, by claiming science is gray and uncertain.

First of all, Walensky admitted she doesn't remotely, "lead with science," when she makes the point about running with a headline by the propagandist clowns at CNN. But second, recall Walensky's early 2021 claim that, "Vaccinated people do not carry the virus, don't get sick." Does that statement appear to be in any way tempered by an understanding that science is gray and uncertain? Do *any* of the unprecedented actions and tyrannies of the CDC appear to have been tempered? What about her abuse of the term, "misinformation," as it related to potential side effects she could not have possibly known would or wouldn't occur?[36] She claims, "no one said 'waning,'" so one has to assume they also didn't say, "side effects." Those side effects most definitely have occurred (as we will cover) and no matter how stupid Walensky plays or how she tries to blame CNN, she is directly responsible for the damage she did do because of her, "lack of caution."

So it doesn't matter whether it's utter incompetence or intentional fraud, but this question seems to define every action made by the current head of the CDC. Another example is a CDC/DHHS study on infections and hospitalizations in Los Angeles County, California, from May-July 2021.[37] What the study claimed to show was the following:

- Of 43,127, "Covid," infections:
  - ○ 25.3% in, "fully vaccinated," persons
  - ○ 3.3% in, "partially vaccinated," persons
  - ○ 71.4% in, "unvaccinated," persons
- Of the same 43,127, "Covid," infections:
  - ○ 3.2% of, "fully vaccinated," persons were hospitalized, 0.5% admitted to ICU, and 0.2% required mechanical ventilation
  - ○ 6.2% of, "partially vaccinated," persons were hospitalized and 1.0% admitted to ICU, and 0.3% required mechanical ventilation
  - ○ 7.6% of, "unvaccinated," persons were hospitalized and 1.5% admitted to ICU, and 0.5% required mechanical ventilation

However, there was a major issue with drawing the conclusion that, "vaccinated," people were better protected, which was conveniently hidden several pages down in the asterisks of an exhibit. The asterisk revealed that the following was the definition used for an, "unvaccinated," person:

> *"<14 days receipt of the first dose of a 2 dose series or 1 dose of the single-dose vaccine or if no vaccination registry data were available."*

The above definition of, "unvaccinated," is among the most egregiously dishonest scientific practices I've seen throughout this Covid era, and that's *really* saying something considering all we've discussed to this point. Including people who *did* receive the, "vaccine," amongst the, "unvaccinated," is not only deceitful on the face of it, but based on the CDC's own Vaccine Adverse Event Reporting System (VAERS), the majority of serious reported adverse events potentially leading to death occur within the first 14 days of inoculation.[38] Such serious events which could put someone in a hospital—a hospital where, "Covid," PCR testing is now standard practice for hospital doctors, many of whom are admittedly willing to blame anything but the, "vaccine," for the reactions which occur immediately following its administration, as reported to *Project Veritas* by whistleblower Jodi O'Malley, among others.[39]

We will return to VAERS soon, but this distortion reveals a tremendous flaw with the term, "unvaccinated," which must be brought into question anytime the CDC has used or will use the word in the future. Even the assumption that a person is truly, "unvaccinated," if no data is available seems dubious. No data in what system? Is every single, "vaccinated," person in that system? If so, how and where is it reported? Also, why is the data provided in this study not broken out between people with, "<14 days since," and people who are simply not in the system? Again, these are questions which, if you were going to make that your definition, should be answered immediately before any results are demonstrated. But they aren't, and the motivation for that seems to be consistent with the demonstrated intent of these corrupt organizations.

A Pandemic of the "Vaccinated"

Following these initial data manipulation lies by US officials, they unsurprisingly continued moving and/or erasing the goal posts until there was nothing left but empty rhetoric. And this rhetoric continued even as the experience of the highest uptake countries proved to be the exact opposite of what they were saying when they claimed there was a, "pandemic of the unvaccinated."

One key example is Israel, one of the earliest and strictest nations in the world as far as requiring inoculation. The media, like their masters, was celebrating Israel's success in the spring of 2021— a mere three months after the inoculation campaign had begun and at the end of cold/flu season. The *Washington Post*, for example, published on April 21, 2021 that, "With most adults now vaccinated, Israelis are busting loose," and that, "Israel is partying like it's 2019."[40] Quite the giddy headline for an organization that had nothing

258

so kind to say at the same time in March 2021 about US states such as Texas and Florida doing the same thing despite much lower inoculation rates.[41] The only difference between these states and Israel was the organization's agenda wasn't met in those places, since both saw the same massive drop in, "cases," at the end of cold/flu season.

The story of this integrity-less bias is the story of the mainstream media itself, and it continued even when Israel's situation started to rapidly deteriorate to a point worse than any it experienced prior. The refusal to acknowledge reality over agenda can be summarized no better than this astonishing sub-headline from *Deseret* in late-July 2021[42]:

> *"The first country to reach vaccine herd immunity has seen a recent rise in cases among vaccinated people."*

How can a country with herd immunity see a rise in—oh, nevermind. There's just no point in trying to understand these types of statements with logic or science anymore because they're not written with those things in mind. What is important to recognize here though is that by late-August, early-September 2021 Israel would see its largest, "case," spike of the entire Covid era.[43] The failure of the inoculations was so impossible to ignore too that according to the *Times of Israel*, Portugal and Sweden, among others, banned Israelis from entry, regardless of, "vaccination," status.[44] And don't get me wrong—I don't agree with the concept of banning travel in the name of this scheme. However, these countries were right to not discriminate against the, "unvaccinated," alone, when considering Israeli outcomes from July 4, 2021 to July 31, 2021, which have been summarized based the Israeli government's databases as follows[45]:

Age Group	Cases Fully Vaccinated	Cases Unvaccinated	Percent of Cases Fully Vaccinated	Percentage of Population Fully Vaccinated
20-29	2,689	795	77.2%	71.9%
30-39	3,176	881	78.3%	77.4%
40-49	3,303	635	83.9%	80.9%
50-59	2,200	359	86.0%	84.4%
60-69	2,200	187	92.2%	86.9%
70-79	1,384	100	93.3%	92.8%
80-89	540	61	89.9%	91.2%
90+	142	20	87.7%	89.7%

Total	Total	Total	Average	Average
20-90+	15,634	3,038	86.0%	84.4%

As can be seen on the final two columns, all age bands from age 20-79 saw a greater percentage of cases in, "fully vaccinated," people than the percentage of people in those bands in the population which were, "fully vaccinated," demonstrating an overrepresentation. In fact, the *overall* percentage of, "fully vaccinated," cases during this time period was greater than the percentage of, "fully vaccinated," people in the population as well.

For this to occur just over six months into the mass inoculation campaign too, means it's impossible to spin this as anything other than a failure of the program and of the mRNA gene therapy itself. Any efforts to claim it was, "effective during the first six months," are barren of any logical support, as we've discussed, when considering the reduced case rates almost everywhere in the world during those time periods. Also, we've already mentioned the CDC's point that people get 2-3 colds (coronavirus infections) per year. This means one can expect an infection every 4-6 months in general. So to insinuate the inoculations, "protect," a person for the same period of time is absurd and implies the shots are pointless. The excuse of, "variants," for the eventual case spike in Israel is equally pitiful, but we will get into that shortly.

Still, though they must face crimes against humanity tribunals for the economic and social coercion of this failure, Israel's leadership can at least take solace in the fact that it was not alone. A 2021 study by Subramanian et al. in the *European Journal of Epidemiology* which tracked September 2021 7-day outcomes across 68 countries and 2,947 counties in the United States found[46]:

> "At the country-level, there appears to be no discernable relationship between percentage of fully vaccinated and new COVID-19 cases. In fact, the trend line suggests a marginally positive association such that countries with higher percentage of population fully vaccinated have higher COVID-19 cases per 1 million people. Notably, Israel with over 60% of their population fully vaccinated had the highest COVID-19 cases per 1 million people in the last 7 days.

... Across the US counties too, the median new COVID-19 cases per 100,000 people in the last 7 days is largely similar across the categories of percent population fully vaccinated.
... The sole reliance on vaccination as a primary strategy to mitigate COVID-19 and its adverse consequences needs to be re-examined."

And this study's findings on the worse-than-uselessness infection/transmission prevention (the whole point of vaccines) has also been confirmed by at least 28 others provided in an ongoing list (which apparently started at 16) by the Brownstone Institute.[47] Here are a few notables:

1. Given that someone was infected, a 2021 Acharya et al. study in *medRxiv* found using PCR, "no significant difference in viral load between vaccinated and unvaccinated, asymptomatic and symptomatic groups."[48] And as a side note, if this asymptomatic/symptomatic point doesn't also serve as an indictment of the disconnect between the, "load," of the alleged virus and the extent to which someone actually gets sick, I don't know what does. In fact, it also reveals the misguidance of PCR in general.

2. A 2021 study by Riemersma et al. in *medRxiv* found[49]: *"no difference in viral loads when comparing unvaccinated individuals to those who have vaccine, 'breakthrough,' infections. Furthermore, individuals with vaccine breakthrough infections frequently test positive with viral loads consistent with the ability to shed infectious viruses."*

3. A 2021 study by Chemaitelly et al. in *medRxiv* found the level of, "protection," from infection of the Pfizer inoculation dropped to 30% within 4 months[50]

4. A 2021 study by Riemersma et al. in *medRxiv* reported elevated viral loads of 82% in the asymptomatic, "vaccinated," compared to 29% in the asymptomatic, "unvaccinated"[51]

5. A 2021 study by Chau et al. in the *SSRN Electronic Journal* reviewed an outbreak among entirely, "vaccinated," healthcare workers at a Vietnam hospital.[52] Among those who recovered, they found viral loads 251 times higher than average pre-inoculation cases.

6. A 2021 study by Brown et al. in the CDC's own *Morbidity And Mortality Weekly Report* found 74% of cases among those reviewed were, "fully vaccinated," and that, "the vaccinated had on average more virus in their nose than the unvaccinated who were infected"[53]

7. A 2021 study by Nordström et al. in the *SSRN Electronic Journal* observed, "vaccine effectiveness," wane from 92% in month 1, to 47% by month 4-6, down to 0% by month 8 and onward[54]

Perhaps the most fascinating report in this entire list, however, also comes from the CDC itself. On November 5, 2021 the CDC published a study which reviewed hospitalizations among, "immunocompromised," adults with both doses of inoculation, compared to, "immunocompetent adults," with both doses.[55] The data they analyzed came from 9 states and spanned January to September 2021. Now, we've already discussed the problem with using data that spans through January and how this would over-represent the, "unvaccinated." However, even including January, this report shows that among 89K people *hospitalized* with, "Covid-like," illness, 43% of the immunocompetent (healthy) were, "fully vaccinated," and 53% of the immunocompromised were, "fully vaccinated." Recall the 97%, "unvaccinated," hospitalization lie Walensky cited months earlier and how far a cry this is from that, even still using the same bunk timing methodology.

Recall also the CDC and mainstream goal post shift that though the inoculations don't prevent transmission, they're allegedly effective against hospitalization and death. This study single-handedly eviscerates that notion by demonstrating that whether immunocompromised or not, those who are, "fully vaccinated," are still being hospitalized in increasingly significant numbers for, "Covid-like," illnesses. In fact, they're almost certainly being hospitalized in *greater* numbers, considering the time period and lack of accounting for inoculation rates over time in the report. And finally, given what we know about testing, the CDC's suggestion in this study that the inoculations are still effective because, "less of the hospitalized fully vaccinated tested positive using PCR than unvaccinated," the uniformity of testing between the two groups can't be trusted any more than the CDC's definition of, "unvaccinated," itself. For example, where are the numbers in this study that confirm all, "fully vaccinated," patients were tested at all? In the absence of those numbers, is the assumption that there aren't doctors who would dismiss the possibility of a, "Covid," diagnosis and simply not provide a test when they hear a person is, "fully vaccinated?" If so, I flatly reject that assumption based on my own simple observation of doctor behaviors during this time.

To make matters worse, the CDC has engaged in a blatant deception related to, "cases," once the inoculations were unleashed. Specifically, guidance was released in the spring of 2021 stating that, "clinical specimens for sequencing should have an RT-PCR Ct value $\leq$ 28," for those infected post-inoculation, according to Alex Berenson.[56] This guidance was later removed upon intense pushback, but what remains is a CDC standard to *not even track*, "breakthrough cases," which do not involve hospitalization or death.[57] This change, among others, makes meaningful comparison of 2020 and 2021 results impossible. But by all accounts that seems to be the point.

All of the above information presented a huge problem toward every case the CDC made in favor of inoculation—they knew this. How do I know they knew this? Because they intentionally and admittedly hide vast swathes of data which, according to a CDC spokesperson, "might be misinterpreted as the vaccines being ineffective."[58] In this open confession you can see inoculation effectiveness is a foregone conclusion of this broken organization. What they work to do, in their own words, is *not* to determine effectiveness or ineffectiveness based on the data, but rather to figure out how to make the data show effectiveness—a task I can attest would not be difficult for a data scientist no matter what the data actually showed.

The CDC's cover-up has not been exclusive to that organization either. As reported by the *Glasgow Times*, "Public Health Scotland will stop publishing data on covid deaths and hospitalisations by vaccination status — over concerns it is misrepresented by anti-vaxx campaigners."[59] Once again, we see the globally-coordinated effort to push this agenda, as these in-unison cover-ups both happened to also be initiated in February 2022.

Additionally, the FDA inexplicably recommends against antibody tests for the, "vaccinated," to assess immunity, despite them having been controversially used to *count cases* for periods of time in

2020, as we covered.[60] Isn't the entire point of getting, "vaccinated," to stimulate antibodies? If the antibody test is accurate at all, doesn't a negative antibody test for a, "vaccinated," person imply the inoculation isn't working? Isn't the alternative to admit the antibody test is just simply inaccurate? And if so, what does that say about these organizations' understanding (or lack thereof) of the alleged virus and its antibodies? These are questions that remain unanswered to date.

Given the litany of studies which show there would be a clear, "pandemic of the vaccinated," if the same absurd standards were used in 2021 as were used in 2020 to establish the alleged pandemic in the first place, the only way to describe these actions is fraud—obvious, unmitigated fraud. It's an embarrassing attempt at fraud too when one simply observes outcomes in the rest of the world. For example, does the CDC seriously expect a thinking person to believe that 97% of hospitalizations and deaths were, "unvaccinated," in the US, when public health data out of Scotland (before it stopped being reported) showed 9 out of 10, "Covid," deaths and about 7 out of every 10, "Covid," hospitalizations since August 2021 had been, "vaccinated," people?[61] Surely one of the two countries has to be lying if that's the case, don't they? Also, even if one does foolishly want to argue this is due to the, "delta variant," how can they explain the fact that Scotland shows worse death outcomes amongst the inoculated even for that variant, relative to both hospitalization outcomes *and* the percent of the population "vaccinated?"

To demonstrate the latter, Scottish inoculation uptake around August 2021 is alleged to have been around 90% among the 18+ population according to Public Health Scotland.[62] At the same time, the hospitalization and death data previously referred to is *not* generalized to the 18+ population. This means the comparable inoculation percentage (the entire population) should be well below 90%, since a significant chunk of the Scottish population would be below this age group, and the large majority of that chunk would have been, "unvaccinated," at that time. So if we assume Scotland has a similar age distribution to the US (about 25% under 18, per *Statista*), and use conservative estimates for the, "vaccinated," percentages in each age band (we will assume 90% "vaccinated" over 18 as stated and 5% below 18, which is also extremely conservative), we can estimate the appropriate percentage to be around 68.8%.[63] This would demonstrate a far worsened, "Covid," deaths outcome for the inoculated relative to the population, and a slightly worse than neutral hospitalization outcome.

The idea of a reduction in deaths becomes an even more absurd notion when adverse events are considered, which will be addressed in a bit. For now, we have seen that these inoculations do not prevent transmission (aka, positive PCR tests), do not protect against infection, and do not protect against hospitalization or death. In fact, according to coverage out of Israel, today the, "vast majority," of those severely ill in Israeli hospitals are inoculated and experiencing an, "immuno-erosion," which is reflective of the hypersensitivity experienced by animals in SARS inoculation studies a decade ago.[64]

Epidemiological Disaster

But what about, "herd immunity?" Is it possible these places just haven't reached the threshold necessary yet? Also, what even is the goal to achieve, "herd immunity?" The answers, as demonstrated by Israel's 84.4% inoculation rate in July 2021, are no it isn't possible, and no, there never was a goal.

> *"When polls said only about half of all Americans would take a vaccine, I was saying herd immunity would take 70 to 75 percent ... Then, when newer surveys said 60 percent or more would take it, I thought, 'I can nudge this up a bit,' so I went to 80, 85. We need to have some humility here ... We really don't know what the real number is. I think the real range is somewhere between 70 to 90 percent. But, I'm not going to say 90 percent."*

—Anthony Fauci[65]

According to *New York Times* writer Donald G. McNeil Jr., the reason Fauci is overtly lying the way he confesses he is above is, "partly based on new science, and partly on his gut feeling that the country is finally ready to hear what he really thinks." Fortunately for us, Fauci already admitted what he really thinks immediately prior to the alleged pandemic, so we know how narcissistic and psychopathic the way he, "really thinks," is. Unfortunately for us, the director of NIAID openly lies about basing his sales goals on, "science," he simultaneously admits he doesn't have and is just guessing on. Does this guesswork sound like it satisfies the hallmark oath of medicine to, "first, do not harm," to you? Also, observe his negotiation tactic above of simply saying a number larger than whatever surveys suggest. Again, we observe the tactics of a salesman, *not* a doctor.

And if what Fauci, "thinks," is the necessary threshold for, "herd immunity," were actually that, any one of the below countries would have achieved it. Unfortunately for them, as represented in the Subramanian study and the below outcomes, they did so to no avail:

- Gibraltar – 100%, "fully vaccinated," per CNN as of November 24, 2021.[66] Experienced second highest case outbreak of the Covid era in November 2021, per *Worldometers.*[67]
- Singapore – 91.9%, "fully vaccinated," per CNN as of November 24, 2021. Experienced highest cases (more than twice the 2020 daily peak) and deaths (more than eight times the daily 2020 peak) of the Covid era in October 2021, per *Worldometers.*
- Iceland – 81.7%, "fully vaccinated," per CNN as of November 24, 2021. Experienced highest cases of the Covid era in both August 2021 (almost twice the 2020 daily peak) and September 2021 (more than twice the 2020 daily peak), per *Worldometers.*
- Cuba – 80.3%, "fully vaccinated," per CNN as of November 24, 2021. Experienced by-far highest cases and deaths of the Covid era in August-September 2021, per *Worldometers.*
- South Korea – 79.2%, "fully vaccinated," per CNN as of November 24, 2021. Experienced highest cases and deaths of the Covid era in November 2021, per *Worldometers.*
- Finland – 72.0%, "fully vaccinated," per CNN as of November 24, 2021. Experienced highest cases and deaths of the Covid era November 2021, per *Worldometers.*
- Denmark – 76.4%, "fully vaccinated," per CNN as of November 24, 2021. Experienced highest cases of the Covid era November 2021, per *Worldometers.*
- Norway – 69.5%, "fully vaccinated," per CNN as of November 24, 2021. Experienced by-far highest cases and deaths of the Covid era November 2021, per *Worldometers.*
- Per *Forbes*, the Island of Seychelles, Israel, the UAE, Chile, and Bahrain—the top 5 most inoculated countries in the world

as of May 2021—all experienced the highest surges in the world at the time on a per-capita basis, other than Israel.[68] Israel did, however, go on to experience its highest ever surge a few months later, as we've discussed.

- As of August 2021 the CDC considered 12 of the top 13 most inoculated countries to be travel risks[69]

And countries weren't the only observable examples of the failure of the inoculations. Mass inoculation as a primary strategy proved a failure in various other venues as well. The following are just a notable few:

- The 100%, "fully vaccinated," Arizona Cardinals lost their head coach, two assistants, the GM, and two players to testing positive in the same week[70]
- A 100%, "fully vaccinated," Royal Navy flotilla reported a 100-case, "outbreak"[71]
- A 96%, "fully vaccinated," Israeli hospital outbreak was highlighted in a report in *Eurosurveillance*.[72] The paper noted transmission likely occurred between two individuals both wearing surgical masks, and in one instance using full PPE, including N-95 mask, face shield, gown, and gloves. There were 42 cases diagnosed, 8 of whom became severely ill, 6 of whom became critically ill, and 5 of whom died. All of those severely ill, critically ill, or who died were, "fully vaccinated." The paper concluded: *"This communication ... challenges the assumption that high universal vaccination rates will lead to herd immunity and prevent COVID-19 outbreaks."*
- A 99%, "fully vaccinated," nursing home experienced an outbreak resulting in 8 deaths out of the 70 residents housed there[73]
- 99.98% of the crew and 96.5% of the passengers were, "fully vaccinated," on a Carnival cruise which experienced 27 infected people—all, "fully vaccinated"[74]
- The Dept. of Defense's Joint Artificial Intelligence Center AI Program titled, "Project Salus," found the majority of Medicare beneficiaries inoculated later tested positive[75]

Natural Immunity

267

On August 25, 2021, Gazit et al. published a study in *medRxiv* showing that those who received the inoculation, "had a 13-fold (95% CI, 8-21) increased risk for breakthrough infection," compared to those who previously recovered from illness, as well as a 7-fold hospitalization risk.[76] When adjusting for the time of disease/inoculation, there was a 27-fold increased risk. The findings of this Israeli study on natural immunity would go on to be corroborated by 131 others to date as well, all of which have been documented by the Brownstone Institute.[77] Like their list on the lack of protection provided by the inoculations, this list started at 79 studies and has worked its way up over time. The conclusions of just 3 of those 131 are as follows:

- In 2021 Shrestha et al., published in *medRxiv*, found[78]: *"Not one of the 1359 previously infected subjects who remained unvaccinated had a SARS-CoV-2 infection over the duration of the study. Individuals who have had SARS-CoV-2 infection are unlikely to benefit from COVID-19 vaccination."*

- In 2020 Le Bert et al., published in *Nature*, took it a step further and found that, "patients (n = 23) who recovered from SARS possess long-lasting memory T cells that are reactive to the N protein of SARS-CoV 17 years after the outbreak of SARS in 2003; these T cells displayed robust cross-reactivity to the N protein of SARS-CoV-2."[79] What this effectively confirms is that immunity already existed to the cold/flu attributed to what is alleged to be a novel coronavirus. If the alleged virus *was* actually novel and meaningfully distinct, this should not be possible.

- In 2021 Pilz et al., published in the *European Journal of Clinical Investigation*, found[80]: *"40 tentative re-infections in 14,840 COVID-19 survivors of the first wave (0.27%) and 253,581 infections in 8,885,640 individuals of the remaining general population (2.85%) translating into an odds ratio (95% confidence interval) of 0.09 (0.07 to 0.13)...relatively low re-infection rate of SARS-CoV-2 in Austria. Protection against SARS-CoV-2 after natural infection is comparable with the highest available estimates on vaccine efficacies."* Additionally, hospitalization in only five out of 14,840 (0.03%) people and death in one out of 14,840 (0.01%).

Despite all this evidence that a person who had fallen seriously ill was far less likely to fall seriously ill again in the same period of time it would take a, "fully vaccinated," person to fall ill, public health officials who knew this information perfectly well carried forward with their coercive, senseless universal inoculation campaigns anyway. They did so without any good explanation whatsoever, as well. Their behavior further solidifies the allegation that their only objective was to sell mRNA inoculations without any regard for health.

> "CNN's Sanjay Gupta: *There was a study that came out of Israel about natural immunity and basically the headline was that natural immunity provides a lot of protection—even better than the vaccines alone. What are people to make of that? As we talk about vaccine mandates, I get calls all the time from people, 'I've already had Covid, I'm protected, and now the study says maybe even more protected than the vaccine alone.' Should they also get the vaccine? How do you make the case to them?"*
> Anthony Fauci: *"You know, that's a really good point Sanjay. I don't have a really firm answer for you on that. That's something that we're going to have to discuss."*
> —Sanjay Gupta and Anthony Fauci, early September 2021[81]

Interesting. So Fauci, the man who was confident enough to publicly hail an unpublished, non-peer-reviewed, placebo-group-sabotaged study by his own organization on remdesivir, now all of a sudden is going to exercise restraint when it comes to a litany of peer-reviewed studies released months before. Only, he's not going to exercise the far more relevant type of restraint in pausing or shifting his hardline stance on universal inoculations based on this information. Hell, even a CNN anchor knew about these studies and what they showed. So how could someone like Fauci *not* know and not have an opinion on the course of action those studies suggest? He would've known, and he would've needed a narrative to explain them away—a narrative he'd promptly craft and return to CNN's Jake Tapper to broadcast days later, where he was asked the following[82]:

> "*I want to ask you about people who were previously infected with Covid, who—you and I had previously discussed this*

before—have some lingering antibody protections. I understand that vaccination offers stronger protections, but what's your answer when people say, 'why does Biden's new federal vaccine mandate have to apply to people that have had Covid, given that they have some protection already?'"

While I usually don't find it worth it to highlight the statements of propagandists, this question is built on such a perverse lie that I think it helps clarify who Fauci is, for entertaining it alone. The lie, which you probably noticed, is that the mRNA, "vaccination," all of a sudden apparently offers *stronger* protection from illness than natural immunity. We've already covered the litany of studies that demonstrate this to be a falsehood. And before anyone suggests Tapper might not have known about these studies, the studies are the only reason this is even a talking point on his propaganda show at all. In fact, we just saw Sanjay Gupta of the same network also talking about them in an interview which preceded this one. Tapper obviously knows and is obviously lying about it to misguide people. Will he be censored for, "dangerous misinformation?" Of course not. Fauci goes on to answer this without addressing the lie, which is as much a testament to who he is (a liar and a salesman) as who he isn't (a scientist):

> *"Yeah, it is true, they do have protection. The one thing we are not aware of yet—and hopefully we will get that data—is what the durability of protection is and, looking ahead, whether or not that type of protection that is induced by natural infection—how that will be against a variety of variants as they arrive. I'm not denying at all that people who get infected and recover have a considerable degree of immunity. We also know ... that when you get infected and recover, a) you get a good degree of immunity, but b) when you get vaccinated you dramatically increase that protection—which is something that is really quite good."*

The liar not only doesn't correct the lie, he doubles down on it and lies again. First of all, Fauci doesn't even answer the question, nor does he provide new evidence for his claims since the first time he was asked the same question. There's no justification to economically coerce a medical intervention without informed consent in any situation, as defined by the Nuremberg Code and Hippocratic Oath. Still, Fauci's best excuse to support this nonsensical mandate despite the evidence against it is that natural immunity protection is, "considerable," but natural immunity plus, "vaccination," is, "dramatically," better than "considerable." This is, yet again, a lie though, as we saw in the findings of 131 different studies. The Shrestha study, to use an example we highlighted already, saw no difference at all in the benefit of those with previous infection who did or didn't get the shot. In fact, they concluded, "individuals who have had SARS-CoV-2 infection are unlikely to benefit from COVID-19 vaccination." And like the Israel study, this study was published more than three months prior to this interview so, again, Fauci would have either been well aware of it or derelict of his duty.

To respond to the waterfall of evidence suggesting natural immunity was superior to any alleged protection provided by the inoculations, the CDC published the first study suggesting the opposite in November 2021—two months *after* Fauci's interviews.[83] This study is a true demonstration, however, of the danger of drawing your conclusion and then conducting a study to simply support your conclusion. To be specific, a previous meta-analysis had also been conducted by the CDC, which found, "no significant difference," in protection between, "vaccination," and natural immunity.[84] They pointed to these findings at that time to support the power of the inoculations, until the aforementioned questions were later raised around why then a previously infected person would need to get inoculated. And so, like manna from heaven, the November study came and changed the narrative in support of *greater* protection provided by the shots. This did not go unnoticed, as the November study was torn apart by observers:

- Attorney Jenin Younes pointed out this difference in study findings before saying that, "one should begin to question everything the CDC has ever said about COVID-19 (or perhaps anything)," based on this fraud[85]
- Immunologist Hooman Noorchashm called the study, "another teleological piece of propaganda," by the CDC because it excludes the Johnson & Johnson shots and likely includes recovered people in the, "vaccinated," group[86]

271

- Harvard Medical School epidemiologist Martin Kulldorff said the study has a, "major statistical flaw," which is that it falsely portrays hospitalized respiratory patients as, "representative of the population."[87] Kulldorff claims this renders the odds ratio, "wrong."
- Journalist Alex Berenson determined the study to be, "meaningless gibberish that would have never been published if the agency did not face huge political pressure to get people vaccinated."[88] Berenson acknowledged that the raw data actually showed almost four times as many, "fully vaccinated," people being hospitalized with, "Covid," as those with natural immunity—and *fifteen* times as many over the summer.

After continuing to get lambasted for its political bastardization of science, the CDC once again showed its reactive nature by again changing position and admitting natural immunity was more effective than inoculation in January 2022.[89,90] This would have been the third position change on the issue in less than a year, from an organization whose director repeatedly endorsed mass informed consent violations via illegal EUA-authorized inoculation mandates, committed against the American people.[91]

As is common knowledge, the more serious cold/flu symptoms in my opinion falsely attributed to the alleged novel disease, "Covid," are not likely to recur in a 6-month to 2-year period. This is considered, "protection," and for our purposes, I'm fine with that argument, even though I think it'd be more appropriate to say that during a cold/flu the immune system does its job flushing out an overload of toxicity built up over time, which afterwards it can go back to regulating without fanfare until the next overload is built up and/or acutely introduced. The reason that an, "unvaccinated," person is less likely to recur these cold flu symptoms in my opinion is that they did not introduce a toxic substance into their body, as we've already established the inoculations to likely be in theory, thanks to the extreme amounts of spike-producing, lipid-nanoparticle-enveloped mRNA packages.

Endnotes

1   "The Voice Of Truth (19 November 2021) With Dr Zev Zelenko, Prof Dolores Cahill And Craig Kelly MP, Leader Of The United Australia Party.". 2021. *Rumble*. https://www.rumble.com/vpk7a1-the-voice-of-truth.html.

2   Erickson, Jon. 2020. "CDC Estimates COVID-19 Fatality Rate, Including Asymptomatic Cases". *Nbc26.Com*. https://www.nbc26.com/news/coronavirus/cdc-estimates-covid-19-fatality-rate-including-asymptomatic-cases.

3   "Albert Bourla On Twitter April 1, 2021 8:46 AM". 2021. *Twitter*. https://twitter.com/AlbertBourla/status/1377618480527257606.

4   Pavlich, Katie. 2022. "Pfizer CEO: Our Vaccines Offer 'Limited, If Any Protection'". *Townhall*. https://townhall.com/tipsheet/katiepavlich/2022/01/11/pfizer-ceo-our-vaccines-offer-little-protection-n2601670.

5   "Biden: 'Get Vaccinated Or Wear A Mask Until You Do'". 2021. *MSNBC.Com*. https://www.msnbc.com/msnbc/watch/biden-says-you-don-t-need-a-mask-if-you-re-fully-vaccinated-after-cdc-updated-guidance-111897669835.

6   "US Coronavirus Vaccine Tracker". 2021. *Usafacts.Org*. https://www.usafacts.org/visualizations/covid-vaccine-tracker-states/.

7   The White House. 2021. "Remarks By President Biden In A CNN Town Hall With Don Lemon". whitehouse.gov.

8   "US Coronavirus Vaccine Tracker". 2021. *Usafacts.Org*. https://www.usafacts.org/visualizations/covid-vaccine-tracker-states/.

9   Miller, Andrew Mark. 2021. "Biden Defends Previously Saying Vaccinated Don't Need Masks: 'That Was True At The Time'". *Fox News*. https://www.foxnews.com/politics/biden-vaccinated-need-masks-true-at-time.

10 "US Coronavirus Vaccine Tracker". 2021. *Usafacts.Org*. https://www.usafacts.org/visualizations/covid-vaccine-tracker-states/.

11 "They Lied About The Mrna Vaccines". 2021. *Rumble*. https://www.rumble.com/vpeqy0-the-covid-19-vaccine-booster-circus.html.

12 Ibid.

13 Ibid.

14 Ashworth, Nate. 2021. "Fauci: Families Should Require Vaccination Proof Before Holiday Gatherings - Election Central". *Uspresidentialelectionnews.Com*, https://www.uspresidentialelectionnews.com/2021/12/fauci-families-should-require-vaccination-proof-before-holiday-gatherings/.

15 Takala, Rudy. 2021. "Biden CDC Director: Data Suggests 'Vaccinated People Do Not Carry The Virus'". *Mediaite*. https://www.mediaite.com/news/biden-cdc-director-data-suggests-vaccinated-people-do-not-carry-the-virus/.

16 "US Coronavirus Vaccine Tracker". 2021. *Usafacts.Org*. https://www.usafacts.org/visualizations/covid-vaccine-tracker-states/.

17   " CDC Eases Guidance On Mask Wearing For People Who Are Fully Vaccinated; Gov. Pritzker To Revise State's Mask Mandate ". 2021. *Msn.Com*. https://www.msn.com/en-us/health/medical/cdc-eases-guidance-on-mask-wearing-for-people-who-are-fully-vaccinated-gov-pritzker-to-revise-state-e2-80-99s-mask-mandate/ar-BB1gHxag.

18   "US Coronavirus Vaccine Tracker". 2021. *Usafacts.Org*. https://www.usafacts.org/visualizations/covid-vaccine-tracker-states/.

19   "CDC Director Rochelle Walensky Admitted COVID-19 Vaccines Cannot 'Prevent Transmission'". 2021. *National File*. https://www.nationalfile.com/cdc-director-rochelle-walensky-admitted-covid-19-vaccines-cannot-prevent-transmission/.

20   "US Coronavirus Vaccine Tracker". 2021. *Usafacts.Org*. https://www.usafacts.org/visualizations/covid-vaccine-tracker-states/.

21   White, Andrew. 2021. "CDC Director Admits Those Who Were 'Vaccinated Early' At 'Increased Risk Of SEVERE Disease,' Vaccine Effectiveness Is 'Waning'". *National File*. https://www.nationalfile.com/cdc-director-admits-those-who-were-vaccinated-early-at-increased-risk-of-severe-disease-vaccine-effectiveness-is-waning/.

22   "US Coronavirus Vaccine Tracker". 2021. *Usafacts.Org*. https://www.usafacts.org/visualizations/covid-vaccine-tracker-states/.

23   "They Lied About The Mrna Vaccines". 2021. *Rumble*. https://www.rumble.com/vpeqy0-the-covid-19-vaccine-booster-circus.html.

24   Ibid.

25   Ibid.

26   Swenson, Ali. 2021. "COVID Vaccine Package Insert Is Blank Because Up-To-Date Information Is Online". *AP NEWS*. https://www.apnews.com/article/fact-checking-956865924140.

27   MORRIS, DAVID Z., and SY MUKHERJEE. 2021. "It's Official: Vaccinated People Don'T Transmit COVID-19". *Fortune*. https://www.fortune.com/2021/04/01/its-official-vaccinated-people-dont-transmit-covid-19/.

28   Aubrey, Allison. 2021. "97% Of People Entering Hospitals For COVID-19 Are Unvaccinated". *Npr.Org*. https://www.npr.org/2021/07/16/1017012853/97-of-people-entering-hospitals-for-covid-19-are-unvaccinated.

29   The White House. 2021. "Press Briefing By White House COVID-19 Response Team And Public Health Officials". The White House Briefing Room. https://www.whitehouse.gov/briefing-room/press-briefings/2021/08/05/press-briefing-by-white-house-covid-19-response-team-and-public-health-officials-48/.

30   "US COVID-19 Cases And Deaths By State". 2020. *Usafacts.Org*. https://usafacts.org/visualizations/coronavirus-covid-19-spread-map/.

31   Walia, Arjun. 2022. ""We Had Too Little Caution & Too Much Optimism" CDC Director On COVID Vaccines". *The Pulse*.

https://thepulse.one/2022/03/08/we-had-too-little-caution-too-much-optimism-cdc-director-on-covid-vaccines/.

32   Bursztynsky, Jessica. 2021. "Sexual Misconduct Allegation Against Chris Cuomo Led To His Firing From CNN, Attorney Says". *CNBC*. https://www.cnbc.com/2021/12/05/attorney-sexual-misconduct-allegation-led-to-cnns-chris-cuomo-firing.html.

33   Smith, Emily. 2022. "Jeff Zucker And Allison Gollust 'Lied' For Years About 'Open Secret' Affair". *Nypost.Com*. https://nypost.com/2022/02/02/ousted-cnn-boss-jeff-zuckers-affair-with-his-colleague-allison-gollust-was-the-worst-kept-secret-in-tv-but-they-conspired-to-keep-it-out-of-the-media-for-years-with-a-web-of-lies-sources-told-the-post/.

34   Lungariello, Mark. 2021. "Accuser Details Sex Assault Allegations Against CNN's Don Lemon". *Nypost.Com*. https://nypost.com/2021/11/08/accuser-details-sex-assault-allegations-against-cnns-don-lemon/.

35   Sheehy, Kate. 2020. "Jeffrey Toobin Was Masturbating In Front Of New Yorker Bigs: Report". *Nypost.Com*. https://nypost.com/2020/10/19/jeffrey-toobin-was-masturbating-in-front-of-new-yorker-bigs-report/.

36   Galvin, Beth. 2021. "CDC Director Says 'Disinformation' May Be Driving Some To Refuse COVID-19 Vaccine". *FOX 5 Atlanta*. https://www.fox5atlanta.com/news/cdc-director-says-disinformation-may-be-driving-some-to-refuse-covid-19-vaccine.

37   US Department of Health and Human Services / The Centers for Disease Control and Prevention. 2021. "Morbidity And Mortality Weekly Report / August 27, 2021 / Vol. 70 / No. 34." https://www.cdc.gov/mmwr/volumes/70/wr/pdfs/mm7034e5-H.pdf.

38   "VAERS COVID Vaccine Adverse Event Reports". 2022. *Openvaers*. Accessed March 14. https://www.openvaers.com/covid-data.

39   "Jodi O'malley - HHS". 2021. *Projectveritas.Com*. https://www.projectveritas.com/news/jodi-omalley-hhs/.

40   Hendrix, Steve, and Shira Rubin. 2021. "With Most Adults Now Vaccinated, Israelis Are Busting Loose". *The Washington Post*. https://www.washingtonpost.com/world/middle_east/israel-coronavirus-vaccine-herd-immunity/2021/04/20/e4e1199c-a118-11eb-b314-2e993bd83e31_story.html.

41   Shammas, Brittany, Brittney Martin, Richard Webner, and Dan Diamond. 2021. "Coronavirus Hospitalizations Drop As Officials, Wary Of States Reopening, Urge Caution". *The Washington Post*. https://www.washingtonpost.com/health/2021/03/10/covid-hospitalizations-fall/.

42   Pflughoeft, Aspen. 2021. "Inside Israel's Recent Outbreak: Why Mostly Vaccinated People Are Testing Positive". *Deseret*. https://www.deseret.com/coronavirus/2021/7/20/22584134/whats-going-on-in-israels-outbreak-among-vaccinated-people.

43   "Israel COVID - Coronavirus Statistics - Worldometer".
      2022. *Worldometers.Info*. Accessed March 14.
      https://www.worldometers.info/coronavirus/country/israel/.

44   Jeffay, Nathan. 2021. "Portugal, Sweden Slap COVID Entry Ban On
      Israelis, Including Those Vaccinated". *Timesofisrael.Com*.
      https://www.timesofisrael.com/portugal-sweden-slap-covid-entry-ban-on-
      israelis-including-those-vaccinated/.

45   Day, Vox. 2021. "A Pandemic Of The Vaccinated - Vox Popoli". *Vox
      Popoli*. https://www.voxday.net/2021/09/08/a-pandemic-of-the-
      vaccinated/.

46   Subramanian, S. V., and Akhil Kumar. 2021. "Increases In COVID-19
      Are Unrelated To Levels Of Vaccination Across 68 Countries And 2947
      Counties In The United States". *European Journal Of Epidemiology* 36
      (12): 1237-1240. doi:10.1007/s10654-021-00808-7.

47   ALEXANDER, PAUL ELIAS. 2021. "43 Studies On Vaccine
      Efficacy That Raise Doubts On Vaccine Mandates ★ Brownstone
      Institute". *Brownstone Institute*. https://brownstone.org/articles/16-
      studies-on-vaccine-efficacy/.

48   Acharya, Charlotte B., John Schrom, Anthea M. Mitchell, David A. Coil,
      Carina Marquez, Susana Rojas, and Chung Yu Wang et al. 2021. "No
      Significant Difference In Viral Load Between Vaccinated And
      Unvaccinated, Asymptomatic And Symptomatic Groups When Infected
      With SARS-Cov-2 Delta Variant". doi:10.1101/2021.09.28.21264262.

49   Riemersma, Kasen K., Brittany E. Grogan, Amanda Kita-Yarbro, Peter J.
      Halfmann, Hannah E. Segaloff, Anna Kocharian, and Kelsey R. Florek et
      al. 2021. "Shedding Of Infectious SARS-Cov-2 Despite Vaccination".
      doi:10.1101/2021.07.31.21261387.

50   Chemaitelly, Hiam, Patrick Tang, Mohammad R. Hasan, Sawsan
      AlMukdad, Hadi M. Yassine, Fatiha M. Benslimane, and Hebah A. Al
      Khatib et al. 2021. "Waning Of Bnt162b2 Vaccine Protection Against
      SARS-Cov-2 Infection In Qatar". doi:10.1101/2021.08.25.21262584.

51   Riemersma, Kasen K., Brittany E. Grogan, Amanda Kita-Yarbro, Peter J.
      Halfmann, Hannah E. Segaloff, Anna Kocharian, and Kelsey R. Florek et
      al. 2021. "Shedding Of Infectious SARS-Cov-2 Despite Vaccination".
      doi:10.1101/2021.07.31.21261387.

52   Chau, Nguyen Van Vinh, Nghiem My Ngoc, Lam Anh Nguyet, Vo Minh
      Quang, Nguyen Thi Han Ny, Dao Bach Khoa, and Nguyen Thanh Phong
      et al. 2021. "Transmission Of SARS-Cov-2 Delta Variant Among
      Vaccinated Healthcare Workers, Vietnam". *SSRN Electronic Journal*.
      doi:10.2139/ssrn.3897733.

53   Brown, Catherine M., Johanna Vostok, Hillary Johnson, Meagan Burns,
      Radhika Gharpure, Samira Sami, and Rebecca T. Sabo et al. 2021.
      "Outbreak Of SARS-Cov-2 Infections, Including COVID-19 Vaccine
      Breakthrough Infections, Associated With Large Public Gatherings —
      Barnstable County, Massachusetts, July 2021". *MMWR. Morbidity And*

Mortality Weekly Report 70 (31): 1059-1062.
doi:10.15585/mmwr.mm7031e2.

54   Nordström, Peter, Marcel Ballin, and Anna Nordström. 2021.
      "Effectiveness Of Covid-19 Vaccination Against Risk Of Symptomatic
      Infection, Hospitalization, And Death Up To 9 Months: A Swedish Total-
      Population Cohort Study". *SSRN Electronic Journal.*
      doi:10.2139/ssrn.3949410.

55   The Centers for Disease Control and Prevention. 2021. "Effectiveness Of
      2-Dose Vaccination With Mrna COVID-19 Vaccines Against COVID-
      19–Associated Hospitalizations Among Immunocompromised Adults —
      Nine States, January–September 2021."

56   Horowitz, Daniel. 2021. "Horowitz: CDC Issues Guidance For
      Evaluating Post-Vaccination COVID Tests At A Lower
      Standard". *Theblaze.* https://www.theblaze.com/op-ed/horowitz-cdc-
      issues-guidance-for-evaluating-post-vaccination-covid-tests-at-a-lower-
      standard.

57   Tayag, Yasmin. 2021. "Why Has The CDC Stopped Collecting Data On
      Breakthrough Covid Cases? | Yasmin Tayag". *The Guardian.*
      https://www.theguardian.com/commentisfree/2021/aug/06/cdc-covid-
      coronavirus-data-breakthrough-cases.

58   Mandavilli, Apoorva. 2022. "The C.D.C. Isn'T Publishing Large Portions
      Of The Covid Data It Collects". *Nytimes.Com.*
      https://www.nytimes.com/2022/02/20/health/covid-cdc-data.html.

59   Brownlie, Lauren. 2022. "Covid Data Will Not Be Published Over
      Concerns It's Misrepresented By Anti-Vaxxers". *Glasgow Times.*
      https://www.glasgowtimes.co.uk/news/19931641.covid-data-will-not-
      published-concerns-misrepresented-anti-vaxxers/?ref=rss.

60   The Food and Drug Administration. 2021. "Antibody Testing Is Not
      Currently Recommended To Assess Immunity After COVID-19
      Vaccination: FDA Safety Communication".
      https://www.fda.gov/medical-devices/safety-communications/antibody-
      testing-not-currently-recommended-to-assess-immunity-after-covid-19-
      vaccination-fda-safety.

61   "Fully Vaccinated Account For 9 In Every 10 Covid-19 Deaths Since
      August According To Latest Official Data". 2021. *The Expose.*
      https://dailyexpose.uk/2021/12/03/fully-vaccinated-account-for-9-in-
      every-10-covid-19-deaths-since-august-according-to-latest-official-data/.

62   Public Health Scotland. 2021. "Public Health Scotland COVID-19
      Statistical Report As At 29 November 2021."

63   "U.S. Population By Age And Gender 2019 | Statista". 2021. *Statista.*
      https://www.statista.com/statistics/241488/population-of-the-us-by-sex-
      and-age/.

64   "Press Secretary For Israeli PM: Vaccinated People Now Dying, And
      Going To Hospital Very Sick". 2021. *Bitchute.*
      https://www.bitchute.com/video/eosnwyX7qNUT/.

65   Allen, Mike. 2020. "NYT: Fauci Acknowledges Moving Goalposts On Herd Immunity From COVID-19". *Axios*. https://www.axios.com/fauci-goalposts-herd-immunity-c83c7500-d8f9-4960-a334-06cc03d9a220.html.

66   Pettersson, Henrik, Byron Manley, Sergio Hernandez, Deidre McPhillips, and Tatiana Arias. 2021. "Covid-19 Vaccine Tracker: View Vaccinations By Country". *CNN*. https://www.cnn.com/interactive/2021/health/global-covid-vaccinations/.

67   "Gibraltar COVID - Coronavirus Statistics - Worldometer". 2020. *Worldometers.Info*. https://www.worldometers.info/coronavirus/country/gibraltar.

68   Hart, Robert. 2021. "Covid Surges In 4 Of 5 Most Vaccinated Countries—Here's Why The U.S. Should Worry". *Forbes*. https://www.forbes.com/sites/roberthart/2021/05/11/covid-surges-in-4-of-5-worlds-most-vaccinated-countries-heres-why-the-us-should-worry/?sh=52363ab2d677.

69   "CDC Considers 12 Of The 13 Most Vaccinated Countries A Travel Risk". 2021. *The Watch Towers*. https://www.thewatchtowers.org/cdc-considers-12-of-the-13-most-vaccinated-countries-a-travel-risk/?amp=1.

70   Rucker, JD. 2021. "100% 'Vaccinated' NFL Team Loses Their Head Coach, Two Assistants, The GM, And Two Players Due To Covid". *NOQ Report - Conservative Christian News, Opinions, And Quotes*. https://www.noqreport.com/2021/10/16/100-vaccinated-nfl-team-loses-their-head-coach-two-assistants-the-gm-and-two-players-due-to-covid/.

71   Singh, Namita. 2021. "Royal Navy Flotilla Reports Covid Outbreak With 100 Cases Despite All Sailors Being Vaccinated". *The Independent*. https://www.independent.co.uk/news/uk/home-news/hms-queen-elizabeth-covid-royal-navy-b1883699.html.

72   Redshaw, Megan. 2021. "COVID Outbreak Sparked By Fully Vaccinated Patient Challenges Vaccine-Induced Herd Immunity Theory". *Children's Health Defense*. https://www.childrenshealthdefense.org/defender/covid-outbreak-vaccinated-patient-herd-immunity-theory/.

73   Miller, Joshua Rhett. 2021. "COVID-19 Outbreak Kills 8 In Connecticut Nursing Home". *Nypost.Com*. https://www.nypost.com/2021/11/16/covid-19-outbreak-kills-8-in-connecticut-nursing-home/.

74   Brooks, Kristopher, and Kate Gibson. 2021. "27 People Aboard A Carnival Cruise Test Positive For COVID-19". *Cbsnews.Com*. https://www.cbsnews.com/news/carnival-cruise-covid-outbreak/.

75   "New Data From Department Of Defense 'Project Salus' Shows Waning Immunity From COVID-19 Vaccine To Its 5.6 Million Vaccinated Medicare Beneficiaries (VIDEO)". 2021. *Survival Magazine & News - Bushcraft Prepper Offgrid SHTF Blog & Conservative News*. https://survivalmagazine.org/news/new-data-from-department-of-defense-project-salus-shows-waning-immunity-from-covid-19-vaccine-to-its-5-6-million-vaccinated-medicare-beneficiaries-video/.

76   Gazit, Sivan, Roei Shlezinger, Galit Perez, Roni Lotan, Asaf Peretz, Amir Ben-Tov, Dani Cohen, Khitam Muhsen, Gabriel Chodick, and Tal Patalon. 2021. "Comparing SARS-Cov-2 Natural Immunity To Vaccine-Induced Immunity: Reinfections Versus Breakthrough Infections". doi:10.1101/2021.08.24.21262415.

77   ALEXANDER, PAUL ELIAS. 2021. "150 Research Studies Affirm Naturally Acquired Immunity To Covid-19: Documented, Linked, And Quoted ★ Brownstone Institute". *Brownstone Institute.* https://brownstone.org/articles/79-research-studies-affirm-naturally-acquired-immunity-to-covid-19-documented-linked-and-quoted/.

78   Shrestha, Nabin K., Patrick C. Burke, Amy S. Nowacki, Paul Terpeluk, and Steven M. Gordon. 2021. "Necessity Of COVID-19 Vaccination In Previously Infected Individuals". doi:10.1101/2021.06.01.21258176.

79   Le Bert, Nina, Anthony T. Tan, Kamini Kunasegaran, Christine Y. L. Tham, Morteza Hafezi, Adeline Chia, and Melissa Hui Yen Chng et al. 2020. "SARS-Cov-2-Specific T Cell Immunity In Cases Of COVID-19 And SARS, And Uninfected Controls". *Nature* 584 (7821): 457-462. doi:10.1038/s41586-020-2550-z.

80   Pilz, Stefan, Ali Chakeri, John PA Ioannidis, Lukas Richter, Verena Theiler-Schwetz, Christian Trummer, Robert Krause, and Franz Allerberger. 2021. "SARS-Cov-2 Re-Infection Risk In Austria". *European Journal Of Clinical Investigation* 51 (4). doi:10.1111/eci.13520.

81   Hains, Tim. 2021. "Fauci: Natural Immunity Vs. Vaccine For COVID-19 Needs To Be Discussed Seriously". *Realclearpolitics.* https://www.realclearpolitics.com/video/2021/09/10/fauci_natural_immunity_vs_vaccine_for_covid-19_needs_to_be_discussed_seriously.html#1.

82   Dietrich, Ray. 2021. "Fauci Admits Natural Immunity After Recovery From COVID Gives A "Considerable Degree Of Immunity"". *Red Voice Media.* https://www.redvoicemedia.com/2021/09/fauci-admits-natural-immunity-after-recovery-from-covid-gives-a-considerable-degree-of-immunity/.

83   The Centers for Disease Control and Prevention. 2021. "Laboratory-Confirmed COVID-19 Among Adults Hospitalized With COVID-19–Like Illness With Infection-Induced Or Mrna Vaccine-Induced SARS-Cov-2 Immunity — Nine States, January–September 2021". CDC.

84   The Centers for Disease Control and Prevention. 2021. "Science Brief: SARS-Cov-2 Infection-Induced And Vaccine-Induced Immunity" CDC. https://www.cdc.gov/coronavirus/2019-ncov/science/science-briefs/vaccine-induced-immunity.html/#anchor_1635540449320.

85   Younes, Jenin. 2021. "Jenin Younes Tweet, October 31, 2021 8:46 PM". *Twitter.* https://www.twitter.com/Leftylockdowns1/status/1454988276415098882.

86   Noorchashm, Hooman. 2021. "Hooman Noorchashm Tweet (Account Since Banned)". *Twitter.* https://www.twitter.com/noorchashm/status/1454187971339489282.

279

87   Kulldorf, Martin. 2021. "Martin Kulldorf Tweet October 29, 2021 11:20 PM". *Twitter*. https://www.twitter.com/MartinKulldorff/status/1454302176772333572/.

88   Berenson, Alex. 2021. "The CDC Hits A New Low". *Substack*. https://www.alexberenson.substack.com/p/the-cdc-hits-a-new-low/.

89   Siri, Aaron. 2021. "CDC Admits Crushing Rights Of Naturally Immune Without Proof They Transmit The Virus". *Aaronsiri.Substack.Com*. https://aaronsiri.substack.com/p/cdc-admits-crushing-rights-of-naturally?s=r.

90   Miltimore, Jon. 2022. "CDC: Natural Immunity Offered Stronger Protection Against COVID Than Vaccines During Delta Wave | Jon Miltimore". *Fee.Org*. https://fee.org/articles/cdc-natural-immunity-offered-stronger-protection-against-covid-than-vaccines-during-delta-wave/.

91   Adl-Tabatabai, Sean. 2021. "CDC Director: Unvaccinated Police, Government Workers To Be Forcibly Re-Educated". *News Punch*. https://newspunch.com/cdc-director-unvaccinated-police-government-workers-to-be-forcibly-re-educated/.

Chapter 12

Inoculations Pt. 3: Turning Failure into Opportunity

The Covid inoculations failed to do what those whose mission it was to sell them promised they'd do—promises they made with a certainty they couldn't have had. This failure has led to a pathetic amount of defensiveness and ever shifting goalposts on their part, as well as a troubling psychosis on the part of those who they deceived. Consider any of the following examples:

> *"I learned today that I tested positive for COVID-19 after first feeling symptoms on Saturday. My symptoms are relatively mild. I'm beyond grateful to have received two doses of vaccine and, more recently, a booster – I'm certain that without them I would be doing much worse."*
> —Senator Cory, "Spartacus," Booker social media post[1]

> *"I regularly test for COVID & while I tested negative earlier this week, today I tested positive with a breakthrough case. Thankfully, I am only experiencing mild symptoms & am grateful for the protection provided against serious illness that comes from being vaccinated & boosted."*
> —Senator Elizabeth, "Pocahantas," Warren social media post[2]

> *"A woman's **fully vaccinated father died** (my emphasis) from COVID-19. **Doctors said the condition of the father could have been worse** (my emphasis) if he was not vaccinated at all."*
> —The Hill, August 2021[3]

> *"Were Utah a truly civilized place, the governor's next move would be to find a way to mandate the kind of mass vaccination campaign we should have launched a year ago, going as far as to deploy the National Guard to ensure that people without proof of vaccination would not be allowed, well, anywhere."*
> — The Sake Lake Tribune Editorial Board, January 2022[4]

> *"She was vaccinated but was infected by others who chose not to be. The cost was her life."*
> —The Independent, September 2021[5]

"Remaining unvaccinated & going out in public is equivalent to driving under the influence. You want to be intoxicated? That's your choice, but if you want to drive a car, that endangers others. No one should have the 'choice' to infect others with a potentially deadly disease."
—CNN regular and TV Doctor Leana Wen[6]

*"People who are vaccinated, we now know based on the CDC—they are now able, with the delta variant—**because they carry so much more virus** (my emphasis)—they can transmit to their unvaccinated family members."*
—Also Leana Wen[7]

In order to keep the cognitive dissonance of the above types of people from snapping, the perpetrators have to ensure their narrative survives above all else. The way they have achieved this is by overwhelming ("flooding," to quote Event 201) the prevailing consciousness with increasing pressure and an endless supply of new, ever-more-complex layers on top of the original, nonsensical story. And while it might sound like increasing irrationality would weaken their narrative, as propagandist Joseph Goebbels is credited with saying, "If you tell a lie big enough and keep repeating it, people will eventually come to believe it."[8] The following are the tactics employed with disorienting, relentless intensity to divert attention away from inoculation failure.

"Variants" and why They Destroy the Entire Narrative
The first half of 2021 was categorized by a tremendous drop in, "cases." At the midway point of the year, "cases," started to spike again, in many places beyond any levels previously seen in the Covid era. This was also a time when inoculation uptake was on a trajectory to reach Fauci's initial sales penetration goals of 70% or higher. And so, the concept of virus, "variants," was introduced, largely for three purposes:

1. To explain away the inevitable cold/flu symptoms and subsequent positive PCR tests of the, "fully vaccinated"
2. To justify boosters
3. To maintain the culture of fear

According to the CDC, variants are genetic mutations of the original virus, and there were at least 10 officially being tracked in late 2021.[9] Variants are not identified by PCR test obviously, since not even the alleged original, "variant," of SARS-CoV-2 is specifically identified using those, as we've covered.[10] They are, however, claimed to be identified using genomic sequencing of the extracted RNA of the virus. Don't ask me how laboratories can possibly know the RNA they're extracting is from the virus itself, when not even the official process of, "isolation," involves actually *isolating* and labs are certainly not going through the process that *is* done with every single test sample. We're as unlikely to get answers on that as they are to be able to demonstrate their findings to the layperson in a way that makes any sense.

But according to the NIH itself, the, "vaccines," were designed to deliver a *general*—not SARS-CoV-2 specific—coronavirus spike protein, which was created immediately before the first cases of the alleged pandemic were even officially identified. The official story, per *Axios*, says that this spike protein was derived based on SARS-CoV-1 and also applies to SARS-CoV-2. Also, according to the aforementioned La Bert study on natural immunity, natural immunity to SARS-CoV-1 also carries over to SARS-CoV-2.

The CDC claims there are *nine* other, "variants being monitored," of which they claim have had no apparent consequence and for which the same immunity, "rules," apply. In fact, some of these alleged strains have been considered, "more infectious than Delta," yet are at the same time, "symptomless."[11] What purpose is there to make such a claim of an infectious, yet symptomless virus other than to maintain the control-facilitating fear narrative that other human beings are diseased and to be avoided? Actual headlines like *Bloomberg*'s, "What's Worst About Omicron So Far Is the Uncertainty," prove there is no other purpose.[12] Given the fact that asymptomatic spread is an impossible concept to begin with, such claims are just more nonsense to throw on a mountain of nonsense.

Meanwhile, outside scientists have discovered there to be closer to 100,000 distinct genomes sampled from patients around the world.[13] So, given the lack of consequence of all this variation, is the, "delta variant," considered to be *so significantly* different to both SARS-CoV-1 and SARS-CoV-2 that its immunity profile is also different? Clearly SARS1 and SARS2 must have been similar enough for the same shot to be considered appropriate for both. If this isn't the case for, "delta," which it clearly isn't based on larger-than-ever case spikes and inoculated sick people, how could, "delta," even be considered in the same family of virus?

Another glaring issue all these, "variants," present is the extent of, "variation." Even with at *least* 100,000 distinct genomes, to assume all variations have been identified is not probable at all. So clearly *most*, if not *all*, of the viruses in question have a distinct genetic code. And this is where the problem comes because when the CDC alleges a, "delta," variant outbreak for example, it is not doing genomic testing on each sample to confirm, but is rather making assumptions about increases in, "cases," based on extrapolation. With so much variation though, this does not seem like a good assumption at all.

The questions start to pile up behind this topic because it's a claim which follows from bad claims, and it's made with even less evidence. For example, the newest, "variant," as of late November has been called the, "omicron," or, "nu," variant.[14] It was also alleged by *the Telegraph* to somehow itself have an, "eye-watering number of mutations," on November 26, 2021, despite having only been allegedly identified in 10 cases worldwide. It was initially called out only three days earlier on *Twitter* by Tom Peacock, who is employed at, of all places, Imperial College London—the same Imperial College London behind the horrendously wrong, tyranny-justifying projection models. Despite the demonstrable failure of lockdowns since the Covid era began, countries have wasted no time shutting down travel from African countries and announcing new restrictive measures based on this alleged, "variant."[15] Also, despite the fact that there were only 10 identified cases in the entire world, the WHO suggested there could be, "re-infection risk."

News of this, "variant," comes only 3 months after the natural immunity studies which largely made the public realize how irrationally coercive public health's obsession with, "vaccinating," the population was. It also conveniently came within a week of a November 18, 2021 *Yahoo News* article acknowledging that Africa was less than 6% vaccinated but Covid cases were practically non-existent on the continent.[16] This left the, "experts," *Yahoo* cited baffled, but apparently did not lead a single one to admit the obvious conclusions it would imply for both the efficacy of the inoculations and the existence of an indiscriminate viral pandemic in general. Such obvious truths made it difficult for Fauci and his collaborators to come up with a reason why people should still get the shots and/or boosters. And this culminated in Pfizer CEO Albert Bourla making the confusing claim that a, "variant," which could, "escape the protection of our vaccine," would eventually emerge.[17]

First of all, if this was, "likely," as Bourla says it was, and if the old strains simply become irrelevant once the new ones come around, what's the point of, "vaccinating," for last year's strain, as was done in 2021? Second, if these, "variants," occur in nature, it is simply impossible—not unlikely—*impossible*—for Bourla to make this kind of prediction and for it to come true precisely as predicted, only three months later … that is, other than if he had foreknowledge his product was going to fail—foreknowledge Bourla *was shown* to have had, as a March 2022 document dump revealed Pfizer's own data from as early as September 2020 showed efficacy waned by as much as 50% in as little as 1 month after the second dose (aka, no efficacy).[18,19]

No matter how little sense it might seem to make though, what Bourla is attempting to do here for mRNA inoculations is a tried and true strategy at this point in the world of pharma vaccines. For example, the vaccine industry talks of new flu, "strains," every year and literally says their goal is to simply make a, "best guess," at what the next year's strain will be.[20] Many people who get those vaccines however, are the very same who find themselves getting the flu every year. I know of several people in my own family who have stopped taking them for this reason, as each year they'd take a flu shot they'd, "mysteriously," come down with the flu. The racket continues though as any time this failure to immunize happens it can be explained away with the convenient, perpetual excuse of, "strains," or, "variants."

We will discuss the very specific business/financial reasons Bourla employs this strategy in the final section of this chapter. But for now the most obvious medical reason is that he knows inoculated individuals will get sick eventually (as we all do when our bodies build up toxicity via poor lifestyle habits). So, this inevitability of cold or flu-like symptoms leads to an inevitability of positive PCR tests. In fact, based on previous studies of spike protein based inoculations, he would know that the vaccine-enhanced disease and hypersensitivity we previously covered were also very real possibilities that would need to have some kind of explanation prepared.

Fauci himself acknowledged this as early as March of 2020 during an interview with *Facebook* CEO Mark Zuckerberg.[21] During that interview he admitted, "This would not be the first time, if it happened, that a vaccine that looked good in initial safety actually made people worse," citing a previous RSV vaccine. As a necessary aside, think about this statement with the context of Fauci's premeditation to skip the standard, decade-long safety process he cited vaccines are supposed to go through. This quote shows Fauci knew there could be potentially catastrophic risks to skipping over this process, yet he made it his mission to do so anyway. And he did so while urging people universally to take this risk, in some cases even suggesting it be mandatory, as he suggested it should be even for school age children.[22] This is just another notch in the belt of evidence of Fauci's crimes, but it's a significant one. In the next chapter we will cover how much of a gross, criminal informed consent violation it is that every single person who ultimately received a shot was not required to acknowledge this risk immediately prior, despite Fauci's admission.

For now though, a few things should be pretty clear. The first is that, "the science," (the narrative) of, "variants," is not coherent. And what makes this even more pronounced is how little sense the people who introduce these, "variants," make in order to sell the inoculations. For example, take Moderna chief medical officer Dr. Paul Burton, who claimed two variants could strike at the same time, "swap genes," and combine into a super variant.[23] You heard the man—be afraid of the Super Megatron Variant and pray Moderna's genius, "innovators," (in reality, NIH scientists) will come through with some new solution! Besides providing comic relief, these impossible-to-substantiate claims demonstrate there is truly no limit to the mental gymnastics these companies will go through in order to explain away the failure of their products.

So if, "variants," are the reason the inoculated get sick and new, "variants," continuously become the dominant strain, why do our institutions continue telling us to get inoculated? Additionally, for those who are already inoculated, why get a booster of the same shot when the first two doses were overcome by, "variants," in less than a year? This narrative breaks the entire inoculation campaign because it requires an impossible balancing act between convincing people the inoculations are both ineffective without continuous boosters (to sell the inoculated), but also still somehow effective enough to be worth taking at all (to sell the, "unvaccinated").

The message also became even more badly mixed, when in December of 2021 the news broke that the US army had developed a new, "super-vaccine," which was claimed to be, "effective against all COVID variants."[24] This should have been extremely confusing to anyone who was inoculated however, considering the incessant messaging at the same time that the current, EUA-approved inoculations were, "safe and effective." It is also strange when considering the downright abusive prodding and polarization by those inhabiting the White House for people to get those shots with the, "omicron variant," allegedly spreading[25]:

> *"We are intent on not letting omicron disrupt work and school for the vaccinated. You've done the right thing, and we will get through this.*
> ***For the unvaccinated, you're looking at a winter of severe illness and death for yourselves, your families, and the hospitals you may soon overwhelm*** *(my emphasis)."*

Merry Christmas and a happy New Year to all (the compliant)! Many hilarious memes followed this message, ridiculing its exceptionally wicked tone by an administration of which 41% of its own Democrat voter base believed could be illegitimate according to *Rasmussen* polling.[26] It's also not as if the messages of the public health oligarchs themselves were any less wicked. Consider the following senseless panic-inducing drivel from WHO Director Ghebreyesus during the same Christmas 2021 season[27]:

> *"... an event cancelled is better than a life cancelled. It's better to cancel now and celebrate later than to celebrate now and grieve later."*

Back to the, "super-vaccine," why would anyone take it if Biden, Fauci, and their cabal are saying the current ones do the job? They'd have to admit those initial shots aren't doing the job at some point. And if I was a betting man, I'd guess that's exactly what they'll do, for reasons I will address shortly.

To close off on this section though, even alternative, non-fear mongering, non-pharma-tied doctors who attempt to speak in the context of, "variants," struggle to make coherent sense of them, in my opinion. Now I have to say this so I'm not misinterpreted: I have nothing but respect for people like Dr. Zelenko and Dr. McCullough—in fact I believe their actions during this time have been historically heroic. Unlike the censorious psychopaths of public health, I simply believe it's possible to agree on the situation and agree to disagree on the conclusions about the situation.

That said, the reason why I think they are off as it relates to, "variants," is that they are adopting the language of people who started from a place of fraudulent pseudoscience. Again, if the narrative of the initial, "alpha variant," of the alleged SARS-CoV-2 virus doesn't make sense, and the issues with it are never addressed, the conclusions you make on topics that extend from it (like variants of it) are naturally going to end up impossible to logically follow. For example, comparing the mortality/morbidity risk of, "delta," or, "omicron," to, "alpha," is pointless when you know for a fact both mortality and morbidity statistics for, "alpha," were made meaningless by the garbage methodology used to collect them. And that's not to say that methodology has even improved in 2021—it hasn't, because it's built on selling a story and not identifying and/or comparing meaningful phenomena.

For those alternative doctors, many draw two conclusions:

1. With the virus left to its own devices, any, "variants," which emerge will increasingly become less impactful, as they are so similar to the original that the body will still recognize them[28]
2. Per Dr. Zelenko, the inoculations create a kind of, "evolutionary pressure," on the alleged virus that causes it to mutate.[29] This is posited as opposed to the downright silly mainstream narrative that the, "unvaccinated," cause this variation and if only every single person (or some percentage they never accurately or definitively pronounce) got the shot, the, "herd," would become immune—this despite the fact that those shots don't make the individual immune. Per Dr. Luc Montagnier (2008 Nobel Prize for discovery of the AIDS virus—a discovery we've pointed out has been disputed by many, including PCR inventor Kary Mullis), the, "vaccines,"

actually, "feed the virus," and facilitate its development into stronger and more transmittable variants.[30]

For #1, I believe it *is* logical that a person who recently experienced a cold/flu is less likely to experience one again within a time period of 6 months to a year. This is, based on my conclusions, because the body has flushed out, via the symptoms of cold and flu, much of the toxicity built up within it by the time the illness has run its course. Therefore, it would be reasonable to expect it to take time to build up the levels of toxicity again which bring on illness. Applying this to the conclusions of those who think in terms of, "variant," terminology, if a new variant is allegedly observed within a year, the people who were already sick with a previous variant are, of course, going to have superior immunity (less toxicity), assuming their lifestyle remains unchanged. It is therefore easy to see how the identification of, "variants," could be conflated with simple processes, the same way, "Covid," was conflated with the simple processes of cold and flu before being exacerbated by experimental drugs.

Another explanation is seasonal activity, as people tend to travel more, exercise less, eat far more, and drink far more alcohol during the winter holiday seasons. These poor nutrition/lifestyle changes during a time of reduced vitamin D intake from reduced sunlight are a recipe for what is referred to as cold/flu season. In fact, Mayo-Clinic-trained, Board-Certified Pathologist Dr. Ryan Cole of Idaho gave a presentation in 2020 where he explained that, "there is no such thing as, 'flu and cold season,' only low vitamin D season," and how the lack of public health messaging on basic vitamin/nutritional health during the Covid era was a complete failure.[31]

To address #2 about inoculation-caused evolutionary pressure, Dr. Montagnier's claim that the inoculation can cause worsened disease is easily explained by the hypersensitivity, vaccine-enhanced disease, and/or antibody dependent enhancement we've discussed previously that vaccines can cause. Those things do *not* necessarily imply vaccines caused a worsened outbreak, but could rather suggest the vaccines damaged the immune system's natural ability to cope with the usual things it faces and handles by introducing something foreign and/or toxic. So what Dr. Montagnier says here is a theory which could be reasonable but to me seems better explained by observable phenomena that make more sense in my opinion (vaccine complications).

I also don't believe it makes sense this claim of evolutionary pressure would apply to the Covid inoculations since they clearly provide no immunity and therefore would put no pressure on the alleged virus to mutate. One might counter this by saying, "but the 'alpha' variant vanished after the inoculations so the inoculations must be what led to the new variant." While I agree this is a logical conclusion based on the public-health-organized data related to, "variants," we've already discussed the faults of that data and how the methodology used to collect it perverts any conclusions. The first issue with interpreting the false data in this way is that the final, "alpha," case spike did not fall off a cliff in January 2021 because of the inoculations, as we've discussed. In fact, it started dropping significantly prior to the first inoculations even entering arms. Therefore, since the inoculations were not responsible for suppressing, "alpha," I don't think it makes much sense to say they caused any kind of pressure enough to lead to variation.

The second issue with the data collection is as it relates to there being evidence of a viral pandemic at all. For example, if what was alleged to be a pandemic was actually a hospital-centric, public health genocide thanks to dangerous, novel medications, lack of early care, and false diagnoses—as I've laid out the case for to this point—then the entire idea there was a virus outbreak (and subsequent mutations) is false. I'm not saying that theory isn't a possibility at all, and I will address all theories and my support for/against each in a future chapter. For now though, I simply think the incoherence of the, "variant," narrative and the conclusions that flow from it imply it is not a meaningful way to explain what is happening—and this is reflected in the unmitigated failure of the public health officials who've alleged it to prevent any suffering and death despite the awareness/understanding they claim to have of it.

Boosters (Subscription Inoculations) and the Mix-and-Match Meme Comes to Life

As we saw via the experiences of the senators at the beginning of this chapter, boosters were introduced in the second half of 2021 and they, like the inoculations they are meant to supplement, do not work at all by any intended or discernable metric. What they do work to do however, is to ensure a taxpayer-funded income stream in perpetuity. No one understands the value of this subscription-medicine scheme better than apparent-oracle Bill Gates, from whom the following social media post was prophetically (ominously) posted on December **19, 2019**, two weeks before the Chinese identified the first pneumonia cases and two months after Gates' foundation simulated a coronavirus pandemic[32]:

> *"What's next for our foundation? I'm particularly excited about what the next year could mean for one of the **best buys in global health: vaccines** (my emphasis)."*

Gates, Fauci, and their co-conspirators at the CDC create an endless cycle of confusion via boosters by pressuring people to take them instead of ever addressing the questions which have arisen with the original two doses. This is the same strategy employed with virus, "variants," versus the alleged original—maximum claims, maximum confusion. We covered the impossible balancing act this creates in the previous section, but the logical is not important to them. What is important is that they flex their authority with hollow slogans and big (if illogical) ideas, while slandering any opposition through their media PR teams as, "anti-vax," "anti-science," and/or, "conspiracy theorists." The average person then assumes they themself are either, "too dumb," or, "not an expert," and therefore must just be unable to make sense of things due to a lack of education—nevermind the fact that countless highly-educated and experienced scientists/doctors are among the slandered, with PhDs acknowledged by the media to be the most reluctant to get inoculated.[33]

So the rest—not stupid, just misinformed and lacking in confidence—go along with things like the term, "fully vaccinated." This term is, like all definitions in the opinion of the perpetrators, open to any change at any time. Today it could mean one dose, tomorrow it could mean three, and next month it might mean six or more. In September for example, Fauci, along with countries like Israel, decided to increase the definition from two shots, to two shots and a booster.[34] This came in the wake of the, "delta variant," wave demonstrating the first signs of inoculation failure. Fauci's solution was another shot, but it was easy then to see that this was a cycle which would never end. And it hasn't ended, as the solution for the, "omicron variant," is now a fourth shot, as Fauci shrugs and claims that for some reason, "We'll just have to deal with it."[35]

What anyone who accepts the term, "fully vaccinated" (I can't imagine why anyone would still at this point) will, "just have to deal with," is an endless game being played with their life and health. Like we covered before, the CDC can't even define, "unvaccinated," the way any rational, honest person would define it. These words mean whatever they want them to mean, whenever they need them to mean something new. Because of this constant shifting, whenever the term, "fully-vaccinated," is used to represent something in data or studies it must now be carefully scrutinized. This adds yet another layer of complexity that intentionally obfuscates "Covid," data and analyses.

Matters get even more complicated when considering the CDC and FDA also recommend a, "third shot," *not* considered a booster, for immunocompromised people.[36] Without saying the word, "boost," the CDC claims this shot is an additional boost to the protection which they allege will be provided to these people—but it's *not* a booster, so don't call it one! You can see at this point there is no rhyme or reason to any of this reckless behavior. The CDC seemingly has no limit on the number of shots a person should get. A person who receives a, "third shot," should still get a, "booster," shot in their opinion. For those people that's a total of four inoculations in one year, with Fauci talking currently about a likely fifth on the way, as countries like Israel have already been giving people.[37] In fact, Israeli Health Ministry Vaccination Advisory Committeeman Arnon Afek admitted[38]:

> *"Those who think we won't need to take more boosters are wrong. We will need to take the 4th shot, the 5th shot, the 6th shot, the 7th shot. As long as the pandemic continues in places like Africa, where only few are vaccinated, new variants of COVID-19 will develop and the need to protect against them with vaccines, will continue."*

To translate for those who don't understand that countries like Africa will never reach Afek's desired, undefined threshold: continuous, subscription inoculations will not end if these people have it their way. And even without this confession, does anyone seriously think it would or should end, given the argument they give of, "waning immunity," to justify it? After what number of shots does, "immunity," stop, "waning?" They can't possibly know the answer to that question and they don't even care to find it because their goal isn't immunity or improved health—it's shots in arms, no matter how reckless the extent of intervention gets. The credo, "do no harm," does not apply here. Thanks to Fauci's stated goal of making people think differently about the flu, the Hippocratic Oath has been abandoned for a regime of what can only be described as senseless experimentation.

So anyone still on the train would be foolish to expect anything less than at *least* two or three more shots in 2022, likely more. And the saddest part is that despite claims of this being based on newly-discovered, "science," the ridiculous nature of the boosting regimen (along with pretty much every other aspect of this scheme) was, "predicted," (the pre-meditation was observed and pointed-out) by those paying attention as soon as, "Operation Warp Speed," was announced. In fact, little did those of us who were hip to it know, our memes about mixing a little Pfizer with a double shot of Johnson & Johnson & Johnson (third Johnson for the additional boost) would soon become a hilarious reality. Shockingly, despite differences in dosage and the nature of each brand as a whole, in 2022 mixing shot types remains official policy of the major US public health organizations.[39] And it remains so without any official recommendations to date for which to mix or not to mix, or which order to mix them or not mix them—proving once again that the official policy is pharma profit viability and experimentation.

"Vaccine" Passports, Senseless Coercions, and Societal Sabotage

> *"Eventually what we'll have to have is certificates of who's a recovered person, who's a vaccinated person ... so eventually there will be this digital immunity proof that will help facilitate the global reopening up."*

—Bill Gates, March 2020[40]

The above sentence on, "digital immunity proof," said by Bill Gates was edited out of the video it's sourced from by TED Talk producers. I can only assume his having said it makes Gates a, "conspiracy theorist," who spouted, "dangerous misinformation," when considering the following February 28, 2020 blogpost headline by *Vice*[41]:

"Anti-Vaxxers Are Terrified the Government Will 'Enforce' a Vaccine for Coronavirus: Anti-vax groups on social media are claiming that the spread of the disease will lead to mandatory vaccinations and 'unlimited surveillance.'"

It appears the, "anti-vaxxers," propagandists like *Vice* are paid to slander were simply listening to and taking seriously the insane comments of Gates and his fellow oligarchs. Like all the perpetrators of these crimes, Gates made claims here he couldn't have possibly made without foreknowledge and motive. For example, how could he have known in March 2020 that inoculations and the enforcement of those inoculations for public engagement were even a viable solution, let alone a necessary one? In doing so he effectively ruled out the possibility of an effective, cheap, repurposed treatment in the earliest days of the alleged pandemic. Why? And, given our understanding of the damage caused by the suppression of early treatment he helped facilitate, at what cost?

The only possible answer is that he had a predetermined plan to do so, a plan we know he did have thanks to his actions during both the, "decade of vaccines," and the months immediately preceding the alleged Covid outbreak in China. But there is more evidence of pre-meditation too, such as the April 2020 sprouting of tech platforms like the Covid Credentials Initiative and Covi-Pass, each designed to facilitate vaccine passport programs at a time well before the inoculations were even an available option.[42,43]

As we know, Gates now admits his promises were wrong and the, "vaccines," do not prevent transmission. Preventing transmission is literally the only thing that could even theoretically be used to justify a, "vaccine passport," and the mRNA inoculations, by all accounts, do not achieve this. Even if they did though, there would remain no justification whatsoever to entertain the notion of such an oppressive, evil thing, especially without the opportunity for religious, personal, or any other exemption a person could desire to declare. And this has even been admitted by the very officials pushing for it. Israeli Health Minister Nitzan Horowitz, for example, was caught on a hot mic in the fall of 2021 saying[44]:

"There is no medical or epidemiological justification for the Covid passport. It is only intended to pressure the unvaccinated to vaccinate."

While this type of boldness is unsurprising in our time, one has to ask why someone like Horowitz isn't forced by any kind of law enforcement to answer for his actions, given these remarks. Medical and epidemiological excuses were all there was since the beginning to attempt to justify the widespread violation of inalienable human rights. Am I still to be considered a, "conspiracy theorist," for acknowledging that the only possible excuses left are financial, tyrannical, and/or downright wicked? People like me who wished not to comply with this madness were considered, "selfish," and were ridiculed for laying claim to those rights which our societies previously acknowledged are bestowed upon us by God alone. How can there be no consequences for the unjustified tyrannies which have sought to subvert that acknowledgement, in the name of a technology the people selling it publicly admit they'd rather not honestly advertise or even have to prove works?

Again, despite admissions of program failure, criminal attempts at enforcement and deceit including but not limited to the following have continued:

- Those who run the Joe Biden Regime sought to mandate inoculations at companies of 100 or more via OSHA.[45] This came just months after OSHA removed its work-related vaccine injury reporting requirement for the Covid inoculations.[46] The organization admitted the decision for removal of this requirement was not logical or ethical, but strictly to, "encourage COVID-19 vaccinations." The combination of these moves with pharma liability protection and the lack of any medical or epidemiological support whatsoever represents a disgusting, criminal disregard for human life, dignity, and protection under the law. The corrupt White House knows this too, as it absurdly claims the term, "vaccination mandate," is, "misinformation," and the proper term is, "vaccination requirement."[47] With or without these illegal OSHA mandates receiving support from the courts, many companies have already illegally fired people for their refusal to engage in a medical experiment.

- Directly on the heels of airline executives acknowledging to Congress the futility of mask-wearing and lack of infection potential on flights due to airplane filtration systems, unelected bureaucrat Anthony Fauci went on his usual propaganda tour.[48] First, Fauci not only denounced the perfectly rational point made by the airline executives, he took it a step further by saying he doesn't think we will *ever* reach a point, "where we don't have to wear masks on airplanes."[49] As always, he said this without any supporting evidence whatsoever. Still, he wasn't done. Even though Fauci included the, "vaccinated," among those who'd need to wear masks forever, he still suggested that, "A vaccine requirement for a person getting on a plane is just another level of getting people to have a mechanism that would spur them to get vaccinated; namely, you can't get on a plane unless you're vaccinated." Again, Fauci's only justification for this is getting people, "vaccinated." This criminal salesman does not care about even attempting to provide any medical or epidemiological reasoning, because he knows they don't exist. Thus, what he is doing is calling for the human rights violation of forbidding the free movement of people by the heavily government-subsidized (and therefore public-entitled) airline industry, with no cause but profit. This is just one of a long list of crimes against humanity he has yet to answer for.
- On January 5th, 2022 the state of New York was set to vote on a variety of human-rights-violating bills as follows[50]:
  - Assembly Bill A8378 – Mandatory, "Covid," inoculations to attend school[51]
  - Bill A279a/S75a – All adult inoculation records into state database[52]
  - Bill A7829/S6495 – Mandatory inoculations to attend college[53]
  - Assembly Bill A8398 – Eliminates religious exemptions for work and college[54]
  - Bill A3091/S3041 – Eliminates parental consent for inoculation once child reaches 14 years of age[55]

- o Assembly Bill A416 – Allows Governor to imprison without trial anyone considered a threat to public health[56]
- o Assemblyman Patrick Burke proposed bill to allow denial of insurance coverage to, "unvaccinated," people for, "Covid-related," treatment (cold, flu, pneumonia, and all other diseases relabeled, thanks to PCR).[57] Side note: in fairness, this would be fantastic for the, "unvaccinated," since, "Covid-related treatments," sanctioned by the government and utilized in hospitals are a death sentence 80% of the time, as we've covered.

- The WHO defines an, "implied consent," process for inoculating children as, "the physical presence of the child or adolescent, with or without an accompanying parent at the vaccination session, is considered to imply consent."[58] They worm their way into an attempted justification by saying the parent should be informed by, "social mobilization and communication," beforehand. However, they explicitly differentiate this from direct written or verbal parental consent, meaning those who don't actually notice such communications prior to sending their kids to a school during an inoculation campaign would be out-of-luck. This is wrong and yet another human rights violation related to children by a globalist organization with a troubling history of committing such violations.[59]

- Austria implemented a November 2021 lockdown of only the, "unvaccinated," which was followed by its largest case spike in the Covid era.[60] Police patrolled the streets of Vienna demanding proof of a, "vaccination," with no medical or epidemiological benefit. Vienna saw a December protest in response including an estimated 44,000 people, a massive number considering the size of the city.[61] Germany and others pushed toward following suit despite tremendous protests of their own and vast majority opposition as high as 89%, according to a removed-in-shame Good Morning Britain poll.[62,63]

- WHO director Tedros Adhanom acknowledged, "vaccine passports," were discriminatory in a discussion with Brazilian president Jair Bolsonaro.[64] Still, he and other world leaders refuse to officially denounce them or declare the inoculation campaign the failure that it is, even by the standards they themselves declared prior to the rollout. *European* Union chief Ursula von Der Leyen, for example, ironically called for scrapping the Nuremberg Code and requiring inoculations throughout the continent.[65] I'm sure von Der Leyen's documented friendship with Pfizer CEO Albert Bourla is a total coincidence as it relates to this stance.

- Per a December 2021 *Bloomberg News* report, the CDC has been over-counting the number of Americans who are inoculated.[66] In the report, it is acknowledged (and admitted by the CDC itself) that the CDC was counting second doses and booster doses as first shots. Specifically, it showed 99.9% of Americans over 65 inoculated for several weeks, before revising it down to 95%. This number is likely still far too high, as state officials from Illinois, Pennsylvania, and West Virginia alone acknowledge over-counting in the current aggregate inoculation rate of 72.5% which would subtract millions of, "vaccinated." The preceding is a dereliction of duty by the CDC beyond just the negligence it implies. It's also extremely deceitful, in that the more people are inoculated, the more the perception will shift toward getting inoculated as a way to fit in with the crowd. This is a marketing tactic and the CDC, which we've demonstrated and will continue to demonstrate is more focused on words and psychology which will sell inoculations than it is on health, is nothing if not a pharma marketing department.

- In Australia, largely the epicenter of some of the world's most shocking tyrannies in the Covid era, State of Victoria Premier Daniel Andrews said the following[67]: *"If you are not vaccinated, and you could be, the chances of you booking a ticket at a sporting event, going to a pub, will be limited ... There is going to be a vaccinated economy, and you get to participate in that if you are vaccinated. We're going to move to a situation where, to protect the health system, we are going* *to lock out people who are not vaccinated and can be ... **It's not going to be safe for people who are not vaccinated to be roaming around the place spreading the virus** (my emphasis)."* Given that no honest person at all pretends the, "vaccinated," do not, "spread the virus," the outright lie Andrews pushes here and the actions he takes in the name of this dogma make him a historically horrendous dictator.

This coercion has also come without compromise or caveat, despite the senseless societal sabotage that's resulted in its wake. The following are some dumbfounding examples of said sabotage:

- Brownfield Regional Medical Center faced closure over a, "vaccine," mandate which would have put out 25% of its workforce.[68] To put that into its astonishing context: it is the job of doctors and nurses to face and care for diseased patients. Brownfield doctors and nurses cared for patients claimed to have, "Covid," for an almost two year period without inoculation. Then, in the name of, "protecting," them from this alleged disease they would've already regularly come in close contact with, as it is their job to do, the hospital implemented a mandate so strict it could lead to the collapse of the entire hospital, since these doctors and nurses were so passionate about not being inoculated.
- A New York Hospital stopped delivering babies after employees were forced out over its, "vaccine," mandate.[69] Again, this comes in the name of an alleged disease which even by false, over-counted official mortality standards has a 99.9% case fatality rate for anyone giving birth or in the profession of helping to give birth.
- The Ronald McDonald House of Vancouver, British Columbia evicted cancer-suffering children over the age of 5 who were, "unvaccinated," once that age group became eligible for the shots.[70] Local father Austin Furgason was one example whose son had Leukemia. Staff informed Furgason his son would be evicted because of the policy despite admitting the, "vaccinated," were still able to get and transmit the alleged virus. The father rightly called the policy, "evil," and, "an abomination."

- Dr. Peter McCullough testified about a young navel cadet patient of his who got a significant heart injury from the first shot.[71] According to McCullough, the cadet's, "commanders and every doctor in the naval academy," still told him to get the second shot.

- In similarly horrific story, 9-year-old Tanner Donaldson was reported as suffering from stage 5 chronic kidney disease and urgently needed a kidney transplant.[72] Miraculously, his father Dane was a perfect match and in early 2018 Cleveland Children's Hospital approved the transplant. However, as of February 2022 the hospital decided to deny the transplant following a new, "cruel, illogical, unscientific," policy demanding the donor—not the patient—be inoculated. The hospital reportedly received approximately $114 million in NIH funding in 2021.[73]

- Supply chain issues already faced in the USA were threatened to be compounded further by the nation's own government, thanks to inoculation mandate threats for truckers.[74] 2.5 million truckers said they'd quit over such mandates. While American truckers currently do not face an imminent threat of such a mandate, the US is set to require foreign cross-border tuckers (people sitting alone in vehicles for many miles at a time) to be inoculated starting January 22, 2022.[75]

- At the same time these supply-chain-facilitating foreign truckers are being economically threatened into a medical experiment, the White House refuses to explain why foreign illegal immigrants crossing the US border are not. In fact, when asked why there are attempts to mandate citizens but not illegals, Press Secretary Psaki simply and snidely replied, "That's correct."[76] For context, the *New York Times* reported 1.7 million illegal immigrant encounters in 2021.[77] And the reason these massive numbers of illegals are not required to inoculate is simple: forcing shots into their arms would be a war-crime, while economic coercion of citizens can be dishonestly portrayed to a court as still being the inoculated individual's own free decision. An inoculated individual, they would argue in criminal court where they belong, could have always quit their job. Sure, they'd have been made to face

300

senseless hardship in their own nation, because of their own government. But in the, "Land of the Free," being free of oligarch puppetry comes at a cost now.

- Los Angeles County Sheriff Alex Villanueva acknowledged the, "imminent threat to public safety posed by the city's inoculation mandates on his police force.[78] With 20-30% of the force refusing to take the shot and homicides continuing to rise in the city, the actions of the local government were rightfully considered, "absolutely absurd," by the Sheriff.
- In order to, "maintain combat readiness," the US military in February 2022 was reported as sabotaging combat readiness by discharging perfectly healthy soldiers who refused to be experimented on[79]
- In a more comical, epic-fail example, the *New York Post* reported on a NYC COVID inspector being kicked out of a bar for failing to show proof of inoculation[80]

In a sane, just society the above would be considered clear violations of the Nuremberg Code points on the illegality of medical coercion of any kind. Based on the intentional, senseless societal sabotage these actions have caused, in my opinion they should also be considered either acts of war, treason, or whatever other appropriate legal term to describe the terrorism inflicted upon nations around the world. Given those violations, which we know *did* occur, tribunals for crimes against humanity should be held for all those responsible. In our society, those trials are currently being sought out via charges filed in December 2021 with the International Criminal Court.[81] Those charges (for now, focused on the UK) hold Gates and Fauci, among others, responsible for genocide related to the damage done in the name of the pandemic they alleged, as well as the experimental inoculations they helped coerce. And while it is hard to have faith in a global judicial system during a globalist coup, the mere fact that the charges were filed is a reason to be hopeful that consciousness is rising.

The FDA's Criminal Bait and Switch

The lawlessness and regulatory capture which characterizes today's western governments and their bureaucratic bodies was perhaps never displayed more prominently than it was by the FDA in

2021. The most egregious example of this was the FDA's bait and switch tactics related to its misleading August 23, 2021 approval of the, "Comirnaty," inoculation. Comirnaty is the brand name given to the EUA-authorized Pfizer/BioNTech inoculations. As such, blogs like the *Washington Post* were quick to report that the Pfizer/BioNTech shots could now be mandated.[82] This spurred New York City Mayor Bill de Blasio to require them for teachers and school staff, the Pentagon to proceed with a mandate for military service members, and countless others to enact similar coercions.[83,84]

However, there were three problems with these actions following the apparent FDA approval. The first and most obvious was that none of the illegal mandates which followed were specific to Comirnaty *or even* the Pfizer/BioNTech shot—the governments and companies who adopted them accepted Moderna and Johnson & Johnson as well. According to the FDA itself, "under section 564 of the Federal Food, Drug, and Cosmetic Act (FD&C Act) … FDA may authorize [for emergency use] unapproved medical products … when certain criteria are met, including there are no adequate, approved, and available alternatives."[85] Therefore, if the FDA had actually approved the Pfizer/BioNTech inoculation on August 23, 2021, from that day forth the Moderna and Johnson & Johnson shots should have lost their EUAs and all uses since then should have been considered illegal until similar approvals were granted to them (which, to-date as of January 2022, they have not).

And this brings us to the second issue, which is that the full approval of an, "adequate, approved, and available alternative," was clearly *not* granted. You see, the FDA provided a specific disclaimer in its approval that the, "Comirnaty," (approved) and, "Pfizer/BioNTech," (EUA-authorized) inoculations are, "legally distinct with certain differences."[86] In November 2021 a federal district court judge also acknowledged these distinctions, rejecting a claim by the US Department of Defense that the two products are interchangeable.[87]

The reason this is extraordinarily relevant is because of the legality of mandating a EUA-authorized inoculation, versus one which is fully-approved—namely, it is not legal to mandate a EUA-authorized drug.[88] The reason for this is that EUA-authorized drugs are legally considered experimental and cannot be mandated in any way per both the Nuremberg Code globally and in the US per the code under which EUAs are defined, 21 US Code Sec.360bbb-3(e)(1)(A)(ii)(iii).[89] The FDA fact sheet also acknowledges this, stating, "Under the EUA, it is your choice to receive or not receive the vaccine."[90] Therefore, unless the product being given to a person is specifically labeled, "Comirnaty," they cannot be required or coerced in any way to take it.

While one might think this is semantics, it is actually fundamental to what makes the FDA's, "approval," a corrupt deception. Like we touched on before, the fine print of what allows the FDA to issue EUAs is that there are no, "adequate, approved, and available alternatives." Since Comirnaty is now considered, "adequate and approved," the only explanation for why the three EUA-authorized shots are not now illegal is that Comirnaty *must not* be, "available." If it were, the FDA has been illegally failing to revoke the EUAs and therefore has officially been allowing people to be experimented on by mandate since August 23rd.

But four months later Comirnaty still wasn't available, and as of December 30, 2021 even the CDC acknowledged, "Comirnaty products are not orderable at this time," and that, "Pfizer does not plan to produce any product with these [Comirnaty] NDCs [National Drug Codes] and labels over the next few months while EUA-authorized product is still available and being made available for US distribution."[91,92] With this definitive confirmation it is clear the, "approval," by the FDA, alleged to be unlawful in at least one court case, can only be explained as a lie spread to encourage inoculation under false premises.[93] This fake approval would and did also provide a mirage of legality to what are actually illegal mandates to take the experimental inoculations, since Comirnaty is *not* interchangeable with the Pfizer/BioNTech experimental EUA shots.

The last but not least detestable issue related to this fake approval brings us back to our chapters on the FDA's slander and rejection of early treatments like ivermectin. Despite the countless controlled randomized studies demonstrating ivermectin (among other cheap, repurposed treatments) to be effective, the FDA refused to acknowledge and approve its use for, "Covid," for a very specific reason: because doing so would mean there was an, "adequate, approved, and available alternative." This would lead to the revocation of the EUAs granted to the shots, making them illegal, and would mean without going through the decade-long period of trials

Fauci openly rejected as the basis for this entire conspiracy, they would not get approval for all ages and the primary goal of universal inoculation would be foiled.

The situation somehow becomes darker when considering the liability shields afforded to EUA-authorized products as well.[94] This liability shield is the reason EUAs are so desirable to pharmaceutical companies and their financial allies in government. As long as the government can declare, "emergency," as a false justification for this scheme, it will. In fact, internal documents from GAVI show major manufacturers are so worried about legal risks from harmful side effects that they would refuse to give inoculations to migrants or countries without the coverage of these shields.[95] This is an extraordinary admission considering the FDA approvals and incessant, "safe and effective," propaganda we've been blasted with.

Actual citizens these governments are designed to represent are, unfortunately, not so lucky. Per the *Defender*, the official method of redressing damages is the, "extremely stingy," Countermeasures Injury Compensation Program.[96] However, the program's administrators have compensated less than 4% of petitioners to date—and not a single Covid, "vaccine," injury, despite the fact that as of December 30, 2021 a total of 1.84M adverse events had been reported to the CDC's VAERS system.[97] We will cover *way* more on these adverse events in the next chapters, but this lack of righting damages represents an objectively cruel system. This is especially so when considering those behind the conspiracy to sell the inoculations are the same as those counting, "cases," and alleging a pandemic, while censoring the questions/concerns of literally tens of thousands of prominent doctors and scientists. To add insult to injury, *Human Events* reported on 180 victims who suffered the consequences of the, "safe and effective," lie and were left with no other option but to turn to GoFundMe for support.[98]

This brings us to the particularly stomach-turning reason Pfizer/BioNTech would rather distribute their drug under EUA labels instead of distributing the approved drug Comirnaty, while still benefiting from the appearance of the FDA's despicable, "approval." The National Childhood Vaccine Injury Act (NCVIA), passed into law in 1986, provides a legal liability shield to drug manufacturers, only if they receive full authorization for all ages.[99] With this in mind, the reason for the aggressive fall 2021 campaign to get children inoculated despite their having zero risk of serious, "Covid," illness (even using incorrect, official Covid numbers) becomes clear: children are being set up as legal human shields in order to secure perpetual, non-emergency liability protection.

Today, this takes the form of testing being done on children under 5.[100] To this point such testing has been found to be, "ineffective," but instead of accepting the lack of risk to this demographic as is and moving on (the obvious thing to do for any moral person), Pfizer has decided to attempt testing a third shot on babies. And despite Pfizer's inability to come up with even a flimsy justification to inoculate this age group, the FDA has managed to raise even more suspicions by moving forward with an authorization plan anyway.[101] This is also why Fauci is pushing for mandatory, "Covid," inoculations in schools—because without this all-ages coverage, an approved Comirnaty would be subject to normal liability like every other product. So the sooner mass adoption takes place, the sooner the FDA will secure the political capital needed for approval.[102]

The reason I say, "political capital," and not, "scientific evidence," is simple: these are not scientific organizations. These are organizations willing to inflict unfathomable damage upon people in order to secure power and money. This is why when asked in court for the documentation it used to approve the Pfizer inoculation in less than a year, the FDA requested (in the age of the internet) the court provide it until the year 2076 to release all the documents.[103] When it came time to submit its brief in this aforementioned case it then doubled-down and requested it be given until 2096.[104] The Plaintiff in the case argued the FDA should need, "only twelve weeks," which still seems extremely generous considering how simple it is these days to click the, "upload," and, "send," buttons.[105] The judge ultimately ruled Pfizer would be given less than a year to release its clinical trial data, at which point the company made the following change to its, "business risk disclosures," in its Q4 2021 earnings presentation:

> *"Risks and uncertainties related to our efforts to develop and commercialize a vaccine to help prevent COVID-19 ... including, among others ... the possibility of unfavorable new pre-clinical, clinical or safety data and further analyses of existing pre-clinical, clinical, or safety data."*

—Pfizer Q3 2021 Earnings Report, business risk
disclosures[106]

*"Risks and uncertainties related to our efforts to develop and commercialize a vaccine to help prevent COVID-19 ... including, among others ... the possibility of unfavorable new pre-clinical, clinical or safety data and further analyses of existing pre-clinical, clinical, or safety data **or further information regarding the quality of pre-clinical, clinical, or safety data, including by audit or inspection** (my emphasis)."*
—Pfizer Q4 2021 Earnings Report, business risk
disclosures[107]

Such changes reveal more and more that both Pfizer and the FDA know what they are doing is wrong. In fact, shortly after top FDA inoculation head Peter Marks, the Biden Regime, and the CDC railroaded through approval of booster shots in August 2021, two of the FDA's most senior officials who disagreed with the decision resigned from the organization.[108] Since-resigned director of the FDA's Office of Vaccines Research & Review Marion Gruber and deputy director Phil Krause even penned a paper in the *Lancet* shortly after, in which they explained how evidence of booster benefit was, "preliminary and difficult to interpret."[109] They and their fellow highly-credentialed co-authors added the following bombshell opinion of the situation:

"Careful and public scrutiny of the evolving data will be needed to assure that decisions about boosting are informed by reliable science more than by politics."

If even two senior officials who support inoculation are recognizing a political problem at the expense of their long-held positions, you can be sure the problem is a significant one. The booster agenda continued forward without evidence anyway, however. The resignations of long-held positions also didn't end there, as NIH Director Francis Collins also announced his resignation in October 2021.[110] This sudden departure of one of the primary figures behind the Covid inoculation push came just as the Biden Regime had, "increasingly put Collins on network shows to urge vaccinations and defend the booster strategy." It also followed a Pfizer insider being caught on camera admitting to a *Project Veritas* reporter that natural immunity is better than inoculation and that their, "organization is run on Covid money now."

While this might seem unrelated and it might seem a stretch to assume guilt plays a role, consider Collins' manic behavior in claiming those who criticize Anthony Fauci should be, "brought to justice."[111] Collins made this unconstitutional assertion as Fauci, an employee of the US government and therefore answerable to the American people, was receiving, "angry messages." Perhaps Fauci would receive less criticism if he and/or Collins would even once address/debate the very critics they prefer to censor than to discourse with, but that's another issue. What we know of Fauci is that he *did* conspire to sell the world on mRNA inoculations in the months immediately prior to the alleged pandemic. That's not a, "theory," it's a video-recorded historical event. Collins surely knows this, and knows that the more this type of information spreads the more likely he too would be on the chopping block. So there is reason to suspect his resignation, like the defensive tone he's adopted as it plays out, comes with a hint of desperation due to the writing on the wall.

Of course, Collins is right to not want to be associated with this crime, especially at a time when it involves the experimentation on children the FDA signed off on in the fall of 2021. During that time, the organization held an advisory panel open forum in which outside experts were able to present on whether or not EUAs should be granted for Covid shots for the 5-11 year-old demographic. In an example of the utter disregard for human life which has come to plague the FDA, this meeting and consideration was still given despite a troubling University of California study which came out weeks before about this very age group.[112] The study, led by Dr. Tracy Heog, found that the teenage boys were six times more likely to suffer heart problems caused by the inoculations than they were to be hospitalized with a positive PCR test for, "Covid." And what was Pfizer's answer for this? Their briefing document for inoculation in kids 5 to 11 admits they have none and won't for the foreseeable future[113]:

"The number of participants in the current clinical development program is too small to detect any potential risks of myocarditis associated with vaccination. Long-term safety of COVID-19 vaccine in participants 5 to <12 years of age

will be studied in 5 post-authorization safety studies, including a 5-year follow-up study to evaluate long-term sequelae of post-vaccination myocarditis/pericarditis."

It is obviously outrageous that Pfizer plainly admits they're experimenting on children, and doing so on what they desire to be a universal scale. With states mandating these shots for children to attend school, for the FDA to ignore studies like the one conducted by Dr. Heog is madness. But the warning signs didn't end with the Cal study, either. When the advisory panel convened several doctors and experts who presented to the FDA testified that the inoculations were killing more than they were saving.[114] Dr. Jessica Rose for example pointed out how:

- VAERS-reported death counts for Covid inoculations showed a more-than 1,000% increase over any previous year's worth of vaccine-related deaths
- This translates to 1/660 individuals inoculated *reporting* (*without* considering significant under-reporting factors) an immunological adverse event
- Inoculations demonstrated clear transmission failure in Israel, regardless of number of shots administered
- Her belief the aforementioned failure could suggest the shots contribute to the emergence of, "variants"

Another contributor to the panel was Dr. Richard Fleming, who discussed his team's findings on the impact these mRNA inoculations have on the blood.[115] In his presentation, Dr. Fleming showed images of how the Pfizer/BioNTech inoculation directly caused blood clots and oxygen deprivation. He finished the two minutes he was allotted by urging the FDA and CDC to do their jobs.

A third presenter was Dr. Steve Kirsch, who cited the deaths of several children as the immediate result of inoculation, as well as the following[116]:

- His estimate of the VAERS under-reporting factor (more on this in the next chapter) and question of why the CDC misleads by making no attempt to define one
- A 2021 study by Kostoff et al. in *Toxicology Reports* which shows that, "people in the 65+ demographic are **five times as**

likely to die from the inoculation as from COVID-19 under the most favorable assumptions (my emphasis)," and that the rate is even worse for those younger[117]

Dr. Kirsch then went on to ask the following prudent questions, among others, which remain unanswered:

- Is there any, "stop," condition which, if met, would trigger the inoculation program to be halted?
- Why are there no post-inoculation-death autopsies?
- Why didn't the highly unusual reported deaths post-inoculation in children including pulmonary embolism and intracranial hemorrhage in the CDC's own 12-17 safety study raise red flags?[118]
- Why are the 1,200 public comments, "against," and 1 comment, "for," inoculating kids ignored?
- Why is the FDA calling a 559-fold increase in myocarditis reported to VAERS from 2020 to 2021 a, "slightly elevated risk?"

Another presenter was Dr. Brian Dressen, who urged the committee to reject the EUA not only as a matter of his professional expertise on analyzing such technologies, but also since his wife Brianne suffered significant neurological damage after the first dose of AstraZeneca.[119] Dr. Dressen told the advisory panel their, "decision was being rushed, based on incomplete data from underpowered trials, insufficient to predict rates of severe and long-lasting adverse reactions." But Dr. Dressen's most shocking revelation was that his wife was, "dropped from the trial, her access to the study app deleted," because the study required two doses. What is the FDA's explanation for the 266 participants described as having adverse events leading to discontinuation and 56 neurological reactions? What's their justification for ignoring them?

Finally, a review was posted at this same time by Dr. Toby Rogers which explained how the FDA was actually violating the CDC's own, "Guidance for Health Economic Studies Presented to Advisory Committee on Immunization Practices (ACIP), 2019 Update," which is meant to serve as an outline for such actions as these 5-11 EUA recommendations.[120,121] Per Dr. Rogers, at least half of the 21 things that the CDC says every health economics study in

309

connection with vaccines must contain were violated by the FDA risk-benefit analysis. And the crucial piece (per the CDC's own guidance) pointed out as missing/ignored in the FDA's analysis was a metric called Number Needed to Vaccinate (NNTV), a risk-benefit metric for those, "saved," versus harmed. In four separate places the CDC mentions the importance of this metric, yet the FDA makes no mention of it in their analysis. Dr. Rogers conducted his own NNTV however, which suggests why it was disregarded. He came to the following conclusion:

> *"So, to put it simply, the Biden administration plan would kill 5,248 children via Pfizer mRNA shots in order to save 45 children from dying of coronavirus. **For every one child saved by the shot, another 117 would be killed by the shot** (my emphasis)."*

Despite these warnings and unanswered questions, the FDA committee members approved the EUA anyway, with a 17-0 vote. And while this approval is unconscionable, it is not surprising in the least, seeing as members of this committee included, "the former vice president of Pfizer Vaccines, a recent Pfizer consultant, a recent Pfizer research grant recipient, a man who mentored a current top Pfizer vaccine executive, a man who runs a center that gives out Pfizer vaccines, the chair of a Pfizer data group, a guy who was proudly photographed taking a Pfizer vaccine, and numerous people who are already on the record supporting Covid vaccines for children."[122] Oh, and recent FDA Commissioner Scott Gottlieb also happens to be on Pfizer's board of directors.

More on this insane web of conflicts of interest later, but you can see the means, motive, and opportunity come together when considering the background of those behind this otherwise-unfathomable scheme. And whether or not the decision was intentionally malicious is irrelevant when it comes to the consequences of it. What matters is that these people knew the risks and knew they were significant. They knew their decision would impact potentially hundreds of millions of children in the US and around the world, a group which—and this can't be restated enough—had a 1 in a million risk of severe disease, even using false attribution methodology. Yet still, when it came time to either condemn or defend the most innocent demographic, they didn't exercise even the least bit of care/restraint. Their goal would be achieved at all costs, and they knew they wouldn't be liable (at least financially) for their choice either way. And so, it was fitting that at such a hearing one of the most reckless, chilling, unethical statements in the history of medicine came courtesy of Committeeman Dr. Eric Rubin[123]:

> *"We're never gonna learn about how safe the vaccine is* [for children] *until we start giving it. That's just the way it goes."*

Endnotes

1   Balagtas, Tristan. 2021. "Sen. Cory Booker Reveals He Tested Positive For Breakthrough COVID-19: 'Relatively Mild'". *PEOPLE.Com.* https://people.com/politics/cory-booker-tests-positive-breakthrough-covid-19-vaccinated/.

2   Ibid.

3   Spencer, Christian. 2021. "Fully Vaccinated Man Dies Of COVID-19, Daughter Says He Was Cautious". *Thehill.* https://www.thehill.com/changing-america/well-being/prevention-cures/567402-fully-vaccinated-man-dies-of-covid-19-daughter.

4   "Utah Leaders Have Surrendered To COVID Pandemic, The Editorial Board Writes". 2022. *The Salt Lake Tribune.* https://www.sltrib.com/opinion/editorial/2022/01/15/utah-leaders-have/.

5   Sharma, Shweta. 2021. "Obituary Blames Unvaccinated People For Woman's Death, Says 'The Cost Was Her Life'". *The Independent.* https://www.independent.co.uk/news/world/americas/obituary-blames-unvaccinated-people-illinois-b1921091.html.

6   "Leana Wen: Being Unvaccinated And Going Out In Public Is Like Drunk Driving". 2021. *Hotair.Com.* https://www.hotair.com/allahpundit/2021/09/10/leana-wen-being-unvaccinated-and-going-out-in-public-is-like-drunk-driving-n415075.

7   "Dr. Leana Wen Warns Americans That Vaccinated People Carry More Virus And Are Superspreaders - The Last Refuge". 2021. *The Last Refuge.* https://theconservativetreehouse.com/blog/2021/09/26/dr-leana-wen-warns-americans-that-vaccinated-people-carry-more-virus-and-are-superspreaders/.

8   "Joseph Goebbels On The "Big Lie"". 2022. *Jewishvirtuallibrary.Org.* Accessed March 16. https://www.jewishvirtuallibrary.org/joseph-goebbels-on-the-quot-big-lie-quot.

9   "SARS-Cov-2 Variant Classifications And Definitions". 2021. *Cdc.Gov.* https://www.cdc.gov/coronavirus/2019-ncov/variants/variant-info.html.

10   Holt, Dejaris. 2021. "Delta Variant: How Do I Get Tested For It?". *Fox News.* https://www.foxnews.com/health/delta-variant-testing.

11   Isgin, Kieran, and Alexander Smail. 2021. "New Symptomless Covid Strain 'More Infectious Than Delta' Being Investigated". *Glasgowlive.*

https://www.glasgowlive.co.uk/news/new-symptomless-covid-strain-more-22218807.

12   Kluth, Andreas. 2021. "What's Worst About Omicron So Far Is The Uncertainty". *Bloombergquint.* https://www.bloombergquint.com/gadfly/omicron-has-a-lot-of-unknowns-and-waiting-for-answers-leads-to-anxiety.

13   van Dorp, Lucy. 2020. "Coronavirus Mutations: What We've Learned So Far". *The Conversation.* https://www.theconversation.com/coronavirus-mutations-what-weve-learned-so-far-145864.

14   Schachtel, Jordan. 2021. "New Variant Hysteria Comes From Same Institution That Popularized Lockdowns & Previous COVID Scares". *Dossier.Substack.Com.* https://dossier.substack.com/p/nu-variant-hysteria-originated-with.

15   Phillips, Jack. 2021. "WHO Labels New COVID-19 Variant 'Omicron,' Possible Increased Re-Infection Risk". *Www.Theepochtimes.Com.* https://www.theepochtimes.com/who-labels-new-covid-19-variant-omicron-possible-increased-re-infection-risk_4125906.html?slsuccess=1.

16   CHENG, MARIA, and FARAI MUTSAKA. 2021. "Scientists Mystified, Wary, As Africa Avoids COVID Disaster". *News.Yahoo.Com.* https://news.yahoo.com/scientists-mystified-wary-africa-avoids-074905034.html.

17   Rivas, Kayla. 2021. "Pfizer CEO Says COVID-19 Vaccine-Resistant Variant Likely To Emerge". *Fox News.* https://www.foxnews.com/health/pfizer-bourla-covid-19-vaccine-resistant-variant-likely-emerge.

18   Kesslen, Ben. 2021. "'Striking' Vaccine Resistance In Omicron Variant: Columbia University". *Nypost.Com.* https://www.nypost.com/2021/12/16/columbia-university-finds-omicron-vaccine-resistance/.

19   Kirsch, Steve. 2022. "Things You Should Know About The New Pfizer Documents". *Stevekirsch.Substack.Com.* https://stevekirsch.substack.com/p/10-things-you-should-know-about-the?s=r.

20   Hammond, A.M. 2020. "How Does The Flu Shot Work? How It Protects Against The Flu And Why It Changes Every Year". *Insider.* https://www.insider.com/how-does-the-flu-shot-work.

21   Becker, Kyle. 2021. "Dr. Fauci Admits That Covid Vaccines May Actually Make People 'Worse': "It Would Not Be The First Time"". *Trending Politics.* https://www.trendingpolitics.com/dr-fauci-admits-that-covid-vaccines-may-actually-make-people-worse-it-would-not-be-the-first-time-knab/.

22   Lungariello, Mark. 2021. "Dr. Fauci Says He Supports COVID Vaccine Mandate For Children". *Nypost.Com.* https://www.nypost.com/2021/09/21/dr-fauci-says-he-supports-covid-vaccine-mandate-for-children/.

23   "Omicron And Delta Variants May Strike People At The Same Time And
        Combine To Create An Even Worse Covid Variant In The Coming
        Weeks - Moderna Boss Warns". 2021. *Globaltake News.*
        https://www.globaltake.com/omicron-and-delta-variants-may-strike-
        people-the-same-time-and-combine-create-even-worse-covid-variant-the-
        coming-weeks-moderna-boss-warns/.

24   Dutton, Jack. 2021. "Super Vaccine Effective Against All COVID
        Variants Created By U.S. Army". *Newsweek.*
        https://www.newsweek.com/super-vaccine-effective-against-all-covid-
        variants-omicron-created-army-1662000.

25   Pavlich, Katie. 2021. "The Latest White House Statement About The
        'Unvaccinated' Is Making People's Skin Crawl". *Townhall.*
        https://www.townhall.com/tipsheet/katiepavlich/2021/12/20/the-latest-
        white-house-statement-about-the-unvaccinated-is-making-peoples-skin-
        crawl-n2600842.

26   "Voters Against 'Zuckerbucks' Influencing Elections".
        2021. *Rasmussenreports.Com.*
        https://www.rasmussenreports.com/public_content/politics/general_politi
        cs/december_2021/voters_against_zuckerbucks_influencing_elections.

27   Charles, Nathaniel. 2021. "W.H.O. Says Cancel Christmas Now Or
        'Grieve Later'". *Breitbart.*
        https://www.breitbart.com/politics/2021/12/22/w-h-o-says-cancel-
        christmas-now-or-grieve-later/.

28   Lewnard, Joseph A., Vennis X. Hong, Manish M. Patel, Rebecca Kahn,
        Marc Lipsitch, and Sara Y. Tartof. 2022. "Clinical Outcomes Among
        Patients Infected With Omicron (B.1.1.529) SARS-Cov-2 Variant In
        Southern California". doi:10.1101/2022.01.11.22269045.

29   Zelenko, Vladimir. 2021. "December 26, 2021 Telegram Post By Dr.
        Vladimir Zelenko". *Telegram.* https://t.me/zelenkoprotocol/2448.

30   "Two Top Virologists' Frightening Warnings About COVID Injections:
        Ignored By Government And Big Media — News From The Perimeter".
        2021. *News From The Perimeter.*
        https://www.newsfromtheperimeter.com/home/2021/8/27/two-top-
        virologists-frightening-warnings-about-covid-injections-ignored-by-
        government-and-big-media.

31   "Dr. Ryan Cole - Covid Mistakes". 2021. *Bitchute.*
        https://www.bitchute.com/video/hfzL5gUeQvxr/.

32   Gates, Bill. 2019. "Bill Gates On Twitter December 19, 2019 9:20
        AM". *Twitter.*
        https://mobile.twitter.com/BillGates/status/1207681997612748801/.

33   Thaler, Shannon. 2021. "Americans With Phds Are Most Reluctant To
        Get Vaccinated Against COVID". *Msn.Com.* https://www.msn.com/en-
        us/news/us/americans-with-phds-are-most-reluctant-to-get-vaccinated-
        against-covid/ar-AANjRHh.

34   Hoft, Jim. 2021. "Crazy Fauci Moves The Goalposts Again -- "Fully
        Vaccinated" Now Means 2 Shots Plus One Booster". *The Gateway*

313

Pundit. https://www.thegatewaypundit.com/2021/09/crazy-fauci-moves-goalposts-fully-vaccinated-now-means-2-shots-plus-one-booster/.

35   Schnell, Mychael. 2021. "Fauci: 'If It Becomes Necessary To Get Yet Another Boost, Then We'll Just Have To Deal With It'". *Thehill*. https://www.thehill.com/news/administration/585462-fauci-if-it-becomes-necessary-to-get-yet-another-boost-then-well-just-have.

36   "COVID-19 Vaccines For Moderately Or Severely Immunocompromised People". 2022. *Cdc.Gov*. https://www.cdc.gov/coronavirus/2019-ncov/vaccines/recommendations/immuno.html.

37   Efrati, Ido. 2021. "Why Israel Went For A Second COVID Booster Shot". *Haaretz.Com*. https://www.haaretz.com/israel-news/why-israel-went-for-a-second-covid-booster-shot-1.10487608.

38   Huff, Ethan. 2021. "Israel Says Covid Booster Shots Will Now Be ENDLESS". *Truth11.Com*. https://www.truth11.com/2021/12/13/israel-says-covid-booster-shots-will-now-be-endless/.

39   "COVID-19 Vaccine Booster Shots". 2022. *Cdc.Gov*. https://www.cdc.gov/coronavirus/2019-ncov/vaccines/booster-shot.html.

40   ""Eventually What We'Ll Have To Have Is Certificates Of Who's A Recovered Person..." - Bill Gates". 2020. *Bitchute*. https://www.bitchute.com/video/eNR3ebBNzvFT/

41   Merlan, Anna. 2020. "Anti-Vaxxers Are Terrified The Government Will 'Enforce' A Vaccine For Coronavirus". *Vice.Com*. https://www.vice.com/en/article/m7q5vv/anti-vaxxers-are-terrified-the-government-will-enforce-a-vaccine-for-coronavirus.

42   "COVI-PASS™ | HEALTH AUTHENTICATED | COVI-PASS™". 2020. *COVI-PASS*. https://web.archive.org/web/20200525204351/https://www.covipass.com/#CoviPassEndorse.

43   "Covid Credentials Initiative : Home". 2020. *Web.Archive.Org*. https://web.archive.org/web/20200415021233/https://www.covidcreds.com/.

44   Cohen, Josh. 2021. "No "Medical Justification"; Israel Health Minister Caught On Hot Mic Moment". *The Raging Patriot*. https://theragingpatriot.org/2021/09/28/no-medical-justification-israel-health-minister-caught-on-hot-mic-moment/.

45   "APPEALS COURT PERMANENTLY ENDS BIDEN OSHA CIVILIAN VAX MANDATE". 2021. *CD Media*. https://creativedestructionmedia.com/news/politics/2021/11/12/busy-evening-for-vax-tyranny-ok-national-guard-general-ends-vax-mandate-appeals-court-upholds-stay-on-biden-civilian-corporate-mandate/.

46   Hamachek, Brent. 2021. "Employers Are No Longer Required By OSHA To Record Worker Side Effects From COVID Vaccine | Human Events". *Humanevents.Com*. https://humanevents.com/2021/06/29/employers-are-no-longer-required-by-osha-to-record-worker-side-effects-from-covid-vaccine/.

47   Nelson, Steven. 2021. "White House: Calling Vaccine Policy 'Mandate' Is 'Misinformation'". *Nypost.Com*. https://www.nypost.com/2021/11/05/white-house-calling-vaccine-policy-mandate-is-misinformation/.

48   Solomon, John. 2021. "Fauci Pushes Masks, Vaccine Mandates For Airline Travel In Apparent Shot Against Industry". *Just The News*. https://www.justthenews.com/politics-policy/coronavirus/fauci-pushes-masks-vaccine-mandates-airline-travel-apparent-shot.

49   "Fauci Says People Should Wear Masks Forever, Even After Vaccination". 2021. *ADN América*. https://www.adnamerica.com/en/united-states/fauci-says-people-should-wear-masks-forever-even-after-vaccination.

50   Smythe, Kay. 2021. "New York Legislation Provides For Indefinite Detention Of Unvaccinated At Governor's Whim.". *Rights And Freedoms*. https://rightsfreedoms.wordpress.com/2021/12/20/new-york-legislation-provides-for-indefinite-detention-of-unvaccinated-at-governors-whim/.

51   *Assembly Bill A8378*. 2021. Amd 2164 & 613, Pub Health L. The New York State Senate.

52   *Assembly Bill A279A*. 2021. Amd 2168, Pub Health L. The New York State Senate.

53   *Assembly Bill A7829*. 2021. Amd 2165, Pub Health L. The New York State Senate.

54   *Assembly Bill A8398*. 2021. Add 2164-a, rpld 2165 sub 9, Pub Health L. The New York State Senate.

55   *Assembly Bill S3041*. 2021. Add 2167-a, Pub Health L. The New York State Senate.

56   *Assembly Bill A416*. 2021. Add 2120-a, Pub Health L. The New York State Senate.

57   "Assemblyman Pat Burke Proposing Bill To Allow Insurance To Deny COVID Treatment Coverage For Unvaccinated". 2021. *Wkbw.Com*. https://www.wkbw.com/news/local-news/assemblyman-pat-burke-proposing-bill-to-allow-insurance-to-deny-covid-treatment-coverage-for-unvaccinated.

58   "Considerations Regarding Consent In Vaccinating Children And Adolescents Between 6 And 17 Years Old". 2014. *Who.Int*. https://www.who.int/immunization/programmes_systems/policies_strategies/consent note en.pdf.

59   BUCKS, JONATHAN. 2015. "UN Officials 'Force Children To Perform Oral Sex For Food' In Warzones | World | News | Express.Co.Uk". *Express.Co.Uk*. https://www.express.co.uk/news/world/627783/Starving-children-as-young-as-NINE-forced-to-give-UN-officials-oral-sex-to-get-food/amp.

60   Watson, Paul Joseph. 2021. "Days After Locking Down The Unvaccinated, Austria Hits COVID Case Record". *Summit.News*.

https://summit.news/2021/11/18/days-after-locking-down-the-unvaccinated-austria-hits-covid-case-record/.

61   "Tens Of Thousands Protest Against Compulsory
Covid Jabs In Austria". 2021. *Lucianne*. https://www.lucianne.com/2021/12/11/tens_of_thousands_protest_against_compulsory_covid_jabs_in_austria_74773.html.

62   Haddad, Mohammed. 2021. "Mapping Coronavirus Anti-Lockdown Protests Around The World". *Aljazeera.Com*. https://www.aljazeera.com/news/2021/2/2/mapping-coronavirus-anti-lockdown-protests-around-the-world/.

63   "TV Show Deletes Poll After 89% Oppose Mandatory Vaccination". 2022. *Nexus Newsfeed*. https://nexusnewsfeed.com/article/geopolitics/tv-show-deletes-poll-after-89-oppose-mandatory-vaccination/.

64   Shilhavy, Brian. 2021. "Brazilian President Tells WHO Director "People Are Dying" After COVID Shots – Pleads With WHO To Publicly NOT Recommend It For Children - Medical Kidnap". *Medical Kidnap - News On Medical Abductions By Hospitals And Government Social Agencies.*. https://medicalkidnap.com/2021/11/11/brazilian-president-tells-who-director-people-are-dying-after-covid-shots-pleads-with-who-to-publicly-not-recommend-it-for-children/.

65   "SHOCKING: In The Wake Of Austria's Drastic Lockdown Of Unvaccinated People, EU Chief Calls For Throwing Out Nuremberg Code". 2021. *FIGHT4USA*. https://fight4usanews.wordpress.com/2021/12/05/shocking-in-the-wake-of-austrias-drastic-lockdown-of-unvaccinated-people-eu-chief-calls-for-throwing-out-nuremberg-code/.

66   Wingrove, Josh. 2021. "Vaccine Data Gaps Point To Millions More In U.S. Who Lack Shots". *Bloomberg.Com*. https://www.bloomberg.com/news/articles/2021-12-18/vaccine-data-gaps-point-to-millions-more-in-u-s-who-lack-shots.

67   Hansen, Stevie Ray. 2021. "Australian Government Says Unvaccinated People Will Be "Locked Out" Of The - Www.Hnewswire.Com". *Www.Hnewswire.Com*. https://hnewswire.com/australian-government-says-unvaccinated-people-will-be-locked-out-of-the/.

68   Heilman, Zach. 2021. "Vaccine Mandate Causes Healthcare Worker Shortage, TX Hospital May Close". *Red Voice Media*. https://www.redvoicemedia.com/2021/09/vaccine-mandate-causes-healthcare-worker-shortage-tx-hospital-may-close/.

69   LANDEN, XANDER. 2021. "New York Hospital To Stop Delivering Babies After Employees Resign Over Vaccine Mandate". *Newsweek*. https://www.newsweek.com/new-york-hospital-stop-delivering-babies-after-employees-resign-over-vaccine-mandate-1628177.

70   "'This Is Some Kind Of Crazy Evil': Father Of Boy With Leukemia Rips Ronald Mcdonald House Vaccine Mandate | Charlie Kirk". 2022. *Charlie Kirk*. https://charliekirk.com/news/this-is.

71   "Dr. Peter Mccullough Becomes Emotional Speaking About The Societal Impact Of Group Think [VIDEO] - Walls-Work.Org". 2022. *Walls-Work.Org*. https://walls-work.org/dr-peter-mccullough-becomes-emotional-speaking-about-the-societal-impact-of-group-think-video/.

72   Edwards, Michelle. 2022. "9-Year-Old Boy Denied Kidney Transplant Because Donor Dad Isn't Vaccinated - Uncoverdc". *Uncoverdc*. https://uncoverdc.com/2022/02/23/9-year-old-boy-denied-kidney-transplant-because-donor-dad-isnt-vaccinated/.

73   The National Institutes of Health. 2022. "NIH Awards By Location & Organization". NIH. https://report.nih.gov/award/index.cfm?ot=&fy=2021&state=&ic=&fm=&orgid=10000858&distr=&rfa=&om=n&pid=&view=state.

74   Richards, Tori. 2021. "2.5 Million Truckers Say They'll Quit Over Vaccine Mandate, Industry Warns Biden". *Washington Examiner*. https://www.washingtonexaminer.com/policy/2-5-million-truckers-say-theyll-quit-over-vaccine-mandate-industry-warns-biden.

75   Tabak, Nate. 2021. "Report: US To Require Vaccines For Cross-Border Foreign Truckers Starting Jan. 22". *Freightwaves*. https://www.freightwaves.com/news/report-us-to-require-vaccines-for-cross-border-foreign-truckers-starting-jan-22.

76   Brown, Spencer. 2021. "Psaki Can't Explain Why Biden Mandated Vaccines For Americans But Not Illegals". *Townhall*. https://www.townhall.com/tipsheet/spencerbrown/2021/09/10/psaki-cant-explain-why-biden-mandated-vaccines-for-americans-but-not-illegals-n2595705.

77   Sullivan, Eileen, and Miriam Jordan. 2021. "Illegal Border Crossings, Driven By Pandemic And Natural Disasters, Soar To Record High". *Nytimes.Com*. https://www.nytimes.com/2021/10/22/us/politics/border-crossings-immigration-record-high.html.

78   "'Threat To Public Safety.' L.A. Sheriff Villanueva To Discuss COVID Vaccine Mandate". 2021. *Msn.Com*. https://www.msn.com/en-us/news/crime/threat-to-public-safety-la-sheriff-villanueva-to-discuss-covid-vaccine-mandate/ar-AAQehOp.

79   "U.S. Army Begins Discharging Soldiers Who Refuse COVID-19 Vaccine". 2022. *Reuters*. https://www.reuters.com/world/us/us-army-discharge-soldiers-who-refuse-covid-19-vaccine-2022-02-02/.

80   Brown, Lee. 2021. "NYC COVID Inspector Booted From Bar For Failing To Show Proof Of Vaccination". *Nypost.Com*. https://nypost.com/2021/12/17/nyc-covid-inspector-booted-from-bar-for-failing-to-show-proof-of-vaccination/.

81   Hope, Justus R. 2021. "Gates, Fauci, And Daszak Charged With Genocide In Court Filing". *The Desert Review*. https://www.thedesertreview.com/opinion/columnists/gates-fauci-and-daszak-charged-with-genocide-in-court-filing/article_76c6081c-61b8-11ec-ae59-7718e6d063ed.html.

82   Guarino, Ben, Laurie McGinley, and Tyler Pager. 2021. "Pfizer-Biontech
      Coronavirus Vaccine Gets Full FDA Approval, Potentially Persuading
      The Hesitant To Get A Shot". *The Washington Post.*
      https://www.washingtonpost.com/health/2021/08/23/pfizer-vaccine-full-
      approval/.

83   ELSEN-ROONEY, MICHAEL, and MICHAEL GARTLAND. 2021.
      "Mayor De Blasio Announces Vaccine Mandate For All NYC Public
      Schools Staff". *The New York Daily News.*
      https://www.nydailynews.com/new-york/ny-schools-vax-mandate-
      20210823-4oszhp6nfnbh7bexjftqflnhai-story.html.

84   Long, Pam. 2021. "Will Military Mandate COVID Vaccines? Know Your
      Rights.". *Children's Health Defense.*
      https://www.childrenshealthdefense.org/defender/military-mandate-
      covid-vaccines-exemption-rights/.

85   "Emergency Use Authorization". 2022. *U.S. Food And Drug
      Administration.* https://www.fda.gov/emergency-preparedness-and-
      response/mcm-legal-regulatory-and-policy-framework/emergency-use-
      authorization/.

86   "Q&A For Comirnaty (COVID-19 Vaccine Mrna)". 2022. *U.S. Food And
      Drug Administration.* https://www.fda.gov/vaccines-blood-biologics/qa-
      comirnaty-covid-19-vaccine-mrna.

87   "BREAKING: Federal Judge Rejects DOD Claim That Pfizer EUA And
      Comirnaty Vaccines Are 'Interchangeable' - CD Media". 2021. *CD
      Media.*
      https://www.creativedestructionmedia.com/news/2021/12/01/breaking-
      federal-judge-rejects-dod-claim-that-pfizer-eua-and-comirnaty-vaccines-
      are-interchangeable/.

88   Nevradakis, Michael. 2021. "Federal Judge Rejects DOD Claim That
      Pfizer EUA And Comirnaty Vaccines Are 'Interchangeable'". *Children's
      Health Defense.* https://www.childrenshealthdefense.org/defender/judge-
      allen-winsor-pfizer-eua-comirnaty-vaccines-interchangeable/.

89   *21 U.S. Code § 360Bbb–3 - Authorization For Medical Products For Use
      In Emergencies.* 2018.

90   The Food and Drug Administration. 2022. "Pfizer-Biontech Fact Sheet."

91   Schachtel, Jordan. 2021. "Bait And Switch: There Remains No FDA
      Approved COVID Vaccine In The United States". *Dossier.Substack.Com.*
      https://dossier.substack.com/p/bait-and-switch-there-remains-no.

92   "Preview Posting Of COVID-19 Vaccine Codes And Crosswalk For
      Currently Authorized Vaccines And Anticipation Of Potential Vaccine
      Availability Under Emergency Use Authorization (EUA)".
      2021. *Cdc.Gov.* https://www.cdc.gov/vaccines/programs/iis/COVID-19-
      related-codes.html.

93   "Covid - Defending The Republic". 2021. *Defending The Republic.*
      https://defendingtherepublic.org/Covid/#_ftn9.

94   Kennedy, Jr., Robert F., and Meryl Nass. 2021. "2 Things Mainstream
      Media Didn'T Tell You About FDA's Approval Of Pfizer

Vaccine". *Children's Health Defense.*
https://childrenshealthdefense.org/defender/mainstream-media-fda-approval-pfizer-vaccine/.

95   Guarascio, Francesco, and Panu Wongcha-um. 2021. "Refugees Lack COVID Shots Because Drugmakers Fear Lawsuits, Documents Show". *Reuters.* https://www.reuters.com/world/refugees-lack-covid-shots-because-drugmakers-fear-lawsuits-documents-2021-12-16/.

96   Kennedy, Jr., Robert F., and Meryl Nass. 2021. "2 Things Mainstream Media Didn'T Tell You About FDA's Approval Of Pfizer Vaccine". *Children's Health Defense.*
https://childrenshealthdefense.org/defender/mainstream-media-fda-approval-pfizer-vaccine/.

97   "Open VAERS". 2022. *Openvaers.Com.* Accessed March 16. https://openvaers.com/.

98   Hamachek, Brent. 2021. "People Injured By Vaccine Turn To Gofundme For Support | Human Events". *Humanevents.Com.*
https://www.humanevents.com/2021/06/28/people-injured-by-vaccine-turn-to-gofundme-for-support/.

99   Kirsch, Steve. 2021. "Here's The Real Reason Comirnaty Is Not Available". *Stevekirsch.Substack.Com.*
https://stevekirsch.substack.com/p/heres-the-real-reason-comirnaty-is.

100   Redshaw, Megan. 2021. "Pfizer To Test 3Rd COVID Shot In Kids Under 5 After Two Doses Fall Short". *Children's Health Defense.*
https://childrenshealthdefense.org/defender/pfizer-test-third-covid-shot-kids-under-five/.

101   "Doctors Question Unusual COVID Vaccine Authorization Plan For Kids". 2022. *Youtube.* https://youtu.be/thSzr4rRU9k.

102   Samson, James. 2021. "Fauci Says Children Should Be Forced To Get COVID-19 Vaccine". *Red Voice Media.*
https://www.redvoicemedia.com/2021/09/fauci-says-children-should-be-forced-to-get-covid-19-vaccine/.

103   PUBLIC HEALTH AND MEDICAL PROFESSIONALS FOR TRANSPARENCY against FOOD AND DRUG ADMINISTRATION. 2021, Case 4:21-cv-01058-P Second Joint Report. UNITED STATES DISTRICT COURT NORTHERN DISTRICT OF TEXAS.
https://www.sirillp.com/wp-content/uploads/2021/11/020-Second-Joint-Status-Report-8989f1fed17e2d919391d8df1978006e.pdf.

104   Siri, Aaron. 2021. "FDA Doubles Down: Asks Federal Judge To Grant It Until At Least The Year 2096 To Fully Release Pfizer's COVID-19 Vaccine Data". *Aaronsiri.Substack.Com.*
https://aaronsiri.substack.com/p/fda-doubles-down-asks-federal-judge?r=8ocly&utm_campaign=post&utm_medium=web&utm_source=copy.

105   Hancock, Seth. 2021. "FDA Should Need Only '12 Weeks' To Release Pfizer Data, Not 75 Years, Plaintiff Calculates". *Children's Health*

Defense. https://childrenshealthdefense.org/defender/fda-pfizer-comirnaty-vaccine-data-twelve-weeks/.

106   Pfizer. 2021. "Third-Quarter 2021 Earnings Conference Call Prepared Remarks November 2, 2021". https://s28.q4cdn.com/781576035/files/doc_downloads/event-announcement/2021/11/02/Q3-2021-Earnings-Conference-Call-Prepared-Remarks-FINAL.pdf.

107   Pfizer. 2022. "Fourth-Quarter And Full-Year 2021 Earnings Conference Call Prepared Remarks February 8, 2022". https://s28.q4cdn.com/781576035/files/doc_financials/2021/q4/Q4-2021-Earnings-Conference-Call-Prepared-Remarks-FINAL.pdf.

108   Brennan, Zachary. 2021. "In A Major Blow To Vaccine Efforts, Senior FDA Leaders Stepping Down". *Endpoints News.* https://endpts.com/breaking-in-a-major-blow-to-vaccine-efforts-senior-fda-leaders-stepping-down-report/.

109   Krause, Philip R, Thomas R Fleming, Richard Peto, Ira M Longini, J Peter Figueroa, Jonathan A C Sterne, and Alejandro Cravioto et al. 2021. "Considerations In Boosting COVID-19 Vaccine Immune Responses". *The Lancet* 398 (10308): 1377-1380. doi:10.1016/s0140-6736(21)02046-8.

110   Becker, Kyle. 2021. "Top Figure Behind United States' Covid Vaccine Push Is Unexpectedly Stepping Down". *Becker News.* https://beckernews.com/top-figure-behind-united-states-covid-vaccine-push-is-unexpectedly-stepping-down-42311/.

111   Watson, Paul Joseph. 2021. "NIH Director Calls For COVID Conspiracists To Be "Brought To Justice"". *Summit.News.* https://summit.news/2021/11/20/nih-director-calls-for-covid-conspiracists-to-be-brought-to-justice/.

112   Watson, Paul Joseph. 2021. "Study Finds Teenage Boys Six Times More Likely To Suffer Heart Problems From Vaccine Than Be Hospitalized By COVID". *Summit.News.* https://summit.news/2021/09/10/study-finds-teenage-boys-6-times-more-likely-to-suffer-heart-problems-from-vaccine-than-be-hospitalized-by-covid/.

113   The Food and Drug Administration. 2021. "Vaccines And Related Biological Products Advisory Committee October 26, 2021 Meeting Document."

114   "FDA Vaxx Panel Comes Out Against "COVID INJECT ABLE PRODUCTS" – BREAKING-NEWS.CA". 2021. *Breaking-News.Ca.* https://breaking-news.ca/fda-vaxx-panel-comes-out-against-covid-inject-able-products/.

115   "Dr. Richard Fleming: Pfizer Vaccine Causes Blood Clots Under Microscope". 2021. *Rumble.* https://rumble.com/voalls-dr.-richard-fleming-pfizer-vaccine-causes-blood-clots-under-microscope.html.

116   "Steve Kirsch Gives Presentation To FDA On EUA Pfizer 5-11 Vaccine". 2021. *Rumble.* https://rumble.com/vp4ypd-steve-kirsch-gives-presentation-to-fda-on-eua-pfizer-5-11-vaccine.html.

117   Kostoff, Ronald N., Daniela Calina, Darja Kanduc, Michael B. Briggs, Panayiotis Vlachoyiannopoulos, Andrey A. Svistunov, and Aristidis Tsatsakis. 2021. "Why Are We Vaccinating Children Against COVID-19?". *Toxicology Reports* 8: 1665-1684. doi:10.1016/j.toxrep.2021.08.010.

118   The Centers for Disease Control and Prevention. 2022. "COVID-19 Vaccine Safety In Adolescents Aged 12–17 Years — United States, December 14, 2020–July 16, 2021."

119   HATCH, HEIDI. 2021. "Utah Scientist Testifies Before FDA Panel, Asks Not To Approve COVID-19 Vaccine For Kids". *KUTV*. https://kutv.com/news/local/utah-scientist-testifies-before-fda-panel-asks-not-to-approve-covid-19-vaccine-for-kids.

120   Rogers, Toby. 2021. "What Is The Number Needed To Vaccinate (NNTV) To Prevent A Single COVID-19 Fatality In Kids 5 To 11 Based On The Pfizer EUA Application?". *Tobyrogers.Substack.Com*. https://tobyrogers.substack.com/p/what-is-the-number-needed-to-vaccinate?s=r.

121   The Centers for Disease Control and Prevention. 2019. "Guidance For Health Economics Studies Presented To The Advisory Committee On Immunization Practices (ACIP), 2019 Update."

122   Howley, Patrick. 2021. "FDA Committee Members Reviewing Pfizer Vaccine For Children Have Worked For Pfizer, Have Big Pfizer Connections". *National File*. https://www.nationalfile.com/fda-committee-members-reviewing-pfizer-vaccine-for-children-have-worked-for-pfizer-have-big-pfizer-connections/.

123   Morefield, Scott. 2021. "FDA Panel Member: 'We're Never Gonna Learn About How Safe The Vaccine Is Until We Start Giving It'". *Townhall*. https://www.townhall.com/tipsheet/scottmorefield/2021/10/26/fda-panel-member-were-never-gonna-learn-about-how-safe-the-vaccine-is-until-we-start-giving-it-n2598090.

Chapter 13

Adverse Events Pt. 1: A Mortality Catastrophe

In chapters 1-10 we covered how, "Covid," was used as a premeditated means of changing the perception of the flu, and how this was a plan devised in order to sell the world on universal mRNA inoculations. Then, in chapter 11, we covered how those mRNA inoculations were marketed using lies about a prevention of transmission which never materialized. Finally, in chapters 9 (early treatment) and 12, we saw how this well-anticipated failure was turned into opportunity in order to continue the campaign, despite a host of dangerous risk factors and the existence of safer, more effective treatments which were well known/established. Now, in the next two chapters, we will discuss the impact they have had in reality, and how the psychopathic, reckless effort to make this experiment happen constitutes attempted genocide.

The Violation of Informed Consent in Action

"Before you inject your child—a decision that is irreversible—I wanted to let you know the scientific facts about this genetic vaccine, which is based on the mRNA vaccine technology I created:

There are three issues parents need to understand:

The first is that a viral gene will be injected into your children's cells. This gene focuses your child's body to make toxic spike proteins. These proteins often cause permanent damage in children's critical organs, including their brain and nervous system, their heart and blood vessels including blood clots, their reproductive system, and this vaccine can trigger fundamental changes to their immune system.

... The second thing you need to know about is the fact that this novel technology has not been adequately tested. We need at least 5 years of testing/research before we can really understand the risks. Harms and risks from new medicines often become revealed many years later.

... In summary: there is no benefit for your children or your family to be vaccinating your children against the small risks

of the virus, given the known health risks of the vaccine that as a parent, you and your children may have to live with for the rest of their lives.

The risk/benefit analysis isn't even close.

As a parent and grandparent, my recommendation to you is to resist and fight to protect your children."

—Dr. Robert Malone, inventor of mRNA technology, December 2021[1]

It is one thing to have heard such damning statements by the inventor of PCR, Kary Mullis, about the improper use of his technology by the very public health officials currently in power; it is another thing for Mullis' disdain for those officials to be accompanied by the same from the inventor of the other technology at the heart of this disaster, mRNA; and finally, it is an absolutely outrageous third thing to see those public health officials masquerade on propagandist TV shows calling the opinions of the actual scientists whose inventions they pervert, "misinformation." The term "dystopian," does not begin to describe the phenomenon of Dr. Malone recently having also been kicked off of platforms like *Twitter* in the age when the technology he invented decades ago has seen a push toward forced popularization.[2,3]

But here we are. And thankfully, in the absence of a force like Mullis, Dr. Malone fights on for what he believes to be true. As we covered in the chapter on censorship, there should be nothing remotely controversial about that. If someone like this believes there to be an issue with a product built off of their invention, the world should not only want to hear their opinion, any attempt to silence and/or censor that opinion is and should be widely considered nefarious, by default. This isn't to say one can't disagree with said opinion either, nor should anyone submit to it without questioning. But there is only one side of this issue which, in the absence of a convincing narrative, aggressively and at times lawlessly (Psaki's *Facebook* free speech violations, for example) attempts to silence dissent.

It would seem the opinion of these people is that the less everyone knows, the better. This is supported by the atrocious lack of informed consent throughout this inoculation rollout. We've already touched on how package inserts were left entirely blank with nothing but links to a website, and how this was explained away as being due to evolving findings in the experiment. It can be added here that a full review was conducted by Cardozo et al. and published in the *International Journal of Clinical Practice*, which specifically found informed consent had not been provided as it relates to the very real risk of these inoculations worsening clinical disease.[4] Beyond that though, what we also did not go over, is that the FDA knew full well what all the risks were—and it knew this information in 2020, months before the eventual January 2021 rollout.

In a meeting titled, "Vaccines and Related Biological Products," presented online on October 22, 2020, the FDA advisory committee included a slide on a, "working list of possible adverse event outcomes."[5] The list included a variety of entirely possible side effects, all of which should have been provided on each and every package insert, with required risk acknowledgement by each and every experiment participant for the past year. If they cared at all about humanity, all appearances Fauci and his ilk made on TV should have included warnings of these possible outcomes. We know they not only didn't provide the slightest recommendation of caution, but also that many impossible promises (lies) were made.

The result is as follows. The following table is a comparison of the specific risks identified in this FDA meeting, versus the to-date, actually-reported adverse reactions in the CDC's VAERS[6]:

FDA Adverse Reaction Risks Identified	Present in VAERS
Guillian-Barré syndrome	✓
Death	✓
Encephalitis/myelitis/meningitis	✓
Pregnancy and birth outcomes	✓
Non-anaphylactic allergic reactions	✓
Convulsions/seizures	✓
Thrombocytopenia	✓
Stroke	✓
Disseminated intravascular coagulation	✓
Narcolepsy and cataplexy	✓
Venous thromboembolism	
Anaphylaxis	✓

Arthritis and arthralgia / joint pain	✓
Acute myocardial infarction	✓
Kawasaki disease	✓
Myocarditis/pericarditis	✓
Multisystem Inflammatory Syndrome	✓
Autoimmune disease	✓
Vaccine enhanced disease	✓

We will go much further into VAERS and the baffling reaction by the public health propagandists to anyone who cites it shortly. But as you can see above, basically all possible adverse reactions identified in October 2020 by the FDA have ultimately been reported to the VAERS system to-date (January 1, 2022). This alone makes it impossible to believe that the FDA and Pfizer were not aware these side effects could occur specific to these shots.

Still, if the FDA had its way, we wouldn't know whether this is the case until 2096... fortunately however, they didn't. The first court-ordered data dump of clinical trial information the FDA used to authorize Pfizer's inoculation came in March 2022. It included a list of **1,294** known, "adverse events of special interest," that the FDA hid from the public prior to the rollout.[7] I considered including the entire list here but it took up almost ten pages, so feel free to check the citation link to see for yourself. The FDA has not been made to answer for this crime to date.

So the trial results themselves in which these adverse events were identified could not have possibly gone well, despite claims of the contrary used to justify authorization. As covered in a video by Dr. Malone and a presentation by the Canadian Covid Care Alliance, a network of over 500 independent doctors, scientists, and health care providers, Pfizer's own trial saw 20 deaths in the, "vaccinated," group versus 14 in the placebo, with nearly double the amount of cardiovascular deaths among the, "vaccinated."[8,9] They also found the following violations of the best practices of such studies[10]:

- Un-blinding of the trial participants after only 2 months despite the fact that the trial was meant to go for 3 years
- Failure to track any subclinical biomarkers which would be valuable early warning signs of inoculation damage

- Introduction of tremendous subjectivity by failing to even test as many as 3,410 participants. While we know the tests are not reliable as is, even by their own nonsensical standards this is dishonest.
- Reporting of one 12-year-old trial participant as, "functional abdominal pain," who has been paralyzed to a wheelchair and forced to eat from a feeding tube for the last 10 months
- Report authors had conflicts of interest, with 84% of them either employed by Pfizer, owning Pfizer stock, receiving grants from Pfizer, hired as consultants by Pfizer, or previously running clinical trials for Pfizer. Two of the Pfizer report authors actually even made $9B in stock market profit directly from the Pfizer vaccines because they also happened to be the co-founders of BioNTech.

Perhaps the most egregious aspect of this trial however, was what the results recorded occurred prior to the un-blinding. Hidden in the supplementary appendix of the report, one can find that there were 5,241 adverse events in the inoculated group (out of 21,926 participants), versus 1,311 in the placebo group (out of 21,921 participants).[11] Of those, 262 were severe in the inoculated group, versus 150 in the placebo group. These represent a 300% increase in adverse events and a 75% increase in severe adverse events.

As we've covered in our section on remdesivir, Anthony Fauci has made a habit of sabotaging placebo groups in the name of, "ethics." Pfizer's study—and, as *NPR* admits, Moderna's too—demonstrates that this is actually a deceitful practice.[12] And it's easy to see why if you apply these numbers to the total American population inoculated. For example, let's say 200M Americans get inoculated. According to this study, there should be about 47.8M adverse events (23.9%, as seen in the study) and 2.4M severe adverse events (1.2%). However, we must take into account the baseline events should they have theoretically done nothing (placebo), meaning 12.0M adverse events (6.0%) and 1.4M severe adverse events (0.7%). This would translate to a net inoculation-caused 35.8M adverse events and 1M severe adverse events. What makes such an outcome tolerable? And if it is somehow considered tolerable, is there any number where it wouldn't be?

These actual study results and demonstrably shady practices are also further confirmed by additional allegations made of both the Pfizer and Moderna trials as follows:

- Allegations of a claimed Moderna insider[13]: *"He had worked at a research center 6 years testing various drugs and was in charge of describing and filling reports for serious adverse reactions (SAEs) ... For a normal week, he'd have 1 or 2 SAEs to file and report. When they started the Moderna trial, within a week he was having to come in early and stay late to get through stacks of SAEs. The normal acceptable threshold for SAEs is 5%. Once you cross that threshold, and more than 5% of your patients are reporting SAEs, you have to stop the trial and investigate for cause. Well, they had a rate of at least 16% after a few weeks. So, confused as to why the trial had not been flagged and halted, they looked into their SAE database and found that the majority of the ones they had reported to the agency responsible (I think FDA) were missing. They called said agency and were told that there were a high volume of SAEs being reported from multiple centers, so they were going through and removing the, 'irrelevant ones.' They claimed that the state of the pandemic warranted an unconventional approach to research."*

- Allegation by whistleblower from research organization Ventavia Research Group published in the *BMJ* about the Pfizer trial[14]: *"Revelations of poor practices at a contract research company helping to carry out Pfizer's pivotal covid-19 vaccine trial raise questions about data integrity and regulatory oversight ... for researchers who were testing Pfizer's vaccine at several sites in Texas during that autumn, speed may have come at the cost of data integrity and patient safety ... told The BMJ that the company falsified data, unblinded patients, employed inadequately trained vaccinators, and was slow to follow up on adverse events reported in Pfizer's pivotal phase III trial."*

These companies knew the dangers during the trials, and they know now after the rollout. Pfizer's, "Cumulative Analysis of Post-Authorization Adverse Event Reports," through February 2021 acknowledged 42K adverse events including 1.2K which were fatal.[15] Understand, the Swine Flu vaccination program of 1976, which had the same goal of vaccinating every American by the end of 1976, was first cut short in 9 states after only *3 deaths* occurred.[16] So where did that type of caution go? Who gave the CDC, FDA, and NIH the authority to take bigger gambles with people's lives since then, with little to no informed consent standards abided by?

What's actually in the Shots?

According to the CDC, the following are the listed ingredients of the Pfizer/BioNTech shots[17]:

- Messenger ribonucleic acid (mRNA) – mRNA encoding spike protein
- Lipids (fats) – to help mRNA enter cells. Includes polyethylene glycol.
- Salts and sugar – to stabilize molecules during shipment process

Seems innocent enough. And you can be sure it is too, because the very first sentence on the CDC's webpage under the, "Pfizer-BioNTech COVID-19 Vaccine Ingredients," header is, "All COVID-19 vaccine ingredients are safe." While you might think I'm biased toward trusting the CDC (*wink*), I will admit it is strange they find the need to say this at all, nevermind it being the first thing said prior to providing any real information. It also understandably seems a little odd when considering their acknowledgement at the top of said webpage that, "if you have had a severe allergic reaction to any ingredient in the Pfizer-BioNTech COVID-19 vaccine (such as polyethylene glycol), you should not get this vaccine." Now, I don't know about you, but I've never heard of a person being allergic to polyethylene glycol at all. In fact, I'd never even heard of polyethylene glycol prior to this situation. So I wonder how many people would even be aware of such a, "severe allergy," and why, if it's a possibility worth calling out, the CDC still finds the need to say the, "ingredients are safe."

I'm being a bit facetious here, of course, but from our previous review of Moderna's past struggles with mRNA technology we know toxicity associated with the lipid nanoparticle delivery system was their biggest ongoing roadblock—especially as it related to diseases where you'd theoretically need more protein to have an effect (i.e. 40 trillion packages worth in the current shots). In fact, the *STAT* report which covered this unanswered challenge specifically called out, "troubling safety concerns for any mRNA treatment that needs to be delivered in multiple doses, **covering almost everything that isn't a vaccine** (my emphasis)."[18] And there it is, as if we needed more evidence what is being administered aren't vaccines! The publication *Nature* also ridiculed Moderna in 2016 for never so much as publishing a single paper answering any outstanding questions and, "thinking they are better off if no one knows what they do or how they do it."[19]

This brings us back to why the CDC's description of the ingredients is so concerning—namely, there is no background on the past and potential dangers this delivery system presents, nor is there any description of how those dangers were overcome. What is provided instead is, again, simply: "the ingredients are safe." It is one thing if Moderna wants to be secretive as a private company, but it is unacceptable for the CDC to do so as it relates to an experimental, pressure-driven inoculation campaign pushed on such a vast number of Americans.

This behavior is just another among the litany of examples already provided demonstrating the CDC's lack of transparency and blatant dishonesty. It makes questioning their claims imperative, especially considering the growing body of evidence suggesting they *did not* solve the lipid nanoparticle toxicity problem. One study by Ndeupen et al. published in *iScience* in 2021, for example, determined the lipid nanoparticles to be, "highly inflammatory in mice," with injection leading to, "rapid and robust inflammatory responses, characterized by massive neutrophil infiltration, activation of diverse inflammatory pathways, and production of various inflammatory cytokines and chemokines."[20]

These predictable outcomes have also led various scientists to raise relevant questions about whether the composition of the shots is even accurate as described. While I will not provide any opinion on these claims as I have no expertise in microscopy, I find it important to at least point out here that several separate sources have alleged discovering troubling things when looking at what was in the inoculation vials under a microscope. I can neither confirm nor deny such claims in any way, as even if I myself were looking I wouldn't know what I was looking at. However, the mere existence of the claims warrants ongoing investigation and concern:

- La Quinta Columna (biostatistician Ricardo Delgado and Dr. José Luis Sevillano) alleged to have seen and provided images they claimed show graphene oxide when looking at the inoculations under the microscope[21]
- In two separate 2021 reports, Dr. Pablo Campra confirms the graphene oxide findings of Drs. Delgado and Sevillano[22,23]
- Dr. Carrie Madej alleged to have seen and provided images she claimed show strange, unidentified objects including metallic fragments, "graphene-like structures," and an unidentified organism[24]
- Dr. Robert Young alleged to have seen and provided images he claimed show graphene oxide in all four inoculation brands, as well as try-panosoma cruzi parasites in the Pfizer inoculation, which he claims is composed of carbon, oxygen chromium, Sulphur, aluminum, chloride, and nitrogen[25]
- Dr. Larry Pavlevsky at a panel in Nashville, TN cited a German doctor's determination there was graphene hydroxide in the vials, which that doctor understood, "breaks apart in the bloodstream and causes razor blade cuts into the endothelial lining of the blood vessels."[26] Pavlevsky pointed to the FDA-acknowledged phenomenon of blood-clotting and heart issues as a supporting complication for this conclusion.
- At the same panel Dr. James Neueschwander pointed out that the lipids in the shot are not naturally occurring and, "have the opposite polarity of any other phospholipid."[27] He decried the lack of animal or human study on the impact this would have on the body, as well as the known toxicity of the spike protein.

"Fact-checkers," (like *Forbes'* self-described, "avocado-eater," Bruce Lee) with no background in microscopy have slandered the backgrounds of those making these claims instead of scientifically demonstrating the falsehood of the claims themselves.[28] For example, Lee could have simply described what the actual pictures provided by the above doctors are and explained why he thinks the doctors' assessments of what those pictures represent are wrong. He instead

331

opted to question their background and use, "but the CDC said so," as a refutation.

However, the problem with this is there have been *several* peer-reviewed studies about the use of graphene oxide in this very technology. These include a February 2021 report by Yin et al. in *Nano Letters*, a March 2021 report by Feng et al. in *Small*, and an August 2020 report by Cao et al. in *Acta Biomaterialia*, the latter of which analyzed, "Recent progress of graphene oxide as a potential vaccine carrier and adjuvant."[29,30,31] The Yin and Feng reports even identify how polyethylenimine and/or polyethylene glycol are used alongside graphene oxide in gene-based inoculation technologies like the Covid shots. So clearly, despite the words of the, "avocado-eater," above, it would be a perfectly reasonable expectation that graphene oxide could have been an ingredient of the shot related to the very lipids you will recall the CDC identified (polyethylene glycol). And the concern about graphene oxide as a potentially dangerous, undesirable substance to inject oneself with is also a valid one, given the Cao study's acknowledgement that it, "aggregates in biological liquid and induces cell death, and it also exhibits poor biosolubility and biocompatibility."

Beyond the intended ingredients, there has also been mainstream news reporting of, "contaminated," vials, which in one instance led to the death of at least two Japanese men and caused an eventual halting of a 1.63 million Moderna dose lot (batch).[32] How do 1.63 million doses get contaminated and why should anyone believe this lot is an exception, given the VAERS data we are about to discuss next? This is a rhetorical question, of course.

VAERS and Other Reporting Systems Light Up

> *"We have the most robust safety system that we have ever had in this country in the rollout of this vaccine. Our Vaccine Adverse Events Reporting System [VAERS], as senator Murphy just described, has over 600,000 reports publicly available."*
> —CDC director Rochelle Walensky, November 2021[33]

> *"Social media posts repeatedly misuse unverified data from the Vaccine Adverse Event Reporting System to falsely claim that COVID-19 vaccines are dangerous, and even lethal. But*

332

the government database is not designed to determine if vaccines cause health problems (my emphasis)."

—"Fact-check," by *SciCheck*, March 2021[34]

Um… what is it used for then, *SciCheck*? Let's check in with a, "more reputable fact-checker," like *Reuters* (whose former CEO James C. Smith is on the international business council of the World Economic Forum and is *also* on the board of Pfizer) so we can get a better explanation[35,36]:

"Viewed more than 21,000 times on Facebook, a video showing data collected by the U.S. Vaccine Adverse Event Reporting System (VAERS) claims that thousands of people died from receiving COVID-19 vaccines. The video, which fails to mention that anyone can report events to VAERS and that the database contains unverified information, **describes reported deaths of individuals who died after receiving the vaccine as deaths caused by the vaccine** *(my emphasis)."*

Well, I'll be damned—in one of the most epic heel-turns you'll ever see, *Reuters* now cares about cause of death! I can't wait for their article when they launch a full blown assault on the false, "Covid death," counts since, as Dr. Ngozi Ezike explained, "everyone who's listed as a COVID death doesn't mean that that was the cause of the death." In fact, *Reuters* should just go ahead and, "fact-check," their own, "COVID-19 Tracker," graphic which peddles, "dangerous misinformation," when it claims there have been, "828,879 coronavirus-related deaths reported," in the US since the pandemic began.[37] This number too is just as unverified, since the CDC itself said a death could be counted as, "coronavirus-related," if that was even suspected to be the case.

Digressing from the dishonesty of the PR teams our society falsely identifies as, "journalists," VAERS *is* an early-warning reporting system designed to determine if vaccines are causing health problems—because what the hell else would it be for? Whether or not its reports are verified at any given time, they are there to be followed up on and if anomalies in the system weren't relevant then the system itself wouldn't be relevant. For example, let's say that in 30 years there had been 6,214 total VAERS-reported deaths in the system since its inception, or about 207 per year.[38] Now, let's imagine that you roll out a new shot and within ten months there are 16,310 new VAERS-reported deaths, more than the entire prior 30 year period and a 79-fold increase over the annual average. Would you think it wise to dismiss this? Or, perhaps a better question: do you think it wise that it *has been dismissed*—since these numbers are what's actually happened?

This is the actual narrative of the alleged Covid pandemic, as pushed by, "public health," departments. Nevermind the fact that the overwhelming majority of these severe adverse events and deaths occured in the first *three* days of inoculation, while their official numbers for the alleged virus counted and falsely implied/advertised causation at a window as high as *sixty* days. Somehow it is, "misinformation," to accept the former as relevant but not the latter. And it is so despite the fact that the former is an experimental substance you know was injected into someone's vein, while the latter is based on a test which doesn't test for the thing being alleged as causative of the problem a person is facing—a problem which is not new (cold/flu/pneumonia/respiratory issues), but for which the methods of, "treatment," are brand new.

So is the CDC really saying that *none* of the 21,002 deaths identified in VAERS to-date as related to the Covid inoculations are caused by those inoculations? According to their *Politifact* public relations wing, it seems so[39]:

> *"According to the CDC, there is no evidence in the U.S. that the vaccines have caused any deaths, though it is continuing to investigate cases of death that are reported following vaccination."*

The first and second part of this sentence are verifiable lies, based on the multiple coroner reports and even regulators who *are* documented as having identified the inoculations as a cause of death.[40,41,42,43,44] The problem here is the CDC and its collaborators haven't been interested in autopsy confirmation at all during the Covid era. In fact, this disinterest is confirmed by both a May 2020 study by Salerno et al. in the *Journal of Clinical Medicine* and by Dr. Ryan Cole, who acknowledged, "you cannot find that for which you do not look," as he lamented the death of one of his own nine-year-old post-inoculation patients.[45,46] A causal relationship is also strongly suggested by the simple fact that the deaths slope downward so dramatically as time since inoculation increases. If there was no relationship and the deaths were all naturally/otherwise occurring, their distribution in days after receiving the shot should be more uniform than they are. And for one last example, consider the CDC-acknowledged side effect of myocarditis. As we will cover in the next chapter, myocarditis, like any heart-related injury, is a disease which causes death. So to say there's no evidence the shots cause death when you acknowledge they cause myocarditis, is a lie.

But even if none of these deaths were inoculation-related—an absurd notion—what is the point of this database or any like it? Why wouldn't there be some kind of marking on a VAERS, "vaccine death," record that confirms whether or not the CDC has reviewed it and, if it has, shows whether or not they determined it to be inoculation-related? This clarification would both avoid confusion ("misinformation," as liars call it) and would be immediately verifiable by the public. And if the reports are all unverified that's fine, but until they are verified as being causative or not, this many reports of death will remain no less concerning.

In the meantime, the CDC claims the lack of verification caused them to rely upon a new system called, "v-safe," which is a smartphone app that allows the inoculated to tell, "the CDC about any side effects," after getting the shot.[47,48] Unfortunately however, like the FDA before it, the CDC has taken it upon itself to hide v-safe data from the public. Following a FOIA request by attorney Aaron Siri, on behalf of ICAN, the CDC acknowledged that since January 2020, "v-safe data contains approximately **119 million medical entries** (my emphasis)," but refused to produce the data behind those entries by claiming that the, "information in the app is not de-identified."[49]

Before I get to the second part of that, please understand that the somehow, "less reliable," yet, "most robust," VAERS safety system contains only 1.85 million records to date. This means that the ease of use of the app allows for the full spectrum of adverse events to be reported, and at 119 million it would seem an exceptional amount of inoculation recipients experience adverse events. Is this somehow *better* than the picture the VAERS system paints? Of course not. Also, if someone were to die or be badly incapacitated after taking the inoculation, how exactly would the info even be entered on the v-safe app which that person is supposed to be the one using? This flaw clearly suggests it'd be better to use VAERS, which a doctor can report to, and v-safe together.

But the CDC, as by now we are used to, also wasn't being honest with this request in their claim about the data not being de-identified. The CDC's own protocol document on v-safe explains that data submitted to v-safe is, "collected, managed, and housed on a secure server by Oracle," a private computer technology company, and that Oracle can access, "aggregate de-identified data for reporting."[50] As such, Siri's team submitted another request to appeal this decision, on the grounds that it was obviously untrue.[51] Perhaps shockingly, perhaps not, the CDC followed up by administratively closing the request, stating that it was duplicative of the original.[52] The fact that this runaway bureaucracy can get away with this and still exist is beyond me.

Back to VAERS though (the obviously relevant data we do have access to), what makes matters even worse is that VAERS has not historically been assumed to be *over*-reported, but rather is by all accounts assumed to be significantly *under*-reported. In fact, in a report by Harvard Pilgrim Health to the DHHS it was stated that, "fewer than 1% of vaccine adverse events are reported."[53] And while during a massive inoculation campaign it might be safe to assume there would be more inclination to report, there are also several factors that suggest there would be less:

1. Corruption – Consider a *Project Veritas* insider video from a DHHS facility, in which a DHHS doctor admits doctors there are not reporting the, "dozens," of inoculation-related side effects they are observing.[54] The reasons why can obviously vary by the doctor, but there are several to consider:
   a. As the DHHS doctor admits in the video, covering up the damage caused by something a doctor told a patient to take. This could be for avoiding the financial/professional consequences as stated in that video, a subconscious bias toward ruling out inoculations as a potential cause of illness, or the consequences of conscience. For an example of the latter, guilt/denial was significant enough to lead to suicide in the case of the head of the Chemnitz Clinic in Germany, Dr. Thomas Jendges.[55] An alleged suicide

letter found at the scene where Jendges jumped from the top of the clinic's building cited guilt over providing patients what the letter referred to as, "bio-warfare agents," which constituted, "genocide and a crime against humanity."

    b. Under-reporting does not have to be assumed nefarious though, either. Another possibility is simply a doctor's failing to realize an inoculation had a role. For example, if you go to a pharmacy today to get a shot and then 5 days later end up in the hospital. You may or may not register the shot could have had any role in said hospitalization, and if you don't then your doctor at the hospital certainly won't.

2. <u>Time consuming</u> – From the same *Project Veritas* insider footage, a registered nurse explains that reports are also time consuming to fill out. She says that, "it takes over a half hour to write the damn thing." In line with these claims, about two dozen Minnesota nurses came forward during an August 2021 town hall to share their experiences about inoculation injuries they were seeing amongst their patients.[56] One said her and her friends at other hospitals were, "seeing more reactions with their patients post-vaccination than they're seeing COVID patients." The other nurses concurred and another additionally mentioned that, "nurses are being discouraged from reporting it because first of all it takes about 30 minutes to report on VAERS."

3. <u>Bullying/pressure</u> – The same Minnesota nurse who discussed the time-consuming nature of reporting added she believed VAERS reports, "hold a lot of clout because whoever put that in took their time to put that in," and that those who did, "risk people walking by, seeing them doing this and belittling them." This too was echoed as nurses brought up being, "laughed at," and, "an insane sense of bullying," related to those who report or bring up reporting.

4. <u>General lack of awareness of the VAERS system</u>

5. <u>General lack of awareness that the inoculations can even be a cause of harm</u> due to the criminal censorship of the doctors who have been identifying it

6. <u>Simple clerical error</u>

Several doctors/scientists have attempted to estimate this VAERS under-reporting in the Covid era, using a variety of methods. The following are examples of their findings, support, and subsequent estimates:

- Covid, "vaccination," mortality risk review by Pantazatos and Seligmann of Columbia University, New York, published in *ResearchGate*[57]: *"… **146K to 187K vaccine-associated US deaths between February and August, 2021 … suggests VAERS deaths are underreported by a factor of 20** (my emphasis), consistent with known VAERS under-ascertainment bias … suggests the risks of COVID vaccines and boosters outweigh the benefits in children, young adults, and older adults with low occupational risk or previous coronavirus exposure."*

- Kirsch, Rose, and Crawford underreporting factor estimate based on anaphylaxis rates reported in the Blumenthal paper published in *JAMA*[58,59,60]: *"… we computed a 41X under-reporting factor for serious adverse events in VAERS, leading to an estimate of over 150,000 excess deaths caused by the vaccines."* This report was dated August 28, 2021. When looking at the most recent US-only death total in VAERS of 9,623 (through December 24, 2021), an under-reporting factor of 41 would put the death toll at about 394K for the year 2021.

- Independent analysis of CMS data-integrity whistleblower (who claimed the CDC was sweeping tens of thousands of inoculation-related deaths under the rug) data revealed by lawyer Tom Renz[61,62]: *"… which gives us an Under-Reporting Factor for VAERS of 44.64. This corresponds to a true reporting rate in VAERS of 2.2% of all adverse events. If we multiply the current number of deaths in VAERS (as of the 12/10 data release) by our URF, we will get: 887,711 deaths. If we want US deaths only, we will have: 407,831."*

- VAERS review by Dr. Jessica Rose in *Science, Public Health Policy, and the Law*, October 2021[63]: *"suggesting a URF of 31 ($N_{SAE\_Pfizer\_trial}$ / $N_{SAE\_Pfizer\_VAERS}$ = ~1.4M / 43,948). Using this URF for all VAERS-classified SAEs, estimates to date are as follows: 205,809 dead, 818,462 hospitalizations."*

- A *Baris* poll found 5.2% of inoculated respondents identified as having, "serious adverse effects," from the inoculations, specifically defined as events so serious they, "prevent daily activity."[64] Using a low-ball (according to the CDC) assumption of 200 million Americans inoculated, this would very conservatively estimate the true serious adverse event total to be at least 10.4 million—which obviously doesn't even include deaths.

These numbers are, of course, estimates. However, in the absence of quality data thanks to the CDC's poor data collection and presentation methods, and with the CDC intentionally hiding the additional data they claim to somehow be better, these estimates alongside the historical understanding of VAERS under-reporting provide a reasonable, conservative range for the actual impact this standard-safety-process-skipping inoculation program has had. In the paper by Dr. Rose, she cites the CDC itself, in a quote which raises even more questions for why Walensky seems to have no concern or explanation for her lack thereof[65]:

> *"Patterns of adverse events, or an unusually high number of adverse events reported after a particular vaccine, are called 'signals.' If a signal is identified through VAERS, scientist(s) may conduct further studies to find out if the signal represents an actual risk."*

Is a 79-fold year-over-year increase *not* a, "signal?" Of course it is. If the CDC was not a captured organization it wouldn't label the people acknowledging this, "signal," as, "conspiracy theorists," spreading, "misinformation." This is *entirely* the CDC's own information and terms we are even discussing/interpreting here to begin with! And the truth of the matter is this: so are the conclusions. Yes—the CDC is fully aware that VAERS is, in fact, *under*-reported, and we know this because as recently as November 2020 five scientists from the CDC itself published a paper in *ScienceDirect* specifically acknowledging it.[66] The authors determined that VAERS captured only 12% of cases of Guillian-Baré syndrome caused by the 2012-2013 inactivated seasonal influenza vaccine. This translates to an under-reporting factor of 8.3 (1 / 0.12).

339

So clearly, from Harvard Pilgrim, to the scientific papers we discussed, to the CDC itself, it is commonly understood that VAERS is under-reported. And while the CDC attributes tremendous numbers in the system to a higher, "propensity to report," than usual, Dr. Steve Kirsch explains why this is not the case using the example of pulmonary embolism (PE) reports[67]:

"... the average number of reports of PE per year in VAERS for all vaccines was 1.4. So we'd expect to see at most 11.6 PE events this year (1.4 avg * 8.3 URF) according to the belief system of the FDA and CDC. Well, one tiny problem: with the COVID vaccines, there were 1,131 reports, nearly a 100-fold increase over the 'best case' scenario."

For another issue with the VAERS data, recall Japan's experience with bad Moderna lots (batches) which was acknowledged to have led to the deaths of two men. An October 31, 2021 review of VAERS data by *The Exposé* suggested this was not a freak occurrence, as it determined that almost 100% of the identified inoculation deaths identified in VAERS were attributed to just 5% of the lots produced.[68] Also, when comparing against influenza vaccine-related VAERS deaths, the greatest death count in a single lot was 26, versus 3,563 for a single Covid inoculation lot. This wasn't an anomaly either, as several of the 4,522 total lots had thousands of reports made. This phenomenon obviously warrants further investigation, but it also implies something nefarious is going on, especially when considering the following:

1. No official investigation has been made into this by the CDC/FDA
2. The inoculation program has not been halted despite tremendous orders of magnitude increases of adverse event and death reports compared to influenza vaccines
3. The inoculations are experimental and phase III clinical trials are scheduled to continue until 2023.[69] This suggests those lots could potentially be non-placebo lots. If this were the case and the program was not halted long ago, consider the number of people being dangerously experimented on here without consent.

One possible explanation for this occurrence is mRNA, "integrity." Per a report in the *BMJ*, integrity refers to the extent of which the mRNA molecules in the vial are intact and a, "complete, intact mRNA molecule is essential to the potency of the vaccine."[70] However, in the *BMJ* report they cite a leaked European Medicines Agency document, which showed a significant variance in the intact mRNA in Pfizer's doses. In fact, the report showed some vials demonstrated as low as 50% integrity. This wide variance in active ingredient was one among, "a raft of issues," outlined by a high ranking EMA official to the *BMJ*, which included the admission that, "commercial manufacturing was not producing vaccines to the specifications expected, and regulators were unsure of the implications on safety and efficacy." The *BMJ* was unable to get any information on acceptable integrity from any of the companies (Pfizer, Moderna, etc.) or regulatory agencies, and despite, "major objections," the shots continued receiving approvals anyway. Still, this variance points back to the aforementioned *STAT* article outlining Moderna's toxicity problem as it related to high active-ingredient diseases. High active ingredient doses would, based on that understanding, seem the most likely explanation for high adverse event lots.

Still, the CDC's VAERS also isn't the only system reporting horrific numbers. Per *Natural News*, as of November 13, 2021 the total deaths connected to the Covid shots in the EU's EudraVigilance adverse event tracking database was 30,551.[71] A search of the WHO's VigiAccess for, "Covid-19 Vaccine," doesn't show a count of events which proved fatal, but it does yield 2,878,217 reports in 2021 alone.[72] This should qualify as what the CDC would call a clear, "signal," considering our previous search of ivermectin yielded less than 6K total results *since 1992*.

There are also many studies and observations which support the under-reporting factors mentioned previously, beyond even the support those scientists documented. One example is a report by Dr. Sucharit Bhakdi and Dr. Arne Burkhardt, who examined the organs of 15 deceased patients who had died within 0-2 months of inoculation.[73] Since the, "macroscopic appearance of the organs seemed unremarkable," the initial coroner reports uncovered no obvious hints of anything other than a postulation of death by, "rhythmogenic heart failure." However, upon histopathologic (tissue-based) reexamination of the subjects, 14 of the 15 patients' organ tissues showed signs of a, "process of immunological self-attack," which were described as, "without precedent." The heart (14 out of 15) and lungs (13 out of 15) were the most impacted by what the report describes as, "autoimmune-like pathology in multiple organs." Because the inoculations were the single common denominator between all these cases (only 4 out of the 15 died in the hospital), the authors determined there to be, "no doubt," the shots were the trigger of the tissue destruction which led to their deaths. Further explanation for this conclusion is provided as the doctors explain:

> *"... the vaccines cause cells deep inside our body to express viral spike protein, which they were never meant to do by nature. Any cell which expresses this foreign antigen will come under attack by the immune system ... This may occur in any organ. We are seeing now that the heart is affected in many young people, leading to myocarditis or even sudden cardiac arrest and death."*

This report, in which 14 out of 15 post-inoculation deaths are alleged by these prominent microbiologists to have been falsely identified as not related to said inoculations, demonstrates just how significant under-reporting can be expected to be. And with the CDC having assumed the products, "safe and effective," right off the bat, it is worth asking what their criteria would be to determine an inoculation-caused death, if they have any at all. If a person has a heart attack for example, what characteristics, if not the abnormal tissue damage mentioned above, would be used to make such a determination? Since experience shows they are firmly opposed to transparency as far as their data goes, receiving an answer to such a question is almost certainly wishful thinking.

Fortunately however, there are other countries and data sources out there to consider when making determinations. Much like our findings to this point, those sources directly contradict both the, "safe and effective," and, "reduced hospitalization and death," pivot-narratives regurgitated by the very people who regularly lied about how certain they were the inoculations would prevent, "transmission." Instead, they suggest a catastrophic, "one-in-200-year," disaster:

- An Indiana life insurance CEO said deaths across their entire book of business were up a stunning 40% among working-age people in Q3 2021 compared to pre-pandemic levels.[74] "Just to give you an idea of how bad that is, a three-sigma or a one-in-200-year catastrophe would be [a] 10% increase," he is reported as saying. It is also acknowledged that most of the claims being filed are not labeled as, "Covid," deaths and that the company was also experiencing an uptick in disability claims.

- Former Blackrock portfolio manager Edward Dowd summarized group (employer) life insurance loss ratios in Q4 2021 versus the rate in 2019.[75] The increases ranged from 21-57% among seven of the major insurers, including Prudential, MetLife, and Unum.

- Per the *Defender*, the CEO of one of Germany's largest health insurance companies, Andreas Schofbeck of BKK/ProVita, was fired in early 2022 after he released data suggesting German health authorities were significantly underreporting COVID-19 vaccine injuries.[76] In a whistleblower letter to the German equivalent of the CDC, Schofbeck reported, "If these figures are extrapolated to the whole year and to the population in Germany, probably 2.5-3 million people in Germany have received medical treatment for vaccination side effects after Corona vaccination." In fact, his data even pointed to a 4-5% rate of treatment-requiring adverse events, in line with the aforementioned *Baris* poll. In return for identifying this important safety signal he was dismissed and the data was scrubbed from the company's website.

- Per Petr Svab of the *Epoch Times*, several states have confirmed they are investigating massive 2021 increases in mortality rates among people aged 18-49.[77] These increases reportedly amount to 40% and more, in line with the aforementioned group insurance observations. Texas, for example, saw an incredible 61% jump. This trend was also identified in many other countries following the introduction of the mass inoculation campaign by *The Exposé*, including Denmark, Finland, Norway, Germany, and Scotland, among others.[78]

343

- A running list has been kept by *The COVID Blog* of doctors passing away, "suddenly," and before their time of heart issues, including one 32 year-old doctor who died of pulmonary embolism—a known complication of the inoculations[79,80]
- Alex Berenson demonstrates that twice-inoculated Swedish people are dying at a far-more-than 20% greater rate than the average mortality rate in the first two weeks following their second dose, based on a large 2022 study by Nordström et al. in the *Lancet*.[81,82] In the study, 3,949 twice-inoculated individuals (pulled from a subset of twice-inoculated Swedes, so not necessarily even *all* twice-inoculated Swedes) died with 14 days of their inoculation. Reviewing Swedish mortality statistics from 2015-2019, Berenson points out that during spring and summer Sweden normally has about 3,300 deaths every two weeks *amongst the entire population*[83]
- The aforementioned Pfizer-Ventavia subcontractor scandal prompted a group of 16 Swedish doctors and researchers to circulate a petition calling on the Pfizer inoculation to no longer be administered there.[84] The signatories called the revelations, "extremely serious," adding that adverse reactions to Pfizer's inoculations are, "gigantic." They expanded[85]: *"For instance, in Sweden alone during the ten months that vaccination has taken place wholly 83,744 suspected side effects have been reported—which is **more than ten times more than all side effects reported for all drugs and vaccines per year in the immediately preceding years, for a total of 25,000 substances** (my emphasis)."*
- *The Exposé* summarized official UK Health Security Agency surveillance reports for weeks 34-45 (August – November) of 2021, showing the following[86,87,88,89]:
  - Case rates per 100,000 were higher for, "fully-vaccinated," than the, "unvaccinated," in *all* age groups
  - The case-hospitalization rate for the, "fully-vaccinated," was 38% higher than the case-hospitalization rate for the, "unvaccinated," and was worsening at a more rapid pace over time for the

former group. This data demonstrates the exact opposite situation being claimed of, "reduced hospitalization and death."

- o While the, "fully-vaccinated," accounted for 60% of the total cases, they accounted for 80% of the deaths, a margin that has also worsened at a more rapid pace over time. Again, the exact opposite of, "reduced hospitalization and death."
- o The hospitalization-fatality rate of the, "fully-vaccinated," population during this period was 124% higher than that of the, "unvaccinated," again, worsening over time

- Journalist Alex Berenson confirmed *The Exposé*'s findings, demonstrating in November 2021 that the official UK government data showed all-cause deaths for those who received two doses were twice that of the, "unvaccinated," on a per 100,000 basis[90]
- The *UK Telegraph* also reported in November 2021 that, "nearly 10,000 more people than usual have died in the past four months from non-Covid reasons."[91] This time period represented the height of the inoculation and booster campaign of 2021 and no other explanation is provided for these excess deaths.
- "Covid-19," daily deaths reached never-before-seen, often exponentially higher levels *after* the start dates of the inoculation campaigns of *at least* each of the following countries[92]: Afghanistan, Albania, Algeria, Bahamas, Bahrain, Bangladesh, Brazil, Brunei, Burma, Cambodia, Cote d'Ivoire, Cuba, Djibouti, Fiji, Grenada, Guinea, Guyana, India, Indonesia, Israel, Jamaica, Jordan, Latvia, Malaysia, Mauritius, Mosambique, Nepal, Curacao, Paraguay, Portugal, Qatar, Seychelles, Sri Lanka, Taiwan, Tanzania, Timor, Thailand, Trinidad & Tobago, Tunisia, Uganda, Uruguay, Vietnam, Zambia, and Zimbabwe
- Taiwan, "vaccine," deaths surpassed total deaths attributed to, "Covid," throughout the entire alleged pandemic as of October 2021[93]

- A German study of 16, "countries," (similar to what we call, "counties," in the US) by Dr. Rolf Steyer and Dr. Gregor Kappler, translated into English, concluded that, "complete vaccination increases the likelihood of death."[94] This was based on the following observation: *"The correlation is +.31, is amazingly high and especially in an unexpected direction. Actually, it should be negative, so that one could say: 'the higher the vaccination rate, the lower the excess mortality.' However, the opposite is the case and this urgently needs to be clarified. Excess mortality can be observed in all 16 countries."*

And the astonishing correlation this German study makes between inoculation rate and excess mortality is what brings us to how the CDC actually counts, "Covid deaths." We already know the method in which, "Covid deaths," are reported is fraudulent. Since, "Covid," does not have to be the cause of death at all, fraudulent PCR tests are the only method for claiming the alleged virus (which PCR doesn't test for) was even present in the dying/dead person. We also know that the CDC even allows for those, "suspected," to have had, "Covid," to be counted as, "Covid deaths."

What we did not yet touch on however, relates to the fact that nearly 100% of excess mortality identified by the CDC is attributed to, "Covid."[95] Now, this might make sense if the CDC was collecting death data honestly. For example, if there were an abnormal metric ton of car accidents in an otherwise normal year, I could add the additional deaths I know were caused by those accidents to the expected mortality and most likely match excess mortality. This isn't what the CDC does though. The CDC itself acknowledges it goes backwards, stating the following[96]:

> *"COVID-19 deaths are estimated using a statistical model to calculate the number of COVID-19 deaths that were unrecognized and those that were not recorded on death certificates and, as a result, were never reported as a death related to COVID-19.*
>
> *To estimate these unrecognized COVID-19 deaths, all-cause deaths are obtained from the National Center of Health Statistics. Before applying the statistical mode, reported*

346

COVID-19 deaths are subtracted by age, state and week from all-cause deaths, so that these reported COVID-19 deaths are not included in the calculation of the expected deaths for the statistical model.

*… **To obtain the number of unrecognized COVID-19 deaths, the number of expected all-cause deaths (without COVID-19 circulation) are subtracted from the number of predicted all-cause deaths (with COVID-19 circulation)** (my emphasis)."*

And there you have it—the CDC admits it assumes all excess mortality is, "Covid," excess mortality, and uses this absurd assumption to provide its, "Covid death," estimates. We now know this assumption to be false based on any/all of the following things which we've covered and which could just as easily be posited as alternate contributors/causes of excess mortality with *more* evidence than what is given for the current, "Covid," false-identification:

- Lockdowns – economic destruction
- Lockdowns – negative impact on health (closing gyms, staying home, etc.)
- Deaths of despair due to the oppressive, inhuman measures taken/enforced
- Use of novel, experimental, dangerous drugs like remdesivir and death penalty drugs, as well as the over-use of ventilators in hospitals, some of which experienced 80% death rates or higher
- Misdiagnosis (and subsequent mistreatment) on a massive scale
- Senseless, intentional suppression of safe, effective drugs like IVM, HCQ, etc.

And now, thanks to studies like the German one previously mentioned, we can add another cause/contributor to the list: the inoculations themselves. In fact, whether or not the CDC acknowledges the point I've just made is irrelevant, because it's worked itself into an impossible corner. The CDC either has to admit that its attribution of, "Covid," to all excess mortality is false and the pandemic was a fraud, or that it is correct. If it continues to falsely claim it is correct however, it also needs to explain why excess mortality it alleges is caused by, "Covid," has *worsened* in 2021 (the year of the mass inoculation campaign it endorsed to the point of coercion) when compared to 2020. Either way, this organization, among many others, has committed insane, senseless crimes against humanity it needs to be held accountable for.

Endnotes

1   Malone, Robert. 2022. "Before Your Child Is Injected, Watch Dr. Robert Malone's Statement On Child COVID Vaccinations". *Global Covid Summit*. https://www.globalcovidsummit.org/news/live-stream-event-physicians-alerting-parents.

2   PANDOLFO, CHRIS. 2021. "Twitter Suspends Dr. Robert Malone, 'Inventor' Of Mrna Vaccines And COVID-19 Vaccine Skeptic". *Theblaze*. https://www.theblaze.com/news/twitter-suspends-dr-robert-malone-inventor-of-mrna-vaccines-and-covid-19-vaccine-skeptic.

3   "Robert W Malone MD". 2022. *Robert W Malone MD*. Accessed March 17. https://www.rwmalonemd.com/.

4   Cardozo, Timothy, and Ronald Veazey. 2020. "Informed Consent Disclosure To Vaccine Trial Subjects Of Risk Of COVID-19 Vaccines Worsening Clinical Disease". *International Journal Of Clinical Practice* 75 (3). doi:10.1111/ijcp.13795.

5   "COVID-19 Vaccine Bombshell: FDA Reveals 21 Adverse Outcomes | Principia Scientific Intl.". 2020. *Principia Scientific Intl. | A Science-Based Community*. https://principia-scientific.com/covid-19-vaccine-bombshell-fda-reveals-21-adverse-outcomes/.

6   "VAERS COVID Vaccine Adverse Event Reports". 2022. *Openvaers*. Accessed March 14. https://www.openvaers.com/covid-data.

7   Macdonald, Steve. 2022. "Here Is The FDA's List Of Pfizer's 1,290+ Known Adverse Side Effects For Its Experimental COVID19 "Vaccine" - Granite Grok". *Granite Grok*. https://granitegrok.com/blog/2022/03/fdas-list-of-1290-known-adverse-side-effects-from-the-pfizer-covid-vaccine.

8   "The Pfizer Inoculations Do More Harm Than Good". 2021. *Rumble*. https://www.rumble.com/vqx3kb-the-pfizer-inoculations-do-more-harm-than-good.html.

9   "THE PFIZER INOCULATIONS FOR COVID-19: MORE HARM THAN GOOD". 2021. *Canadian COVID Care Alliance*. https://www.canadiancovidcarealliance.org/wp-content/uploads/2021/12/The-COVID-19-Inoculations-More-Harm-Than-Good-REV-Dec-16-2021.pdf.

10   "The Powerful Pfizer Presentation That Got Dr. Robert Malone Kicked Off Twitter". 2022. *Kanekoa.Substack.Com*. https://kanekoa.substack.com/p/the-powerful-pfizer-presentation.

11   Ibid.

12   Harris, Richard. 2021. "Long-Term Studies Of COVID-19 Vaccines Hurt By Placebo Recipients Getting Immunized". *Npr.Org*. https://www.npr.org/sections/health-shots/2021/02/19/969143015/long-

term-studies-of-covid-19-vaccines-hurt-by-placebo-recipients-getting-immuni.

13   Day, Vox. 2021. "Why They Didn't Stop The Trials - Vox Popoli". *Vox Popoli*. https://voxday.net/2021/11/09/why-they-didnt-stop-the-trials/.

14   Thacker, Paul D. 2021. "Covid-19: Researcher Blows The Whistle On Data Integrity Issues In Pfizer's Vaccine Trial: Video 1". *BMJ*, n2635. doi:10.1136/bmj.n2635.

15   Pfizer. 2021. "5.3.6 CUMULATIVE ANALYSIS OF POST-AUTHORIZATION ADVERSE EVENT REPORTS OF PF-07302048 (BNT162B2) RECEIVED THROUGH 28-FEB-2021". Worldwide Safety Pfizer. https://phmpt.org/wp-content/uploads/2021/11/5.3.6-postmarketing-experience.pdf.

16   Schmeck Jr., Harold M. 1976. "SWINE FLU PROGRAM IS HALTED IN 9 STATES AS 3 DIE AFTER SHOTS (Published 1976)". *Nytimes.Com*. https://www.nytimes.com/1976/10/13/archives/swine-flu-program-is-halted-in-9-states-as-3-die-after-shots.html.

17   "Pfizer-Biontech COVID-19 Vaccine (Also Known As COMIRNATY) Overview And Safety". 2022. *Cdc.Gov*. https://www.cdc.gov/coronavirus/2019-ncov/vaccines/different-vaccines/Pfizer-BioNTech.html.

18   Garde, Damian. 2017. "Lavishly Funded Moderna Hits Safety Problems In Bold Bid To Revolutionize Medicine". *STAT*. https://www.statnews.com/2017/01/10/moderna-trouble-mrna/.

19   "Research Not Fit To Print". 2016. *Nature Biotechnology* 34 (2): 115-115. doi:10.1038/nbt.3488.

20   Ndeupen, Sonia, Zhen Qin, Sonya Jacobsen, Aurélie Bouteau, Henri Estanbouli, and Botond Z. Igyártó. 2021. "The Mrna-LNP Platform's Lipid Nanoparticle Component Used In Preclinical Vaccine Studies Is Highly Inflammatory". *Iscience* 24 (12): 103479. doi:10.1016/j.isci.2021.103479.

21   "ORWELL CITY: La Quinta Columna: Analysis Of Vaccination Vial Confirms Presence Of Graphene Nanoparticles". 2021. *ORWELL CITY*. https://www.orwell.city/2021/06/graphene-oxide-in-vaccination-vials.html?m=1.

22   Playne, Mark. 2021. "GRAPHENE OXIDE 'DISCOVERED' IN PFIZER VACCINE BY DR CAMPRA - THE ALMERIA PAPER - ENG TRANSLATION". Notonthebeeb. https://www.notonthebeeb.co.uk/post/englis-translation-of-the-graphene-oxide-almeria-paper.

23   Playne, Mark. 2021. "NEW - DR CAMPRA PROVES GRAPHENE OXIDE IN COVID VACCINES". Notonthebeeb. https://www.notonthebeeb.co.uk/post/breaking-dr-campra-proves-graphene-in-vaccine.

24   "Dr. Carrie Madej Took A Look At The Moderna, Pfizer, And J&J Shot Contents Under A Microscope". 2021. *Algora Blog*.

https://www.algora.com/Algora_blog/2021/10/25/dr-carrie-madej-took-a-look-at-the-moderna-pfizer-and-jj-shot-contents-under-a-microscope.

25   "Dr. Robert Young Finds Graphene Oxide Or Graphene Hydroxide In All Four Vaccines And Other Disturbing Ingredients". 2021. *Algora Blog*. https://www.algora.com/Algora_blog/2021/12/25/dr-robert-young-finds-graphene-oxide-in-all-four-vaccines-and-other-disturbing-ingredients.

26   "Panel 4 Doctors Discuss Vaccine: Drs: Pavlevsky, Reinders, Moss, Neueschwander". 2022. *Rumble*. https://rumble.com/vsu4fc-panel-4-doctors-discuss-vaccine-drs-pavlevsky-reinders-moss-neueschwander.html.

27   Ibid.

28   Lee, Bruce. 2021. "Graphene Oxide In Pfizer Covid-19 Vaccines? Here Are The Latest Unsupported Claims". *Forbes*. https://www.forbes.com/sites/brucelee/2021/07/10/graphene-oxide-in-pfizer-covid-19-vaccines-here-are-the-latest-unsupported-claims/?sh=632a26fe74d.

29   Yin, Yue, Xiaoyang Li, Haixia Ma, Jie Zhang, Di Yu, Ruifang Zhao, Shengji Yu, Guangjun Nie, and Hai Wang. 2021. "In Situ Transforming RNA Nanovaccines From Polyethylenimine Functionalized Graphene Oxide Hydrogel For Durable Cancer Immunotherapy". Nano Letters 21 (5): 2224-2231. doi:10.1021/acs.nanolett.0c05039.

30   Feng, Liangzhu, Xianzhu Yang, Xiaoze Shi, Xiaofang Tan, Rui Peng, Jun Wang, and Zhuang Liu. 2013. "Polyethylene Glycol And Polyethylenimine Dual-Functionalized Nano-Graphene Oxide For Photothermally Enhanced Gene Delivery". Small 9 (11): 1989-1997. doi:10.1002/smll.201202538.

31   Cao, Wanjun, Lin He, Weidong Cao, Xiaobing Huang, Kun Jia, and Jingying Dai. 2020. "Recent Progress Of Graphene Oxide As A Potential Vaccine Carrier And Adjuvant". Acta Biomaterialia 112: 14-28. doi:10.1016/j.actbio.2020.06.009.

32   Swift, Rocky. 2021. "Two Die In Japan After Shots From Suspended Moderna Vaccines - Japan Govt". *Yahoo.Com*. https://www.yahoo.com/news/two-die-japan-shots-suspended-061929001.html.

33   Johnson, Ron. 2021. "Senator Ron Johnson Tweet November 4, 2021". *Twitter*. https://www.twitter.com/SenRonJohnson/status/1456321897801699330.

34   Jaramillo, Catalina. 2021. "Viral Posts Misuse VAERS Data To Make False Claims About COVID-19 Vaccines - Factcheck.Org". *Factcheck.Org*. https://www.factcheck.org/2021/03/scicheck-viral-posts-misuse-vaers-data-to-make-false-claims-about-covid-19-vaccines/.

35   "Jim Smith (Business Executive) - Wikipedia". 2022. *En.M.Wikipedia.Org*. Accessed March 17. https://en.m.wikipedia.org/wiki/Jim_Smith_(business_executive).

36   "Fact Check-VAERS Data Does Not Prove Thousands Died From Receiving COVID-19 Vaccines". 2021. *Reuters*. https://www.reuters.com/article/factcheck-vaers-deaths-idUSL1N2LV0NY.

37   "United States: The Latest Coronavirus Counts, Charts And Maps". 2020. *Reuters*. https://graphics.reuters.com/world-coronavirus-tracker-and-maps/countries-and-territories/united-states/.

38   "Until October, VAERS Records 2.5 Times More Deaths After Covid Vaccines Than After All Vaccines In Last 30 Years". 2021. *The Rio Times*. https://www.riotimesonline.com/brazil-news/modern-day-censorship/until-october-vaers-records-2-5-times-more-deaths-after-covid-vaccines-than-after-all-vaccines-in-the-last-30-years/.

39   Kertscher, Tom. 2021. "Politifact - No Evidence Of COVID-19 Vaccines Causing Deaths". @Politifact. https://www.politifact.com/factchecks/2021/sep/20/facebook-posts/no-evidence-covid-19-vaccines-causing-deaths/.

40   Sutton, Stephanie. 2021. "Battling The Blood Clots". The Medicine Maker. https://themedicinemaker.com/discovery-development/battling-the-blood-clots.

41   Dawson, Bethany. 2022. "Mother Died Due To Rare 'Brain Bleed' Side Effect Of COVID-19 Vaccine, Coroner Rules". Business Insider. https://www.businessinsider.in/science/news/mother-died-due-to-rare-brain-bleed-side-effect-of-covid-19-vaccine-coroner-rules/articleshow/90321245.cms.

42   "COVID-19 Vaccine To Blame For 24-Year-Old Man's Death". 2022. News.Yahoo.Com. https://news.yahoo.com/covid-19-vaccine-blame-24-001800059.html.

43   Phillips, Jamie. 2021. "Pianist, 40, Suffered Brain Haemorrhage 'Induced Astrazeneca Vaccine'". *Mail Online*. https://www.dailymail.co.uk/news/article-10233341/Musician-40-suffered-brain-haemorrhage-induced-AstraZeneca-Covid-vaccine-inquest-hears.html.

44   Penley, Taylor. 2021. "Coroner Confirms COVID Vaccine Complications Were Behind BBC News Presenter's Death". *The Western Journal*. https://www.westernjournal.com/coroner-confirms-covid-vaccine-fault-news-presenters-death/.

45   Salerno, Monica, Francesco Sessa, Amalia Piscopo, Angelo Montana, Marco Torrisi, Federico Patanè, Paolo Murabito, Giovanni Li Volti, and Cristoforo Pomara. 2020. "No Autopsies On COVID-19 Deaths: A Missed Opportunity And The Lockdown Of Science". Journal Of Clinical Medicine 9 (5): 1472. doi:10.3390/jcm9051472.

46   Cole, Ryan. 2022. "Fauci Told Medical Professionals Not To Do Autopsies". Bitchute. https://www.bitchute.com/video/cKvBBBUA11M1/.

47   Siri, Aaron. 2021. "The FDA Wants To Hide Pre-Licensure Data Until You're Dead And Now The CDC Wants To Hide The Post-Licensure

Safety Data". *Aaronsiri.Substack.Com.*
https://aaronsiri.substack.com/p/the-fda-wants-to-hide-pre-licensure.

48   "V-Safe After Vaccination Health Checker". 2021. *Cdc.Gov.*
https://www.cdc.gov/coronavirus/2019-ncov/vaccines/safety/vsafe.html.

49   Brehm, Elizabeth A. Letter Roger Andoh to . 2021. "V-Safe De-
Identified Data (IR#0519)". Email, , 2021.
https://www.icandecide.org/wp-content/uploads/2021/12/IR0519-CDC-
V-Safe-De-identified-Data-final.pdf.

50   The Centers for Disease Control and Prevention. 2021. "V-Safe Active
Surveillance For COVID-19 Vaccine Safety."
https://www.cdc.gov/vaccinesafety/pdf/V-safe-Protocol-508.pdf.

51   Siri, Aaron Letter Roger Andoh to . 2021. "V-Safe De-Identified Data
(IR#0547)". Email, , 2021. https://www.icandecide.org/wp-
content/uploads/2021/12/IR0547-CDC-V-Safe-De-identified-
Data_v.2.pdf.

52   Andoh, Roger Letter Elizabeth Brehm to . 2021. "Duplicate Request
Letter". Email, , 2021. https://www.icandecide.org/wp-
content/uploads/2021/12/2021-09-03-Duplicate-Request-Letter.pdf

53   Lazarus, Ross, Michael Klompas, and Steve Bernstein. 2011. "Electronic
Support For Public Health–Vaccine Adverse Event Reporting System
(ESP:VAERS)". Harvard Pilgrim Health Care, Inc.
https://digital.ahrq.gov/sites/default/files/docs/publication/r18hs017045-
lazarus-final-report-
2011.pdf#:~:text=Adverse%20events%20from%20drugs%20and,and%20
Drug%20Administration%20(FDA).

54   "Jodi O'malley - HHS". 2021. *Projectveritas.Com.*
https://www.projectveritas.com/news/jodi-omalley-hhs/.

55   Cardiny, Jessica. 2021. "Germany | Dr Thomas Jendges Head Of Clinic,
Commits Suicide "COVID-19 Vaccine Is A Genocide"". *STESS News.*
https://archive.md/qQRso#selection-877.14-877.29.

56   Hooten, Kyle. 2021. "Minnesota Nurses Say Vaccine Injuries Likely
Underreported". *Alpha News.* https://alphanews.org/minnesota-nurses-
say-vaccine-injuries-likely-underreported/.

57   Pantazatos, Spiro, and Herve Seligmann. 2021. "COVID Vaccination
And Age-Stratified All-Cause Mortality Risk". *Researchgate.*
doi:10.13140/RG.2.2.28257.43366.

58   Kirsch, Steve, Jessica Rose, and Mathew Crawford. 2021. "Estimating
The Number Of COVID Vaccine Deaths In America".
https://www.skirsch.com/covid/Deaths.pdf.

59   Kirsch, Steve. 2021. "Latest VAERS Estimate: 388,000 Americans Killed
By The COVID Vaccines". *Stevekirsch.Substack.Com.*
https://stevekirsch.substack.com/p/latest-vaers-estimate-388000-
americans.

60   Blumenthal, Kimberly G., Lacey B. Robinson, Carlos A. Camargo, Erica
S. Shenoy, Aleena Banerji, Adam B. Landman, and Paige Wickner. 2021.

"Acute Allergic Reactions To Mrna COVID-19 Vaccines". *JAMA* 325 (15): 1562. doi:10.1001/jama.2021.3976.

61   "Using CMS Whistleblower Data To Approximate The Under-Reporting Factor For VAERS – VAERS Analysis". 2021. *Vaersanalysis.Info.* https://vaersanalysis.info/2021/12/13/using-cms-whistleblower-data-to-approximate-the-under-reporting-factor-for-vaers/.

62   "Study: COVID-19 Lockdowns Caused More Deaths Instead Of Reducing Them". 2021. *Humans Be Free.* https://humansarefree.com/2021/09/govt-data-50k-deaths-within-14-days-of-covid-19-vax.html/.

63   Rose, Jessica. 2021. "Critical Appraisal Of VAERS Pharmacovigilance: Is The U.S. Vaccine Adverse Events Reporting System (VAERS) A Functioning Pharmacovigilance System?". The Institute for Pure and Applied Knowledge. https://cf5e727d-d02d-4d71-89ff-9fe2d3ad957f.filesusr.com/ugd/adf864_0490c898f7514df4b6fbc5935da07322.pdf.

64   Becker, Kyle. 2021. "'Severe Reactions' To Covid Vaccines Are Far More Common Than Official Data Show: Here Is The Stunning New Evidence". *Becker News.* https://beckernews.com/severe-reactions-to-covid-vaccines-43196/.

65   Rose, Jessica. 2021. "Critical Appraisal Of VAERS Pharmacovigilance: Is The U.S. Vaccine Adverse Events Reporting System (VAERS) A Functioning Pharmacovigilance System?". The Institute for Pure and Applied Knowledge. https://cf5e727d-d02d-4d71-89ff-9fe2d3ad957f.filesusr.com/ugd/adf864_0490c898f7514df4b6fbc5935da07322.pdf.

66   Miller, Elaine R., Michael M. McNeil, Pedro L. Moro, Jonathan Duffy, and John R. Su. 2020. "The Reporting Sensitivity Of The Vaccine Adverse Event Reporting System (VAERS) For Anaphylaxis And For Guillain-Barré Syndrome". *Vaccine* 38 (47): 7458-7463. doi:10.1016/j.vaccine.2020.09.072.

67   Kirsch, Steve. 2021. "Proof That The CDC Is Lying To The World About COVID Vaccine Safety". *Trialsitenews.* https://trialsitenews.com/proof-that-the-cdc-is-lying-to-the-world-about-covid-vaccine-safety/.

68   "EXCLUSIVE - 100% Of Covid-19 Vaccine Deaths Were Caused By Just 5% Of The Batches Produced According To Official Government Data". 2021. *The Expose.* https://dailyexpose.uk/2021/10/31/100-percent-of-covid-19-vaccine-deaths-caused-by-just-5-percent-of-the-batches-produced/.

69   The National Institutes of Health. 2020. "Study To Describe The Safety, Tolerability, Immunogenicity, And Efficacy Of RNA Vaccine Candidates Against COVID-19 In Healthy Individuals". Pfizer & BioNTech. https://clinicaltrials.gov/ct2/show/NCT04368728?term=NCT04368728&draw=2&rank=1.

70   "Concerns Over Integrity Of Mrna Molecules In Some COVID-19 Vaccines". 2021. Medicalxpress.Com.

https://medicalxpress.com/news/2021-03-mrna-molecules-covid-vaccines.html.

71   Huff, Ethan. 2021. "Europe Logs 1,163,356 Adverse Reactions, 30,551 Deaths Caused By Covid "Vaccines"". *Naturalnews.Com*. https://www.naturalnews.com/2021-11-23-europe-1163356-reactions-30551-deaths-covid-vaccines.html.

72   "WHO Collaborating Center For International Drug Monitoring". 2021. *Vigiaccess*. Accessed October. https://vigiaccess.org/.

73   Bhakdi, Sucharit, and Arne Burkhardt. 2021. "On COVID Vaccines: Why They Cannot Work, And Irrefutable Evidence Of Their Causative Role In Deaths After Vaccination". Doctors 4 Covid Ethics. https://doctors4covidethics.org/wp-content/uploads/2021/12/end-covax.pdf.

74   Menge, Margaret. 2022. "Indiana Life Insurance CEO Says Deaths Are Up 40% Among People Ages 18-64". *The Center Square*. https://www.thecentersquare.com/indiana/indiana-life-insurance-ceo-says-deaths-are-up-40-among-people-ages-18-64/article_71473b12-6b1e-11ec-8641-5b2c06725e2c.html.

75   Rucker, JD. 2022. "Bombshell Report: Insurance Companies Increase U.S. Mortality Expectations By 300,000 Due To Covid And "INDIRECT Covid,&#8". NOQ Report - Conservative Christian News, Opinions, And Quotes. https://noqreport.com/2022/02/16/bombshell-report-insurance-companies-increase-u-s-mortality-expectations-by-300000-due-to-covid-and-indirect-covid-aka-the-jabs/.

76   Bowman, Nolan E. 2022. "German Insurance Company Fires CEO Who Released COVID Vaccine Injury Data, Then Scrubs Data From Website". Children's Health Defense. https://childrenshealthdefense.org/defender/german-insurance-fires-andreas-schofbeck-covid-vaccine-injuries-data/.

77   Svab, Petr. 2022. "EXCLUSIVE: States Investigating Surge In Mortality Rate Among 18–49-Year-Olds, Majority Unrelated To COVID-19". Www.Theepochtimes.Com. https://www.theepochtimes.com/mkt_app/several-states-examine-2021-mortality-surge-in-americans-aged-18-49_4213438.html.

78   "Countries With High Covid-19 Vaccination Rates All Suffered An Extraordinary Rise In Excess Deaths In 2021 Suggesting The Jabs Are To Blame". 2022. Dailyexpose.Uk. https://dailyexpose.uk/2022/01/31/high-excess-deaths-worldwide-linked-to-covid-vaccine/.

79   "Reap What You Sow? Doctors Dropping Like Flies In Deaths Described As "Died Unexpectedly" And "Died Suddenly" Since Mid-October - The COVID Blog™". 2021. *The COVID Blog™*. https://thecovidblog.com/2021/11/17/reap-what-you-sow-doctors-dropping-like-flies-died-suddenly-unexpectedly/.

80   "Pulmonary Embolism". 2022. *The COVID Blog™*. Accessed March 18. https://thecovidblog.com/?s=pulmonary+embolism.

81 Berenson, Alex. 2021. "Another Major Red Flag About Covid Vaccines And Death". *Alexberenson.Substack.Com.* https://alexberenson.substack.com/p/another-major-red-flag-about-covid.

82 Nordström, Peter, Marcel Ballin, and Anna Nordström. 2022. "Risk Of Infection, Hospitalisation, And Death Up To 9 Months After A Second Dose Of COVID-19 Vaccine: A Retrospective, Total Population Cohort Study In Sweden". *The Lancet* 399 (10327): 814-823. doi:10.1016/s0140-6736(22)00089-7.

83 Statistics Sweden, Population and Economic Welfare. 2022. "Population Statistics". SCB.

84 Kuznetsov, Igor. 2021. "Swedish Doctors Pen Petition To Stop Pfizer Vaccine After Suspected Subcontractor Fraud". *Sputnik.* https://sputniknews.com/20211108/swedish-doctors-pen-petition-to-stop-pfizer-vaccine-after-suspected-subcontractor-fraud-1090557515.html.

85 "Swedish Doctors Want Pfizer's Covid-19 Vaccine Banned After Subcontractor Fraud Exposed". 2021. *The Expose.* https://dailyexpose.uk/2021/11/12/swedish-doctors-want-pfizers-covid-19-vaccine-banned-after-subcontractor-fraud-exposed/.

86 "Latest UKHSA Report Proves This Is A 'Pandemic Of The Fully Vaccinated' And The Data Shows The Vaccinated Are TWICE As Likely To Die And Are About To Overwhelm The NHS". 2021. *The Expose.* https://dailyexpose.uk/2021/11/19/latest-ukhsa-report-proves-this-is-a-pandemic-of-the-fully-vaccinated/.

87 UK Health Security Agency. 2021. "Vaccine Surveillance Report Week 38." https://assets.publishing.service.gov.uk/government/uploads/system/uploads/attachment_data/file/1019992/vaccine_surveillance_report_-_week_38.pdf

88 UK Health Security Agency. 2021. "Vaccine Surveillance Report Week 42." https://assets.publishing.service.gov.uk/government/uploads/system/uploads/attachment_data/file/1027511/vaccine_surveillance_report_-_week_42.pdf

89 UK Health Security Agency. 2021. "Vaccine Surveillance Report Week 46." https://assets.publishing.service.gov.uk/government/uploads/system/uploads/attachment_data/file/1034383/vaccine_surveillance_report_-_week_46.pdf

90 Berenson, Alex. 2021. "Vaccinated English Adults Under 60 Are Dying At Twice The Rate Of Unvaccinated People The Same Age". *Alexberenson.Substack.Com.* https://alexberenson.substack.com/p/vaccinated-english-adults-under-60?r=m7jq6&fbclid=IwAR3CkfYQ66OtnZeQibsm21tgFjZpMmOZpLX3gsmC3JhQMMVfADgksHjyCLA.

91 Knapton, Sarah. 2021. "Alarm Grows As Mortuaries Fill With Thousands Of Extra Non-Covid Deaths". *Telegraph.Co.Uk.*

https://www.telegraph.co.uk/news/2021/11/16/nhs-delays-height-pandemic-linked-thousands-extra-non-covid/?utm_content=telegraph&utm_medium=Social&utm_campaign=Echobox&utm_source=Twitter.

92   "Dutch Parliament Member Thierry Baudet Tweeted The Video Of How Vaccines Kill People". 2021. *Lorphic News*. https://lorphicweb.com/videos/.

93   "Taiwan Death From COVID-19 Vaccination Exceeds Death From COVID-19". 2021. *Medical Trend*. https://medicaltrend.org/2021/10/10/taiwan-death-from-covid-19-vaccination-exceeds-death-from-covid-19.

94   Steyer, Rolf, and Gregor Kappler. 2021. "The Higher The Vaccination Rate, The Higher The Excess Mortality". Steve Kirsch. https://www.skirsch.com/covid/GermanAnalysis.pdf.

95   Becker, Kyle. 2022. "The CDC May Be Committing Fraud With Its Reporting On Covid Deaths. Here's Where They Seem To Admit It.". *Becker News*. https://beckernews.com/the-cdc-may-be-committing-fraud-with-its-reporting-on-covid-deaths-heres-where-they-seem-to-admit-it-43693/.

96   "Estimated COVID-19 Burden". 2021. *Cdc.Gov*. https://www.cdc.gov/coronavirus/2019-ncov/cases-updates/burden.html.

Chapter 14

Adverse Events Pt. 2: A Morbidity Catastrophe

In the fall of 2021 into early 2022, the working age population experienced a mortality spike of disastrous proportions. This was evidenced by everything from insurance experience to public excess mortality data from a variety of countries, as documented in the previous chapter. Analyst Edward Dowd calculated this spike to represent around 61,000 excess deaths for US millennials alone, a death toll slightly higher than that suffered by US troops in the Vietnam War.[1] These outcomes show that not only was the mass mRNA inoculation program a failure, but it was far worse than a failure. And the unfortunate kicker at this time in the early spring of 2022 is this: *it's only been **one** year.*

What we've experienced so far are only the short term effects. Because the pre-meditated intention of Fauci and the Covid collaborators was to skip any kind of long term study, we can't yet know how much worse it will get down the road. However, based on the unprecedented mortality outcomes and the 1,294 known, "adverse events of special interest," Pfizer and the FDA knew about prior to the rollout, the outlook is not particularly good. We can start to paint of picture of just how, "not particularly good," it is by looking at the types of morbidity outcomes which have been documented to date.

Myocarditis, Blood Clots, and Heart Attacks

It is not disputed that the inoculations cause myocarditis and other heart-related issues. The FDA fact sheets for the Moderna and Pfizer shots contain explicit warnings of myocarditis/pericarditis risks, while the fact sheet for the Johnson & Johnson shot calls out blood clot risk.[2,3,4] We've also already covered the Cal study which, among others, demonstrated serious inoculation-caused heart risk to be 6-times worse for young boys than the risk of being hospitalized with, "Covid."[5,6] This has become such a prevalent issue for young athletes in particular that starting in the fall of 2021 school districts, such as Orange County Public Schools, have suddenly started recommending electrocardiogram screenings for students who wish to participate in sports.[7] Orange County's warning cites the risk of, "sudden cardiac arrest," in children, an ailment for this age group previously acknowledged in scientific papers to be, "rare," and, "less likely to be a cardiac event."[8] Finally, the European Medicines Agency (EMA) has also acknowledged cases of capillary leak syndrome related to the Moderna inoculation, a disorder involving repeated leaks of large amounts of plasma from blood vessels into nearby body cavities and muscles, according to Mayo Clinic.[9,10]

One would think these clearly relevant risks would be reason enough not to coerce anyone—least of all children—to inoculate in any way, or to at least grant the coerced the dignity to hold the coercer liable so that justice/recompense can be done in the case of injury. Unfortunately and criminally, we now know of the insane push which was made to deny this simple dignity, and to recklessly endanger countless lives by carrying on with coercion anyway.

And when I say, "countless," I say it because the risk of heart and blood related diseases have both been clearly and dramatically misrepresented in both their severity and rarity. As it relates to severity, propagandists like *Popular Science* demonstrated the nerve to call myocarditis, "scary-sounding," while downplaying the danger of this *heart condition*.[11] They specifically cite someone on the CDC vaccine advisory panel itself named Sarah Long who, in reference to this heart condition in children, is actually quoted as saying, "give me a patient with vaccine-associated myocarditis every day," over, "one who has true viral myocarditis."

The reason for the difference, Long claims, is that vaccine-related inflammation isn't concentrated in the heart muscle itself, but in the lining around the heart called the pericardium. She suggests this isn't worth worrying about because, "surgeons sometimes remove it (the pericardium) altogether during heart procedures, and patients do fine." Astonishing. So apparently as long as all those who suffer this side effect just get heart surgery, they should be fine. Joking or not joking (I truly am not sure) aside, what Long recommends is that we, "should be calling the vaccine side-effect pericarditis or perimyocarditis."

This is where the classic deceptive re-definitions that public health departments have become notorious for begins because the FDA fact sheets *do* call out *both* myocarditis and pericarditis, two distinct diseases. If a patient has myocarditis, they have myocarditis. If they have pericarditis, they have pericarditis. Maybe they could have both, and in that case you could call it, "perimyocarditis," if you'd like, as Long suggests. But the FDA acknowledges that people *are* getting *each* condition as a side effect, not just pericarditis. Also, this entire *Popular Science* article was specifically titled and framed to suggest that *myocarditis* isn't, "scary," *not* that pericarditis isn't scary. Perhaps a less deceptive headline and thesis which would accurately reflect the content would have been, "CDC Panelist Believes FDA Misidentifying Myocarditis Risk." Unfortunately, since the goal is strictly to sell inoculations at all costs, accuracy in journalism and explicit criticism of the FDA are antithetical to the goal. But as we've found, it's also difficult to maintain a lie. Long demonstrates this when she goes on to blatantly contradict the entire premise of the article, stating, "If parents were to look up myocarditis, they would be quite upset about this."

Parents certainly would and *should* be upset about the prospect of their child getting myocarditis. As published by the American Heart Association (AHA), myocarditis is defined as an, "inflammation of the myocardium," and its associated morbidity/mortality risks are, "well-established."[12] The AHA cites four studies specifically in relation to this risk, the conclusions of which are as follows:

1. Grogan et al. 1995 publication in the *Journal of the American College of Cardiology* on, "Long-term outcome of patients with biopsy-proved myocarditis: Comparison with idiopathic dilated cardiomyopathy," found[13]: *"There was no difference in the 5-year survival rate between the myocarditis and idiopathic dilated cardiomyopathy groups (56% vs. 54% respectively) ... This study demonstrates that the long-term outcome of patients with biopsy-proved myocarditis seen in a referral setting is poor."*

2. McCarthy et al. 2000 publication in the *New England Journal of Medicine* on, "Long-Term Outcome of Fulminant Myocarditis as Compared with Acute (Nonfulminant) Myocarditis," found[14]: *"Among patients with fulminant myocarditis, 93 percent were alive without having received a heart transplant 11 years after biopsy ... as compared with only 45 percent of those with acute myocarditis."*

3. Mason et al. 1995 publication in the *New England Journal of Medicine* on, "A Clinical Trial of Immunosuppressive Therapy for Myocarditis," found[15]: *"The mortality rate for the*

entire group was 20 percent at 1 year and 56 percent at 4.3 years."

4. Dec et al. 1985 publication in the *New England Journal of Medicine* on, "Active Myocarditis in the Spectrum of Acute Dilated Cardiomyopathies – Clinical Features, Histologic Correlates, and Clinical Outcome," found[16]: *"We conclude that many cases of unexplained dilated cardiomyopathy result from myocarditis."*

Did you know myocarditis was associated with this degree of risk? No? Me neither until I went through this process. Do you think it would be crucial for people to be aware this degree of risk comes with a product they plan on injecting themselves with *multiple times*? It can be alleged all day long that the risk of these outcomes is small and that a tiny fraction of people experience them. The problem is that as of my writing this we are barely over a year into the inoculation campaign (less than that for many people) and you can see above that the timeframe of a myocarditis sufferer's lifespan is approximately 50% survival after 5 years. The number of currently undetected cases is unknown and the clearly intentional effort to suppress the severity gives us reason to expect dishonesty from the same people when they claim the frequency is low. There's also plenty of observable support to back up this suspicion:

- VAERS reports as of December 31, 2021: 10,863 heart attacks, 23,713 myocarditis/pericarditis cases
- A 2021 study by Chua et al. published in *Clinical Infectious Diseases* on, "Epidemiology of Acute Myocarditis/Pericarditis in Hong Kong Adolescents Following Comirnaty Vaccination," found[17]: *"There is a significant increase in the risk of acute myocarditis/pericarditis following Comirnaty vaccination among Chinese male adolescents, especially after the second dose."*
- A 2021 study by Patone et al. published in *medRxiv* on, "Risk of myocarditis following sequential COVID-19 vaccinations by age and sex," found that for all doses of all shots the increased risk of myocarditis was greater than the myocarditis risk associated with getting, "Covid."[18] Specifically, for the

second dose of Moderna the increased risk was almost 15 times greater.

- As-yet un-peer-reviewed analysis posted late December 2021 by Sharff et al. in *medRxiv* which reviewed the CDC's Vaccine Safety Datalink (VSD) methodology used to determine myocarditis and pericarditis cases. The study found[19]: "*... additional valid cases of myopericarditis following an mRNA vaccination that would be missed by the VSD's search algorithm, which depends on select hospital discharge diagnosis codes. **The true incidence of myopericarditis is markedly higher than the incidence reported to US advisory committees** (my emphasis).*"

- Per Steve Kirsch, in a single 4-month period of 2021 there were more athlete deaths and collapses than in the prior 20 years, representing a 60-fold increase in such events.[20] In the FIFA soccer league alone there were 108 players/coaches who had died in the 6-months preceding November 2021. And while heart issues in general are not shocking in a sport with as much physical exertion as soccer, this rate is unprecedented historically. *Wikipedia* confirmed as much when it stopped tracking such events in November 2021, just as many people started recognizing the disturbing, now-regularly-occurring scenes of players simply collapsing, whether they were playing or even just stretching.[21,22] The media also launched an embarrassing campaign to explain away these events, which we will highlight in our chapter on propaganda.

- From the previously cited November 2021 *UK Telegraph* article on increases in, "non-Covid," excess death[23]: "*Data from the UK Health Security Agency show there have been thousands more deaths than the five-year average in heart failure, heart disease, circulatory conditions, and diabetes since the summer.*"

- In October 2021 Dr. Rochagné Kilian came out as a whistleblower on increased D-Dimer levels caused by the inoculations.[24] In her presentation, she explained that D-Dimer levels are an indicator of potential blood clotting issues, and that following the inoculation campaign she was experiencing patients with some of the highest D-Dimer levels she'd ever seen. For example, while a, "maybe positive," reading would be around 500 ng/ml in her experience, she was seeing levels from 3,000 – 5,000 ng/ml. She attributed a tremendous increase in strokes in Ontario to this phenomenon. Finally, Dr. Kilian went on to cite a 2016 study by Schutte et al. published in the *Netherlands Journal of Medicine* titled, "Never ignore extremely elevated D-dimer levels: they are specific for serious illness."[25] This study indicated that, "even if sharply elevated (5,000+ ng/ml) D-dimers are a seemingly solitary finding, clinical suspicion of severe underlying disease should be maintained."

- Dr. Kilian is not alone in her observations either. Dr. Charles Hoffe claims that in D-dimer testing his own inoculated patients he found, "62% of them have evidence of clotting."[26] This phenomenon is even institutionally confirmed by the Salk Institute, which in April 2021 published a report specifically on the damaging effects of the spike protein, which the mRNA in the inoculations are meant to tell the body to create trillions of.[27] The Salk report makes the direct connection between this spike protein and blood clots, explaining, "The spike protein alone was enough to cause disease." To repeat again: *this spike protein is what the mRNA instructs the body to create*.

- The following are five among a list of 226 peer-reviewed studies to-date connecting myocarditis to the inoculations[28]: King et al. August 2021;[29] Montgomery et al. June 2021;[30] Dionne et al. 2021;[31] Marshall et al. September 2021;[32] Luk et al. October 2021[33]

- The following are five among a list of 150 peer-reviewed studies to-date connecting thrombosis (blood vessel and/or clotting damage) to the inoculations[34]: Andraska et al. January 2022;[35] Tajstra et al. May 2021;[36] See et al. June 2021;[37] Stecher et al. August 2021;[38] Gresele et al. July 2021[39]

- The following are five among a list of 115 peer-reviewed studies to-date connecting thrombocytopenia (reduced blood platelets resulting in increased bleeding) to the inoculations[40]: Aladdin et al. September 2021;[41] See et al. June 2021;[42] Gresele et al. July 2021;[43] Sharifian-Dorche et al. September 2021;[44] Long et al. November 2021[45]

- The following are five among a list of 61 peer-reviewed studies to-date connecting cerebral venous thrombosis (a type of stroke) to the inoculations[46]: Bikdeli et al. July 2021;[47] Dutta et al. August 2021;[48] Dias et al. August 2021;[49] Lee et al. September 2021;[50] See et al. June 2021[51]
- The following are three among a list of 43 peer-reviewed studies to-date connecting vasculitis (inflammation of blood vessels which could lead to aneurysm) to the inoculations[52]: Shakoor et al. October 2021;[53] Okuda et al. July 2021;[54] Badier et al. November 2021[55]

It is primarily due to these inoculation-induced heart conditions that several countries have banned or limited the Moderna shot, at least, in some capacity.[56] Iceland, Sweden, Denmark, Norway, and Finland have been the first to take actions. Joining them is a Hasidic rabbinical court in New York, which after hearing eight hours of testimony from a variety of doctors and scientists stated that it is, "absolutely forbidden to administer the mRNA Covid-19 vaccine to children, adolescents, young men, and women."[57]

Maternity and Menstrual Issues

The idea that the inoculations could lead to infertility started off as a theory which was not without motive support. Since Bill Gates was the primary narrative pusher and one of the most obvious beneficiaries of the alleged pandemic, those who were aware of his well-documented background in eugenics started to ask questions.[58] This history began with Gate's father, William H. Gates Sr., who served on the board of Planned Parenthood (a rebranded organization birthed out of the American Eugenics Society), continued into the William H. Gates Foundation, and has to-date culminated in the Bill & Melinda Gates Foundation. You can explore more of that background by diving into either the source I've cited here or the previously mentioned documentary, "Who Is Bill Gates?" by James Corbett. The reason I bring up Gates' history of eugenics though is the following quote many recalled from a Ted Talk Gates gave on, "climate change," in 2010[59]:

> *"Now the world today has 6.8 billion people, and that's headed up to about 9 billion. Now if we do a really great job on **new vaccines** (my emphasis), healthcare, reproductive*

363

health services—we could reduce that by perhaps about 10 or 15%."

What *isn't* important here, despite the deranged effort to tell us otherwise by so many, "fact-checkers," (aka: Gates' PR team) is whether Gates means to apply the, "10 or 15%," reduction to the current 6.8 billion or to the *increase* to 9 billion. What *does* matter is that Gates finds it necessary or in his power at all to control the world's population. He has expressed a belief that there are too many people (fact) and that he or anyone else has the authority to actively seek to do something about it (fact).

This is not even a controversial or contestable point, as the *Wall Street Journal* in 2009 (right before the, "decade of vaccines," began) published the headline, "Billionaires try to shrink the world's population, report says."[60] According to the *Journal*, this meeting included the likes of Gates, Warren Buffett, David Rockefeller, George Soros, Ted Turner (founder of CNN[61]), and Michael Bloomberg, among others. The article also quoted the *London Times* in acknowledging, "Taking their cue from Gates they agreed that overpopulation was a priority," before admitting, "such a stand wouldn't be surprising," since, "Gates, Buffet, and Turner have been quietly worrying about Malthusian population problems for years." Since Michael Bloomberg is both a powerful figure in the propaganda world and his name is on the Event-201-co-organizing John's Hopkins Bloomberg School of Medicine, he too is a prominent Covid era figure to have aligned with such a goal—to say nothing of also-relevant Turner, Soros, or Rockefeller.

While as a Christian I find this worldview obviously detestable, it seems the disdain humanity should have for this position should be universal. Take, "reproductive health services," for example, which is a nicer way to market abortion. Even those in support of abortion should probably be at least somewhat concerned about how Gates brings up abortion not in the context of personal choice, but as a crucial piece in his stated goal of population control. Consider the hypothetical—what if every woman stopped wanting (or in their minds, "needing") abortions? Again, even if you support abortion, this would be the *choice* of women and therefore satisfactory, correct? Well to the pro-choice person, yes it would. To Bill Gates, however, he'd then need a new method of population reduction to achieve the aim of his Ted Talk presentation. Either way, his intention is not your intention, so long as you're not a eugenicist psychopath who wants to reduce the population.

At the same time, Gates says that vaccines are also a solution for this, "problem." According to the members of his PR team at *Poynter*, this is because they claim Gates believes, "expanding access to healthcare will lead people to have smaller families."[62] First of all, to once again acknowledge the intentional deceit that defines, "fact-checkers," the headline of the blog post in which they claim this is called, "Bill Gates didn't say he wanted to use vaccines to reduce the population." Even if Gates' intention was exactly what they suggest it is and nothing more however, he literally did say exactly that in the Ted Talk quote above—a Ted Talk which *Poynter* ironically acknowledges was removed from *YouTube*, "for violating YouTube's Community Guidelines," without any fanfare.

According to *Statista*, the 2020 average number of own children per US family was 1.93.[63] Also, according to the UN, the population replacement rate—the number of children needed for a population to replace themselves—is 2.1 children per couple worldwide, and 2.3 in less developed countries.[64] So, at least in the US, it seems the population is not on pace to replace itself. I'm sure Gates would take pride in having some role in this. However, he himself seems to have hindered the, "progress," he claimed to want to make in, "reducing CO2 emissions by reducing the population," seeing as both his father and he had 3 children and thus replaced themselves.[65]

"Eugenics for thee but not for me," apparently. Either that or maybe the Gates family just doesn't have the same, "access to healthcare," the rest of America, "benefits," from. Either way, this hypocrisy and the stated depopulation motive behind Gates' activity in, "healthcare," demands scrutiny for any relevant project he is involved in. In fact, one would be insane not to make every possible effort to at least understand—if not to reject outright—a product a man with these beliefs has publicly called for the coercive enforcement of on the population (via, "vaccination," certificates/identification, as covered).

All this is what has made reports of reproductive issues in inoculated women all the more troubling. The motive is undeniably there amongst the oligarchs pushing this agenda the hardest. I am not claiming at all that Gates knew or intended for these problems to arise—that is the subject for investigations which will almost certainly never happen, thanks to his tremendous influence around the world. However, the gas-lighting of anyone who raises questions about this obvious motive by the very, "journalists," who should be among those investigating it, simply raises more suspicions. That tremendous amounts of money also happen to flow from the Gates Foundation to those, "journalists," makes matters even worse. The following are the reports in question as it relates to inoculation-related reproductive issues:

- VAERS reports through December 31, 2021: 3,511 miscarriages, 20,608 menstrual disorders, 7,817 vaginal/uterine hemorrhages, 1,406 testicular pain/swelling
- The original *New England Journal of Medicine* study used to justify the CDC and FDA recommendation of pregnant women getting the shots was, by the journal's own admission, riddled with flaws.[66,67] It identified that of 827 completed pregnancies among inoculated women, 104 (12.6%) experienced spontaneous abortions. Now, according to popular estimates this would be within the bounds of average.[68] However, a 2021 study published in *Science, Public Health Policy, and the Law* by Brock and Thornley acknowledged that the *NEJM* study failed to account for the relevant detail that the vast majority of the women in the study were inoculated after 20 weeks' gestation, the period of least risk for spontaneous abortion.[69] In fact, the *NEJM* study author admitted this in the study itself. Upon re-analysis of the original data to account for this however, Brock and Thornley concluded: *"A re-analysis of these figures indicates a cumulative incidence of spontaneous abortion ranging from 82% (104/127) to 91% (104/114), 7-8 times higher than the original author's results."*
- Whistleblowers reported 13 stillborn deaths in a 24 hour period at a single hospital—namely, Lions Gate Hospital in Canada.[70] They allege all involved inoculated women.
- The Regenerative Medicine Center (RMC) did a Biodistribution review to determine where in the body the inoculation material goes.[71] The pharma / public health claim

is that the shot's material is quickly broken down at the site of injection in the arm. The RMC points to a Japanese study, however, which disputed this claim, showing biodistribution beyond the injection site and into the ovaries. The RMC also reviewed Pfizer's own study, PF-07302048 June 2020, which the European Medicine Agency (EMA), the EU agency in charge of the evaluation and supervision of medicinal products, explicitly acknowledged reviewing on February 19, 2021. Shockingly, the following are observations made in this very report: *"The biodistribution was also studied in rats ... results support that injections site and the liver are the major sites of distribution ... Over 48 hours, distribution was mainly observed to liver, adrenal glands, spleen and ovaries."*

- "COVID vaccines may briefly change your menstrual cycle, but you should still get one," reads the headline of a January 6, 2022 propaganda blog post by *NPR*.[72] This came at a time when a 2022 study was published in *Obstetrics & Gynecology* by Edelman et al. which confirmed a change in menstrual cycle length for those inoculated.[73] It was confirmed again in a 2021 *medRxiv* study by Lee et al. which found 42% of women experienced heavier menstrual bleeding and 66% of post-menopausal women even experienced breakthrough bleeding.[74] While the media and public health recklessly claim these changes are not a danger, there is no way they can know that to be true. The NIH admitted as much when it announced on October 5, 2021 that it awarded five institutions grants to explore links between inoculations and menstrual issues.[75] What happens if the findings are grievous? How much pain and suffering could have been avoided by going through the normal long-term safety procedures instead of diving right into a coercive mass-inoculation campaign without any such checks?

Vaccine-Enhanced Disease, Cancer, and all Other Issues

In this final section we will discuss all other issues which have been tied to the inoculations. The first we will touch on is vaccine-enhanced disease. Some people might refer to this as, "VAIDS," (vaccine-induced AIDS) or wrongly as, "HIV," but the overall idea is that the inoculations harm the innate immune system's ability to function as it is supposed to. This is the same concept Anthony Fauci identified in his interview with Mark Zuckerberg, during which he cited examples where, "a vaccine," ultimately, "made people worse." The European Medicines Agency also admitted this when they were reported as saying, "booster doses every four months could eventually weaken the immune system," on January 11, 2022.[76] Fun fact: the same agency also claimed, "Data supports vaccine boosters after three months," just a month before in December 2021.[77]

In the case of the mRNA inoculations, disease-enhancement would theoretically occur due to their reprogramming properties and/or introduction of the unnatural spike protein. The following two studies demonstrate those phenomena, respectively:

1. A 2021 study by Föhse et al. published in *medRxiv* concluded that the Pfizer inoculation, "induces complex function reprogramming of innate immune responses," not just as it relates to specific stimuli (cold/flu/coronavirus-related), but also to non-specific stimuli (fungal/bacterial/etc.)[78]
2. A 2021 study by Jiang and Mei published in *Viruses* found the spike protein, "significantly inhibits DNA damage repair, which is required for effective V(D)J recombination in adaptive immunity"[79]

These findings validate earlier-identified concerns with past SARS inoculations introducing a hypersensitivity and/or weakened ability to fight infection. They are also supported in the real world by both the failure to prevent disease and the increased incidence of hospitalization and excess death seen in many countries, with Scotland being one of the several examples we've covered. The connection also gets more overt when you look to the Netherlands, which by July 2021 reported 90 percent inoculation rates.[80] The country's strategy focused on the Pfizer and Moderna mRNA shots and it clearly hit its goals during the initial round, as by the end of 2021 it announced plans to give people, "up to six doses," of the shots.[81,82] However, this, "public health victory," would be short-lived. In February 2022 the UN claimed a, "fast-spreading HIV variant," which, "doubles rate of immune system decline," had been discovered in the Netherlands."[83]

By now it should be clear that I do not actually give any validity whatsoever to the idea of an, "HIV variant." This goes double when it is alleged by the UN, and triple at a time an explanation is needed for the predictable outcomes of the mass inoculation campaign it has supported. The point here is immune systems are facing an unprecedented decline exactly as all pre- and post-inoculation studies and indications suggested they would. To call the Netherlands story a coincidence of nature is to insult the Dutch as a people. The story also doesn't get better with the adenoviral vector inoculations such as Johnson & Johnson and AstraZeneca, in fact it gets worse.

In October 2020 the *New York Post* reported on the known tendency of these alternative inoculations to cause the same autoimmune failures in question.[84] To this effect they cited a, "cautionary tale," published in the *Lancet*, as well as another in *Science Magazine*.[85,86] Each showed how adenoviral vector injections actually *increased* the prevalence of AIDS when compared to a placebo group, which they then tied to the possibility of the Covid shots contributing to an increased prevalence of AIDS. Fauci would have been well aware of the outcome of the AIDS-era adenoviral shots, yet zero caution or background on this was provided in the opening days of the Covid mass inoculation campaign.

There have been many other papers and articles to-date linking the Covid shots to immune deficiency.[87,88,89] One last example to mention for now is a study published in January 2022 by Seneff et al. in *Authorea* titled, "Innate Immune Suppression by SARS-CoV-2 mRNA Vaccinations: The role of G-quadruplexes, exosomes and microRNAs."[90] The study authors determined that, "vaccination, unlike natural infection, induces a profound impairment in type I interferon signaling, which has diverse adverse consequences to human health." These consequences included all the types of diseases previously mentioned, but also, "increased tumorigenesis," also known as the formation of tumors.[91]

The Seneff paper was also not the only link which has been made between the Covid shots and cancer. Perhaps the most prominent came when lawyer Thomas Renz revealed data from the Defense Medical Epidemiology Database (DMED), the official health surveillance system of the US military, which he received from 3 Department of Defense whistleblowers.[92] When compared to the prior five years, 2021 data showed tremendous increases of between 4 and

369

20 times in all the diseases tied to the Covid inoculations via VAERS and other documented support.[93] They also show spikes in various cancers, including breast (+487%) and testicular (+369%).

After this information was presented to Senator Ron Johnson at a hearing he organized, he sent a letter outlining the details to the Secretary of the Department of Defense, Lloyd Austin.[94] Even worse than the results however, was the DOD's response to what they showed. Instead of honestly acknowledging and investigating, the DOD actually claimed that, "the data in the system accessed by several military doctors working with Thomas Renz was only a 'fraction' of the true numbers that existed," for all years except 2021, due to a, "glitch in the database."[95] To reiterate: the DOD claimed that their database used to monitor the US military's health readiness was wrong for five years at least, corrected somehow in 2021 for that year only, and none of this was acknowledged or documented until 2022— just after the results demonstrated a dramatic increase in inoculation-connected illnesses and that increase was brought to the public's attention by whistleblower military doctors—whistleblower military doctors who apparently didn't know the database they utilize was underreported by a factor of between 4 and 20 for the prior 5 years. They are then meant to have, "corrected," this data, for the same 5 years (2016-2020) used as a benchmark by Renz and team to compare against 2021.

As a data scientist, let me provide my expertise here: this is one of the most obvious examples of fraud in this book, and we've already covered *a lot* of extremely obvious examples. The following is a long list of reasons why, including contributions by Steve Kirsch and Daniel Horowitz[96,97]:

1. The convenience of the explanation and the manner in which it was explained away, which the US DOD actually did via a source as disreputable as *PolitiFact*[98]
2. There is no explanation given for why data was allegedly missing from 2016-2020 but not 2021. For this to be possible, a correction would've had to have been made in 2021, but such a correction is not documented, nor was the deficiency which is now claimed to have existed with older, uncorrected data. This 2021 correction, if it had occurred, would've led to a lack

of comparability from year-to-year and thus, made the historical data useless for its purpose.

3. The lack of awareness of this glaring issue by military doctors with access to and who are dependent in some capacity on the accuracy of DMED is incomprehensible

4. Per Kirsch, the, "corrections," made to 2016-2020 only included the symptoms which were elevated in connection with the inoculations. Other illnesses were not, "corrected." This is not possible by a glitch or programming issue.

5. Horowitz shows the changes as they relate to pericarditis, among other illnesses, are not believable because they show a *drop* in pericarditis cases for both 2020 and 2021, relative to the prior period. This means despite pericarditis being tied to both, "Covid," and to the inoculations, the military incidence is alleged to have gone down. This does not make sense.

6. Horowitz also shows how vaccine injury diagnosis codes, which were apparently not explicitly called out by the Renz whistleblowers, remain at 6- to 17-fold increases relative to 2016-2020 data and were apparently spared the, "glitch." This further points to the DOD simply making the Renz-identified illnesses look better. It also invalidates the, "corrections," which were made, because how can inoculation injuries increase by a factor of 6 to 17, while other diseases remain flat or drop?

7. Kirsch also points out that the DOD only, "corrected," the 2016-2020 period, though the years prior to 2016 continue to reflect the averages seen prior to the, "correction"

8. As mentioned by Kirsch, both before and after the, "correction," total hospital event rates *declined* from 2019 to 2020. This is relevant to the discussion on, "Covid," as well because military hospitals do not get the same government Covid incentives the civilian hospitals do (more on those in a bit).

9. The inoculation injury data, as well as the illness data, "pre-correction," were both available to the military and CDC throughout 2021 and neither paid any mind to them despite the massive increases they showed. No investigations into the cause were made, not even into the possibility of a, "glitch," until called out by the Renz whistleblowers. This implies fraud

371

in the, "correction," or reckless negligence even if the, "correction," was accurate.

10. The DMED data before the, "correction," matches both VAERS and other civilian data points on post-inoculation outcomes

Whether it's DMED or VAERS, the Covid-collaborating US government bureaucracies have demonstrated a consistent pattern of claiming their own databases are, "robust," until the time comes when those resources show something antithetical to their mass inoculation mission. During such times, those bureaucracies are happy to hide their blatant culpability behind a veil of what would still be an inexcusable degree of incompetence, as we've seen with both the CDC and DOD. The problem is they aren't incompetent—not the CDC with its conflicts we will yet cover, nor the DOD, which we saw had a hand in funding the mRNA inoculations they now run cover for.

Additional support for a link between the shots and cancer are as follows:

- Bioinformatic analysis published in *Translational Oncology* in June 2020 by Singh and Bharara determined that the spike protein interacts with tumor suppressor proteins[99]
- A November 2021 study by Goldman et al. published in *Frontiers in Medicine* observed a man who was discovered to have cancer on September 1, 2021, 5 months after receiving his first two Pfizer doses.[100] The man then received a booster shot on September 22, 2021. By September 30, 2021 his cancer had rapidly progressed. The study authors concluded that the, "vaccine might induce rapid progression of AITL," and, "dedicated studies are needed," to conclude this connection.
- Dr. Ryan Cole observed an increase in cancers and recurrences among inoculated patients, saying, "I'm seeing a 20 times increase of endometrial cancers over what I see on an annual basis."[101] Dr. Cole cites an observed drop in killer T-cells post-inoculation as well as the Föhse study on altered immune responses for this increase.
- Hundreds of Chinese people formed a social media group for people suffering from leukemia, the symptoms of which

presented following their Covid inoculation.[102] This group includes parents of previously healthy children as young as 4 as well, following China's push to inoculate 3-11 year-olds.

To end this chapter, the following is a list of several other anomalies and concerns reported around inoculation side effects and complications. They are supported as side effects by both the reporting data and biological issues discussed related to the problems with both the spike proteins and mRNA delivery toxicity:

- A 2022 systematic review and meta-analysis in *JAMA* by Haas et al. found there to be about 30% more adverse events in the inoculated group than the placebo group after one dose and about 100% more in the inoculated group after the second[103]

- Per Attorney Aaron Siri, physician assistant and whistleblower Deborah Conrad's hospital tracks the inoculation status of every patient admitted.[104] According to Conrad, while less than 50% of the community her hospital serves were inoculated, during the same time period approximately 90% of the individuals admitted were documented as having been inoculated. What was particularly troubling to Conrad was that, "there were many individuals who were young, many who presented with unusual or unexpected health events."

- Whistleblower Dr. Patricia Lee penned a letter to the FDA and CDC after witnessing serious harms and death following the inoculations.[105] A return letter was sent by the FDA's director of communications, not a medical officer, which sought no additional information regarding the injuries described. Instead, the letter simply touted VAERS—the same system both called, "robust," by the CDC and also considered incapable of identifying an issue despite a tremendous number of reports. Nonetheless, Dr. Lee's bravery led 11 more physicians to provide attorney Aaron Siri declarations attesting to serious harms from the inoculations.[106]

- US Senator Ron Johnson held a panel discussion on November 2, 2021 with at least 11 doctors and medical researchers who have treat inoculation injuries, as well as at least 8 patients who have experienced these injuries.[107] Invitations to this discussion were sent to CDC Director Rochelle Walensky, FDA Commissioner Janet Woodcock, NIH Director Francis Collins, NIAID Director Anthony Fauci, and the CEOs of each of the major pharmaceutical companies, among others. None attended.

- A second hearing titled, "COVID-19: A Second Opinion," was also hosted by Senator Johnson on January 24, 2022.[108] The hearing featured Drs. Peter McCullough, Jay Bhattacharya, Pierre Kory, Harvey Risch, and Robert Malone, among others, who summarized their findings on the dangers of the Covid inoculations, among other criticisms of the public health apparatus. Again the aforementioned public health and pharma officials were invited, and again they refused to attend and defend their position.

- Dr. Stephanie Seneff, a Senior Research Scientist at MIT's Computer Science and Artificial Intelligence Laboratory in Cambridge, Massachusetts, shared a presentation with the World Council for Health in which she tied the Covid inoculations to neurodegenerative disease[109]

- ABC affiliate WXYZ Detroit posted on *Facebook* asking its followers if they lost an, "unvaccinated," loved one to, "Covid."[110] The post went on to garner well over 100K comments; however, nearly all the comments contained stories of adverse reactions to the inoculations.

- A documentary called *I Am Not Misinformation* was released in December 2021 which chronicles the testimony of a variety of patients and doctors who have been injured by the inoculations[111]

- The following are five among a list of 43 peer-reviewed studies to-date connecting Guillain-Baré Syndrome (neurological disorder ranging from mild case of weakness to severe paralysis) to the inoculations[112]: Dufour et al. March 2021;[113] Introna et al. September 2021;[114] Min et al. October 2021;[115] Ogbebor et al. 2021;[116] Rossetti et al. December 2021[117]

- The following are five among a list of 35 peer-reviewed studies to-date connecting lymphadenopathy (disease affecting the lymph nodes where the sizes of the lymph can be

374

affected) to the inoculations[118]: Park et al. October 2021;[119] Xu et al. April 2021;[120] Özütemiz et al. July 2021;[121] Cohen et al. June 2021;[122] Keshavarz et al. August 2021[123]

- The following are five among a list of 30 peer-reviewed studies to-date connecting anaphylaxis (severe, potentially life-threatening allergic reaction) to the inoculations[124]: Turner et al. February 2021;[125] Shimabukuro et al. February 2021;[126] "Allergic Reactions Including Anaphylaxis After Receipt Of The First Dose Of Pfizer-Biontech COVID-19 Vaccine — United States, December 14–23, 2020" 2021;[127] "Allergic Reactions Including Anaphylaxis After Receipt Of The First Dose Of Moderna COVID-19 Vaccine — United States, December 21, 2020–January 10, 2021" 2021;[128] Lee et al. August 2021[129]

- The following are three among a list of 18 peer-reviewed studies to-date connecting Bell's Palsy (facial muscle weakness or paralysis resulting in damage to the facial nerve) to the inoculations[130]: Cirillo et al. September 2021;[131] Repajic et al. May 2021;[132] Gómez de Terreros Caro et al. September 2021[133]

- The following are three among a list of 15 peer-reviewed studies to-date connecting acute myelitis (inflammation of the spinal cord which can disrupt the normal responses from the brain to the rest of the body, and from the rest of the body to the brain, resulting in sensory loss and paralysis) to the inoculations[134]: Vegezzi et al. October 2021;[135] Román et al. April 2021;[136] Tahir et al. July 2021[137]

Endnotes

1   Hill, James. 2022. "Excess Mortality Up 84% In Millennials (Ages 25-44) Since 2021 Vaccine Rollout: Former Blackrock Executive". Hillmd.Substack.Com. https://hillmd.substack.com/p/excess-mortality-up-84-in-millennials?s=r.

2   The Food & Drug Administration. 2022. "FACT SHEET FOR HEALTHCARE PROVIDERS ADMINISTERING VACCINE (VACCINATION PROVIDERS) EMERGENCY USE AUTHORIZATION (EUA) OF THE MODERNA COVID-19 VACCINE TO PREVENT CORONAVIRUS DISEASE 2019 (COVID-19)." https://www.fda.gov/media/144637/download.

3   The Food and Drug Administration. 2021. "Pfizer-Biontech/Comirnaty
         Concentrate For Dispersion For Injection COVID-19 Mrna Vaccine
         (Nucleoside Modified)." https://www.fda.gov.ph/wp-
         content/uploads/2021/11/Pfizer-BioNTech-and-Comirnaty-Product-
         Information-for-vaccine-recipients.pdf.

4   The Food and Drug Administration. 2022. "FACT SHEET FOR
         RECIPIENTS AND CAREGIVERS EMERGENCY USE
         AUTHORIZATION (EUA) OF THE JANSSEN COVID-19 VACCINE
         TO PREVENT CORONAVIRUS DISEASE 2019 (COVID-19) IN
         INDIVIDUALS 18 YEARS OF AGE AND OLDER."
         https://www.fda.gov/media/146305/download.

5   Cambridge, Ellie. 2021. "Teen Boys '14 Times More Likely To Suffer
         Heart Complication From Pfizer Jab'". The US Sun. https://www.the-
         sun.com/health/3451600/teen-boys-heart-compilations-pfizer-vaccine/.

6   "Official Data Shows Children Are Up To 52 Times More Likely To Die
         Following Covid-19 Vaccination Than Unvaccinated Children & The
         ONS Is Trying To Hide It". 2022. The Expose.
         https://dailyexpose.uk/2022/01/29/ons-data-covid-vaccinated-children-
         52x-more-likely-to-die/.

7   "Sports Physicals". 2022. Ocps.Net. Accessed March 25.
         https://www.ocps.net/departments/athletics/sports_physicals?aff_id=1262
         .

8   Vega, Roy M., Hersimran Kaur, and Peter F. Edemekong. 2021.
         "Cardiopulmonary Arrest In Children". Statpearls.
         https://www.ncbi.nlm.nih.gov/books/NBK436018/.

9   Phillips, Jack. 2021. "Regulator Reviewing Reports Of 'Rare' And Serious
         Condition Linked To Moderna Vaccine". *Www.Theepochtimes.Com.*
         https://www.theepochtimes.com/mkt_breakingnews/regulator-
         investigating-moderna-vaccine-over-rare-but-serious-blood-
         condition_4099180.html.

10   "Systemic Capillary Leak Syndrome - Symptoms And Causes".
         2021. *Mayo Clinic.* https://www.mayoclinic.org/diseases-
         conditions/systemic-capillary-leak-syndrome/symptoms-causes/syc-
         20378147.

11   Kiefer, Philip. 2021. "How Dangerous Is Myocarditis? The Truth About
         The Scary-Sounding Condition.". *Popular Science.*
         https://www.popsci.com/health/how-dangerous-is-myocarditis-the-truth-
         about-the-scary-sounding-condition/.

12   Magnani, Jared W., and G. William Dec. 2006.
         "Myocarditis". *Circulation* 113 (6): 876-890.
         doi:10.1161/circulationaha.105.584532.

13   Grogan, Martha, Margaret M. Redfield, Kent R. Bailey, Guy S. Reeder,
         Bernard J. Gersh, William D. Edwards, and Richard J. Rodeheffer. 1995.
         "Long-Term Outcome Of Patients With Biopsy-Proved Myocarditis:
         Comparison With Idiopathic Dilated Cardiomyopathy". *Journal Of The*

American College Of Cardiology 26 (1): 80-84. doi:10.1016/0735-1097(95)00148-s.

14   McCarthy, Robert E., John P. Boehmer, Ralph H. Hruban, Grover M. Hutchins, Edward K. Kasper, Joshua M. Hare, and Kenneth L. Baughman. 2000. "Long-Term Outcome Of Fulminant Myocarditis As Compared With Acute (Nonfulminant) Myocarditis". *New England Journal Of Medicine* 342 (10): 690-695. doi:10.1056/nejm200003093421003.

15   Mason, Jay W., John B. O'Connell, Ahvie Herskowitz, Noel R. Rose, Bruce M. McManus, Margaret E. Billingham, and Thomas E. Moon. 1995. "A Clinical Trial Of Immunosuppressive Therapy For Myocarditis". *New England Journal Of Medicine* 333 (5): 269-275. doi:10.1056/nejm199508033330501.

16   Dec, G. William, Igor F. Palacios, John T. Fallon, H. Thomas Aretz, John Mills, Daniel C-S. Lee, and Robert Arnold Johnson. 1985. "Active Myocarditis In The Spectrum Of Acute Dilated Cardiomyopathies". *New England Journal Of Medicine* 312 (14): 885-890. doi:10.1056/nejm198504043121404.

17   Chua, Gilbert T, Mike Yat Wah Kwan, Celine S L Chui, Robert David Smith, Edmund Chi-Lok Cheung, Tian Ma, and Miriam T Y Leung et al. 2021. "Epidemiology Of Acute Myocarditis/Pericarditis In Hong Kong Adolescents Following Comirnaty Vaccination". *Clinical Infectious Diseases*. doi:10.1093/cid/ciab989.

18   Patone, Martina, Xue W Mei, Lahiru Handunnetthi, Sharon Dixon, Francesco Zaccardi, Manu Shankar-Hari, and Peter Watkinson et al. 2021. "Risk Of Myocarditis Following Sequential COVID-19 Vaccinations By Age And Sex". doi:10.1101/2021.12.23.21268276.

19   Sharff, Katie A, David M Dancoes, Jodi L Longueil, Eric S Johnson, and Paul F Lewis. 2021. "Risk Of Myopericarditis Following COVID-19 Mrna Vaccination In A Large Integrated Health System: A Comparison Of Completeness And Timeliness Of Two Methods". doi:10.1101/2021.12.21.21268209.

20   Kirsch, Steve. 2021. "Dramatic Increase In Pro Sports Adverse Events Since The Vaccines Rolled Out". *Stevekirsch.Substack.Com*. https://stevekirsch.substack.com/p/over-a-60x-increase-in-serious-adverse.

21   Westall, Sarah. 2021. "Wikipedia Stops Listing Athletes Who Died While Playing Soccer As The Number Explodes - Business Game Changers". *Business Game Changers*. https://www.sarahwestall.com/wikipedia-stops-listing-athletes-who-died-while-playing-soccer-as-the-number-explodes/.

22   Playne, Mark. 2022. "WORLDWIDE SURGE OF SPORTS PEOPLE SUFFERING SUDDEN HEALTH ISSUES AND DEATH". *Not On The Beeb*. https://www.notonthebeeb.co.uk/post/surge-of-sports-people-worldwide-suffering-unexpected-ill-health.

23   Knapton, Sarah. 2021. "Alarm Grows As Mortuaries Fill With Thousands Of Extra Non-Covid Deaths". *Telegraph.Co.Uk*. https://www.telegraph.co.uk/news/2021/11/16/nhs-delays-height-pandemic-linked-thousands-extra-non-covid/?utm_content=telegraph&utm_medium=Social&utm_campaign=Echobox&utm_source=Twitter.

24   "Dr Rochagné Kilian - Blows The Whistle On Covid-19 Vaccines And D-Dimer Levels". 2021. *Rumble*. https://rumble.com/vohbts-dr-rochagn-kilian-blows-the-whistle-on-covid-19-vaccines-and-d-dimer-levels.html.

25   Schutte, T., A. Thijs, and Y. M. Smulders. 2016. "Never Ignore Extremely Elevated D-Dimer Levels: They Are Specific For Serious Illness". *The Netherlands Journal Of Medicine* 74 (10): 443-448. https://pubmed.ncbi.nlm.nih.gov/27966438/.

26   Harding, Lee. 2021. "BC Doc Says He's Found Blood Clots In 62% Of Post-Jab Patients". *Westernstandardonline.Com*. https://westernstandardonline.com/2021/07/bc-doc-says-hes-found-blood-clots-in-62-of-post-jab-patients/.

27   "The Novel Coronavirus' Spike Protein Plays Additional Key Role In Illness - Salk Institute For Biological Studies". 2021. *Salk Institute For Biological Studies*. https://www.salk.edu/news-release/the-novel-coronavirus-spike-protein-plays-additional-key-role-in-illness/.

28   "COMPILATION: PEER REVIEWED MEDICAL PAPERS OF COVID VACCINE INJURIES - A COVIDVACCINEINJURIES.COM COMMUNITY". 2022. *A COVIDVACCINEINJURIES.COM COMMUNITY*. https://community.covidvaccineinjuries.com/compilation-peer-reviewed-medical-papers-of-covid-vaccine-injuries/.

29   King, William W., Matthew R. Petersen, Ralph M. Matar, Jeffery B. Budweg, Lyda Cuervo Pardo, and John W. Petersen. 2021. "Myocarditis Following Mrna Vaccination Against SARS-Cov-2, A Case Series". *American Heart Journal Plus: Cardiology Research And Practice* 8: 100042. doi:10.1016/j.ahjo.2021.100042.

30   Montgomery, Jay, Margaret Ryan, Renata Engler, Donna Hoffman, Bruce McClenathan, Limone Collins, and David Loran et al. 2021. "Myocarditis Following Immunization With Mrna COVID-19 Vaccines In Members Of The US Military". *JAMA Cardiology* 6 (10): 1202. doi:10.1001/jamacardio.2021.2833.

31   Dionne, Audrey, Francesca Sperotto, Stephanie Chamberlain, Annette L. Baker, Andrew J. Powell, Ashwin Prakash, and Daniel A. Castellanos et al. 2021. "Association Of Myocarditis With Bnt162b2 Messenger RNA COVID-19 Vaccine In A Case Series Of Children". *JAMA Cardiology* 6 (12): 1446. doi:10.1001/jamacardio.2021.3471.

32   Marshall, Mayme, Ian D. Ferguson, Paul Lewis, Preeti Jaggi, Christina Gagliardo, James Stewart Collins, and Robin Shaughnessy et al. 2021. "Symptomatic Acute Myocarditis In 7 Adolescents After Pfizer-Biontech COVID-19 Vaccination". *Pediatrics* 148 (3). doi:10.1542/peds.2021-052478.

33   Luk, Adriana, Brian Clarke, Nagib Dahdah, Anique Ducharme, Andrew Krahn, Brian McCrindle, and Trent Mizzi et al. 2021. "Myocarditis And Pericarditis After COVID-19 Mrna Vaccination: Practical Considerations For Care Providers". *Canadian Journal Of Cardiology* 37 (10): 1629-1634. doi:10.1016/j.cjca.2021.08.001.

34   "COMPILATION: PEER REVIEWED MEDICAL PAPERS OF COVID VACCINE INJURIES - A COVIDVACCINEINJURIES.COM COMMUNITY". 2022. *A COVIDVACCINEINJURIES.COM COMMUNITY.* https://community.covidvaccineinjuries.com/compilation-peer-reviewed-medical-papers-of-covid-vaccine-injuries/.

35   Andraska, Elizabeth A., Rohan Kulkarni, Mirnal Chaudhary, and Ulka Sachdev. 2022. "Three Cases Of Acute Venous Thromboembolism In Females After Vaccination For Coronavirus Disease 2019". *Journal Of Vascular Surgery: Venous And Lymphatic Disorders* 10 (1): 14-17. doi:10.1016/j.jvsv.2021.07.009.

36   Tajstra, Mateusz, Jerzy Jaroszewicz, and Mariusz Gąsior. 2021. "Acute Coronary Tree Thrombosis After Vaccination For COVID-19". *JACC: Cardiovascular Interventions* 14 (9): e103-e104. doi:10.1016/j.jcin.2021.03.003.

37   See, Isaac, John R. Su, Allison Lale, Emily Jane Woo, Alice Y. Guh, Tom T. Shimabukuro, and Michael B. Streiff et al. 2021. "US Case Reports Of Cerebral Venous Sinus Thrombosis With Thrombocytopenia After Ad26.COV2.S Vaccination, March 2 To April 21, 2021". *JAMA* 325 (24): 2448. doi:10.1001/jama.2021.7517.

38   Öcal, Osman, Stephanie-Susanne Stecher, and Moritz Wildgruber. 2021. "Portal Vein Thrombosis Associated With Chadox1 Ncov-19 Vaccination". *The Lancet Gastroenterology & Hepatology* 6 (8): 676. doi:10.1016/s2468-1253(21)00197-7.

39   Gresele, P., Marietta, M., Ageno, W., Marcucci, R., Contino, L., Donadini, M. P., Russo, L., Tiscia, G. L., Palareti, G., Tripodi, A., Mannucci, P. M., & De Stefano, V. (2021). "Management of cerebral and splanchnic vein thrombosis associated with thrombocytopenia in subjects previously vaccinated with Vaxzevria (AstraZeneca): a position statement from the Italian Society for the Study of Haemostasis and Thrombosis (SISET)." *Blood transfusion = Trasfusione del sangue, 19*(4), 281–283. https://doi.org/10.2450/2021.0117-21

40   "COMPILATION: PEER REVIEWED MEDICAL PAPERS OF COVID VACCINE INJURIES - A COVIDVACCINEINJURIES.COM COMMUNITY". 2022. *A COVIDVACCINEINJURIES.COM COMMUNITY.* https://community.covidvaccineinjuries.com/compilation-peer-reviewed-medical-papers-of-covid-vaccine-injuries/.

41   Aladdin, Yasser, Hussein Algahtani, and Bader Shirah. 2021. "Vaccine-Induced Immune Thrombotic Thrombocytopenia With Disseminated Intravascular Coagulation And Death Following The Chadox1 Ncov-19 Vaccine". *Journal Of Stroke And Cerebrovascular Diseases* 30 (9): 105938. doi:10.1016/j.jstrokecerebrovasdis.2021.105938.

42 See, Isaac, John R. Su, Allison Lale, Emily Jane Woo, Alice Y. Guh, Tom T. Shimabukuro, and Michael B. Streiff et al. 2021. "US Case Reports Of Cerebral Venous Sinus Thrombosis With Thrombocytopenia After Ad26.COV2.S Vaccination, March 2 To April 21, 2021". *JAMA* 325 (24): 2448. doi:10.1001/jama.2021.7517.

43 Gresele, P., Marietta, M., Ageno, W., Marcucci, R., Contino, L., Donadini, M. P., Russo, L., Tiscia, G. L., Palareti, G., Tripodi, A., Mannucci, P. M., & De Stefano, V. (2021). "Management of cerebral and splanchnic vein thrombosis associated with thrombocytopenia in subjects previously vaccinated with Vaxzevria (AstraZeneca): a position statement from the Italian Society for the Study of Haemostasis and Thrombosis (SISET)." *Blood transfusion = Trasfusione del sangue, 19*(4), 281–283. https://doi.org/10.2450/2021.0117-21

44 Sharifian-Dorche, Maryam, Mohammad Bahmanyar, Amirhossein Sharifian-Dorche, Pegah Mohammadi, Masood Nomovi, and Ashkan Mowla. 2021. "Vaccine-Induced Immune Thrombotic Thrombocytopenia And Cerebral Venous Sinus Thrombosis Post COVID-19 Vaccination; A Systematic Review". *Journal Of The Neurological Sciences* 428: 117607. doi:10.1016/j.jns.2021.117607.

45 Long, Brit, Rachel Bridwell, and Michael Gottlieb. 2021. "Thrombosis With Thrombocytopenia Syndrome Associated With COVID-19 Vaccines". *The American Journal Of Emergency Medicine* 49: 58-61. doi:10.1016/j.ajem.2021.05.054.

46 "COMPILATION: PEER REVIEWED MEDICAL PAPERS OF COVID VACCINE INJURIES - A COVIDVACCINEINJURIES.COM COMMUNITY". 2022. *A COVIDVACCINEINJURIES.COM COMMUNITY.* https://community.covidvaccineinjuries.com/compilation-peer-reviewed-medical-papers-of-covid-vaccine-injuries/.

47 Bikdeli, Behnood, Saurav Chatterjee, Shilpkumar Arora, Manuel Monreal, David Jimenez, Harlan M. Krumholz, Samuel Z. Goldhaber, Mitchell S.V. Elkind, and Gregory Piazza. 2021. "Cerebral Venous Sinus Thrombosis In The U.S. Population, After Adenovirus-Based SARS-Cov-2 Vaccination, And After COVID-19". *Journal Of The American College Of Cardiology* 78 (4): 408-411. doi:10.1016/j.jacc.2021.06.001.

48 Dutta, Ajitava, Ritwik Ghosh, Dwaipayan Bhattacharya, Saumen Bhat, Adrija Ray, Alak Pandit, Shambaditya Das, and Souvik Dubey. 2021. "Anti-PF4 Antibody Negative Cerebral Venous Sinus Thrombosis Without Thrombocytopenia Following Immunization With COVID-19 Vaccine In An Elderly Non-Comorbid Indian Male, Managed With Conventional Heparin-Warfarin Based Anticoagulation". *Diabetes & Metabolic Syndrome: Clinical Research & Reviews* 15 (4): 102184. doi:10.1016/j.dsx.2021.06.021.

49 Dias, Leonor, Ricardo Soares-dos-Reis, João Meira, Diana Ferrão, Pedro Ribeirinho Soares, Ana Pastor, Guilherme Gama, Luísa Fonseca, Vítor Fagundes, and Marta Carvalho. 2021. "Cerebral Venous Thrombosis After Bnt162b2 Mrna SARS-Cov-2 Vaccine". *Journal Of Stroke And*

Cerebrovascular Diseases 30 (8): 105906.
doi:10.1016/j.jstrokecerebrovasdis.2021.105906.

50   Lee, Eun-Ju, and Alfred I Lee. 2021. "Cerebral Venous Sinus Thrombosis After Vaccination: The UK Experience". *The Lancet* 398 (10306): 1107-1109. doi:10.1016/s0140-6736(21)01788-8.

51   See, Isaac, John R. Su, Allison Lale, Emily Jane Woo, Alice Y. Guh, Tom T. Shimabukuro, and Michael B. Streiff et al. 2021. "US Case Reports Of Cerebral Venous Sinus Thrombosis With Thrombocytopenia After Ad26.COV2.S Vaccination, March 2 To April 21, 2021". *JAMA* 325 (24): 2448. doi:10.1001/jama.2021.7517.

52   "COMPILATION: PEER REVIEWED MEDICAL PAPERS OF COVID VACCINE INJURIES - A COVIDVACCINEINJURIES.COM COMMUNITY". 2022. *A COVIDVACCINEINJURIES.COM COMMUNITY*. https://community.covidvaccineinjuries.com/compilation-peer-reviewed-medical-papers-of-covid-vaccine-injuries/.

53   Shakoor, Muhammad Tariq, Mark P. Birkenbach, and Matthew Lynch. 2021. "ANCA-Associated Vasculitis Following Pfizer-Biontech COVID-19 Vaccine". *American Journal Of Kidney Diseases* 78 (4): 611-613. doi:10.1053/j.ajkd.2021.06.016.

54   Okuda, Saki, Yasuaki Hirooka, and Masafumi Sugiyama. 2021. "Propylthiouracil-Induced Antineutrophil Cytoplasmic Antibody-Associated Vasculitis After COVID-19 Vaccination". *Vaccines* 9 (8): 842. doi:10.3390/vaccines9080842.

55   Badier, Laure, Albanie Toledano, Tiphaine Porel, Sylvain Dumond, Julien Jouglen, Laurent Sailler, Haleh Bagheri, Guillaume Moulis, and Margaux Lafaurie. 2021. "Iga Vasculitis In Adult Patient Following Vaccination By Chadox1 Ncov-19". *Autoimmunity Reviews* 20 (11): 102951. doi:10.1016/j.autrev.2021.102951.

56   Moore, Art. 2021. "Moderna COVID Shot Halted For All Ages In Iceland". *WND*. https://www.wnd.com/2021/10/4951474/.

57   Hall, Kennedy. 2021. "'Absolutely Forbidden' To Give COVID Shots To Kids, Young Men And Women, Jewish Court Rules - Lifesite". *Lifesite*. https://www.lifesitenews.com/news/absolutely-forbidden-to-give-covid-shots-to-children-and-youth-jewish-court-rules/.

58   Ungurean, Geri. 2020. "Bill Gates, His Father And Eugenics :: By Geri Ungurean". *Rapture Ready*. https://www.raptureready.com/2020/12/29/bill-gates-his-father-and-eugenics-by-geri-ungurean/.

59   Gates, Bill. 2010. "Bill Gates: Innovating To Zero!". *Ted.Com*. https://www.ted.com/talks/bill_gates_innovating_to_zero/transcript.

60   Frank, Robert. 2009. "Billionaires Try To Shrink World's Population, Report Says". The Wall Street Journal. https://www.wsj.com/articles/BL-WHB-1322.

61   "Ted Turner - Infogalactic: The Planetary Knowledge Core". 2022. Infogalactic.Com. https://infogalactic.com/info/Ted_Turner.

62   Settles, Gabrielle. 2021. "Bill Gates Didn'T Say He Wanted To Use Vaccines To Reduce The Population - Poynter". *Poynter.* https://www.poynter.org/fact-checking/2021/bill-gates-didnt-say-he-wanted-to-use-vaccines-to-reduce-the-population/.

63   "Average Number Of Own Children Per Family U.S. | Statista". 2020. *Statista.* https://www.statista.com/statistics/718084/average-number-of-own-children-per-family/.

64   "Population Replacement Rate - Energy Education". 2018. *Energyeducation.Ca.* https://www.energyeducation.ca/encyclopedia/Population_replacement_rate.

65   "Bill Gates` Family: Parents, Wife, Siblings And Children". 2022. *Starschanges.Com.* Accessed March 18. https://starschanges.com/bill-gates-family/.

66   Riley, Laura E. 2021. "Mrna Covid-19 Vaccines In Pregnant Women". *New England Journal Of Medicine* 384 (24): 2342-2343. doi:10.1056/nejme2107070.

67   "Mrna Covid-19 Vaccines In Pregnant Women". 2021. *New England Journal Of Medicine* 385 (16): 1536-1536. doi:10.1056/nejmx210017.

68   Dulay, Antonette T. 2020. "Spontaneous Abortion - Gynecology And Obstetrics - MSD Manual Professional Edition". *MSD Manual Professional Edition.* https://www.merckmanuals.com/professional/gynecology-and-obstetrics/abnormalities-of-pregnancy/spontaneous-abortion.

69   Brock, Aleisha R., and Simon Thornley. 2021. "Spontaneous Abortions And Policies On COVID-19 Mrna Vaccine Use During Pregnancy". Science, Public Health Policy, And The Law Volume 4:130–143. Institute for Pure and Applied Knowledge. https://cf5e727d-d02d-4d71-89ff-9fe2d3ad957f.filesusr.com/ugd/adf864_2bd97450072f4364a65e5cf1d7384dd4.pdf.

70   Huff, Ethan. 2021. "Whistleblowers Expose 13 Stillborn Deaths In 24 Hours At Lions Gates Hospital Caused By Covid "Vaccines"". *Naturalnews.Com.* https://www.naturalnews.com/2021-11-23-whistleblower-exposes-stillborn-deaths-babies-hospital-covid-vaccines.html.

71   Donaldson, Valerie. 2021. "Biodistribution Of Pfizer Covid-19 Vaccine | Regenerative Medicine Center - Dr. Valerie Donaldson MD Pittsburgh, Pennsylvania PA". *Regenerativemc.Com.* https://regenerativemc.com/biodistribution-of-pfizer-covid-19-vaccine/.

72   Brumfiel, Geoff. 2022. "COVID Vaccines May Briefly Change Your Menstrual Cycle, But You Should Still Get One". *Npr.Org.* https://www.npr.org/sections/health-shots/2022/01/06/1070796638/covid-vaccine-periods.

73   Edelman, Alison, Emily R. Boniface, Eleonora Benhar, Leo Han, Kristen A. Matteson, Carlotta Favaro, Jack T. Pearson, and Blair G. Darney.

2022. "Association Between Menstrual Cycle Length And Coronavirus Disease 2019 (COVID-19) Vaccination". *Obstetrics & Gynecology* Publish Ahead of Print. doi:10.1097/aog.0000000000004695.

74 Lee, Katharine MN, Eleanor J Junkins, Chongliang Luo, Urooba A Fatima, Maria L Cox, and Kathryn BH Clancy. 2021. "Investigating Trends In Those Who Experience Menstrual Bleeding Changes After SARS-Cov-2 Vaccination". doi:10.1101/2021.10.11.21264863.

75 "COVID-19 Vaccines And The Menstrual Cycle | NIH COVID-19 Research". 2021. *NIH COVID-19 Research.* https://covid19.nih.gov/news-and-stories/covid-19-vaccines-and-menstrual-cycle.

76 Anghel, Irina. 2022. "Frequent Boosters Spur Warning On Immune Response". Bloomberg.Com. https://www.bloomberg.com/news/articles/2022-01-11/repeat-booster-shots-risk-overloading-immune-system-ema-says.

77 Burger, Ludwig, and Pushkala Aripaka. 2021. "EU Drugs Regulator Says Data Supports Vaccine Boosters After Three Months". Reuters. https://www.reuters.com/world/europe/eu-drugs-regulator-says-data-supports-vaccine-boosters-after-three-months-2021-12-09/.

78 Föhse, F. Konstantin, Büsranur Geckin, Gijs J. Overheul, Josephine van de Maat, Gizem Kilic, Ozlem Bulut, and Helga Dijkstra et al. 2021. "The Bnt162b2 Mrna Vaccine Against SARS-Cov-2 Reprograms Both Adaptive And Innate Immune Responses". doi:10.1101/2021.05.03.21256520.

79 Jiang, Hui, and Ya-Fang Mei. 2021. "SARS–Cov–2 Spike Impairs DNA Damage Repair And Inhibits V(D)J Recombination In Vitro". Viruses 13 (10): 2056. doi:10.3390/v13102056.

80 Séveno, Victoria. 2021. "Vaccination Turnout In The Netherlands Rises To 90 Percent". Iamexpat. https://www.iamexpat.nl/expat-info/dutch-expat-news/vaccination-turnout-netherlands-rises-90-percent.

81 "COVID-19 Vaccination Campaign In The Netherlands". 2022. Government.Nl. Accessed March 24. https://www.government.nl/topics/coronavirus-covid-19/dutch-vaccination-programme/covid-19-vaccination-campaign.

82 KAONGA, GERRARD. 2021. "Netherlands Announces Plan To Give People Up To Six Doses Of COVID Vaccine". Newsweek. https://www.newsweek.com/netherlands-vaccination-booster-coronavirus-covid-shot-1664296.

83 "Fast-Spreading HIV Variant Doubles Rate Of Immune System Decline". 2022. UN News. https://news.un.org/en/story/2022/02/1111372.

84 O'Neill, Jesse. 2020. "Some COVID-19 Vaccines Could Increase HIV Risk: Researchers". Nypost.Com. https://nypost.com/2020/10/20/some-covid-19-vaccines-could-increase-hiv-risk-researchers/.

85 Buchbinder, Susan P, M Juliana McElrath, Carl Dieffenbach, and Lawrence Corey. 2020. "Use Of Adenovirus Type-5 Vectored Vaccines:

A Cautionary Tale". The Lancet 396 (10260): E68-E69.
doi:10.1016/S0140-6736(20)32156-5.

86   Cohen, Jon. 2020. "Could Certain COVID-19 Vaccines Leave People
More Vulnerable To The AIDS Virus?". Science.Org.
https://www.science.org/content/article/could-certain-covid-19-vaccines-
leave-people-more-vulnerable-aids-virus.

87   Shwe Zin Tun, Gloria, Dermot Gleeson, Amer Al-Joudeh, and Asha
Dube. 2022. "Immune-Mediated Hepatitis With The Moderna Vaccine,
No Longer A Coincidence But Confirmed". Journal Of Hepatology 76
(3): 747-749. doi:10.1016/j.jhep.2021.09.031.

88   Talotta, Rossella. 2021. "Do COVID-19 RNA-Based Vaccines Put At
Risk Of Immune-Mediated Diseases? In Reply To "Potential Antigenic
Cross-Reactivity Between SARS-Cov-2 And Human Tissue With A
Possible Link To An Increase In Autoimmune Diseases"". Clinical
Immunology 224 (108665). doi:10.1016/j.clim.2021.108665.

89   Liu, Jiping, Junbang Wang, Jinfang Xu, Han Xia, Yue Wang, Chunxue
Zhang, and Wei Chen et al. 2021. "Comprehensive Investigations
Revealed Consistent Pathophysiological Alterations After Vaccination
With COVID-19 Vaccines". Cell Discovery 7 (99). doi:10.1038/s41421-
021-00329-3.

90   Seneff, Stephanie, Greg Nigh, Anthony M. Kyriakopoulos, and Peter A
McCullough. 2022. "Innate Immune Suppression By SARS-Cov-2 Mrna
Vaccinations: The Role Of G-Quadruplexes, Exosomes And Micrornas".
Authorea. doi:10.22541/au.164276411.10570847.

91   Hinton-Sheley, Phoebe. 2020. "What Is Tumorigenesis?". News-
Medical.Net. https://www.news-medical.net/life-sciences/What-is-
Tumorigenesis.aspx.

92   "Special Notice Regarding Evidentiary Findings Related To The Official
Renz Law Covid-19 Investigation – Renz Law". 2022. Renz-Law.Com.
https://renz-law.com/special-notice-regarding-evidentiary-findings-
related-to-the-official-renz-law-covid-19-investigation/.

93   "Renz Whistleblowers DMED DATA Reveals Incredibly Disturbing
Spikes In Vaccine Injuries Across The Board". 2022. Renz-Law.
Accessed March 24. https://renz-law.com/attorney-tom-renz-
whistleblowers-dmed-defense-medical-epidemiology-database-reveals-
incredibly-disturbing-spikes-in-diseases-infertility-injuries-across-the-
board-after-the-military-was-forced-to/.

94   US Committee on Homeland Security and Governmental Affairs. 2022.
"Letter From Senator Ron Johnson To Department Of Defense Secretary
Lloyd Austin". Washington, DC: United States Senate.

95   Horowitz, Daniel. 2022. "Horowitz: The Pentagon's RESPONSE To The
Explosive DOD Medical Data Is An Even Bigger Story Than The Data".
Theblaze. https://www.theblaze.com/op-ed/horowitz-the-pentagons-
response-to-the-explosive-dod-medical-data-is-an-even-bigger-story-
than-the-data.

96   Kirsch, Steve. 2022. "DMED Data Is Explosive. Mainstream Media Has Been Ordered To Ignore It.". Stevekirsch.Substack.Com. https://stevekirsch.substack.com/p/this-medical-data-from-the-us-dod?s=r.

97   Horowitz, Daniel. 2022. "Horowitz: 5 Ways DOD's Recalibrated Health Surveillance Data Looks Like A Fraudulent Attempt To Cover Vaccine Injury". Theblaze. https://www.theblaze.com/op-ed/horowitz-5-ways-dods-recalibrated-health-surveillance-data-looks-like-a-fraudulent-attempt-to-cover-vaccine-injury.

98   Cercone, Jeff. 2022. "Politifact - Numbers Were Based On Faulty Data, Military Spokesperson Says". @Politifact. https://www.politifact.com/factchecks/2022/jan/31/instagram-posts/numbers-were-based-faulty-data-military-spokespers/.

99   Singh, Nishant, and Anuradha Bharara Singh. 2020. "S2 Subunit Of SARS-Ncov-2 Interacts With Tumor Suppressor Protein P53 And BRCA: An In Silico Study". *Translational Oncology* 13 (10): 100814. doi:10.1016/j.tranon.2020.100814.

100   Goldman, Serge, Dominique Bron, Thomas Tousseyn, Irina Vierasu, Laurent Dewispelaere, Pierre Heimann, Elie Cogan, and Michel Goldman. 2021. "Rapid Progression Of Angioimmunoblastic T Cell Lymphoma Following Bnt162b2 Mrna Vaccine Booster Shot: A Case Report". *Frontiers In Medicine* 8. doi:10.3389/fmed.2021.798095.

101   Bingham, Jack. 2021. "Idaho Doctor Reports A '20 Times Increase' Of Cancer In Vaccinated Patients". *Lifesite.* https://www.lifesitenews.com/news/idaho-doctor-reports-a-20-times-increase-of-cancer-in-vaccinated-patients/.

102   Fu, Eva. 2022. "Children In China Diagnosed With Leukemia After Taking Chinese Vaccines". Www.Theepochtimes.Com. https://www.theepochtimes.com/children-in-china-contract-leukemia-after-taking-chinese-vaccines_4332657.html.

103   Haas, Julia W., Friederike L. Bender, Sarah Ballou, John M. Kelley, Marcel Wilhelm, Franklin G. Miller, Winfried Rief, and Ted J. Kaptchuk. 2022. "Frequency Of Adverse Events In The Placebo Arms Of COVID-19 Vaccine Trials". JAMA Network Open 5 (1): e2143955. doi:10.1001/jamanetworkopen.2021.43955.

104   Siri, Aaron. 2021. "Whistleblower: FDA And CDC Ignore Damning Report That Over 90% Of A Hospital's Admissions Were Vaccinated For Covid-19 And No One Was Reporting This To VAERS". *Aaronsiri.Substack.Com.* https://aaronsiri.substack.com/p/whistleblower-fda-and-cdc-ignore-3e2.

105   Siri, Aaron. 2021. "Whistleblower: FDA And CDC Ignore Reports Of Serious Covid-19 Vaccine Injuries From Highly Credentialed Pro-Vaccine ICU Physician". *Aaronsiri.Substack.Com.* https://aaronsiri.substack.com/p/whistleblower-fda-and-cdc-ignore.

106 Siri, Aaron. 2021. "One Brave ICU Physician Reporting Covid-19 Vaccine Injuries Leads To A Dozen More". *Aaronsiri.Substack.Com*. https://aaronsiri.substack.com/p/one-brave-icu-physician-reporting.

107 "WATCH: Sen. Johnson Holds Expert Panel On COVID Vaccine Injuries, Federal Vaccine Mandates". 2021. *Children's Health Defense*. https://www.childrenshealthdefense.org/defender/nov-2-sen-ron-johnson-cdh-covid-vaccine-injuries-federal-mandates/.

108 Zempel, Kylee. 2022. "Ron Johnson's Covid Panel Shows 800K Seeking 'A Second Opinion'". The Federalist. https://thefederalist.com/2022/01/25/sen-ron-johnsons-latest-covid-panel-reveals-800000-people-and-counting-want-a-second-opinion/.

109 Senef, Stephanie. 2022. "Dr. Stephanie Seneff: Covid-19 Vaccines And Neurodegenerative Disease". *World Council For Health*. https://worldcouncilforhealth.org/multimedia/stephanie-seneff-covid-vaccines-disease/.

110 Edwards, Michelle. 2021. "Anecdotal Comments Of Death After The Jab Flood WXYZ-TV's FB Post - Uncoverdc". *Uncoverdc*. https://uncoverdc.com/2021/09/13/anecdotal-comments-of-death-after-the-jab-flood-wxyz-tvs-fb-post/.

111 Peruzzo, Dan. 2021. I Am Not Misinformation. Video. Freelance Projects Portfolio.

112 "COMPILATION: PEER REVIEWED MEDICAL PAPERS OF COVID VACCINE INJURIES - A COVIDVACCINEINJURIES.COM COMMUNITY". 2022. *A COVIDVACCINEINJURIES.COM COMMUNITY*. https://community.covidvaccineinjuries.com/compilation-peer-reviewed-medical-papers-of-covid-vaccine-injuries/.

113 Dufour, Catherine, Thien-Kim Co, and Antonio Liu. 2021. "GM1 Ganglioside Antibody And COVID-19 Related Guillain Barre Syndrome – A Case Report, Systemic Review And Implication For Vaccine Development". *Brain, Behavior, & Immunity - Health* 12: 100203. doi:10.1016/j.bbih.2021.100203.

114 Introna, Alessandro, Francesca Caputo, Carlo Santoro, Tommaso Guerra, Maria Ucci, Domenico Maria Mezzapesa, and Maria Trojano. 2021. "Guillain-Barré Syndrome After Astrazeneca COVID-19-Vaccination: A Causal Or Casual Association?". *Clinical Neurology And Neurosurgery* 208: 106887. doi:10.1016/j.clineuro.2021.106887.

115 Min, Young Gi, Woohee Ju, Ye-Eun Ha, Jae-Jun Ban, Seol Ah Lee, Jung-Joon Sung, and Je-Young Shin. 2021. "Sensory Guillain-Barre Syndrome Following The Chadox1 Ncov-19 Vaccine: Report Of Two Cases And Review Of Literature". *Journal Of Neuroimmunology* 359: 577691. doi:10.1016/j.jneuroim.2021.577691.

116 Ogbebor, Osakpolor, Harshit Seth, Zaw Min, and Nitin Bhanot. 2021. "Guillain-Barré Syndrome Following The First Dose Of SARS-Cov-2 Vaccine: A Temporal Occurrence, Not A Causal Association". *Idcases* 24: e01143. doi:10.1016/j.idcr.2021.e01143.

117   Rossetti, Arianna, Galina Gheihman, Meabh O'Hare, and Joshua M. Kosowsky. 2021. "Guillain-Barré Syndrome Presenting As Facial Diplegia After COVID-19 Vaccination: A Case Report". *The Journal Of Emergency Medicine* 61 (6): e141-e145. doi:10.1016/j.jemermed.2021.07.062.

118   "COMPILATION: PEER REVIEWED MEDICAL PAPERS OF COVID VACCINE INJURIES - A COVIDVACCINEINJURIES.COM COMMUNITY". 2022. *A COVIDVACCINEINJURIES.COM COMMUNITY*. https://community.covidvaccineinjuries.com/compilation-peer-reviewed-medical-papers-of-covid-vaccine-injuries/.

119   Park, Ji Yeon, and Seong Yoon Yi. 2021. "Rare Case Of Contralateral Supraclavicular Lymphadenopathy After COVID-19 Vaccination: Computed Tomography And Ultrasonography Findings". *Radiology Case Reports* 16 (12): 3879-3881. doi:10.1016/j.radcr.2021.09.042.

120   Xu, Guofan, and Yang Lu. 2021. "COVID-19 Mrna Vaccination–Induced Lymphadenopathy Mimics Lymphoma Progression On FDG PET/CT". *Clinical Nuclear Medicine* 46 (4): 353-354. doi:10.1097/rlu.0000000000003597.

121   Özütemiz, Can, Luke A. Krystosek, An L. Church, Anil Chauhan, Jutta M. Ellermann, Evidio Domingo-Musibay, and Daniel Steinberger. 2021. "Lymphadenopathy In COVID-19 Vaccine Recipients: Diagnostic Dilemma In Oncologic Patients". *Radiology* 300 (1): E296-E300. doi:10.1148/radiol.2021210275.

122   Cohen, Dan, Shir Hazut Krauthammer, Ido Wolf, and Einat Even-Sapir. 2021. "Hypermetabolic Lymphadenopathy Following Administration Of Bnt162b2 Mrna Covid-19 Vaccine: Incidence Assessed By [18F]FDG PET-CT And Relevance To Study Interpretation". *European Journal Of Nuclear Medicine And Molecular Imaging* 48 (6): 1854-1863. doi:10.1007/s00259-021-05314-2.

123   Keshavarz, Pedram, Fereshteh Yazdanpanah, Faranak Rafiee, and Malkhaz Mizandari. 2021. "Lymphadenopathy Following COVID-19 Vaccination: Imaging Findings Review". *Academic Radiology* 28 (8): 1058-1071. doi:10.1016/j.acra.2021.04.007.

124   "COMPILATION: PEER REVIEWED MEDICAL PAPERS OF COVID VACCINE INJURIES - A COVIDVACCINEINJURIES.COM COMMUNITY". 2022. *A COVIDVACCINEINJURIES.COM COMMUNITY*. https://community.covidvaccineinjuries.com/compilation-peer-reviewed-medical-papers-of-covid-vaccine-injuries/.

125   Turner, Paul J., Ignacio J. Ansotegui, Dianne E. Campbell, Victoria Cardona, Motohiro Ebisawa, Yehia El-Gamal, and Stanley Fineman et al. 2021. "COVID-19 Vaccine-Associated Anaphylaxis: A Statement Of The World Allergy Organization Anaphylaxis Committee". *World Allergy Organization Journal* 14 (2): 100517. doi:10.1016/j.waojou.2021.100517.

126   Shimabukuro, Tom, and Narayan Nair. 2021. "Allergic Reactions Including Anaphylaxis After Receipt Of The First Dose Of Pfizer-

Biontech COVID-19 Vaccine". *JAMA* 325 (8): 780. doi:10.1001/jama.2021.0600.

127   "Allergic Reactions Including Anaphylaxis After Receipt Of The First Dose Of Pfizer-Biontech COVID-19 Vaccine — United States, December 14–23, 2020". 2021. *MMWR. Morbidity And Mortality Weekly Report* 70 (2): 46-51. doi:10.15585/mmwr.mm7002e1.

128   "Allergic Reactions Including Anaphylaxis After Receipt Of The First Dose Of Moderna COVID-19 Vaccine — United States, December 21, 2020–January 10, 2021". 2021. *MMWR. Morbidity And Mortality Weekly Report* 70 (4): 125-129. doi:10.15585/mmwr.mm7004e1.

129   Lee, Eunju, Yeon-kyeong Lee, Tae Eun Kim, Insob Hwang, Yeon Haw Jung, Hye Ryeon Lee, Jeongsuk Song, Youngjoon Park, Enhi Cho, and Yeon-Kyeng Lee. 2021. "Reports Of Anaphylaxis After Coronavirus Disease 2019 Vaccination, South Korea, 26 February To 30 April 2021". *Eurosurveillance* 26 (33). doi:10.2807/1560-7917.es.2021.26.33.2100694.

130   "COMPILATION: PEER REVIEWED MEDICAL PAPERS OF COVID VACCINE INJURIES - A COVIDVACCINEINJURIES.COM COMMUNITY". 2022. *A COVIDVACCINEINJURIES.COM COMMUNITY*. https://community.covidvaccineinjuries.com/compilation-peer-reviewed-medical-papers-of-covid-vaccine-injuries/.

131   Cirillo, Nicola, and Richard Doan. 2021. "Bell's Palsy And SARS-Cov-2 Vaccines—An Unfolding Story". *The Lancet Infectious Diseases* 21 (9): 1210-1211. doi:10.1016/s1473-3099(21)00273-5.

132   Repajic, Michael, Xue Lei Lai, Prissilla Xu, and Antonio Liu. 2021. "Bell's Palsy After Second Dose Of Pfizer COVID-19 Vaccination In A Patient With History Of Recurrent Bell's Palsy". *Brain, Behavior, & Immunity - Health* 13: 100217. doi:10.1016/j.bbih.2021.100217.

133   Gómez de Terreros Caro, G., S. Gil Díaz, M. Pérez Alé, and M.L. Martínez Gimeno. 2021. "Bell's Palsy Following COVID-19 Vaccination: A Case Report". *Neurología (English Edition)* 36 (7): 567-568. doi:10.1016/j.nrleng.2021.04.002.

134   "COMPILATION: PEER REVIEWED MEDICAL PAPERS OF COVID VACCINE INJURIES - A COVIDVACCINEINJURIES.COM COMMUNITY". 2022. *A COVIDVACCINEINJURIES.COM COMMUNITY*. https://community.covidvaccineinjuries.com/compilation-peer-reviewed-medical-papers-of-covid-vaccine-injuries/.

135   Vegezzi, Elisa, Sabrina Ravaglia, Gabriele Buongarzone, Paola Bini, Luca Diamanti, Matteo Gastaldi, Paolo Prunetti, Elisa Rognone, and Enrico Marchioni. 2021. "Acute Myelitis And Chadox1 Ncov-19 Vaccine: Casual Or Causal Association?". *Journal Of Neuroimmunology* 359: 577686. doi:10.1016/j.jneuroim.2021.577686.

136   Román, Gustavo C., Fernando Gracia, Antonio Torres, Alexis Palacios, Karla Gracia, and Diógenes Harris. 2021. "Acute Transverse Myelitis (ATM):Clinical Review Of 43 Patients With COVID-19-Associated ATM And 3 Post-Vaccination ATM Serious Adverse Events With The

Chadox1 Ncov-19 Vaccine (AZD1222)". *Frontiers In Immunology* 12. doi:10.3389/fimmu.2021.653786.

137   Tahir, Nayha, Gowthami Koorapati, Sonika Prasad, Hafiz Muhammad Jeelani, Robin Sherchan, Jishna Shrestha, and Maryna Shayuk. 2021. "SARS-Cov-2 Vaccination-Induced Transverse Myelitis". *Cureus*. doi:10.7759/cureus.16624.

Chapter 15

Gain of Function: The Only Possible Alternative

There are three posited theories as to the origin of the alleged Covid pandemic:

1. An animal (zoonotic) virus jumped to humans in Wuhan
2. A virus was leaked (either accidentally or not) in Wuhan
3. There was no novel viral pandemic

Right off the bat (pun intended) I am going to outright dismiss #1, because it is impossible. And I don't even need to use science to make that determination—though it can be dismissed on scientific grounds as well, as we will cover. The simple reason a zoonotic origin is impossible is because of the timing and content of the Milken Institute and Event 201 gatherings. To have premeditated the sale of universal mRNA shots two months before, for Rick Bright to have correctly predicted an origin in China which exactly fit the circumstances needed to sell the public on those shots, and for the unprecedented global policy responses including censorship to be universally implemented as they were war-gamed—these premeditations and all the rest we've discussed make it impossibly convenient for such a once-in-a-century-or-more type of event to have occurred in nature on cue.

This convenience also rules out an *accidental* lab leak. To be sure, it is statistically less impossible for a lab to have accidentally had a leak at the exact time these people needed it to than it would be for nature to provide those circumstances. However, for the leak to also happen to be the exact type of contagion which would justify the product they conspired to sell *and* signed a contract affirming their part ownership of *weeks* before is, frankly, not believable. So this leaves us with two believable possibilities: intentional lab leak or no novel viral pandemic.

By this point in the book I can imagine you probably know on which side I heavily lean. To clarify, I will end this chapter with my full opinion and a summary of why I think everything I've mentioned to this point supports that opinion. Before we get there though, I will provide a background on the history of the intentional lab leak theory.

Gain of Function Research and the Lab Leak Theory

As documented by long-time patent tracker David E. Martin, Ph.D., the scientists Anthony Fauci has funded to do the coronavirus research mentioned have been filing patents on these coronaviruses since 1999.[1,2] One such scientist is the University of North Carolina's Ralph Baric, who the NIH/NIAID have funded to do such work for decades.[3] In April 2002, for example, UNC filed patent US7279327B2, "methods for producing recombinant coronavirus," with Baric credited as the inventor.[4] It was immediately following this patent filing that the alleged SARS1 outbreak began—it spanned 2002-2004 according to the official narrative—raising obvious suspicions.[5] However, Martin claims 120 patents he cites show there is no real difference between that SARS virus and what was dealt with in 2020.

By 2003, SARS genome patenting had become such a documented, regular occurrence that the CDC too filed a patent. E. Richard Gold acknowledged this in the *Lancet*, claiming the reason public health agencies did this was because they, "want the genome to remain in the public domain, free to all researchers."[6] Gold also admitted this demonstrated a need to revise the patent system, since these organizations should have just been able to publish the genome to achieve the same effect of preventing others from patenting it. Still, they file patents and receive, "the exclusive right to use and sell molecular forms of the genome."[7] This creates an obvious conflict of interest however, seeing as the CDC is meant to *control* the disease it now has a patented financial interest in keeping relevant.

Let's fast forward to the October 2019 Event 201 pandemic simulation hosted by the Bill & Melinda Gates Foundation and the strange amount of emphasis it placed on, "conspiracy theories that are around about the potential that pharmaceutical companies or the UN have released this (virus) for their own benefit." A few months later, in January 2020, the WHO announced a coronavirus pandemic and adopted the since-externally-peer-reviewed and deemed-flawed PCR protocol developed by Christian Drosten. Immediately on the heels of this announcement, in February 19, 2020, a statement by, "public health scientists," was published in the *Lancet* which addressed the same alleged, "conspiracy theories," so-feared during Event 201.[8] The signees of the *Lancet* declaration included, among others, Peter

Daszak of the EcoHealth Alliance and Christian Drosten himself. Their statement included the following:

> *"The rapid, open, and transparent sharing of data on this outbreak is now being threatened by rumors and misinformation around its origins. We stand together to strongly condemn conspiracy theories suggesting that COVID-19 does not have a natural origin."*

The first glaring problem with this statement is that it came before restrictions even began in essentially every country but China. Coronavirus was not yet more than a distant concern of the average citizen in the majority of the world when this article was penned. So if the signatories really were dispassionate scientists just trying to continue facilitating the, "rapid, open, and transparent sharing of data," with the hope of figuring more out about the alleged virus, this letter would have run counter to their aim.

As we can see with the Event 201 pre-coordination however, this was not a statement by dispassionate scientists. Take lesser-known co-author Charles Calisher, for example. Calisher was the lead signatory of the letter, who also happened to be part of a controversial 1975 CDC/WHO dengue fever expedition to Cuba.[9] His trip apparently coincided with hundreds of Cubans being sickened and around 150 children dying, prompting the Cuban government to allege Calisher was an undercover CIA asset and that the disease was actually caused by a bioterror attack he instigated. While these remain unproven allegations, author Nicholson Baker is noted as having considered them credible and they are worth note when considering the topic/aim of the *Lancet* article, in general.[10]

Another example is Christian Drosten, the original PCR test designer considered to be, "Germany's Fauci," for his ceaseless advocacy of failed policies like mass testing, masking, closed schools, and lockdowns.[11] To distract from the evident, on-going failure of every policy Drosten supported, he now simply rambles out non-sequiturs like, "I want to have vaccine immunity and then, on top of that, I want to have my first infection, and my second, and my third at some point." We can also recall how distinctly aware Drosten is documented as having been about the potential abuses of PCR, "asymptomatic infection," and media hype, as well as his conflicts of interest with the very testing companies which could profit from those things.

This is a consistent thread with all those who are involved in the Covid crimes against humanity and are mainstream-authorized to speak on it. They *all* support *all* the policies *no matter* the outcome, *especially* inoculations, and they *never* admit failure or recommend caution. They move in such an unnatural, tyrannical lockstep toward the goal of selling inoculations at all costs that they can't help but make mistakes. Recall the certainty of Walensky, Gates, and Fauci for example, as it related to the shots preventing transmission—a certainty they *couldn't* have had if they were being honest rather than selling a narrative. Any questioning of the narrative or their policies is automatically deemed, "misinformation," a word an actual, honest scientist would never use but which those like Drosten pen propaganda letters about.

Back to the timeline, by late April 2020 *Newsweek*'s Fred Guterl authored what was seemingly the first publication in the Covid era on Anthony Fauci's financial ties to the Wuhan Institute of Virology, the EcoHealth Alliance, and gain-of-function research.[12] Guterl outlined a $3.7 million, five-year contract NIAID granted to the Wuhan lab's Shi Zheng-Li in 2014, to investigate and catalogue bat coronaviruses in the wild. While this contract was claimed to not involve gain-of-function research, the president of the EcoHealth Alliance, Peter Daszak, said the following at a 2016 forum[13]:

> *"We found other coronaviruses in bats, a whole host of them. Some of them looked very similar to SARS. So we sequenced the spike protein: the protein that attaches to cells. Then we— well, I didn't do this work, but my colleagues in China did the work—you create pseudo particles. You insert spike proteins from those viruses, see if they bind to human cells. At each step of this, you move closer and closer to this virus could really become pathogenic in people. You end up with a small number of viruses that really do look like killers."*

All the same, that contract ended in 2019, at which time a new six-year $3.7 million contract was then granted to EcoHealth Alliance.[14] This new contract explicitly, "included additional surveillance work but also gain-of-function research for the purpose of understanding how bat coronaviruses could mutate to attack humans." Gain-of-function specifically refers to research which involves manipulating viruses in the lab to explore their potential for infecting humans, and is considered risky.[15] The NIH reportedly cancelled the new project on April 24, 2020, but not before Guterl and *Newsweek* apparently got their hands on the since-deleted EcoHealth proposal, citing its words[16]:

> *"We will use S protein sequence data, infectious clone technology, in vitro and in vivo infection experiments and analysis of receptor binding to test the hypothesis that % divergence thresholds in S protein sequences predict spillover potential."*

At the beginning of the decade of the 2010's, gain-of-function research was enough of a hot-button topic that well over 300 scientists with the Cambridge Working Group called for it to be halted, despite Fauci's support for it.[17] By 2014, the pressure mounted and resulted in a moratorium on the work.[18] Three years later however, the NIH ended the moratorium with DHHS setting up a framework of justifying the risk under which the work could be approved.[19] Guterl of *Newsweek* alleged the reviews with which this framework was carried out were done in secret, while the NIH, NIAID, and EcoHealth deny they did gain-of-function research. Instead, the NIH claims they aimed to, "characterize the function of newly discovered bat spike proteins."[20] However, Richard Ebright, a professor of chemistry and chemical biology at Rutgers University and long-time critic of gain-of-function research, said the EcoHealth/Wuhan research, "was—unequivocally—gain-of-function research."[21,22,23] Fauci himself also specifically called the research which would be permitted by the ending of the moratorium, "gain-of-function," in January 2018.[24]

The *Newsweek* article was one of the earliest major cracks in the public health narrative. It was from here more details began to seep out on what was ultimately affirmed as a cover-up. First, as if Daszak's conflict of interest wasn't bad enough, the *Lancet* letter failed to disclose that four other signers of the statement also had positions with EcoHealth.[25] Rather than correct this mistake, the *Lancet* doubled down on this exceptional corruption. On November 23, 2020 it named a 12-member panel to a, "COVID-19

Commission," which would investigate the origins of the alleged virus.[26] Guess who was selected as the chairman of this task force? You guessed it—Peter Daszak. Half the taskforce members were even signers of the original *Lancet* statement which claimed to already know the origin within weeks of the first allegedly identified case. Due to pushback it seems this original panel has since been cancelled (in shame, one would hope).

Those behind the February 2020 statement made matters even worse for themselves when in July 2021 they responded to the growing tension behind it. It was at that time they published another statement in the *Lancet*, in which they backtracked on their original claims.[27] This time, instead of calling perfectly reasonable questions about the origin, "misinformation," they suddenly decided it was in their best interest to act out the part of scientist again, admitting:

> *"The critical question we must address now is, how did SARS-CoV-2 reach the human population?"*

You might be wondering how this can be a, "critical question," in July 2021 when it was a, "strongly condemned," form of, "misinformation," which prevented the, "sharing of data," in February 2020. If so, the authors of this *Lancet* statement would probably say some kind of platitude about how important science is in order to distract you from that wretched thought. You wouldn't be alone in having it however, as yet another September 2021 statement in the *Lancet*, this time by dissenting scientists, excoriated the authors of the two prior publications.[28] These authors determined that the 2020 letter, "imparted a silencing effect on the wider scientific debate, including among science journalists." This was absolutely the case, as the media and social media PR teams used that paper as an excuse to launch unprecedented censorship, suppression, and slander campaigns against all dissent throughout 2020 and beyond. And again, we can determine this effect to not be an accident, based on both the pre-meditation to achieve it at Event 201 and the glaring conflicts of interest of someone like EcoHealth president and *Lancet* paper co-author Peter Daszak.

The dissenting scientists went further than addressing the propagandistic nature of the two publications, as well. They claimed there was actually, "no direct support for the natural origin of SARS-

CoV-2." They went on to dissect all sources provided in support of this natural origin theory and demonstrated their lack of proof. After doing so, they addressed evidence of a lab-leak origin including, "unusual features," of the alleged virus genome sequence, "which may have resulted from genetic engineering."[29,30,31]

In fact, by October 2021 the NIH even acknowledged in a letter to the US Congress that the EcoHealth Alliance contract did include a, "limited experiment," which tested whether, "spike proteins from naturally occurring bat coronaviruses circulating in China were capable of binding to the human ACE2 receptor in a mouse model."[32] The mice they infected indeed, "became sicker," which is where the implication of gain-of-function comes into play. This letter's author from the NIH also placed blame on this research taking place at all on EcoHealth, stating, "EcoHealth failed to report this finding right away, as was required by the terms of the grant." This offhand acknowledgement of EcoHealth's dishonesty seemingly should have led to an inquiry into a violation of 18 US Code § 175, which prohibits possession of, "any biological agent, toxin, or delivery system of a type or in a quantity that, under the circumstances, is not reasonably justified by a prophylactic, protective, bona fide research, or other peaceful purpose."[33] It didn't however, despite the litany of scientists who today and over the past decade have lambasted gain-of-function as having no such peaceful or scientifically beneficial purpose.

These admissions also took place at a time when Anthony Fauci was being regularly confronted by Kentucky Senator Rand Paul on the matter. Those confrontations have continued into 2022, when in January the undercover journalist group *Project Veritas* released additional documentation in the form of an August 2021 letter by US Marine Corps Major Joseph Murphy on the research in question.[34] Murphy was a former fellow at DARPA and claimed that in March of 2018, EcoHealth Alliance first approached DARPA for the funding of the same gain-of-function research they are alleged as having engaged in with NIAID in 2019 (as covered by *Newsweek*). However, according to Murphy, DARPA rejected this request, calling it too dangerous. Murphy then went on to make an interesting assessment of what he referred to as, "SARS-CoV-WIV," (WIV = Wuhan Institute of Virology) actually is:

"... less a virus than it is engineered spike proteins hitchhiking a ride on a SARSr-CoV quasispecies swarm ... it is a synthetic spike protein chimera engineered to attach to human ACE2 receptors and inserted into a recombinant bat SARSr-CoV backbone."

The report goes on to allege NIAID, "under the direction of," Fauci, went ahead with the research in Wuhan and at several sites across the US. But an irony Murphy acknowledges in his own report is that, "decisions with regards to the vaccines do not appear to be informed by analysis of the documents." What he specifically refers to is the fact that the same DOD which rejected this gain-of-function research has gone on to mandate inoculations which are claimed to cause the body to produce the same spike protein they deemed too dangerous as the basis of said rejection in 2018. He elaborates:

"To me, and to those who were informed by analysis, this situation meets no-go or abort criteria with regards to the vaccines until the toxicity of the spike protein can be investigated ... vaccine approach lacks sufficient coverage to protect against quasispecies of coronavirus."

And this leads to, in my opinion, the most disturbing (though not surprising) part of the letter. Murphy identifies the government knew of early treatments in spring 2020, as follows:

"Many of the early treatment protocols ignored by the authorities work because they inhibit viral replication or modulate the immune response to the spike proteins, which makes sense within the context of what EcoHealth was creating. Some of these treatment protocols also inhibit the action of the engineered spike protein. For instance, Ivermectin (identified as curative in April 2020) works throughout all phases of illness because it both inhibits viral replication and modulates the immune response. Of note, chloroquine phosphate (Hydroxychloroquine, identified April 2020 as curative) is identified in the proposal as a SARSr-CoV inhibitor, as is interferon (identified May 2020 as curative)."

My Opinion on the Matter

I would like to start by saying I do not entirely discount the lab leak theory, nor do I think less of anyone who favors it. It is certainly plausible in that it seems to be supported by a significant amount of relevant historical and perhaps scientific evidence. In fact, I fully believe the evidence shows with 100% certainty that at the very least the aforementioned parties *were* doing gain-of-function research utilizing spike proteins, whether or not their work resulted in an aerosolized novel coronavirus. This research, in my opinion, violates 18 USC 175. Anthony Fauci also blatantly lied to Congress as it relates to this research. Both crimes should absolutely lead to prosecutions.

With that being said however, I personally assign their successful creation of a novel aerosolized virus a lower probability than the alternative theory of a fabricated pandemic. I will now explain why.

> *"... until an infectious disease crisis is very real, present, and at an emergency threshold, it is often largely ignored. To sustain the funding base beyond the crisis, we need to increase public understanding of the need for medical countermeasures such as a pan-influenza or pan-coronavirus vaccine. A key driver is the media, and the economics follow the hype. We need to use that hype to our advantage to get to the real issues. Investors will respond if they see profit at the end of the process."*
> —Peter Daszak, president of NIAID-funded EcoHealth Alliance, 2015[35]

If the above quote sounds awfully similar to Fauci's at the Milken Institute, it should come as no surprise when considering Fauci's NIAID *did* fund Daszak's EcoHealth Alliance. Whether that funding was also aimed at supporting gain-of-function research is irrelevant to the documented fact that funding *was* given to support coronavirus research, specifically in China. So a meaningful relationship existed between Daszak's organization and Fauci's.

Also, this quote demonstrates that the underlying motive of both men was selling the public on the inoculations and creating a sustainable source of funding through perceived crises. To achieve their collective aim, in their own words, they would drum up non-existent demand for those inoculations—not through scientific reasoning or demonstration, but through media-driven, "hype" (to quote Daszak). This hype would solve their problem of, "how the world perceives influenza," by giving them the context needed to skip the process of having to, "prove that this works," and instead allowing them to, "address the problem in a disruptive way and in an iterative way" (to quote Fauci).

This motive is where I start from when approaching my understanding of what comes next. This documented, broad-daylight conspiracy to defy informed consent and potentially put billions of lives in danger in the process is, in my opinion, the first and most important thing to address when approaching the Covid crimes against humanity. It is also by-far the most provable based on the documented evidence, the words of the conspirators themselves, and the timeline. And to me, what is the most provable is what is most relevant and worth focusing on.

The second most provable thing is the suppression of treatments which were already being used to treat disease prior to the alleged pandemic. According to the *Project Veritas* report, as well as past studies we've covered, these men had to have known the benefits of those demonstrably safer treatments. Despite this, they pressed on with their primary objective to sell the experimental, unproven inoculations anyway, while actively dismissing and slandering the alternatives which could have saved countless lives. This is another despicable crime against humanity which should also absolutely be addressed before the origin story.

The reason I say this is because even if the intentional lab leak proves true, the best way the evidence needed to prove it would come out is for criminal investigations and some form of confessions. These investigations would only come if the focus remains on prosecuting the conspiracy to mass inoculate the public and deny early treatment—the two most evident and indisputable crimes. Until then, I as a simple observer and interpreter of the wealth of information I've written down in this book admittedly cannot prove or corroborate an intentional lab leak at a top-secret lab. The best examples of supporting evidence that do exist in my opinion are the patents by Baric and others; however, I tend to side with Dr. Dean Martin in thinking that even those documents demonstrate there to be nothing novel about these alleged coronavirus pandemics. Is it possible we've been living with the consequences of those patents since the alleged SARS1 in 2002? Yes it is. Is it a heinous crime if that is the case? You're damn right it is. But neither you or I or anyone else noticed a significant difference between the before and after of SARS1. It is only now we are conscious of this, in my opinion strictly because of the, "hype."

So even if the evidence Fauci *funded* gain-of-function research is 100% legit and there, which I believe it very well could be and likely is since he's verbally supported it in the past, the next undertaking would be proving that same gain-of-function research ultimately turned into something capable of developing the alleged SARS-CoV-2, which it then needs to be proven causes all the illnesses in question. I don't have the microbiological background to offer anything on proving that, but appreciate the work of those who do and are attempting it! Approaching it from a simply logical perspective however, I lean toward the Covid collaborators not being capable of this and gain-of-function research being a cover story for the purposes of increased, "hype." The reasons I think this and questions I have which give me doubt are as follows:

1. Reviewing the false public health official data, "Covid," has a 99.9% case-survival rate for basically all ages. So even if a virus was created, it would seem they created a moderate flu akin to what is experienced every year anyway. Given that, along with the known phenomena of annually, "overwhelmed hospitals," either way, why bother creating and leaking a virus? Also, why did the flu effectively go to zero and other diagnoses see significant drops if, "Covid," isn't simply a re-categorization/misdiagnosis of known diseases?

2. In the vein of, "why bother," we've covered a metric ton of methods used to over-inflate the alleged problem. From false death and case counts, to false and abused tests with a history of fabricating epidemics, to the brand new asymptomatic illness and transmission concept, to incentives for hospitals to diagnose, and everything in between—the goal was clearly to make the situation look scarier than it was, as supported by this being a stated aim of the co-conspirators. That goal was achieved. As we saw, Christian Drosten knew in 2014 it would be achieved by following this script. But why would this

exaggeration be necessary if there was a lab-created novel virus which should be unknown to immune systems and therefore illness-causing (theoretically at least, more on that later) to everyone it touches?

3. Still in the vein of, "why bother," what if the virus they supposedly created *had* been more dangerous? It is a classic cartoon villain story to create the disease and sell the cure— but in this case they aren't selling the cure. And while it can be argued they did know of the actual treatments, so maybe were just anticipating to use those themselves if they got sick, no treatment is 100%. So they would still be opening themselves up to what seems like an undue degree of risk. Why bother risking your life when you have so much influence/control over the media/numbers and can drum up fear so effectively without having to create anything indiscriminate and dangerous? How are you going to spend your newly acquired fortune or exercise your expanded power if your creation gets out of control?

4. It is entirely plausible, observable, and provable that the dangerous, novel drugs (like remdesivir and midazolam) and processes (like mass ventilation) which were coerced and abused upon, "Covid," patients had a significant role in excess mortality. Lockdowns, unsanitary masking practices, psychosomatic effects of fear, and economic consequences also would have had a role. But the hysteria drummed-up and financial incentives to misdiagnose/mistreat turned hospitals into veritable death camps, some with as high as 80% death rates when it came to, "treating," these, "Covid," patients. As such, I think the Covid pandemic is much more accurately described as an orchestrated collapse of healthcare, if not an outright genocide, rather than a novel coronavirus pandemic. Much if not all the death and disease could have and should have been avoided, and this muddies the water of any potentially relevant analysis which could be made even if there is a SARS-CoV-2.

The gain-of-function story's early 2020 introduction by *Newsweek* with no mainstream or government fanfare at all was also convenient in a way, because it created a binary where both sides automatically accept the existence of a novel virus, whether or not there was evidence of one. In response to these troubling bioweapon allegations however, the DOD/DARPA took zero action. This is also highly suspicious, considering these organizations *were* alerted to them. If they were credible as is and the DOD had no role to play, why didn't they act in defending the homeland from the EcoHealth/NIAID bio-terrorists? Why have they *still* not acted?

Despite Murphy's warnings, the DOD has also gone on to illegally mandate inoculations they had a known role in funding. Because of the *Project Veritas* leak however, the documented rejection of the EcoHealth gain-of-function funding by DARPA served to lionize it, while pinning the blame/attention squarely on the untouchable Anthony Fauci and the origin of the alleged novel virus. The problem with this is the DOD/DARPA *has* provided a variety of other funding contracts to EcoHealth from 2014-2020, in an amount totaling at least $37.5M.[36,37,38,39,40,41,42,43,44,45,46] The descriptions of the purpose of these contracts is mostly unclear, but the DOD's relationship with an organization they admit is doing, "dangerous," work is no less concerning. And while I'm not alleging the *Project Veritas* leak was intentional on the part of DARPA/DOD as a distraction, it has conveniently served that purpose. It has successfully overshadowed what I view as the two much bigger issues there's evidence they were a part of (the inoculation scheme and the associated treatment suppression).

At the same time, despite my lack of microbiologic background, I also have what I feel are unanswered questions on the scientific background as follows:

1. I see no evidence at all in my personal experience or the experience of those around me that excessive amounts of human interaction leads to illness. Despite following none of the CDC guidelines, including around my, "immunocompromised," family members, none of us got abnormally sick. In 2020 I even hung out with friends on July 4 who, "tested positive," because no one else would. Neither my wife, myself, nor anyone we were subsequently in contact with got sick. In fact, the people I know who got sick the most frequently were overwhelmingly those who adopted the CDC's destructive lifestyle recommendations. Also, Africa's

complete lack of pandemic experience and the overall lack of uniform morbidity/mortality geographically makes the viral pandemic theory impossible, in my opinion.

2. If a virus is so tiny it can only be viewed under an electron microscope; if the only apparent way to even confirm its inside someone is to use faulty technology like PCR, which amplifies what is claimed to be the virus' genetic material and *not* the virus itself; if the methods of isolation used by the CDC and their ilk are such an inversion of the concept of actually isolating something as to imply they simply can't isolate it; how exactly then could something as tiny as a virus be, "created?" What technology and/or processes are used to manipulate this infinitesimally tiny thing? Also, how can this possibly be done with any degree of precision to not only, "create a virus," but to create one that does a specific function (i.e. make it dangerous, but not *too* dangerous)? These might be the questions of a layman, but a judge and jury would also be laymen in this regard and would need answers.

3. We now know about the NIH/Moderna inoculation's spike protein being based on a theoretical sequence and therefore not being specific to the alleged novel coronavirus, as confirmed by their December 2019 contracts, by Anthony Fauci in March 2020, and by *Axios* in June 2020. In addition to this, it was also confirmed in a 2022 study by Balamurali et al. in *Frontiers in Virology* that Moderna has a 2017 patent on a proprietary mRNA sequence, SEQ ID11652, which is a 100% match to a sequence claimed to be part of the alleged novel virus.[47] The authors say the probability of such a match occurring in nature is 0.0000000000321. In my opinion this proves the inoculations came first, that what is called the virus wasn't novel as of 2019, and that since it wasn't novel as of 2019, the narrative behind Covid as a 2020 novel virus pandemic can't be either.

4. By all accounts, it seems the toxic spike protein can be present in the absence of the virus it's claimed to be a part of. Given that, perhaps it is more plausible to think the spike protein (which is not novel) could have been aerosolized/weaponized. However, we still run into the same issue with it being very

treatable and not abnormally dangerous to the majority of the population anyway.

5. Outside of maybe Ralph Baric, I simply do not consider Anthony Fauci and his co-conspirators to be scientists. In fact, they are a group of people so focused on marketing psychology that I don't think they are even remotely interested in real scientific analysis or discovery. Ironically, this has been so evident to so many people that it's harmed their marketing efforts. But Fauci himself is a salesman in a white coat. In no way do I see him as being capable of the undertaking of turning human beings into walking biohazards and I will continue to doubt that capability until the day he confesses to it and describes the process in detail. What he does have the capability and a documented history of doing is poisoning people with the novel, dangerous, expensive drugs he fast-tracks. For this he will face justice, in this life or the next.

6. The most glaring scientific issue is the lack of proof the substance claimed to be SARS-CoV-2 causes the disease(s) referred to as, "Covid." In fact, definitive proof it does not cause the disease came from a February 2022 study by Killingley et al. in *Nature Portfolio*, in which 34 people who had no prior infection (showed no antibodies) were intentionally inoculated with said substance.[48] Of the 34, almost *half* never tested positive. This is impossible if the substance is a novel virus they were never exposed to and if the germ theory is true (more on the latter later). It gets more absurd too as even of the 18 who did test positive, only seven ended up with a fever and *zero* had serious symptoms. Again, this is impossible if the SARS-CoV-2 virus exists, is novel, and causes severe acute respiratory syndrome.

Along with all these issues/questions, there is also a breadth of historical precedent on these public health organizations faking and/or misattributing epidemics in order to remain relevant and keep the funding pump flowing. We've already covered some examples as they related to PCR. But there are many issues with everything from AIDS to the Spanish Flu as well, which I will provide as much background on as possible in a later chapter. When taking all these things together though, again, it seems to me most accurate to describe the Covid pandemic as a bureaucratic takeover and orchestrated collapse of healthcare, if not an outright genocide, rather than a novel coronavirus pandemic. As such, and for all the reasons described above, I don't pay as much mind to the gain-of-function details, though they remain relevant and worth investigating.

Endnotes

1   Batistic, Douglas. 2021. "Patents Prove SARS-Cov-2 Is A Manufactured Virus". *Citizens Journal*. https://www.citizensjournal.us/patents-prove-sars-cov-2-is-a-manufactured-virus/.

2   M Cam International LLC. 2020. "The Following Data Is Being Made Publicly Available For The Commons By M·CAM International LLC Based On A Series Of Reviews Of Patent Literature Derived From References". Charlottesville, VA. https://www.m-cam.com/wp-content/uploads/2020/04/20200403_SARS_CoV_Patent_Corpus_Lit_Review.pdf.

3   National Institute of Health, Allergy and Infectious Diseases. 2008. "Grant R01AI075297: SARS-Cov Pathogenic Mechanisms In Senescent Mice."

4   University of North Carolina at Chapel Hill. 2002. Methods for producing recombinant coronavirus. US7279327B2, and issued 2002.

5   "Severe Acute Respiratory Syndrome Coronavirus 1 - Wikipedia". 2022. *En.M.Wikipedia.Org*. Accessed March 26. https://en.m.wikipedia.org/wiki/Severe_acute_respiratory_syndrome_coronavirus_1.

6   Gold, E Richard. 2003. "SARS Genome Patent: Symptom Or Disease?". *The Lancet* 361 (9374): 2002-2003. doi:10.1016/s0140-6736(03)13674-4.

7   Ibid.

8   Calisher, Charles, Dennis Carroll, Rita Colwell, Ronald B Corley, Peter Daszak, Christian Drosten, and Luis Enjuanes et al. 2020. "Statement In Support Of The Scientists, Public Health Professionals, And Medical Professionals Of China Combatting COVID-19". *The Lancet* 395 (10226): e42-e43. doi:10.1016/s0140-6736(20)30418-9.

9   Barrett, Kevin. 2021. "Covid-19 Biowar Investigation: Naming The Persons Of Interest – American Free Press". *Americanfreepress.Net*. https://americanfreepress.net/covid-19-biowar-investigation-naming-the-persons-of-interest/.

10   Ibid.

11   "There Are No Arguments On The Other Side". 2021. *Eugyppius.Substack.Com*. https://eugyppius.substack.com/p/there-are-no-arguments-on-the-other.

12   Guterl, Fred. 2020. "Dr. Fauci Backed Controversial Wuhan Lab With U.S. Dollars For Risky Coronavirus Research". *Newsweek*.

https://www.newsweek.com/dr-fauci-backed-controversial-wuhan-lab-millions-us-dollars-risky-coronavirus-research-1500741.

13   "Was Peter Daszak Working For The Central Intelligence Agency?". 2022. *Kanekoa.Substack.Com.* https://kanekoa.substack.com/p/was-peter-daszak-working-for-the.

14   Guterl, Fred. 2020. "Dr. Fauci Backed Controversial Wuhan Lab With U.S. Dollars For Risky Coronavirus Research". *Newsweek.* https://www.newsweek.com/dr-fauci-backed-controversial-wuhan-lab-millions-us-dollars-risky-coronavirus-research-1500741.

15   Ibid.

16   NATIONAL INSTITUTE OF ALLERGY AND INFECTIOUS DISEASES. 2014. "Project Number 1R01AI110964-01: Understanding The Risk Of Bat Coronavirus Emergence". New York, NY: ECOHEALTH ALLIANCE, INC.

17   "Cambridge Working Group Consensus Statement On The Creation Of Potential Pandemic Pathogens (Ppps)". 2014. *Cambridgeworkinggroup.Org.* http://www.cambridgeworkinggroup.org/.

18   Reardon, Sara. 2014. "US Suspends Risky Disease Research". *Nature* 514 (7523): 411-412. doi:10.1038/514411a.

19   U.S. Department of Health and Human Services. 2017. "Framework For Guiding Funding Decisions About Proposed Research Involving Enhanced Potential Pandemic Pathogens."

20   Freeman, James. 2021. "Opinion | Biden's Latest Jobs Whopper". *WSJ.* https://www.wsj.com/articles/bidens-latest-jobs-whopper-11620685389.

21   "Ebright, Richard". 2022. *Chem.Rutgers.Edu.* Accessed March 26. https://chem.rutgers.edu/people/faculty-bio/140-ebright-richard.

22   Begley, Sharon. 2017. "U.S. Lifts Moratorium On Funding Controversial, High-Risk Virus Research". *Scientific American.* https://www.scientificamerican.com/article/u-s-lifts-moratorium-on-funding-controversial-high-risk-virus-research/.

23   Kessler, Glenn. 2021. "Fact-Checking The Paul-Fauci Flap Over Wuhan Lab Funding". *The Washington Post.* https://www.washingtonpost.com/politics/2021/05/18/fact-checking-senator-paul-dr-fauci-flap-over-wuhan-lab-funding/.

24   Sellers, Ben. 2021. "SMOKING GUN?: Video Suggests Fauci Perjured Himself In Denying Gain-Of-Function Support - Headline USA". *Headline USA,* https://www.headlineusa.com/fauci-perjure-gain-function-denial/.

25   Suryanarayanan, Sainath. 2020. "Scientist With Conflict Of Interest Leading Lancet COVID-19 Commission Task Force On Virus Origins - U.S. Right To Know". *U.S. Right To Know.* https://usrtk.org/biohazards-blog/daszak-conflict-of-interest-lancet-task-force-on-coronavirus-origins/.

26   "The Lancet COVID-19 Commission". 2022. *Lancet Commission On COVID-19.* Accessed March 26. https://covid19commission.org/.

27   Calisher, Charles H, Dennis Carroll, Rita Colwell, Ronald B Corley, Peter Daszak, Christian Drosten, and Luis Enjuanes et al. 2021. "Science, Not Speculation, Is Essential To Determine How SARS-Cov-2 Reached Humans". *The Lancet* 398 (10296): 209-211. doi:10.1016/s0140-6736(21)01419-7.

28   van Helden, Jacques, Colin D Butler, Guillaume Achaz, Bruno Canard, Didier Casane, Jean-Michel Claverie, and Fabien Colombo et al. 2021. "An Appeal For An Objective, Open, And Transparent Scientific Debate About The Origin Of SARS-Cov-2". *The Lancet* 398 (10309): 1402-1404. doi:10.1016/s0140-6736(21)02019-5.

29   Segreto, Rossana, and Yuri Deigin. 2020. "The Genetic Structure Of SARS-Cov-2 Does Not Rule Out A Laboratory Origin". *Bioessays* 43 (3): 2000240. doi:10.1002/bies.202000240.

30   Deigin, Yuri, and Rossana Segreto. 2021. "SARS-Cov-2′S Claimed Natural Origin Is Undermined By Issues With Genome Sequences Of Its Relative Strains". *Bioessays* 43 (7): 2100015. doi:10.1002/bies.202100015.

31   Menachery, Vineet D, Boyd L Yount, Kari Debbink, Sudhakar Agnihothram, Lisa E Gralinski, Jessica A Plante, and Rachel L Graham et al. 2015. "A SARS-Like Cluster Of Circulating Bat Coronaviruses Shows Potential For Human Emergence". *Nature Medicine* 21 (12): 1508-1513. doi:10.1038/nm.3985.

32   Crane, Emily. 2021. "NIH Admits US Funded Gain-Of-Function Research In Wuhan". *Nypost.Com*. https://www.nypost.com/2021/10/21/nih-admits-us-funded-gain-of-function-in-wuhan-despite-faucis-repeated-denials/.

33   *18 U.S. Code*. 2022. Vol. 175. Washington D.C.

34   Mahoney, Wendi Strauch. 2022. "Project Veritas: Former DARPA Fellow Pens Letter Exposing Gov't Secrets - Uncoverdc". *Uncoverdc*. https://uncoverdc.com/2022/01/12/project-veritas-former-darpa-fellow-pens-letter-exposing-govt-secrets/.

35   "Forum on Medical and Public Health Preparedness for Catastrophic Events; Forum on Drug Discovery, Development, and Translation; Forum on Microbial Threats; Board on Health Sciences Policy; Board on Global Health; Institute of Medicine; National Academies of Sciences, Engineering, and Medicine. Rapid Medical Countermeasure Response to Infectious Diseases: Enabling Sustainable Capabilities Through Ongoing Public- and Private-Sector Partnerships: Workshop Summary. Washington (DC)." *National Academies Press (US)*. 2016. 6, Developing MCMs for Coronaviruses. https://www.ncbi.nlm.nih.gov/books/NBK349040/

36   Defense Threat Reduction Agency (DOD). 2015. "Definitive Contract HDTRA115C0041". New York, NY.

37   Defense Threat Reduction Agency (DOD). 2017. "Definitive Contract HDTRA11710037". New York, NY.

38   Defense Threat Reduction Agency (DOD). 2019. "Definitive Contract HDTRA1191033". New York, NY.

39   Defense Threat Reduction Agency (DOD). 2013. "Definitive Contract HDTRA113C0029". New York, NY.

40   Department of Defense. 2014. "Definitive Contract HDTRA11410029 (#1)". New York, NY.

41   Defense Threat Reduction Agency (DOD). 2017. "Definitive Contract HDTRA11410029 (#2)". New York, NY.

42   Defense Threat Reduction Agency (DOD). 2020. "Definitive Contract HDTRA12010016". New York, NY.

43   Defense Threat Reduction Agency (DOD). 2017. "Definitive Contract HDTRA11710064". New York, NY.

44   Defense Threat Reduction Agency (DOD). 2020. "Definitive Contract HDTRA12010018". New York, NY.

45   Uniformed Services University of the Health Services (DOD). 2020. "Definitive Contract HU00012010031". New York, NY.

46   Defense Threat Reduction Agency (DOD). 2020. "Definitive Contract HDTRA12010029". New York, NY.

47   Ambati, Balamurali K., Akhil Varshney, Kenneth Lundstrom, Giorgio Palú, Bruce D. Uhal, Vladimir N. Uversky, and Adam M. Brufsky. 2022. "MSH3 Homology And Potential Recombination Link To SARS-Cov-2 Furin Cleavage Site". *Frontiers In Virology* 2. doi:10.3389/fviro.2022.834808.

48   Killingley, Ben, Alex Mann, Mariya Kalinova, Alison Boyers, Niluka Goonawardane, Jie Zhou, and Kate Lindsell et al. 2022. "Safety, Tolerability And Viral Kinetics During SARS-Cov-2 Human Challenge". doi:10.21203/rs.3.rs-1121993/v1.

Chapter 16

Conflicts of Interest

The scope of entanglements surrounding the major players/organizations involved in the Covid conspiracy are truly incredible. We've already provided tons of evidence they exist and explained how the various global collaborative organizations like the WHO, WEF, and Bill & Melinda Gates Foundation make them possible. So really the purpose of this chapter is to provide a general overview of the conflicts of interest which exist, along with adding several new details we haven't yet covered.

Anthony Fauci, Moderna, NIH/NIAID, Ralph Baric, and Peter Daszak

As for Baric, in the previous chapter we covered his funding connections to the NIH/NIAID, specifically as they related to coronavirus research. You will also recall NIAID and Moderna's joint ownership of the mRNA coronavirus inoculation and sharing of it in a Material Transfer Agreement (MTA) with Ralph Baric himself on December 12th 2019.[1] This puts a man with a documented history of, "producing recombinant coronavirus," and NIH funding at the heart of the NIH/Moderna conspiracy which took place right before the alleged pandemic was even announced.

The plot only thickens from there. Shockingly, UNC also acknowledged that remdesivir—the very drug Fauci pushed at the expense of science and reason—was also, "developed through an academic-corporate partnership between Gilead Sciences and the Baric Lab at the University of North Carolina at Chapel Hill's Gillings School of Global Public Health."[2] Given Baric had a history of being funded by Fauci, his having developed the front-runned drug raises serious questions about remdesivir's selection by NIAID for study and eventual hospital use despite past studies showing it to be dangerous.

Perhaps the most disgraceful thing which ties and implicates both Fauci and Baric in this heinous crime however, is a study we covered at the beginning of our chapter on early treatments.[3] You may or may not have recognized his name when I mentioned it then, but Baric himself was one of the co-authors of the *PLOS Pathogens* report which found that, "Increasing the intracellular Zn^{2+} concentration

411

with zinc-ionophores like pyrithione (PT) can efficiently impair the replication of a variety of RNA viruses." So, given his decades-long connection with Fauci and intensive study on coronaviruses, it is without question that the failure of either of these two men to promote zinc-ionophores vociferously during what they alleged was a coronavirus pandemic is a crime against humanity. Instead, Fauci actively engaged in a suppression campaign of any and all zinc-ionophores. Mass murder via suppression of life saving treatment followed, as his partner's remdesivir was catapulted to both tremendous financial success and disastrous health outcomes in hospitals throughout the US and the world.

We also previously covered Fauci's obvious connection to Daszak in funding the EcoHealth Alliace for more than half a decade. A 2015 report in *Nature* on the risky research being done by these men also ties Daszak's work directly to Baric, who was one of the primary scientists he worked with in the experiments which led to his 2016 claim of engineering viruses.[4] The report alleges they, "created a chimeric virus," which combined the spike protein of a specific virus with, "the backbone of a SARS virus." Ralph Baric himself is even quoted in the report as claiming the NIH allowed this gain-of-function research to proceed while it was still, "under review," by the agency. Virologist Simon Wain-Hobson said this work provided, "little benefit, and reveals little about the risk," these viruses pose to humans. Richard Ebright agreed, saying, "The only impact of this work is the creation, in a lab, of a new, non-natural risk."

In reference to the paper Baric and he co-authored on this work, which can only be described as attempted bioweapons development, Daszak said the study findings, "Move this virus from a candidate emerging pathogen to a clear and present danger." It is hard to disagree with this statement—it is the very point the many who have disagreed with this work were seemingly trying to make in their opposition to it. Again, we must question whether the claims of a known liar like Daszak to create a virus are actually valid, which as I've stated I certainly do. But either way, these connections tie closely together:

1. The head of the US response to the alleged pandemic (Fauci)
2. A mad-scientist who developed the only drug ultimately sanctioned for use, who discovered readily available zinc and

412

zinc-ionophores to be curative, who has been working on coronavirus gain-of-function research, and who even secured a coronavirus patent (Baric)

3. The head of the organization which received millions from the government to research coronaviruses in Wuhan and who used those funds to support the mad-scientist's work (Daszak)

More evidence these co-conspirators knew what they were doing was wrong—outside of how unmistakably wrong their actions were in general—also came in their attempts to cover it up. For example, emails obtained by US Right to Know (USRTK) revealed Daszak actually orchestrated the February 2020 statement in the *Lancet*, hoping to, "avoid the appearance of a political statement."[5] This is said despite one infectious disease expert in the email chain, who drafted the letter but who did not sign it, Trevor Bedford, admitting, "If you start weighing evidence, there's a lot to consider for both scenarios."[6] It is clear from these exchanges that these parties knew all possibilities were on the table, despite their pre-meditation to send their desired message. Daszak even tells Baric in one email exchange that the two, "should not sign this statement, so it has some distance from us and therefore doesn't work in a counterproductive way." If that's not politics, I don't know what is. Baric responded however, by agreeing that they shouldn't sign the statement *which Daszak himself orchestrated*. Daszak ultimately did sign it, while Baric did not.

And so, this deceitful effort by these, "scientists," to sell the public on a natural origin was now-infamously published in the opening days of 2020. It then went on to be endorsed by Fauci and Collins. The respective NIAID/NIH heads also pointed to another propaganda piece to the same effect in *Nature Medicine*, which they themselves were acknowledged by one of the authors as having helped with.[7] Daszak has since rightfully been called out for his offenses, one such example being a November 2021 letter by the US House of Representatives Committee on Energy and Commerce urging the National Academy of Medicine to suspend his status and investigate him.[8]

Anthony Fauci, Peter Daszak, the CIA, the WHO, Pfizer, and the FBI

By now we've covered the backstory on Peter Daszak's EcoHealth work being funded by Anthony Fauci, NIAID, and the NIH at length. We also covered Daszak's involvement in a propaganda statement in the *Lancet* which sought to stifle dissent in the earliest days of the alleged pandemic. There is much more to his background, however.

First, besides the NIH, Daszak's EcoHealth Alliance also received more than $118 million in grants and contracts from federal agencies, including $53 million from the United States Agency for International Development (USAID) and $42 million from the DOD.[9] In fact, both journalist Sam Husseini and *The Intercept* reported much of the money was not designated for health or ecology, but for bio-warfare and bioterrorism.[10,11]

According to former USAID director John Gilligan in his book *Cold War Anthropology*, USAID is, "infiltrated from top to bottom with CIA people."[12] He explained that, "the idea was to plant operatives in every kind of activity we had overseas; government, volunteer, religious, every kind." From 2009 to 2019, USAID partnered with EcoHealth on its PREDICT virus-identification program.[13] What potentially substantiates the suspicion behind this connection however, is a (suspiciously uncensored) January 12, 2022 *Twitter* thread by former EcoHealth Alliance Associate Vice President Dr. Andrew Huff, who said the following[14]:

> *"For the record: in 2015, Dr. Peter Daszak stopped me as we were leaving work late at night, and asked me if he should work with the CIA. I was shocked given my experience in security. Over the next 2 months he gave me updates on 3 separate occasions about his work with the CIA.*
>
> *When he asked me the question I stated 'Peter, it never hurts to talk with them and there could potentially be money in it.' Meanwhile, I was cringing that he told me this, in a non classified setting (a SCIF), to a person that was not 'read-in,' and to an un-cleared person (me).*
>
> *Then, over the next two months at the break area while getting coffee, or between meetings, he stated that they were interested in the places that we were working, the people involved, the data that we were collecting, and that the work with them was proceeding.*

Looking back, I now believe that EcoHealth Alliance was a CIA front organization to collect viral samples and to collect intelligence on foreign laboratory capacity. There was no way that the data collected of the model being developed, could predict transmission or pandemics.

Contextually, EcoHealth was barely solvent and it was common place to lay off employees with the ebb and flow of federal and private funding. **Peter would do anything or say anything to obtain funding** *(my emphasis). Intelligence organizations often target people in financial distress.*

From the CIA's perspective, it was a great plan in my opinion, if what Dr. Peter Daszak said was true. Since it was common place for Peter to lie, I didn't necessarily believe him when he told me. However...

Based on the past two months of the US government spending millions of dollars surveilling me and MTRX INC employees, including military aircraft, attempting to destroy my house, bugging everything in it stealing my property, and hacking all my devices, I believe that the worst is likely true. EcoHealth Alliance is likely a CIA front organization. COVID-19 is the biggest intelligence failure since 9/11. The coverup is the greatest in US history, far worse than the Iran-Contra scandal. The truth is coming out and I will testify this under oath.

... I wouldn't be surprised if the CIA/IC orchestrated the COVID coverup acting as an intermediary between Fauci, Collins, Daszak, Baric, and many others. At best, it was the biggest criminal conspiracy in US history by bureaucrats or political appointees."

I won't even begin to claim Daszak is definitively a CIA asset. In fact, I find Huff's testimony suspicious, not only because it wasn't censored by *Twitter* (which anything remotely true always is), but also for his own apparently intimate knowledge of the Agency and how it operates. Still, whether or not Daszak himself operated as an asset, the connection and involvement clearly are there. And with all these ties it would almost seem more difficult to imagine Daszak *wasn't* an intelligence asset of some kind. For example, would you be surprised at this point if I told you despite his completely outrageous conflicts of interest, Daszak was *also* chosen by the WHO to lead their team charged with investigating Covid's origin?[15] Short of Fauci himself I cannot possibly think of anyone in the entire world with more conflicts than Daszak to be appointed to such a position, yet the global health body chose him, of all people. The only possible explanation for that is a corrupt connection between the two.

The CIA also factors prominently into the Covid era through other connections as well. The first is Event 201, the pandemic simulation event held by John's Hopkins Bloomberg School of Public Health, the World Economic Forum, and the Bill & Melinda Gates Foundation.[16] One of the 15, "players," in the simulation happened to be Avril Haines, the former Deputy Director of the CIA who went on to become Director of National Intelligence for the Biden Administration.[17] While this might seem like an indirect tie however, consider a recent report by *Project Veritas* about Department of Justice documents obtained by Judicial Watch.[18] The documents showed communications between Pfizer and the FBI specifically about *Project Veritas*, which had recently released several embarrassing undercover videos of Pfizer scientists admitting natural immunity was better than inoculation.[19] The plot thickens however, when we see this *and more* proudly corroborated by Pfizer CEO Albert Bourla himself in an interview:

> *"**We were getting a lot of briefs from the CIA, FBI** (my emphasis) about attacks that may happen to us—cyberattacks I mean—**but also about the spread of misinformation** (my emphasis)."*

Evidence of this CIA/pharma connection is also bolstered by the Agency's extraordinary influence over the media, as covered by Dick Russell of the *Defender*.[20] Russell (a self-professed liberal) points out classic CIA smear tactics which have shown up particularly frequently in liberal media outlets. He also goes into a vast history on several of those outlets such as the *Daily Beast*, describing the intelligence-heavy backgrounds of its former head John Phillips Avlon and his apparent best friend (per *both* of their *Wikipedia* pages) Matthew Pottinger.[21] During Avlon's tenure, the *Beast* actually published a story on October 14, 2016 about the CIA's recruitment program of media assets, titled, "Operation Mockingbird," which, "threatened and blackmailed," journalists into cooperating with the Agency's agenda.[22] Avlon ultimately left the *Beast* in 2018 to become a senior political analyst and anchor at CNN, where he would join former CIA intern Anderson Cooper.[23] You can read Russell's work for much more background on that than I can provide here. But when taken alongside Bourla's confessed collusion, these types of connections only further substantiate the role of this organization's psychological control contributions during the Covid era.

It is one thing for neither the CIA nor the FBI to have done anything at all in the way of investigating, exposing, and holding accountable those responsible for this orchestrated catastrophe. Ignoring the history of these organizations, one would think such a course of action would be their primary responsibility during such a time. So to have failed to do so is an obvious, glaring red flag. But to make matters worse, by now we know the term, "misinformation," means anything at all negative about the inoculations or the overall goals of the Covid conspirators. So for the CIA and FBI to be colluding with Pfizer to suppress speech critical of that company's product—a product the federal government has a significant vested interest in—is an astoundingly bold amount of corruption, even for these historically questionable, untouchable agencies.

The Bill & Melinda Gates Foundation, John's Hopkins, the WEF, and Basically Everyone

These organizations are obviously tied together by Event 201, but each has such vast influence on its own that when combined, their reach/power is significantly amplified. To cover familiar ground first, we've covered how the Bill & Melinda Gates Foundation provided significant funding to Imperial College London, which provided the wildly-inaccurate, tyranny-justifying projections at the beginning of the alleged pandemic. Gates publicly hailed these projections anyway and claimed their dire nature would ultimately have to lead to inoculation certificates he'd long-since theorized.

The former tech mogul behind the tremendously successful Microsoft also bragged in several interviews about how his investments in inoculations were the most profitable in his life, establishing a clear conflict between his Foundation and the pharmaceutical companies, while separating what he does from any claims of, "philanthropy." One specific example of this can be seen in

BioNTech's SEC Filing to Investors in February 2020, which included the following[24]:

> "On **August 30, 2019** (my emphasis), *we entered into a letter agreement and an investment agreement with the Bill & Melinda Gates Foundation, or BMGF, pursuant to which BMGF acquired 3,038,674 of our ordinary shares for $55 million.*"

What miraculous timing to have made such a deal *and* to have scheduled a once-in-a-century pandemic simulation *and* to have been conspiring to connect inoculations to digital ID (but more on that shortly). Gates must be a true visionary! This is especially so when you consider the following disclaimers provided in the same February 2020 statement and prior about BioNTech's business prospects and risks[25]:

> "We are a clinical-stage biopharmaceutical company with no pharmaceutical products approved for commercial sale.
> ... No mRNA immunotherapy has been approved, and none may ever be approved, in this new potential category of therapeutics. mRNA drug development has substantial clinical development and regulatory risks due to the novel and unprecedented nature of this new category of therapeutics.
> ... To our knowledge, there is no current precedent for an mRNA-based immunotherapy such as the type we are developing being approved for sale by the FDA, European Commission or any other regulatory agency elsewhere in the world ... in the European Union, mRNA therapies have been classified as gene therapy medicinal products ..."

The August 2019 Gates-BioNTech agreement saw Gates' Foundation buy shares at approximately $18 per share. Just two years later, BioNTech's stock peaked on the NASDAQ at around $450 per share. If unsold, the 3 million shares would have been worth around $1.3 billion, for a 2,386% return on investment. You will recall Gates informing an interviewer about his, "20-to-1," inoculation returns—the BioNTech deal serves as a great example of this, and it's just *one* such example during the Covid era. But as Gates' manipulation of the situation via corporate media, pandemic war-gaming, and leveraging of institutions like Imperial College London demonstrate, these aren't the shrewd picks of a savvy investor with the added benefit of fortunate timing, but rather an orchestration of the scenario needed to ensure such gargantuan returns.

We also acknowledged that the Gates Foundation is the single largest investor in the WHO, contributing more than any member nation. There really is no greater conflict of interest than this. For such a tremendous pharma funder to also fund the global organization meant to serve as a check on pharma is a big problem, to put it mildly. And even if the WHO didn't have the influence it does over the national public health bureaucracies, Gates funds those through his Foundation as well. Whether it's the US CDC, the UK Medicine and Healthcare products Regulatory Agency (MHRA), or even in eastern nations like China, Gates has a financial influence in seemingly every single public health body in the world—public health bodies which go on to direct government policy actions during a time of perceived health emergency.[26,27,28]

The CDC in particular is funded in part by what's called the CDC Foundation, an entity created to, "Mobilize philanthropic and private-sector resources to support," the CDC.[29] So even beyond the pharma interests of the Gates Foundation, the CDC is also funded directly by pharma companies including Pfizer, Johnson & Johnson, and Gilead, among *many* others. It is through this Foundation that all of Walensky and the CDC's behavior operating as a governmental inoculation sales wing of the pharmaceutical companies starts to make sense.

Even, "fact-checkers," like Sophie Fessl of *HealthFeedback.org* admit Robert F. Kennedy Jr. is correct in asserting that the CDC, "buys and distributes vaccines," with around $4.6 billion, or 40% of its annual budget.[30] The problem is when Fessl then says that the CDC therefore, "isn't a vaccine company; the CDC doesn't sell vaccines." Fessl ~~either doesn't realize or~~ **intentionally ignores** the obvious effects of pharma donating to the CDC Foundation (inoculation revenue), the CDC's admitted royalty collection on the products she admits they license (more inoculation revenue), and the CDC's overt marketing of the inoculations (sales). To summarize, the CDC buys inoculations, heavily markets inoculations, and makes money based on their sales, even if the people taking the shot are not paying them directly. The CDC is therefore, by any honest assessment, an inoculation company.

The NIH/NIAID isn't much better, as we also saw how Anthony Fauci was named to the Leadership Council of the Gates, "Decade of Vaccines Collaboration." And as for the FDA, C. Michael White of the UConn School of Pharmacy has pointed out that almost half of its funding comes from, "user fees," from the pharmaceutical companies themselves.[31] In fact, one such example during the Covid era included an approximately $2.88 million, "application fee," from Pfizer for priority review of their, "Comirnaty," BLA licensing.[32] Understand: that's just *one* of the companies in question and for *one* application of the surely several they would have filed.

A February 2022 *Project Veritas* exposé of FDA Executive Officer Christopher Cole not only validated these conflicts are a relevant problem, but Cole also revealed it is one the FDA intentionally sweeps under the rug[33]:

> *"Well, the dirty stuff is never really publicized, I mean, there's more pressure to approve something ... There's also a billion dollars a year going into the FDA's budget from people we regulate ... A long time ago Congress approved user fees for* [the] *FDA ... Basically, we charge the industry millions of dollars in order to hire more drug reviewers and vaccine reviewers, which will speed up the approval process so they make more money ... **They** [the FDA] **tone down the effect of the user fees on their operations because they know that they're dependent on the drug companies and the vaccine companies and these other companies for their agency to operate** (my emphasis)."*

The story behind John's Hopkins is much less known than that of Gates, but is dark all the same. Given their involvement in and the context of Event 201's recommendations on the suppression of, "misinformation," as well as their ties to Gates-affiliate Michael Bloomberg, it should come as no surprise that one of the John's Hopkins Bloomberg School of Public Health's publicly advertised current projects is called, "Environment of Misinformation."[34] This overt psychological operation is aimed at combatting the spread of, "misinformation," during, "emergencies, disasters, and outbreaks,"

420

because of a perceived increase in, "opportunities for the propagation of misinformation," during such times.

Let me provide a quick example to illustrate how insane and untrue this is. In February of 2021 the state of Texas had an unprecedented blizzard. I personally was without power and water in an all-electric apartment, located at the top of a frozen-over hill, over the course of a week where temperatures were below 10 degrees Fahrenheit. Despite the claims of this John's Hopkins project, there was not one time during this entire, "emergency," where I was doubting the nature of my circumstances—I *was* in a blizzard without power and for as long as my phone would stay on I would turn it on looking for an update from the electric company on when it would come back on. I never considered going to social media to get the scoop on which electric company executive was corrupt and how they were lying. All I cared about was making fires for warmth and figuring out what to eat until the situation was resolved.

It seems the most trivial of concepts that if you were in an emergency, you'd know it. But corrupt oligarch-run institutions like John's Hopkins seem to think it's in their authority to both declare an, "emergency," and to also dictate the response of all living beings to the alleged emergency, without question. This is a psychopathic and psychologically abusive worldview. It should also come as no surprise then that seemingly all, "case counts," including CNN's cite John's Hopkins for their data.[35] I try to imagine what my career would be like if I could just accuse anyone who scrutinizes my data/analysis that they are, "spreading harmful misinformation." I wonder if I'd be promoted or fired. Maybe if I was fired I'd start a, "project," called, "Workplace of Misinformation."

But I digress. To finish off on John's Hopkins and how little this institution is actually focused on public health, consider another project they recently conducted called, "SPARS Pandemic Scenario."[36] This was another crafted pandemic scenario like Event 201, which also was more focused on psychology than anything one would expect, such as medical supply chains, communication system optimization for the free flow of information/debate, or proper data collection methodologies. Key areas of focus inexplicably included, "rumor control," "proactive and reactive media relations," and "cultural competency." If these don't sound familiar to the actual response we've experienced, simply recall the slanderous declarations

421

of, "misinformation," the pathetic refutations of, "fact-checkers," and the willingness to discriminate, respectively. If these things don't make it clear John's Hopkins has had a disturbing role in influence over the media and relevant psychological operations, I don't know what would.

This brings us to the World Economic Forum. I will cover much more on the WEF and its apparent leader Klaus Schwab in the next two chapters on economics and governance in the Covid era. However, it is clear this organization is one which brings many of the players together—and they are not shy in any way to admit it. Take the following 2007 quote by Schwab at the WEF headquarters for a better example than any[37]:

> Schwab: *"We have—if I look at our stakeholders, we have business, of course, as a very important audience; and we have politics, we have continuous partnerships with many governments around the world; then, of course, we have NGOs* [non-government organizations], *we have tribunals— we have all those different parts—media, of course. And, very important, um, experts in science and academia. Because if we are looking at the future I think we should look at new solutions, and the new solutions will be very much driven by technological developments."*
> Interviewer: *"And you even have religious leaders, right?"*
> Schwab: *"Religious leaders, we have social entrepreneurs— very important social entrepreneurs."*

One such stakeholder Schwab is referring to as far as religious leaders go is Justin Welby, the Archbishop of Canterbury and a WEF, "agenda contributor."[38] When asked by a TV outlet if being inoculated was a, "moral issue," the WEF-compromised archbishop unsurprisingly said he thought it was.[39] He continued, "It's not about me and my right to choose. It's about how I love my neighbor." He then seemed to imply Jesus would support this mass experimentation which allegedly involves reprograming the God-given immune system. Such anti-Christian behavior might be surprising if we didn't see the same from the Pope himself, who we will get to.

Another Schwab acolyte is a man named Jim Smith. Jim is the President and CEO of our favorite, "fact-checker," *Reuters*.[40] Now, with all the sloppy, "fact-checks," we've dissected to this point by Jim's rag, it might have seemed puzzling as to why *Reuters* has so relentlessly skirted their duty as an outlet purporting to do journalism. However, things start to make more sense when you realize our boy Jimmy is also a regular at the WEF, with his own bio and everything.[41] But wait, there's more! James is a busy man—so busy, in fact, that he also is on the Board of Directors of Pfizer.[42] Oh … did I say James? Perhaps that's because ole Jim is officially listed as James Smith on his Pfizer biographies. I'm sure this is not a dishonest attempt to keep up appearances though. And if it is, not to worry—Jim is also on the board of the WEF's Partnering Against *Corruption* Initiative, and is on the Forum's International Business Council, so Klaus and he can assure you there is absolutely nothing to worry about here.

While that's an entirely real, serious situation which has inexplicably not led to any criminal investigations at all, I digress. At a January 2022 gathering of the WEF at Davos, Anthony Fauci and Moderna both seemed fixed on alleged, "misinformation," surrounding their product, with Moderna's Bancel even saying they have to, "get people to believe in the vaccines."[43] It is understandable that a faith-like *belief* would seem the only way to convince people, seeing as Bancel also claimed Moderna was expecting a new, "omicron version," of their inoculation to be sent to regulators by March 2022. Didn't world leaders just spend the entire winter saying the only way to protect ourselves from the, "omicron variant," was the current inoculations, and that if we didn't inject ourselves with them our families and ourselves would inevitably overwhelm hospitals? Was it, "misinformation," that the current inoculations protect from the, "omicron variant?" Or will that only *become*, "misinformation," once Moderna is ready to start selling the next round of inoculations?

Anyway, Fauci also said we are in phase one (the, "negative impact," phase) out of five of the pandemic he alleges to be ongoing.[44] Keep in mind, he said this two years after popularizing the phrase, "15 days to slow the spread," as a justification for the largest mass lockdown of non-convicted people the world has ever seen. Those 15 days were supposed to curb the, "negative impact," phase and they didn't, nor did the only-hospital measures he signed off on (remdesivir + sedatives + ventilators), nor did the inoculations. In a logical, uncorrupted system, the, "15 days," failure alone would have led to his being fired in shame, if not an investigation into his motives for recommending measures so un-scientific and inhumane.

For Fauci to speak at a gathering of world leaders at a time when people throughout the world almost universally mock and despise him is a true testament to how out of touch said leaders are. The WEF seems to be realizing the consequences of its actions too, seeing as those leaders who adhere to its agenda have been in the process of a dramatic heel turn the same week this January gathering has taken place. England and the Czech Republic, for example, both announced the removal of restrictions on the same day.[45,46] And while in England's case it could be suggested this was due to Boris Johnson's breaking his own tyrannical rules by throwing parties, the coordination of the actions with many other previously tyrannical leaders also lifting their feet off the gas can hardly be considered a coincidence—especially at a time when crimes against humanity cases are being filed against them in the International Criminal Court.[47]

Anthony Fauci and the Chief of the Department of Bioethics at the NIH

On October 4, 2021, *The Sun* published a propaganda piece called, "POWER COUPLE Who is Dr. Anthony Fauci's wife Christine Grady."[48] As we saw in the emphasis on, "rumor control," which John's Hopkins prepared for, *The Sun*'s piece was a direct response to alleged claims by people on social media that Grady, "was the one to approve the Covid-19 vaccine rather than the FDA." This classic tactic of, "fact-checker," propagandists is well known to us at this point—address an irrelevant, false claim to direct attention away from a relevant issue you do not want addressed. The absolutely relevant issue in this case is that Anthony Fauci's wife is the Chief of the Department of Bioethics at the NIH.

This blog post is particularly interesting to analyze deeper though for several reasons. The first is because we have to ask ourselves: why is *The Sun* groveling about Anthony Fauci? The topic of this article is a perceived conflict of interest between his wife and him and the first words of the title are a capitalized, "POWER COUPLE." It is obvious this is an attempt to reframe the issue, but what incentive does *The Sun* have to be so transparent in this kind of psychological manipulation? This is something of a rhetorical question—the answer should be obvious given the partnerships we know many of these outlets have with the oligarchs/bureaucrats in question. But still, we have to address it because two-thirds or so of the article is simply a puff piece about Grady and Fauci's family life. They even throw in a quote with the clear intention of humanizing Fauci, as if it's relevant to the topic at hand:

> *"He works hard and he does his thing, but he comes home and he's singing opera in the kitchen and dancing around."*

We will cover *way* more ground on the vomit-inducing propaganda campaign surrounding Anthony Fauci in a future chapter. But to address the actual point of this issue, I will repeat myself: *Anthony Fauci's wife is the Chief of the Department of Bioethics at the NIH.* It is so beyond irrelevant whether or not she had any involvement in the FDA's decisions surrounding the inoculations— the FDA has conflicts of interest of its own in the form of pharma, "user fees," as we've already covered, a detail *The Sun* might mention in such a piece if what they were doing was journalism.

What *is* relevant is the endless list of issues with Fauci's conduct we've covered to this point, whether it be the endpoint shifting and control group sabotaging in NIAID's remdesivir trials, any part of his relationships/activities with Baric and Daszak, any of his endless list of conflicts of interest, his sabotaging of the control groups in the inoculation trials, his constant flip-flopping and intentional misdirection in media appearances (for example, on desired inoculation rates and inoculation safety/efficacy), his encouragement of informed consent violations in media appearances, or his willing involvement in too many propaganda pieces to count during an alleged emergency (more on those later). And those are just the issues I can name off the top of my head.

For another particularly indefensible one, consider leaked emails in which NIH director Francis Collins complained to Fauci and others about the Great Barrington Declaration getting, "a lot of attention."[49] Never once did Collins or Fauci publicly address or offer to debate the position of the massive list of scientists and doctors behind the Declaration. Instead, Collins called for, "a quick and devastating takedown of its premises," in the October 2020 emails, on which he copied his to-be successor, Lawrence Tabak. Collins also

425

slandered the prolific epidemiologists behind the Declaration as, "fringe epidemiologists," and asked if there was anything, "on line yet," related to his, "takedown," proposal. Fauci, proving yet *again* he is not a scientist, responded by sending only a *Wired* propaganda blog post titled, "There is no 'scientific divide' over herd immunity."[50]

We've already shown the Covid collaborators themselves can't even reach their own on consensus on a goal/definition of, "herd immunity." Take the following incompetent, translated social media post by Christian Drosten, for yet another example[51]:

> *"If you believe that you can train your immune system by getting an infection, you must also believe that you can train your digestive system by eating a steak."*

Does Drosten not know what a diet is? Does he not think the digestive system reacts in different ways based on what one consumes and how often they consume it? Either way, he as usual proves himself such a dishonest charlatan here that he doesn't even realize he's making a case *against* vaccines—the only nominal point of which is to *train* the *immune* system to build the type of immunity which is meant to occur when one gets a natural infection. This astounding post invalidates the entire, "scientific," basis for Drosten's career, which he gets away with as always because liars lie and the corporate media lies like humans breathe.

But besides the litany of absurd examples like Drosten's, the mere existence of the Great Barrington Declaration alone demonstrates *Wired*'s, "no scientific divide," thesis to be an outright lie. The article too is a predictable mess of slander, including the absurd, baseless claim that the publication of the Declaration was followed by, "clinking champagne glasses before the signatories jetted off to Washington DC." This is the type of immature drivel Fauci considers a, "debunking," worthy of dismissing the valid, published, peer-reviewed concerns of tens of thousands of professionals. Apparently Christine Grady sees no problem with this blatant conspiracy between her husband, Collins, and the incoming NIH director to commit scientific fraud.

A similar example follows reporter Adam Andrzejewski, whose longstanding column with *Forbes* as a senior policy contributor was terminated after he started publishing reports in January 2021 about FOIA requests he'd made surrounding Fauci's financials.[52] Andrzejewski's documentation on the lack of availability of the highest paid government employee's finances was even cited by a senator questioning Fauci at a January 2022 senate hearing. Fauci went on to both call the senator a, "moron," under his breath and then later to admit, "maybe the senator has a point," in a *Washington Post* propaganda piece attempting to defend him.[53] Despite efforts by the NIH in court to make disclosure as difficult as possible for a joint filing by Andrzejewski and Judicial Watch, the financials were eventually discovered and revealed the following[54,55]:

- Fauci's household net-worth exceeded $10.4 million
- Salaries, benefits, royalties, investment gains in the Fauci household exceeded $1.7 million in 2020
- Christine Grady, the chief bioethicist at NIH made $234,284 in 2020
- Fauci made between $100,000 and $1 million as an editor and board member of McGraw-Hill
- In 2021, Fauci was awarded a $1 million prize for, "speaking truth to power," from the Dan David Foundation in Israel

As an aside, the final insulting bullet is like giving an honesty award to a person who just failed a polygraph test—though it is admittedly a very real possibility that when the Dan David Foundation said Fauci, "speaks truth to power," they were actually just referring to conversations he has with the many pictures of himself hanging in his office while he works. I can't confirm or deny Fauci does that, but I'd personally be more surprised if he didn't. Anyway ... none of the above is anywhere near acceptable from an ethics perspective, especially since Fauci is not a scientist—not that it would even be remotely okay for a government scientist to exploit their power to this extent either.

There are so many more of Fauci's ethical indiscretions we've covered and will still cover, both during and before the Covid era, both related-to and unrelated-to Covid. These indiscretions are the responsibility of the Chief of the Department of Bioethics at the NIH to address (if not the FBI or some other criminal investigative body). But Grady clearly hasn't and is not going to hold her, "opera-singing," husband to account for any of them.

Perverse Hospital Incentives and Other Destructive Government Actions

While this final point is not related to how specific individuals and organizations are tied together like the others have been, it is possibly the most important note as far as how conflicts-of-interest were built into the healthcare system itself. We've already touched on the announcement from DHHS in July of 2020, declaring certain hospitals in, "high impact," areas would receive as much as $55,000 per Covid-19 admission, down from $77,000 per admission in earlier months. Analysis by Kaiser Health actually showed states like Minnesota, Nebraska, and Montana were getting more than $300,000 per reported case at one time.[56] The US Centers for Medicare & Medicaid Services (CMS) also provided a, "New COVID-19 Treatments Add-on Payment (NCTAP)," which paid an additional 20% payment for cases treated with remdesivir.[57] We've already covered the dangers of remdesivir, the only drug recommended by public health to treat and only recommended in a hospital setting.

But the horrendous hospital outcomes are not remotely surprising based on this perverse, one-size-fits-all incentive structure for more reasons than the drug itself. Hospitals which abided by this structure in order to reap the NCTAP benefits were not treating patients with known medications based on their unique, observed conditions/ailments, but rather on the government's experimental diagnosis and, "treatment," plan for the country. This led to for-profit experimentation defining the Covid era, as demonstrated by at-this-point commonplace examples such as United Healthcare whistleblower Jeanne Stagg, who reported false, "Covid," diagnoses, including for gunshot patients.[58] Another was an FBI-raided COVID testing company accused of falsifying test results in a scheme that netted $124 million in government reimbursements.[59] The backwardness of the incentives which facilitated such conspiracies was also no mystery to anyone, as they were incredulously questioned and opposed from the beginning by many, including Dr. Kory in his aforementioned early treatment address to the US congress.

These upside-down incentives weren't limited to hospitals either. Per healthcare policy analyst AJ Depriest, a team she worked with out of Tennessee reviewing these policies found schools too were impacted.[60] Specifically, between the CARES Act and other, "relief," packages sent to schools, more than $200 billion was distributed by the government during the alleged pandemic. While this money went to a variety of unsurprising things like remote education and sanitizers, every school has also been required to submit a, "district plan," every 6 months through September 2023 in order to receive the payments. And just like with the hospital payouts being contingent on a harmful medication plan, these school payment plans must also adhere to specific, absurd conditions. Those conditions are as follows:

> "Universal and correct wearing of masks; modifying facilities to allow for physical distancing ... contact tracing in combination with isolation and quarantine, in collaboration with the State, local, territorial, or Tribal health departments; diagnostic and screening testing; efforts to provide vaccinations to school communities..."

These are all issues—masking especially—which parents around the country have for two years now consistently been attending school board meetings demanding be ceased, only to be ignored by glassy eyed administrators. Those administrators certainly know the financial consequences of not enforcing these destructive policies, and their failure to acknowledge the demands of the parents they're supposed to represent is just another in a long list of duty derelictions and betrayals by American institutions. It is even more grotesque when considering it comes at the expense of the youngest, most innocent generation, which faced zero risk and will be damaged for life by the medical, social, and psychological consequences of these horrendous actions.

Reminiscent of the $2.3 trillion then US Secretary of Defense Donald Rumsfeld reported to be mysteriously, "missing," on September 10, 2001, the federal spending watchdog Pandemic Response Accountability Committee (PRAC) has also reported difficulty in determining how the more than $5 trillion in pandemic relief funds have been spent.[61,62] The PRAC was established by the CARES Act itself to, "promote transparency and conduct and support oversight," yet admits the following in the aforementioned report[63]:

> "It's hard to know where pandemic relief money went. It's even harder for us to tell you what it was used for. Government award data is full of dead ends."

Perhaps the government should have simply designated the IRS responsible for this task, since it was apparently considered skilled enough to track the activity of all individual bank accounts over $600 at one point during this alleged pandemic.[64] I can't say for sure what they'd have found if they had, but I would bet the more than $600 in my bank account they'd have also simply hit a, "dead end," in their alleged attempt to uncover it. An honest accounting has led to some ugly findings, including:

- Secret service claims $100 billion in, "pandemic relief," funds stolen[65]
- Roman Catholic Church received $3.5 billion in PPP loan funds[66]
- Kanye West's company, Yeezy LLC., received a PPP loan of $2-5 million[67]
- Joel Osteen's Lakewood Church received $4.4 million in PPP loans[68]
- Tom Brady's TB12 sports performance company took almost $1 million in PPP loans[69]
- The Boston Marathon Bomber got a COVID relief check[70]

It didn't end with financial incentives, either. Another inhumane aspect of the, "CARES," Act included waivers of customary and long-standing patient rights by the Centers for Medicare and Medicaid Services (CMS).[71] These waivers provided to hospitals included patient protections of timeframes in providing a copy of a medical record, of patient visitation rights, and of preventing patient seclusion. Hospitals were allowed to skirt these patient rights in the name of, "public health," with outcomes as horrific as the practices were cruel.

In the next chapter we will cover the larger scale, mostly non-health related economic motives which underpin the Covid era. For now though, these financial conflicts-of-interest explain much of the otherwise completely irrational behavior exhibited throughout this massive collapse of institutions. My analysis has been mostly focused on America, but additional ties have been documented all over the world, thanks to the global reach of the mentioned organizations. Those who set up this scenario—named throughout this chapter—can either admit to the motive of financial gain or of attempted genocide, should they face the tribunals they deserve. While the punishment should be the same either way given the extent of the crimes, no other explanations are acceptable.

Endnotes

1   The National Institutes of Health. 2019. "NIH-Moderna Confidential Disclosure Agreement". Rockville, MD.

2   "Remdesivir, Developed Through A UNC-Chapel Hill Partnership, Proves Effective Against COVID-19 In NIAID Human Clinical Trials - UNC Gillings School Of Global Public Health". 2020. *UNC Gillings School Of Global Public Health*. https://sph.unc.edu/sph-news/remdesivir-developed-at-unc-chapel-hill-proves-effective-against-covid-19-in-niaid-human-clinical-trials/.

3   te Velthuis, Aartjan J. W., Sjoerd H. E. van den Worm, Amy C. Sims, Ralph S. Baric, Eric J. Snijder, and Martijn J. van Hemert. 2010. "Zn2+ Inhibits Coronavirus And Arterivirus RNA Polymerase Activity In Vitro And Zinc Ionophores Block The Replication Of These Viruses In Cell Culture". *Plos Pathogens* 6 (11): e1001176. doi:10.1371/journal.ppat.1001176.

4   Butler, Declan. 2015. "Engineered Bat Virus Stirs Debate Over Risky Research". *Nature*. doi:10.1038/nature.2015.18787.

5   Ruskin, Gary. 2022. "FOI Documents On Origins Of Covid-19, Gain-Of-Function Research And Biolabs - U.S. Right To Know". *U.S. Right To Know*. https://usrtk.org/biohazards/foi-documents-on-origins-of-sars-cov-2-risks-of-gain-of-function-research-and-biosafety-labs/.

6   Suryanarayanan, Sainath. 2020. "New Emails Show Scientists' Deliberations On How To Discuss SARS-Cov-2 Origins - U.S. Right To Know". *U.S. Right To Know*. https://usrtk.org/biohazards-blog/scientists-deliberations-on-sars-cov-2-origins/.

7   Mercola, Joseph. 2021. "Fauci Exposed: Historical Research Of COVID". *Z3news.Com*. https://z3news.com/w/fauci-exposed-historical-research-of-covid/.

8   Congress of the United States House of Representatives COMMITTEE ON ENERGY AND COMMERC. 2021. "November 30, 2021 Letter To National Academy Of Medicine". Washington, DC.

9   "Was Peter Daszak Working For The Central Intelligence Agency?". 2022. *Kanekoa.Substack.Com*. https://kanekoa.substack.com/p/was-peter-daszak-working-for-the.

10 Husseini, Sam. 2020. "Peter Daszak's Ecohealth Alliance Has Hidden Almost $40 Million In Pentagon Funding And Militarized Pandemic Science - Independent Science News | Food, Health And Agriculture Bioscience News". *Independent Science News | Food, Health And Agriculture Bioscience News*. https://www.independentsciencenews.org/news/peter-daszaks-ecohealth-alliance-has-hidden-almost-40-million-in-pentagon-funding/.

11   Lerner, Sharon. 2021. "How The Pursuit Of Unknown Viruses Risks Triggering The Next Pandemic". *The Intercept*. https://theintercept.com/2021/12/28/covid-pandemic-virus-hunters-ecohealth-alliance-peter-daszak-wuhan/.

12   Price, David H. 2016. *Cold War Anthropology*. Durham: Duke University Press.

13   "PREDICT Project". 2022. *PREDICT Project*. Accessed March 27. https://p2.predict.global/.

14   Huff, Andrew. 2022. "Dr. Andrew Huff On Twitter, Jan 12, 2022 Post Thread". *Twitter*. https://twitter.com/AGHuff/status/1481402002995392513?s=20.

15   Nuki, Paul, and Sarah Newey. 2020. "Scientists To Examine Possibility Covid Leaked From Lab As Part Of Investigation Into Virus Origins". *The Telegraph*. https://www.telegraph.co.uk/global-health/science-and-disease/scientists-examine-possibility-covid-leaked-lab-part-investigation/.

16   "About Event 201, A High-Level Pandemic Exercise On October 18, 2019". 2019. *Event 201*. https://www.centerforhealthsecurity.org/event201/about.

17   "Avril Haines - Infogalactic: The Planetary Knowledge Core". 2021. *Infogalactic.Com*. https://infogalactic.com/info/Avril_Haines.

18   "DOJ Docs Obtained By Judicial Watch Confirm Communication Between FBI & Pfizer About Project Veritas". 2022. *Youtube*. https://youtu.be/-WdFxe-xMdY.

19   "Pfizer Scientist: 'Your Antibodies Are Probably Better Than The Vaccination'". 2021. *Projectveritas.Com*. https://www.projectveritas.com/news/pfizer-scientist-your-antibodies-are-probably-better-than-the-vaccination/.

20   Russell, Dick. 2021. "CIA's Extraordinary Role Influencing Liberal Media Outlets Daily Kos, The Daily Beast, Rolling Stone (Part 1)". *Childrenshealthdefence.Org*. https://childrenshealthdefence.org/defender/cia-liberal-media-outlets-the-real-anthony-fauci/.

21   Russell, Dick. 2021. "Part 2: The Belly Of The Daily Beast And Its Perceptible Ties To The CIA". *Children's Health Defense*. https://childrenshealthdefense.org/defender/the-daily-beast-ties-to-cia/.

22   "How The CIA Paid And Threatened Journalists To Do Its Work". 2016. *The Daily Beast*. https://www.thedailybeast.com/cheats/2016/10/14/how-the-cia-paid-and-threatened-journalists-to-do-its-work.

23   "Quoted: Anderson Cooper On His CIA Internship". 2013. *The Washington Post*. https://www.washingtonpost.com/news/reliable-source/wp/2013/10/20/quoted-anderson-cooper-on-his-cia-internship/.

24   BioNTech SE. 2020. "FORM F-1 REGISTRATION STATEMENT UNDER THE SECURITIES ACT OF 1933 - As Filed With The

Securities And Exchange Commission On February 3, 2020". New York, NY. https://investors.biontech.de/node/7171/html.

25   Ibid.

26   "Our Partners | CDC Foundation". 2022. *Cdcfoundation.Org*. Accessed March 27. https://www.cdcfoundation.org/partner-list/foundations.

27   "Why Is The Gates Foundation Funding The UK's Medicines Regulator? | The Liberty Beacon". 2021. *The Liberty Beacon | Bringing Alternative Media Sources Together™*. https://www.thelibertybeacon.com/why-is-the-gates-foundation-funding-the-uks-medicines-regulator/.

28   Winters, Natalie. 2021. "EXC: Gates Foundation Sent Over $54 Million To China Since COVID, Including To Wuhan Collaborators.". *The National Pulse.*. https://thenationalpulse.com/exclusive/exc-gates-foundation-sent-over-54-million-to-china-since-covid-including-to-wuhan-collaborators/.

29   "Our Partners | CDC Foundation". 2022. *Cdcfoundation.Org*. Accessed March 27. https://www.cdcfoundation.org/partner-list/foundations.

30   Fessl, Sophie. 2021. "The CDC Licences Vaccine Technology, But Isn'T A Vaccine Company; The CDC Doesn'T Sell Vaccines, It Buys And Distributes Vaccines Free Of Charge". *Health Feedback*. https://healthfeedback.org/claimreview/the-cdc-licences-vaccine-technology-but-isnt-a-vaccine-company-the-cdc-doesnt-sell-vaccines-it-buys-and-distributes-vaccines-free-of-charge/.

31   White, C. Michael. 2021. "Why Is The FDA Funded In Part By The Companies It Regulates? - Uconn Today". *Uconn Today*. https://today.uconn.edu/2021/05/why-is-the-fda-funded-in-part-by-the-companies-it-regulates-2/.

32   Pfizer. 2021. "Part 1 Of The Original Submission – Rolling Biologics License Application (BLA) - Request For Priority Review Designation". BLA 125742 COVID-19 Mrna Vaccine (BNT162/PF-07302048). Collegeville, PA. https://phmpt.org/wp-content/uploads/2022/03/125742_S1_M1_cover.pdf.

33   "FDA Executive Officer On Hidden Camera Reveals Future COVID Policy: 'Biden Wants To Inoculate As Many People As Possible…Have To Get An Annual Shot'". 2022. *Projectveritas.Com*. https://www.projectveritas.com/news/fda-executive-officer-on-hidden-camera-reveals-future-covid-policy-biden/.

34   Sell, Tara Kirk, Divya Hosangadi, and Marc Trotochaud. 2022. "Project: Environment Of Misinformation | Center For Health Security". *Johns Hopkins Center For Health Security*. Accessed March 27. https://www.centerforhealthsecurity.org/our-work/Center-projects/misinformation.html.

35   Hernandez, Sergio, Byron Manley, Sean O'Key, and Henrik Pettersson. 2020. "Tracking Covid-19 Cases In The US". *CNN*. https://www.cnn.com/interactive/2020/health/coronavirus-us-maps-and-cases/.

36   Schoch-Spana, Monica, Matthew Shearer, Emily Brunson, Sanjana Ravi, Tara Kirk Sell, Gigi Kwik Gronvall, and Hannah Chandler. 2017. "SPARS Pandemic Scenario | Projects: Center For Health Security". *Johns Hopkins Center For Health Security*. https://www.centerforhealthsecurity.org/our-work/Center-projects/completed-projects/spars-pandemic-scenario.html.

37   "Covid Truth Network Video Post Forwarded From Dr. Simon January 23, 2022". 2022. *Telegram*. https://t.me/covidtruthnet/508.

38   "Justin Welby - Agenda Contributor". 2022. *World Economic Forum*. Accessed March 29. https://www.weforum.org/agenda/authors/justin-welby.

39   Newman, Jack, and Jack Wright. 2021. "Jesus Would Get A Vaccine, Archbishop Of Canterbury Suggests". *Mail Online*. https://www.dailymail.co.uk/news/article-10334569/Archbishop-Canterbury-says-unvaccinated-immoral-love-neighbour.html.

40   "Jim Smith - Thomson Reuters Institute". 2022. *Thomson Reuters Institute*. Accessed March 27. https://www.thomsonreuters.com/en-us/posts/authors/jim-smith/.

41   "Jim Smith - Agenda Contributor". 2022. *World Economic Forum*. Accessed March 27. https://www.weforum.org/agenda/authors/jim-smith.

42   "James Smith | Pfizer". 2022. *Pfizer.Com*. Accessed March 27. https://www.pfizer.com/people/leadership/board_of_directors/james_smith.

43   Day, Vox. 2022. "Boosters 4 And 5 On The Way - Vox Popoli". *Vox Popoli*. https://voxday.net/2022/01/19/boosters-4-and-5-on-the-way/.

44   Becker, Kyle. 2022. "Fauci Says We're Just In Phase One Of 'Five Phases Of The Pandemic' — Then Issues A Chilling Warning". *Thekylebecker.Substack.Com*. https://thekylebecker.substack.com/p/fauci-says-were-just-in-phase-one.

45   Ott, Haley. 2022. "England Is About To Drop Virtually All Anti-COVID Restrictions". *Cbsnews.Com*. https://www.cbsnews.com/news/uk-covid-restrictions-cases-boris-johnson-ends-rules-england/.

46   Becker, Kyle. 2022. "Czech Prime Minister Ends Vaccine Mandates: 'We Do Not Want To Deepen The Rifts In Society'". *Trending Politics*. https://trendingpolitics.com/czech-prime-minister-ends-vaccine-mandates-we-do-not-want-to-deepen-the-rifts-in-society-knab/.

47   Ellyatt, Holly. 2022. "UK's Boris Johnson In Leadership Crisis, Accused Of Lying About 'Industrial Scale Partying' During Covid Lockdowns". *CNBC*. https://www.cnbc.com/2022/01/17/uks-boris-johnson-clings-to-power-as-partygate-scandal-rumbles-on.html.

48   Schollenberger, Katrina, and Nikki Main. 2021. "POWER COUPLE Who Is Dr. Anthony Fauci's Wife Christine Grady?". *The US Sun*. https://www.the-sun.com/news/1796332/who-is-dr-fauci-wife-christine-grady/.

49   Nal, Renee. 2021. "LEAKED: Fauci, NIH Head Planned 'Devastating Takedown' Of Non-Compliant Physicians - RAIR". *RAIR*.

https://rairfoundation.com/leaked-fauci-nih-head-planned-devastating-takedown-of-non-compliant-physicians/.

50 Reynolds, Matt. 2020. "There Is No 'Scientific Divide' Over Herd Immunity". *WIRED UK*. https://www.wired.co.uk/article/great-barrington-declaration-herd-immunity-scientific-divide.

51 Drosten, Christian. 2021. "Christian Drosten On Twitter December 29, 2021 Post". *Twitter*. https://twitter.com/c_drosten/status/1476192189793411076?cxt=HHwWi IC9zba-vvwoAAAA.

52 Andrzejewski, Adam. 2022. "How Fact-Finding Fauci Led To My Cancellation At Forbes". *Openthebooks.Substack.Com.* https://openthebooks.substack.com/p/factfindingfaucicanceledforbes?s=r.

53 Zak, Dan, and Roxanne Roberts. 2022. "Anthony Fauci Is Up Against More Than A Virus". *The Washington Post*. https://www.washingtonpost.com/lifestyle/2022/01/27/fauci-pandemic-threats/.

54 Andrzejewski, Adam. 2022. "How Fact-Finding Fauci Led To My Cancellation At Forbes". *Openthebooks.Substack.Com.* https://openthebooks.substack.com/p/factfindingfaucicanceledforbes?s=r.

55 Andrzejewski, Adam. 2022. "No, Fauci's Records Aren't Available Online. Why Won'T NIH Immediately Release Them?". *Forbes*. https://www.forbes.com/sites/adamandrzejewski/2022/01/12/no-faucis-records-arent-available-online-why-wont-nih-immediately-release-them/?sh=561f098646bd.

56 Axelrod, Tal. 2020. "Analysis: Some States Getting $300K Per Coronavirus Case, New York Getting $12K". *Thehill.* https://thehill.com/policy/healthcare/492325-analysis-some-states-getting-300K-per-coronavirus-case-new-york-getting-12k.

57 Centers for Medicare & Medicaid Services. 2020. "New COVID-19 Treatments Add-On Payment (NCTAP)". CMS.

58 "COVID Cases Inflated For Profit: 'The Guy Went In For Multiple Gunshot Wounds And He Was Coded As COVID'". 2022. *Projectveritas.Com*. https://www.projectveritas.com/news/covid-cases-inflated-for-profit-the-guy-went-in-for-multiple-gunshot-wounds/.

59 Atkinson, Grant. 2022. "Update: FBI Raids COVID Testing Company Accused Of Falsifying Test Results In $124 Million Cover-Up". *The Western Journal*. https://www.westernjournal.com/update-fbi-raids-covid-testing-company-accused-falsifyng-test-results-124-million-cover/.

60 Morgan, Edward. 2022. "AJ Depriest Uncovers The Enormous Covid Bribes To All Education And Hospitals From The US Government - Prepare For Change". *Prepare For Change*. https://prepareforchange.net/2022/01/11/aj-depriest-uncovers-the-enormous-covid-bribes-to-all-education-and-hospitals-from-the-us-government/.

61 "Rumsfeld Admitted That The Pentagon Was Missing 2.3 Trillion Dollars | CLG News". 2021. *Legitgov.Org*.

https://www.legitgov.org/rumsfeld-admitted-pentagon-was-missing-23-trillion-dollars.

62   PANDEMIC RESPONSE ACCOUNTABILITY COMMITTEE. 2021. "INCREASING TRANSPARENCY INTO COVID-19 SPENDING". pandemicoversight.gov. https://www.pandemicoversight.gov/sites/default/files/2021-10/increasing-Transparency-Into-COVID-19-Spending_10182021.pdf.

63   Lang, Mary Lou. 2021. "'Hard To Know Where Pandemic Relief Money Went,' Admits Federal Spending Watchdog". *Just The News*. https://justthenews.com/accountability/watchdogs/dead-ends-systemic-transparency-failure-stymies-watchdog-tracking-covid-19.

64   Harper, Casey. 2021. "IRS Would Track All Bank Transactions Over $600 Under Biden Plan; Businesses Revolt". *News.Yahoo.Com*. https://news.yahoo.com/irs-track-bank-transactions-over-140000522.html.

65   "Secret Service: Nearly $100B Stolen In Pandemic Relief Funds". 2021. *NBC News*. https://www.nbcnews.com/politics/politics-news/secret-service-nearly-100b-stolen-pandemic-relief-funds-n1286430.

66   Bostock, Bill. 2020. "The US Catholic Church May Be The Largest Recipient Of Federal Coronavirus Aid, With As Much As $3.5 Billion, AP Analysis Says". *Business Insider*. https://www.businessinsider.com/us-catholic-church-3-billion-coronavirus-loans-not-business-ap-2020-7?op=1.

67   Coleman, Justine. 2020. "Kanye West's Company Got PPP Loan". *Thehill*. https://thehill.com/blogs/in-the-know/in-the-know/506119-kanye-wests-company-got-2m-to-5m-ppp-loan.

68   Meyer, David. 2021. "Joel Osteen's Lakewood Church To Repay $4.4M In PPP Loans". *Nypost.Com*. https://nypost.com/2021/10/10/joel-osteens-lakewood-church-to-repay-4-4m-in-ppp-loans/.

69   Newburger, Emma. 2020. "Tom Brady's Company TB12 Received More Than $960,000 PPP Loan". *CNBC*. https://www.cnbc.com/2020/12/05/tom-bradys-company-tb12-received-more-than-960000-ppp-loan.html.

70   Moore, Mark. 2022. "Boston Marathon Bomber Received $1,400 In COVID Relief Funds". *Nypost.Com*. https://nypost.com/2022/01/06/boston-marathon-bomber-received-1400-in-covid-relief-funds/.

71   The Centers for Medicare and Medicaid Services. 2021. "COVID-19 Emergency Declaration Blanket Waivers For Health Care Providers". CMS.

Chapter 17

Covid: An Economic Conspiracy

There are many layers to the events which have taken place over the last two years. For the purposes of this book, I have focused mostly on one dimension—namely, health and the actions of public health organizations. However, it would be neglectful to not at least address the other factors, which may in some ways be considered even more important and, ultimately, the crux of the entire Covid-19 event. I will start here with one of the primary topics in this regard: economics. While this could be the subject of its own book, I will attempt to be as concise and to-the-point as possible in describing its relevance to the Covid era.

The WEF and "The Great Reset"

Though I've written four fiction books to date, I don't think I could've written anything as subversive or dystopian as the openly declared aspirations and doublespeak of the WEF. If I had though, actual WEF head Klaus Schwab—son of alleged Nazi-supported military contractor, Eugen Schwab—would probably be too cartoonish a villain for me to have designed.[1] As documented by *Swiss Policy Research*, engineer and economist Klaus Schwab founded the WEF in 1971 with the mission of, "shaping global, regional, and industry agendas."[2,3] So with one sentence we've established that Schwab and his organization have taken it upon themselves as unelected oligarchs to direct world agendas. A country based on representative government could stop there and have a legitimate case to consider the WEF a threat to national security/sovereignty, but let's continue.

We've already talked about the WEF orchestrating the October 18, 2019 Event 201 coronavirus pandemic simulation exercise, alongside the Bill & Melinda Gates Foundation and the John's Hopkins University Bloomberg School of Medicine. What we haven't yet covered is that this same day represented the opening of the Wuhan Military World Games. China has made the case that the US military could have, "brought the virus," to China via these games.[4] In my opinion there is enough evidence of a collaboration between the US and China—and not enough serious accusations or military actions in response to such an obvious act of war—to suggest that China doesn't really even believe this to be the case. Consider the connection between Baric, Fauci, Daszak, and the Wuhan lab; or the praise of Chinese public health in the *Lancet* propaganda statement; or the cushy relationship both western leaders and President Xi himself have with Klaus Schwab, who introduced Xi glowingly at the recent January 2022 WEF gathering.[5] The reverence for Xi is so significant, in fact, that the WHO was even reported as skipping the Greek Letter, "Xi," on behalf of the Chinese leader when naming, "variants."[6] Given these things, I see a lot more evidence of international collusion than I do conflict. I will cover more on why that could be in the next chapter.

As for Schwab however, he published a book in July of 2020 called *COVID-19: The Great Reset*, which argued the alleged pandemic necessitated a global reset to exactly the aims of the WEF.[7] These aims included advancing global governance, accelerating digital transformation, tackling, "climate change," and an overall transition to a society with much less privacy and individual autonomy. As a side note on this, it took me two years to gather all the citations, data, and history on the Covid era used in this book. Once I had a lot of it, it took me at least six months to organize it all in a meaningful way and to write this book. It will probably take me another 2 to 6 months to edit, format, and publish it. I'm not going to say it isn't *possible* to write, edit, and publish a book in under 6 months. But that Schwab synthesized a global economic thesis centered specifically on an unprecedented pandemic response in less than that amount of time is, at minimum, enough to raise an eyebrow.

Like collaborator Bill Gates, Schwab and the WEF have been leading proponents of digital biometric identity systems.[8] Schwab has said in interviews that by 2026 everyone will have an implanted technology which will enable them to participate in commerce.[9] To this end, in *July of 2019* his Forum started a project to, "shape the future of travel with biometric-enabled digital traveler identity management."[10] Both the Gates Foundation and the Rockefeller Foundation (which itself theorized in 2010 an eerily familiar totalitarian pandemic response called, "Operation Lockstep") fund a similar project launched in *September of 2019* with the same aim and more, called the ID2020 Alliance.[11,12] ID2020 officially collaborates with the WEF too, on its goal to, "provide digital ID with vaccines," and sees the vaccination of children as, "an entry point for digital identity."[13] One form of this is a Gates-funded, MIT-proposed, "quantum dot tattoo," vaccine-delivery device, which would also embed vaccination records in the skin and be readable by smartphone camera app.[14]

So let's take stock here for a moment. One massive, global agenda-plotting event in 2019 coming to fruition in 2020 would be suspicious … but at this point we are at *more than five* such events carried out by the same players and organizations, which only bolsters our thesis of a conspiracy to sell the world on mRNA inoculations. As if the specific year in the name, "ID2020," wasn't transparent enough as to the self-professed, pre-planned, "agenda," at play here, the inoculations themselves clearly serve as much an economic purpose as a medical one. In fact, it isn't hard to imagine their *primary* aim could be economic at this point.

Either way, economics and social control clearly have a significant role here. Throughout 2020 and into early 2021, "fact-check," gaslighting was directed by dishonest media outlets at people with clearly reasonable concerns about the connection the inoculation developers/funders had to chips and tracking.[15] *Snopes*, for one, ridiculed comparisons and connections of vaccine patches to the Biblical Mark of the Beast, which describes in Revelation 13:17 a now-awfully-familiar phenomenon, that, "no man might buy or sell, save he that had the mark."[16,17] Masks and the economic sanctions put in place to wear them could easily be considered to have been an equivalent of the Mark. In fact, they were likely utilized in a big way to condition people to later accept it when it came to the inoculations, as it took less than a year for the aforementioned concerns to be entirely validated as it related to the latter.

Mandated, "vaccine passports," to buy and sell have been a reality in many totalitarian-controlled locations such as New York Ciy, where healthy, fit under-30 year olds like myself are considered biohazard lepers whose presence is too dangerous to attend venues my family and I grew up enjoying, like Madison Square Garden. And even if the passports are mostly on paper cards for now, it's absurd to have ever thought in this age it would remain that way, even if you had no idea of the intentions of the WEF and ID2020. This obvious reality has also played out by now, as *Newsmax* acknowledged Sweden has begun implanting COVID, "vaccine," passport microchips *inside* of people.[18] Meanwhile, the shills at *Business Insider* in November 2021 were already planting seeds on behalf of the aforementioned oligarchic interests, suggesting, "A COVID-19 vaccine patch could produce a better immune response than injection."[19] This isn't surprising in the least, because *of course* they provide a better response when the outcome (agenda) is pre-determined. And as we saw with remdesivir, if the results of the actual scientific method prove unfavorable, the primary endpoints can always be shifted to make them appear positive.

Such passports are clearly and observably intended by the WEF and ID2020 for purposes far beyond health, since we've already demonstrated and seen them admit that there is no epidemiological benefit whatsoever to the inoculations. In West Africa for example, tests by GAVI, the Gates Foundation, and MasterCard are being carried out for a, "trust stamp," system.[20] The, "trust stamp," would link everything from voting ID, to payment processing, and vaccination records, all in one biometric record keeping system. As if the censorship and privacy breaches/intrusions weren't great enough without this extreme degree of data centralization, it has already been reported by the *Daily Record* that the Scottish government's, "vaccine," passport, for example, has been sending people's private data to Amazon and Microsoft, without the option to opt out or their even having been informed.[21]

In a previous chapter, we covered an admission by the president of Bayer's Pharmaceuticals Division, Stefan Oelrich, that the inoculations were actually a, "Gene and cell therapy," which were marketed as vaccines to gain public trust. During this same 2021 Global Health Summit, Oelrich also said the following[22]:

> *"Our successes over these 18 months* [the duration of the alleged pandemic at the time] *should embolden us to fully focus much more closely on access, innovation, and collaboration to unleash health for all, especially **as we enter, on top of everything else that is happening, a new era of science—a lot of people talk about the Bio Revolution in this context** (my emphasis)."*

According to the McKinsey Global Institute, the, "Bio Revolution," is, "a confluence of advances in biological science and accelerating development of computing, automation, and artificial intelligence [that] is fueling a new wave of innovation."[23] Based on historical precedent, connections, and admissions we can infer that this revolution is also linked in a big way to Schwab's agenda of unprecedented economic and social control. Next, we will show more of the specific economics and tactics used to achieve these aims.

Schwab's Revolution in Action

"Welcome to 2030: I Own Nothing, Have No Privacy and Life Has Never Been Better."
—*Forbes* blog post by the World Economic Forum, 2016[24]

"See, at the start of 2020, 1% of the world's population owned 44% of the world. And since the start of the pandemic, billionaires have increased theirs by more than 25%, whilst 150 million people fell back into extreme poverty. And with climate change set to dwarf the damage caused by the pandemic, the message from 2020 should be abundantly clear: 'capitalism as we know it is dead.'"
—"What is the Great Reset," video by the World Economic Forum, 2021[25]

If the WEF views, "1% of the world's population," owning, "44% of the world," as a problem, how exactly can they *also* consider the average person, "owning nothing," a solution to that problem? Also, we already covered how the senseless Covid era lockdown measures—measures many of the WEF's members are responsible for—destroyed small businesses/incomes the world over and *directly caused* the very 25% shift to the wealthy cited as a problem in this flashy propaganda video. *Also*, as it relates to any environmental issues they pretend to care about, a June 2021 study published in *Chemosphere* by Dharmaraj et al. found the tremendous increase in senseless face mask use has led to a blooming of pollution/waste in the marine environment.[26] Still, servant typists like Michael Hammerl of *Kurier* feature WEF puppet and, "agenda contributor," Greta Thunberg, in blog posts attempting to tie all control mechanisms together with sociopathic claims like, "Compulsory vaccinations are the right test for a climate-neutral future."[27]

Given this body of information, why were the members and allies of the WEF the primary drivers behind each of the very measures which exacerbate the issues they claim to want to solve? Seems more than a little contradictory, don't you think? Seems almost—dare I say it—deceptive? Perhaps the following contradiction could also be considered deceptive.

> *"With everything falling apart, we can reshape the world in ways we couldn't before—ways that address so many of the challenges we currently face. And that's why so many are calling for a Great Reset.* **'A Great Reset? That sounds more like buzzword bingo masking some nefarious plans for world domination' ... But the world isn't so simple. Every one of us has differing priorities, values, and ideas—that's part of why solutions are so hard to come by, and we all need to be involved in the decision-making** (my emphasis)."
> —The same WEF, "What is the Great Reset," video[28]

> *"You know, one of the things that we—I believe the entire world is facing—but we certainly are facing it in a very disconcerting way in the United States—is the amount of disinformation that is accompanying what should be a problem where everyone pulls together against the common enemy which is the virus.* **We have disinformation which is entirely destructive to a comprehensive public health endeavor** (my emphasis)."
> —Anthony Fauci to the WEF gathering at Davos, January 2022[29]

The first thing to point out here is the WEF propaganda says that, "so many are calling for a Great Reset," before immediately echoing the valid, supported concerns many people have voiced about what is in reality the *few* who are calling for said reset. That they actually said this in the video and acknowledged that their, "Great Reset," phrase is, "buzzword bingo," is hilarious. Again though, if the WEF believes that, "every one of us has differing priorities, values, and ideas," why does it endorse Fauci's notion of one-size-fits-all, "comprehensive," medicine and mandates? During a January 2022 panel hosted by Senator Ron Johnson called, "COVID-19: A Second Opinion," Dr. Christina Parks described the disproportionate risk the mRNA inoculations posed to black people as an example of why the one-size-fits-all approach is cruel (not that we still need such an example at this point).[30] Did the WEF, Fauci, and their allies ever once voice any caution for any group taking these shots? Of course they didn't. In fact, any suggestion of caution related to the inoculations by anyone at all prompted these very claims of, "disinformation," and calls for censorship. And censorship, of course, represents the opposite of an honest, moral approach to a world of, "differing priorities, values, and ideas."

The truth of the matter is, a disdain for free speech and differing opinions *defines* WEF policy. This global neo-communist organization, like Karl Marx before it, talks out of both sides of its mouth. In order to combat reduced ownership amongst the lower and middle classes, it proposes *no* ownership amongst the lower and middle classes; in order to support a world full of individuals with differing opinions and needs, it proposes a uniform technocracy which only permits the smallest possible range of opinions and needs; and to achieve order in a world in which it tells you, "everything is falling apart," it suggests the only way to rebuild on the alleged ashes is for the same oligarchs who have presumptively oversaw this destruction to be granted infinitely more control over every aspect of life.

This is a disorienting doublespeak which has sounded great since Marx first posited it because it promises a fairer re-distribution by a strong central government, which it theorizes will lead the wealth gap expansion to cease. But the truth of the matter, when you actually analyze the real world, is that the socialist promises of, "universal (fill-in-the-blank)," are actually just an extreme, non-free-market form of capitalism in which the government merges into a monopoly with the exploitative capitalist oligarch. This establishes a situation where said oligarch can now benefit from the government's enforcement powers, while the government comes to assume the financial motivations of the oligarch, instead of its intended function—namely, to regulate those motivations. If that sounds confusing, consider the following examples:

1. Theory example – let's say I'm an accountant. Considering the laws of supply and demand and assuming the supply of accountants in my area is constant, in order to charge the most for my services I need to maximize demand. Therefore, what

443

is the most ideal scenario to maximize my fees? The answer is to get on the news and cheer, "Accounting services are a human right!" A government promise of accounting services for all citizens guarantees maximum demand (everyone in the economy), while the necessary investment the government will have to make into this scheme will incentivize it to pressure citizens to seek an accountant (consider Obamacare's, "individual mandate," and how healthcare costs were predictably *not* reduced, for a real-world example).[31] But what if some or many people don't need or desire an accountant? Such a system is *not* a free market, but we can see that *is* both desirable and actively sought out by the oligarchs of industry. We are told today because of media influence it is not based on greed, but my accounting income is now through the roof and I'm going to go buy a boat!

2. Covid era – consider the government promise of "free," inoculations during the Covid era and the aggressive interest of oligarchs like Bill Gates to get everyone *in the entire world* inoculated. We've seen the tremendous tens-of-billions financial windfall pharma oligarchs received due to this synthetic, "universal," demand the government created on their behalf—in fact, we heard Gates brag about his 20X returns and saw an example of those returns via his August 2019 BioNTech investment. We've also seen the absurd pressure campaign the government and seemingly all its bureaucracies engaged in to get people to take the shots, in order to justify what amounts to an inoculation tax. It is clear tens to hundreds of millions of Americans don't desire what was purchased with their own money on their behalf, while the extent of oligarch corruption in providing a dangerous, failed product demands regulation/enforcement the government has failed in its responsibility to provide.

So you can see how the exploitation and wealth concentration comes directly from the coercive socialist (aka: non-free-market, ultra-exploitative-capitalist), "re-distribution," tactics. The re-distribution of material wealth is, in fact, still going in the direction of the oligarch in the case of our current *socialist* economic environment. This applied to essentially every action taken during the Covid era,

444

and is what led to the ongoing hospital genocide being directed by this government/pharma serpent in the name of providing these expensive products, "universally."

What should now be clear here is how far off the popular understanding of the economic spectrum is from reality. As covered by Dr. Judd W. Patton of Bellevue University, the popular assumption is that the, "left wing," would be communism and the opposite, "right wing," would be fascism.[32] However, one need only look at China as an example of how absurd this horizontal left/right spectrum is. China is a nationalist ethno-state (popularly assumed, "far right") with a single, "communist," party government (popularly assumed, "far left"), which exerts strict state planning and controls (could be either, "far left," or, "far right") over an extremely industrial, technology-based economy. Now let's do National Socialist Germany, which was a nationalist ethno-state with a single, "fascist," party government, which exerted strict state planning and controls over an extremely industrial, technology-based economy. The differences between these two societies are clearly not articulated by the popular economic spectrum.

Dr. Patton points out Austrian economist Mark Skousen's point-of-view that a top to bottom approach based on degree of economic freedom would be more appropriate.[33] This would definitely seem a more descriptive approach, which we can use to better assess the WEF. To do so, let's define a few metrics of economic freedom as they relate to the WEF, and assess how those metrics contribute to a fair wealth distribution:

- Regulation – the countries of the world each have a tremendous regulatory apparatus, as well as a global regulatory agency in the WHO. However, we have established it to be clear at this point that the majority, if not all, of those regulatory bodies are captured by the industries they're meant to regulate, thanks to a lack of conflict-preventing boundaries. Klaus Schwab of the WEF admits his organization facilitates this collusion via cancerous, "public-private partnerships," and is therefore partly responsible for breaking those necessary boundaries. This effectively nullifies the regulatory apparatus and makes it simply an enforcement arm of oligarchic interests. Verdict: WEF actions contribute to wealth gap expansion.

- Social Control – the WEF, its contributors, and allies have been some of the most aggressive supporters of lockdowns and strict mandates in the world during the Covid era. We've already covered how these policies have decimated local economies, and they themselves admit they've caused a wealth transfer from the poor and middle classes to themselves. Speech control, as justified by WEF-abused terms like, "misinformation," as well as liability protections for WEF member-organizations, have also stolen the ability of the disaffected poor and middle classes to have their grievances addressed. Verdict: WEF actions contribute to wealth gap expansion.

- Technocracy – if you watch five minutes of a WEF meeting, you can be sure you will hear exhaustive rambling about how technology and AI will take over the world and make humans, "irrelevant." Israeli author and WEF contributor Yuval Noah Harari even anticipated there will be an, "exploited class," and, "useless class," with the useless class being comprised of anyone who doesn't work in, or service those who work in, a tech field.[34] Even if that is just the fictional narcissism of an, "elite," technocrat who fantacizes about implanted artificial intelligence telling people, "how gay," they are (as Harari literally does), the WEF doesn't describe this alleged future as a dystopia to be avoided. Instead, it considers a, "useless class," as an inevitability, and their answer is for no one to own anything. Verdict: WEF goal is a complete and total wealth gap

So with these understandings we can make the determination based on this organization's own words and actions of what it actually is. The WEF is a union of the world's wealthiest oligarchs, organized to consolidate their power, influence, and wealth to a degree previously not fathomed in the modern world. The alleged Covid pandemic directly served this purpose in every way imaginable. The actions taken by these forces clearly attempted to push societies not just toward a state of biomedical control, but also one of reduced ownership, increased surveillance, and reduced representative governance.

In some places like Texas, Florida, and Sweden, this seems to have failed, and representative government is clearly rising. As a matter of fact, tremendous rallies in Germany, Australia, Austria, and many other medical dictatorships seem to indicate a rising consciousness which is causing the Great Reset plan to backfire into a Great Awakening.[35,36,37,38] In late January 2022 a massive trucker protest had been ongoing in Canada, where millions of Canadians joined to march on Ottawa seeking the resignation of corrupt Canadian dictator, Justin Trudeau.[39] And it would seem to be in the best interest of Fidel Castro look-alike and extreme Aladdin-enthusiast Trudeau to step down.[40,41] I say this because even people who *are* injected—like self-described progressive liberal and former fearful, "Pringle-can-sprayer," Bari Weiss for example—are recognizing that the house of cards which has been stacked one lie at a time over the years is falling.[42] So even if people like Weiss still pretend we didn't have the data to recognize it two years ago, she represented the only support system globalist tyrants like Trudeau had left to lie to.

Gone are the days when promises of, "equality," were actually believable. The condescending politicians who said blacks couldn't be expected to get an ID to vote and that discrimination is the greatest of all evils, are the same who are now banning them and others from restaurants in places like New York City for the crime of not engaging in a dangerous medical experiment.[43] Whether it's Dr. Christina Parks at Senator Johnson's hearing calling out the damage done to black people by the inoculations, frontline nurse Nicole Sirotek testifying at the same hearing about minorities and the disadvantaged being experimented on by pharmaceutical companies at the hospital she worked at, or an increased awareness of the history surrounding the Tuskegee Experiment, the credibility of elites who spout on about, "tolerance," is waning to a point of non-existence.[44,45] While it was never really believable to begin with, the global consolidation of power in the Covid era has left no one else to blame but the collaborators.

Unfortunately for Anthony Fauci, he's too wrapped up in his own self-interest and preservation to recognize this. Why a national public health figure is even permitted to speak on issues of economics and race—issues he is in a large way responsible for worsening as we've covered—at *global* governance events, is only explainable by his wife holding the position meant to prevent such conflicts.[46] This unelected bureaucrat clearly does not represent the interests of the American people at all. And why would he? What is his incentive to when he will continue to hold his position no matter who is in office and will never experience an adequate, honest scientific audit of any kind? He doesn't have one—and so, Fauci instead demonstrates his servitude of the oligarchs he *does* represent in stunts like the following WEF propaganda piece describing a, "new social contract," no one asked for or consented to, yet the Forum actually theorized to impose on people at least as early as 2018[47]:

> *"COVID-19 has laid bare the systemic social inequities. Addressing these larger problems must be our priority."*

This unsigned, unwritten, "social contract," represents the WEF's attempt to retain power in advance of an economic crisis which first showed serious signs of materializing in 2008 and which has remained a looming threat ever since. The alleged pandemic, "climate change," and inequality have served as cover stories to provide a false explanation for this breakdown. Those cover stories are then used in the typical, "problem, reaction," revolutionary format, to justify their position in providing their pre-determined, "solution." We will cover the true causes of this economic crisis next.

A Series of Macroeconomic Crises

What is capitalism? The American public education system taught me that capitalism was essentially the equivalent of a free-market economy. According to this understanding, capitalism is guided by an, "invisible hand," of competition, as posited by Adam Smith in *The Theory of Moral Sentiments*.[48] Thanks largely to the public education system, I think it is fair to say the average American subscribes to this definition of capitalism and falls into one of three categories:

1. Libertarian – believes competing self-interest (invisible hand) naturally leads to the fairest outcomes and does not want the government to tell them what to do or who they can/can't economically engage with

2. Pro-regulation free-market supporter – believes in a free market within the bounds of a moral system. Does *not* believe the unbounded invisible hand on its own leads to moral outcomes. Opinions on the desirable morals to regulate the market vary by religion (in the US this is predominantly in the form of either Christianity, Judaism, or atheism).
3. Anti-free-market (technocrat) – supporter of top-down control. Rather than just regulating the corporation or business, people in this category believe it is justified to regulate individuals, even if it comes at the expense of human rights. This includes excluding individuals from the economy entirely in order to change their behavior.

The truth is, in category 2 we introduced an important second dimension—namely, regulation. While I admittedly did not always think this way, I believe the libertarian worldview has proven as absurd in the Covid era as the idea firearms aren't a deterrent of government overreach (for example, concentration-camp-erecting Australia, which has strict firearms laws). As I mentioned previously, the problem has not been one of government regulation, it has been a *lack* of it by the very bodies (i.e. the FDA) tasked with protecting consumers from schemes like this. Checks and balances are certainly a good, but corrupt incentive structures (i.e. FDA pharma-paid user fees) have led to a nullification of those checks.

At the same time, I'm not arguing for, "bigger," government—the US federal government is way too big and is also clearly guilty of significant overreach and human rights violations. This book is filled to the brim with examples of many of those violations committed by several oversized government bureaucracies (i.e. the CDC, NIH, FDA, CIA, DOD, and FBI). But lockdowns and mandates, for example, are violations of free expression, bodily autonomy, and peaceable assembly protected by the Constitution, common law, and international law, like the Nuremberg Code. These violations have only been misrepresented as regulation of the corporation, like in the case of mask mandates for businesses to enforce on patrons and the Biden Regime's attempted OSHA inoculation mandates for corporations. The corporation has largely come to be used as the mechanism to violate every human right the government is legally not permitted to violate itself, and this great issue of our time brings us to the anti-free-market technocrats (as I'll call them) in category 3.

Many who are referred to as, "liberals," today have, via propaganda tactics we will yet cover, become technocrats. One of the great ironies of the past decade has been to watch this group cry, "fascist," every chance they get as they religiously regurgitate every talking point of a media/corporate structure they used to be known for opposing. And don't get me wrong—many (perhaps-fewer-but-still-many) of those referred to as, "conservatives," have also gotten there with the right messaging. You can see signs of that in, "conservative," people not just inoculating themselves, but also justifying it with nothing other than they're just doing so in order to travel—and travel to places where they need to identify themselves with proof they aren't lepers in order to engage in society. What modicum of freedom, logic, or morality is being, "conserved," in such cases? Not even free speech has proven sacred either, as alternative, "conservative," social media platforms like GETTR have adopted the same anti-western, technocrat tactic of algorithmic, "hate speech," suppression.[49]

One great example of the technocrat shift is in the music industry. Take former-liberal, "rebel," rock-stars like the Foo Fighters for example, who have required fans to be inoculated to attend their shows, only to have to cancel at least one due to band members testing positive.[50] Outspoken, "anti-capitalist revolutionaries," Rage Against the Machine, have seemingly had an unannounced merger with the machine they claimed to rage against and taken the same tact.[51] Another particularly perplexing case is, "Rockin' in the Free World," singer Neil Young. Despite a history of opposing biotech corporations like Monsanto and being slandered by propagandist media as spreading, "misinformation," for it, Young ironically attempted and failed to cancel podcaster Joe Rogan, also for, "spreading misinformation."[52]

Another example has presented itself in the reaction to the war between Ukraine and Russia. The conflict began over an early 2022 push for Ukraine to join NATO, including suggestions to this effect by US Secretary of State Anthony Blinken.[53] Even a younger, less senile Joe Biden admitted in 1997 that such NATO advances would cause a, "vigorous and hostile reaction," from Russia, but this did not stop his regime from pushing for said advances.[54]

The point here, however, isn't the right and wrong of this war, but rather the reaction to it. A national polling firm called *EKOS* queried Canadian sentiment on the issue by, "vaccination," status and found that more than 80% of the, "vaccinated," overwhelmingly supported measures like sanctions, asset seizures, and cutting off Russian oil supply, compared to less than 20% of the, "unvaccinated."[55] This seems to be directly in line with the same, "vaccinated," group's willingness to support economic warfare measures against its own fellow citizenry, as seen in the Covid era and social media era in general. Perhaps the most telling responses to this poll however, were the percentages who simply answered, "None of the above." While 52% of the, "unvaccinated," group said, "None of the above," in response to taking wartime measures on the other side of the world against a superpower, only 2% of the, "vaccinated," chose that response. One significant explanation for this is the propaganda which followed Russia's attack, and which included absurd, now-familiar tactics, like painting the desired icon—in this case Vladimir Zelensky, and in the case of the Covid era Fauci, Cuomo, etc.—as, "sexy."[56] More on propaganda's hypnosis of technocrats later though.

Besides propaganda, the above irrational behavior is, in my experience, best explained by Catholic historian and author, Dr. E. Michael Jones. In his economics history book *Barren Metal*, Jones specifically mentions the importance in this regard of Occupy Wall Street, a protest movement surrounding mounting student loan debts in the early 2000's.[57] Occupy was comprised of people who would have fallen into category 2 mentioned above, including Jones himself. However, as he points out, the movement was derailed by a subversive corporate and governmental pivot in their messaging to this younger, disaffected generation.[58] In particular, this messaging included a distracting amount of focus on sexual liberation (increased access to pornography via cell phones, as well as incessant focus on, "LGBT issues") and aggressive, faux-egalitarian social causes in the decade which followed.

And so, despite then-President Barack Obama's election promises of, "change," on topics like student loans, the loans actually increased in size and scope—a record even left-wing rag *The Hill* referred to as, "horrible, terrible."[59] This was because instead of focusing on solving the loan issues in question at the time or focusing on cost going forward, the narrative was shifted via promises of egalitarian, "universal," access to loans—promises we've mentioned would *raise* costs, due to the unnaturally increased demand. I would argue this substitution of labor-driven economic concerns with blinding sexual vices and social distractions like race is largely what has led the shift from category 2 into category 3. This generation is being steadily programmed to accept the idea of owning nothing, as Klaus Schwab envisioned for them, thanks to the ever-inescapable bondage of compound interest.

And this brings us to the reason I've found it necessary to provide the above background. As a substitute for debt bondage, those who provided the loans are now offering a, "way out," called the, "Great Reset." Instead of paying the rightful consequences of their bad loans by providing people the ethical-out of bankruptcy, the Reset seeks to retain/consolidate power by transitioning their dependent debtors to a new type of bondage—namely, a centralized-cryptocurrency-enabled technocracy where everything is either rented or, "free," but one's ability to engage with this, "free," economy is dependent on their compliance with the medical, social, and environmental terms and conditions designed for the, "smart cities," the WEF has theorized.

By this point this should sound dystopian but not new. These things are openly documented in WEF presentations and observable by real-world experience in various ways—for example, the Covid era medical dependence state and the ever-expanding relevance of these very terms and conditions associated with everything from social media to payment processors like PayPal. Still, though it is eerie, I'm not saying to be afraid of it at all. What should be clear thanks to the experience of the inoculation passports is that this is an offer which must be accepted. The WEF understands this and acknowledges it in the propaganda we previously referenced.

Unlike the false claims of the book *1984*, "they," do not put a boot to your head. The main character Winston was simply a category 3 person who was hypnotized, dependent, and weak. The primary control mechanism in the real world is economic. It's an offer which for the Winstons of the world will prove too good to refuse, but which you will have the ability to do so if only you say, "no." If I was a gambling man I'd guess these totalitarian smart cities *will* pop up in places, especially places like China and their vassal state Australia.

They will however, present as a stark contrast to the strengthened communities which I believe will stand and be slandered relentlessly by an ever more absurd propaganda machine.

But let's get back to the cause of this crisis: debt and unsustainable social programs. In *Barren Metal* Dr. E. Michael Jones makes a convincing case about what he views to be the true nature of capitalism, distinguishing it from a morally-regulated, free-market economy (as I define in category 2). Jones specifically defines capitalism as, "state-sponsored usury," providing examples throughout history of this system's origins and pushback movements.[60] Such examples demonstrate the pattern of bankers loaning at lucrative interest rates to lavish princes, who inevitably can't conquer at a fast enough rate to keep up with the ever-accruing compound interest. Since the wages of labor also never adequately keep up with interest rates, a conflict is created by the ever-expanding wealth gap this causes. This is the true source of the labor exploitation Marx decried, but did not seem to adequately identify or address in his revolutionary non-solutions. The cycle of debt expansion at usurious rates inevitably leads to periodic economic crashes, which is what leads to Marx-like (Schwab-like) figures calling for economic, societal, and/or governmental, "resets." The problem never ends however, because as long as the bankers are in control, the usury doesn't end.

But even at moderate interest rates, the compound nature of the interest almost always outpaces the growth rates necessary to account for it. The US government, for example, at least greatly expanded its state-sponsorship of usury when President Woodrow Wilson signed over its economic power to the Federal Reserve (Fed) banking cartel in 1913.[61] This has observably led to it being controlled by the usurers. This is why Obama didn't and never would end student loan debt, an action which would harm the banks he is beholden to. Such governmental capture was accidentally admitted to in the Covid era as well, when demented presidential candidate Joe Biden slipped up during a debate, saying of rival Donald Trump, "his position has been totally discredited by the media, by our allies, by the World Bank, by every—."[62] Both Trump and Biden shut their mouths awfully quick after this comical slip.

To me, the influence/power of bankers whose debt levels have reached catastrophic proportions is the best possible explanation for

Trump's heel turn on the inoculations. For example, if Trump really is beholden to the World Bank in some way as Biden suggests, the intense focus its head David Malpass demonstrated in a *Bloomberg* interview on global, "vaccine," distribution points to how important the inoculations are viewed to be to these bankers from an economic perspective.[63] One would think distribution would be a pharmaceutical company problem, yet the World Bank is for some reason determined to get inoculations to every country on earth. Malpass made it clear in a March 2020 speech on a G20 finance ministers conference that the reasons why were the further reduction of representative government and the increased concentration of wealth to the oligarch money class.[64] There he echoed the WEF's agenda to turn the failure of debt-based economies into increasingly globalist-controlled, slave-based economies:

> *"Beyond the severe health impact from the pandemic, we should expect a major recession of the global economy.*
> *We are working to provide a fast response, utilizing all our available instruments. Countries need to move fast to boost health spending, strengthen social safety nets, support the private sector and counter financial-market disruption.*
> ***Countries will need to implement structural reforms to help shorten the time to recovery and create confidence that the recovery can be strong. For those countries that have excessive regulations, subsidies, licensing regimes, trade protection, or litigious obstacles, we will work with them to foster markets, choice, and faster growth prospects during the recovery*** (my emphasis)."

So usury has clearly become a catastrophic problem. In fact, it is *the* problem which has lead the WEF to declare, "Capitalism," to be in crisis, even though they do not diagnose or address the cause of the issue at all, since their collaborators are among those responsible for the situation.

Another thing which makes the problem of usury worse and further expands the wealth gap is the historical tactic of princes/governments to debase the currency in an attempt to more rapidly pay down the debt, as E. Michael Jones also covers.[65] Per Ron Surz of Nasdaq, this presented in the Covid era as the printing of $13 trillion via Covid spending, quantitative easing, and infrastructure.[66] Founder of the world's largest hedge fund, Ray Dalio, refers to this high debt, low-interest rate, and currency-debasing money printing environment as the tail end of a, "long-term debt cycle."[67] According to Dalio, these cycles last approximately 50-100 years, with the current cycle beginning in 1944 when the world entered the US dollar-denominated Bretton Woods financial system. Within such cycles also occur shorter term, "boom and bust cycles," or, "business cycles," which lead to deleveraging periods of recession. But the short term corrections tend to lead to reduced interest rates and an ultimately increased debt burden—that is, until interest rates hit 0%. Interest rates hitting zero signals the beginning of the end of the long-term cycle, according to Dalio. This is when currency debasement and financial asset purchases begin, as they did in the case of the Fed in 2008-2009, for the first time since 1929-1933.

Colin Todhunter of *OffGuardian* also points to a September 16, 2019 spike in repurchase agreement (repo) market interest rates from around 2.5% to an intraday high of 10%.[68] Todhunter cited coverage of this matter by the Brookings Institute, which explained in a January 2020 piece the importance of the repo market in that this spike led to a refusal by banks—who regularly engage in the repo market for its cheap borrowing benefit—to lend.[69] Since the economy is based on debt, the Fed stepped in at this time to prevent short-term economic disaster. For the first time since 2008, their response was to inject $75 billion per day over four days. And according to Cardiff University professor Fabio Vighi, it didn't end there. Vighi actually believes the lockdowns and restrictions are an entirely financial response, rather than one related to public health at all[70]:

> *"... the stock market did not collapse* [in March 2020] *because lockdowns had to be imposed; rather, lockdowns had to be imposed because financial markets were collapsing. With lockdowns came the suspension of business transactions, which drained the demand for credit and stopped the contagion. In other words, restructuring the financial architecture through extraordinary monetary policy was contingent on the economy's engine being turned off."*

455

This would make sense, seeing as not one part of the response to the alleged pandemic made any sense from a public health perspective. From this point of view, it is clear the government's Covid response was just another bailout of big business. Rather than suffering the consequences of unsustainable practices, the largest corporations were injected with government welfare. This spanned all industries too, from Wall Street, to the tech giants, and most evidently, big pharma. Meanwhile, the average debt-dependent citizen and small business owner saw their livelihood destroyed as they were poisoned for profit.

To really hammer home just who the government was bailing out, let's review the *Corporate Research Project*'s history of Pfizer, which propagandists like *Fierce Pharma* today claim, "reigns supreme reputation-wise," despite some of the largest demonstrations in history being carried out on a now-regular basis in opposition to this company's agenda[71,72]:

- In 2009 Pfizer agreed to pay $2.3 billion relating to improper marketing of Bextra and three other medications.[73] This amounted to the largest healthcare fraud settlement ever at the time and the $1.2 billion criminal portion remains the largest criminal fine ever imposed in the US for any matter.[74] The Pfizer whistleblower who helped bring about the investigation told the *New York Times*, "The whole culture of Pfizer is driven by sales, and if you didn't sell drugs illegally, you were not seen as a team player."[75]

- In 2010 Pfizer for the first time disclosed that during a six month period the previous year it paid $20 million to 4,500 doctors and other medical professionals for consulting and speaking on the company's behalf[76]

- In 2000 the *Washington Post* published an exposé accusing Pfizer of experimenting on Nigerian children with a dangerous new antibiotic called Trovan.[77] In 2001 Pfizer was sued by thirty Nigerian families and in 2006 a panel of Nigerian medical experts concluded that Pfizer violated international law.[78,79] By 2009 the company agreed to pay $75 million to settle in Nigerian courts, and an undisclosed amount to settle in American courts.[80,81] Classified US State Department cables made public by *Wikileaks* in 2010 also revealed Pfizer sought dirt on Nigeria's former attorney general in order to gain leverage in a case, as well as making false claims related to the various cases.[82]

- Reports of fatalities in 1986 linked to heart valves produced by Pfizer's Shiley-division led to the ending of their production, which by that time were already implanted in tens of thousands of people.[83,84] In 1991 the FDA charged that Shiley withheld information about safety issues in order to get approval, and a *Wall Street Journal* investigation found them to have deliberately falsified manufacturing records related to valve fractures. Pfizer resisted efforts to address concerns, but ultimately announced $205 million to settle tens of thousands of lawsuits related to the valves, $10.75 million to settle on Justice Department charges of lying to regulators, and $9 million to monitor valve patients and to fund valve removals.[85,86,87]

- In 2004, Merck's painkiller Vioxx demonstrated dangerous side effects. Only in the wake of this scandal did Pfizer pull television advertising for its related medication called Celebrex.[88] It then took until the following year for Pfizer to admit that a 1999 clinical trial of Celebrex found that elderly patients taking it had a significantly elevated risk of heart problems.[89]

- In 2005 Pfizer withdrew Bextra, another painkiller, after the FDA required providing warnings about cardiovascular and gastrointestinal risks.[90] In 2008 Pfizer announced it was setting aside $894 million to settle lawsuits connected to Bextra and Celebrex.[91]

- Pfizer has become the largest pharmaceutical company primarily by buying its competitors, including Warner-Lambert in 2000 and Wyeth in 2009. However, the Warner-Lambert acquisition resulted in a $60 million Pfizer settlement by users of Rezulin for deaths from acute liver failure, and at the time of the Wyeth acquisition the company's most recent financial report included 14 pages of legal proceedings.[92,93] The tens-of-thousands of lawsuits included product liability cases for hormone therapy, childhood vaccines, anti-depressants, contraceptives, and diet drugs.

- In 1958 Pfizer was one of six drug companies accused of price fixing on antibiotics and it was charged with making false statements to the US Patent Office to obtain a patent for tetracycline.[94] The FTC ultimately ruled the six companies, including Pfizer, indeed conspired to fix prices, and found that, "unclean hands and bad faith played a major role," in the issuance of the tetracycline patent to Pfizer.[95]
- In 1961 the Justice Department filed criminal antitrust charges against Pfizer and others, and in 1967 a federal jury found them guilty of conspiring to control the production and distribution of restraint of trade, conspiracy to monopolize, and actual monopoly.[96,97] They were fined the maximum at the time of $150,000.[98]
- In 1996 Pfizer was one of 15 large drug companies which agreed to pay more than $408 million to settle on a price-fixing conspiracy[99]
- In 1999 Pfizer plead guilty to criminal antitrust charges for its Food Science Group engaging in two international price-fixing conspiracies, with fines totaling $20 million[100]
- In 2002 Pfizer resisted cooperating with a General Accounting Office investigation of pricing practices, but relented after its then-chairman and CEO Henry McKinnell was served with a subpoena.[101] Later that year, Pfizer paid $49 million to settle charges for one of its subsidiaries defrauding the federal Medicaid program by overcharging.[102]
- In 2016 the Justice Department announced that Pfizer would pay $784 million that resulted from subsidiary Wyeth underpaying rebates to Medicaid[103]
- Also in 2016, the UK's Competition and Markets Authority fined Pfizer the equivalent of $107 million for charging excessive and unfair prices for an epilepsy drug[104]
- A 1957 advertising scandal saw Pfizer run ads in *JAMA* including shady tactics such as citing endorsements by doctors who turned out to be fictitious[105]
- In 1991 Pfizer paid $70,000 to 10 states for misleading advertising of mouth rinse, before settling for another $6 million with 19 states in 2003 for misleading ads of children's ear infection medication, and then paying $34.7 million in

2007 to settle federal charges related to illegal marketing of a human growth hormone product, before agreeing to pay $14.5 million to resolve federal charges for illegally marketing a bladder drug[106,107]

- In 2004 Pfizer's Warner-Lambert subsidiary agreed to pay $430 million to resolve criminal and civil charges that it paid physicians to prescribe an epilepsy drug to patients with ailments for which the drug was not approved.[108] Documents later came to light which suggested Pfizer arranged for delays of scientific studies undermining the use of this drug for these other ailments.[109] In 2010 a federal jury found Pfizer guilty of committing racketeering fraud related to the drug, resulting in $142 million in ordered damages.[110]

- A 2012 disclosure by Pfizer revealed a $491 million charge against earnings related to an, "agreement in principle," with the Justice Department to settle charges related improper marketing of a kidney transplant drug.[111] The agreement was finalized in 2013 before Pfizer later also reached a $35 million settlement with more than 40 states for the drug.[112,113]

- In 2012 the US Securities and Exchange Commission announced it had reached a $45 million settlement with Pfizer for charges its subsidiaries bribed overseas doctors and other healthcare professionals.[114] Similarly, Dr. Paul Alexander alleged in March 2022 that Pfizer offered him $1 million and a $50,000 per month wage to stop writing negatively about Pfizer, the Covid inoculations, and CEO Albert Bourla—an offer he said he refused.[115]

- In 1971 the EPA asked Pfizer to end its long-time practice of dumping a reported 1 million gallons per year of industrial wastes from its Groton, Connecticut plant into the Long Island Sound[116]

- Additional environmental settlements include $3.1 million in 1991 for damaging the Delaware River, $1.5 million in 1994 for dumping at a toxic waste site in Rhode Island, and $700 million in 2003 for dumping PCBs in Alabama[117,118,119]

- In 2021 the Gravitas news network alleged Pfizer was bullying governments via its Covid inoculations to be compensated for any future lawsuits, among other things.[120] Argentina, as one example, was allegedly pressured by the company to put its bank reserves, its military bases, and its embassy buildings at stake as collateral for potential inoculation liabilities. Demands made to Brazil included waiving sovereignty of its assets abroad, not applying its laws to Pfizer, delaying the delivery of the inoculations without penalty to Pfizer, and exemption from all civil liability. At least nine countries were allegedly subject to similarly humiliating demands, including allowing Pfizer to go after state assets to ensure compensation and muting the government's ability to speak publicly on contracts/issues.

- In December 2021 *Reuters* admitted via Gavi documents that Covid inoculation companies like Pfizer refused to allow refugees to receive the, "safe and effective," inoculations, due to fear of lawsuits from the potential damages[121]

Upon initially typing these out I surpassed 6 pages (in Microsoft Word), so I decided to cut the list down to what seemed like the most telling examples. In reality there is *way* more illicit activity, as summarized by the *Corporate Research Project*. Still, I did the math so you don't have to—the above examples alone account for an astonishing $6.8 billion in settlements and charges, at least. The behavior of the other Covid inoculation companies isn't much better either, as we've covered with Moderna and as we can see with Johnson & Johnson's recently documented attempts to, "worm its way out of paying $3.5 billion to victims of cancer-causing baby talc by forming a new company and declaring bankruptcy," as they, "tried to gag journalists from reporting it."[122]

As a side note, one positive which can be taken from the above is in the timelines of when the crimes occur, versus when they are charged for those crimes. While in the Covid era it may seem hard to keep spirits high in the face of this outrageous corruption we are experiencing, many of the aforementioned examples took a minimum of 2-5 years for the truth to be acknowledged at all. And even though much of the truth of our time has been available since very early on in the alleged pandemic, I can certainly attest having written this book that building the case takes time—a *lot* of time. So to those out there struggling with this I would encourage you to maintain your faith and patience, because the truth winning out is inevitable.

At the same time, why a criminal enterprise of this magnitude has even been allowed to continue operating is beyond me. For the US government and others to have taken it upon themselves to actually *elevate* Pfizer to a position of untouchability is even more impossible to understand or forgive. To put the resulting narcissism into context though, you will recall Pfizer's CEO Albert Bourla projecting, as he described those who suspect his historically-criminal enterprise of further wrong-doing in the Covid era as, "criminals." One has to wonder what would give them such an outlandish idea! You will also recall that this is the company which the federal government has granted immunity from liability related to the novel, experimental Covid inoculations. It is, "misinformation," to discuss any concerns about this though, so let's continue.

A key thing I want to point out here is my opinion that one great solution to this kind of thing actually has nothing to do with economics. The solution I am referring to is to simply re-establish a justice system. Whether it's health-related or economics-related, many of these actions are direct attacks on the well-being of the citizenry and are illegal by the letter of the law. The biggest roadblock is simply a disturbing lack of enforcement as it relates to oligarchs. We've seen from Pfizer's example that the FDA *has* historically been effective in this regard, at least to some extent. It is clear now however, that this organization is currently captured and desperately needs repair. And while this might be an obvious observation about a problem which has spanned the entirety of history—namely, corruption—what's the point of society if we don't identify the problems and seek solutions?

But I digress. Combining this background on the crisis state of the dollar-economy with the rhetoric of Klaus Schwab and the WEF, all signs point to their attempting to become the next Bretton Woods by ushering in and dictating the terms of a new cycle. Their support of cryptocurrencies, as well as the Microsoft-patented ability to integrate those cryptocurrencies with implanted biometrics systems, seems to suggest they might be aiming to do so in the form a digital world reserve currency.[123,124] Doctors and microscopy experts have even speculated the Covid inoculations might constitute said biometrics systems, due to the alleged presence of nanotech under the microscope.[125] Given their desire for the 99% to own nothing, perhaps

461

this new biotech-enabled cycle will even substitute the bondage of debt entirely for a more direct form of slavery.

This is speculation obviously, but it seems it could make sense based on their stated aims and the observable pattern of oligarchs and their institutions buying up more and more of the world. For example, consider how Bill Gates has become the largest owner of US farm land with 269K acres as of January 2021;[126] or how large investment firms like BlackRock are receiving preferred-debtor status via low interest rates and outbidding Americans on real estate by paying 20 to 50% over asking price.[127] The latter has resulted in millennial home ownership dropping by a whopping 8% relative to generation X and baby boomers, a trend which can hardly be considered a coincidence as the US puppet government happily profits off the destruction of the American dream in favor of the WEF/Davos agenda. Besides the example of BlackRock, the proof of this can be seen in a 60 Minutes interview with Gary Berman, the CEO of Toronto-based Tricon Residential, whose company has, "quietly become one of the largest owners of single-family homes in the United States."[128] Instead of acknowledging this as the national security threat it is however, shameless interviewer Lesley Stahl allows Berman to get away with the lie that millennials, "don't necessarily desire to own a home or a car," because, "they've grown up in the sharing economy and what's important to them is lifestyle."

So, when the WEF says, "cryptocurrencies are democratizing the financial world," we can recognize their typical subversion tactics easily enough. The WEF *does not* support democracy and representative government. That isn't a speculative claim, either— they are literally a global, agenda-setting organization and are therefore the antithesis of democratic/representative. This is on top of the obviously totalitarian responses to the alleged pandemic they and their proxies encouraged/performed. So we can safely assume they are not going to ultimately support a decentralized cryptocurrency like Bitcoin—assuming Bitcoin is as decentralized and uncontrollable as it is claimed to be (not that I am claiming it isn't or see overwhelming evidence it isn't). What can be expected is a continued emphasis on central bank digital currencies, which in the absence of alternatives could provide unprecedented financial and social controls.

Medicare and Other Social Programs Contribute to the Crisis

As John Adams prophetically said, "We have no Constitution that functions in the absence of a moral people."[129] The US today suffers greatly from a lack of moral identity which, along with the debt problems, has led to the destruction of its institutions and therefore the viability of potentially effective social programs. One symptom of this is shown in a report by the Center for Immigration Studies, which found that in 2014, 63 percent of households headed by non-citizens used one or more welfare programs, compared to 35 percent of households headed by citizens.[130] For one thing, this uneven distribution puts the financial viability of such programs at risk, due to what is referred to in the related insurance world as, "adverse selection." But it is also an immorality for the government to be redistributing the wealth of those it represents to those it doesn't, especially during difficult financial times. This is just one issue with the current US welfare system.

The collection of additional issues has led the financial situation facing Medicare and social security in particular to become so bad that projections have for some time pointed to their collapsing before or around 2030.[131,132] Despite these dire projections, the general degeneration of the Washington political class has led to the place being filled with insane, endlessly re-elected babblers like Bernie Sanders, who un-ironically suggested in 2021 that Medicare's eligibility age be lowered from 65 to 55.[133] While this might seem like a compassionate plea to get more people healthcare, it would only serve to speed up the collapse so that no one, of any age, gets Medicare in the future. The Hoover Institution and American Action Forum have both acknowledged that such a collapse would also have ripple effects which would further destabilize world economies.[134,135] I'm not going to speculate as to whether this sped-up sabotage of an unsustainable system is intentional or not, but either way, the American welfare doomsday clock seems to be ticking.

The reason these healthcare-related safety nets have become such a disaster is largely thanks to healthcare costs becoming so high in the US. But the reason for the latter is *not* because the US is more free-market-based, as most assume to be the case. It is beyond a shadow of a doubt that during the Covid era, for example, the opposite was true. To demonstrate this we can point to the federal FDA, CDC, and NIH ensuring extremely high-cost, experimental, dangerous remdesivir was the sole treatment option at US hospitals, while cheap, effective ivermectin and hydroxychloroquine were both suppressed here and made directly available to people in Mexican cities south of the border.[136] As we've covered, the subsequent health outcomes for the US were worse than anywhere else in the world as a percent of population, while there was clearly a freer, cheaper, more effective market in Mexico, as demonstrated by ivermectin studies conducted there. The US federal government was therefore more reflective at this time of a socialist/communist (whatever you want to call it) government-monopoly economy.

But this Covid-related observation reveals the deeper underlying issue with the healthcare system itself: Americans are *not* privileged with better healthcare outcomes, despite being privileged with the ability to pay more for healthcare. The truth is that the US subsidizes a medical apparatus which has largely sold out to pharmaceutical companies, at the expense of curing patients. Perhaps nothing makes the genesis of this problem clearer than CNBC quoting Goldman Sachs in April 2018, which asked in a biotech research report, "Is curing patients a sustainable business model?"[137] The answer is it isn't, if your goal is to grow at the speed of debt. If it was, people like Bill Gates who claim to want to improve human health would be focused on much cheaper solutions like clean water, clean food, hygiene, detox, and exercise programs, instead of extraordinarily profitable vaccines and/or drugs. The former collection of good health practices is very much affordable for the majority of Americans, but is not considered to be, "healthcare," as it very much should be. Also, the fact that the Goldman question is being asked at all should make one wary of the products that *are* being offered in this industry.

To make matters worse, as of 2016 the US consumed about 80 percent of the global opioid supply, per CNBC.[138] Bringing us back to the importance of a moral society, for US doctors to be prescribing so abusively instead of focusing on the importance of diet, sleep, and exercise, is indicative of the decay we mentioned previously. But even beyond mental health, to think this type of state-sanctioned drug abuse wouldn't also negatively impact physical health outcomes is both insane and the official stance of the captured public health bureaucracies.

Again, the problem is as simple as supply and demand. Because the US has a tremendous, disproportionate demand for drugs, the US has the highest drug costs. And since the focus remains on a pharmaceutical-centric approach to medicine, rather than natural, lifestyle-based healthcare, the actual causes of the underlying health problems are typically not addressed. Instead those problems are *suppressed* with drugs, which creates the vicious cycle the US finds itself in. Instead of cures and lifestyle changes, demand feeds demand because the medicine either isn't a true cure or, even worse, worsens the disease itself.

So a change of mindset would be the best possible solution to US healthcare costs. The reason my annual medical costs are zero, for example, isn't because I am healthy and therefore almost never need medication. The reason I am healthy is because I understand I almost never need medication, despite a doctor's willingness to prescribe me three different drugs every time I have a runny nose (real, personal example). Throwing the prescriptions I don't need in the trash is what keeps my costs low, while lifestyle is what keeps me away from the doctor and serious illness in general. At the same time, I *do* spend thousands of dollars a month on actual healthcare—namely, clean/organic foods, a gym membership, stress reduction, chiropractic care, and moderate vitamin supplementation.

That's also not to say at times you don't need or can't benefit from the intervention of medicine. There are many things as far as physical care the US healthcare system does extremely well. However, it's clear our public health agencies are steering us in the entirely wrong direction as far as infectious disease goes and have been for some time. We will cover the extent of the history behind this in detail in a future chapter. For now, the unmitigated disaster of centralized medicine, as amplified in the Covid era by public health bureaucracies, will continue to worsen outcomes and costs for those who continue to depend on it, for as long as they continue to depend on it.

Endnotes

1   Vedmore, Johnny. 2021. "Schwab Family Values". *Unlimited Hangout.* https://unlimitedhangout.com/2021/02/investigative-reports/schwab-family-values/.

2   "The WEF And The Pandemic". 2021. *Swiss Policy Research.* https://swprs.org/the-wef-and-the-pandemic/.

3   "Our Mission". 2022. *World Economic Forum.* Accessed March 29. https://www.weforum.org/about/world-economic-forum/.

4   J, Jacob. 2020. "US Military 'Brought' Coronavirus To China? Top Official Refers To Military Games In Wuhan In 2019". *International Business Times, Singapore Edition*. https://www.ibtimes.sg/us-military-brought-coronavirus-china-top-official-refers-military-games-wuhan-2019-40911.

5   "Davos Club: Klaus Schwab Introduces Xi Jinping At 'Reset' Forum Starring Fauci". 2022. *World Tribune: U.S. Politics And Culture, Geopolitics, East Asia Intelligence, China, Geostrategy, Military, National Security, Corporate Watch, Media Watch, North Korea, Iran, Columnists: Dennis Prager, Michelle Malkin, John Metzler, Jeffrey Kuhner, John Mcnabb, Joe Schaeffer, Bill Juneau, Alexander Maistrovoy, Donald Kirk*. https://www.worldtribune.com/davos-club-klaus-schwab-introduces-xi-jinping-at-reset-forum-starring-fauci/.

6   Cacciatore, Luca. 2021. "WHO Skips Over Greek Letter 'Xi' For New Variant". *Newsmax*. https://www.newsmax.com/newsfront/who-china-xijinping-variants/2021/11/26/id/1046350/.

7   Schwab, Klaus. 2020. "Now Is The Time For A 'Great Reset'". *World Economic Forum*. https://www.weforum.org/agenda/2020/06/now-is-the-time-for-a-great-reset/.

8   "On The Agenda / Digital Identity". 2022. *World Economic Forum*. Accessed March 29. https://www.weforum.org/agenda/archive/digital-identity.

9   "Klaus Schwab 2016 Implant Microchip, French With Engl. Translation". 2021. *Youtube*. https://youtu.be/GmmPVipAAio.

10   Burt, Chris. 2019. "WTTC And World Economic Forum Partner To Share Information And Promote Biometric Travel | Biometric Update". *Biometric Update |*. https://www.biometricupdate.com/201907/wttc-and-world-economic-forum-partner-to-share-information-and-promote-biometric-travel.

11   The Rockefeller Foundation and Global Business Network. 2010. "Scenarios For The Future Of Technology And International Development". New York, NY. https://libertynow.com/wp-content/uploads/2021/07/Operation-Lockstep-Rockefeller-Foundation.pdf.

12   Burt, Chris. 2019. "ID2020 And Partners Launch Program To Provide Digital ID With Vaccines | Biometric Update". *Biometric Update |*. https://www.biometricupdate.com/201909/id2020-and-partners-launch-program-to-provide-digital-id-with-vaccines.

13   "ID2020 | Certification". 2022. *ID 2020*. Accessed March 29. https://id2020.org/certification.

14   Tangermann, Victor. 2019. "An Invisible Quantum Dot 'Tattoo' Could Be Used To ID Vaccinated Kids". *Sciencealert*. https://www.sciencealert.com/an-invisible-quantum-dot-tattoo-is-being-suggested-to-id-vaccinated-kids.

15   Cassata, Cathy, and Dana K. Cassell. 2021. "Doctors Debunk Popular COVID-19 Vaccine Myths And Conspiracy Theories". *Healthline*.

https://www.healthline.com/health-news/doctors-debunk-9-popular-covid-19-vaccine-myths-and-conspiracy-theories#Myth:-The-COVID-19-vaccine-makes-you-infertile.

16   Kasprak, Alex. 2020. "Are Bill Gates And The ID2020 Coalition Using COVID-19 To Build Global Surveillance State?". *Snopes.Com*. https://www.snopes.com/fact-check/bill-gates-id2020/.

17   "BIBLE VERSES ABOUT MARK OF THE BEAST". 2022. *Kingjamesbibleonline.Org*. Accessed March 29. https://www.kingjamesbibleonline.org/bible-verses-about-mark-of-the-beast/.

18   Koutsobinas, Nick. 2021. "Sweden Starts Microchipping COVID Passports In People". *Newsmax*. https://www.newsmax.com/newsfront/microchip-covid-passport-sweden/2021/12/18/id/1049202/.

19   Schuster-Bruce, Catherine. 2021. "A COVID-19 Vaccine Patch Could Produce A Better Immune Response Than An Injection, An Early Study Shows". *Business Insider*. https://www.businessinsider.com/covid-19-patch-vaccine-needle-free-strong-immune-response-study-2021-11.

20   Diego, Raul. 2020. "Africa To Become Testing Ground For "Trust Stamp" Vaccine Record And Payment System". *Mintpress News*. https://www.mintpressnews.com/africa-trust-system-covid-19-vaccine-record-payment-system/269346/.

21   Ferguson, John. 2021. "Vaccination Passport App Shares Personal Data With Amazon And Royal Mail". *Daily Record*. https://www.dailyrecord.co.uk/news/scottish-news/vaccination-passport-app-shares-personal-25285887.

22   Bingham, Jack. 2021. "Bayer Executive: Mrna Shots Are 'Gene Therapy' Marketed As 'Vaccines' To Gain Public Trust - Lifesite". *Lifesite*. https://www.lifesitenews.com/news/bayer-executive-mrna-shots-are-gene-therapy-marketed-as-vaccines-to-gain-public-trust/.

23   Chui, Michael, Matthias Evers, James Manyika, Alice Zheng, and Travers Nisbet. 2020. "The Bio Revolution: Innovations Transforming Economies, Societies, And Our Lives". McKinsey Global Institute. https://www.mckinsey.com/industries/life-sciences/our-insights/the-bio-revolution-innovations-transforming-economies-societies-and-our-lives.

24   Auken, Ida. 2016. "Welcome To 2030: I Own Nothing, Have No Privacy And Life Has Never Been Better". *Forbes*. https://www.forbes.com/sites/worldeconomicforum/2016/11/10/shopping-i-cant-really-remember-what-that-is-or-how-differently-well-live-in-2030/.

25   "What Is The Great Reset? | Davos Agenda 2021". 2021. *Youtube*. https://youtu.be/uPYx12xJFUQ.

26   Dharmaraj, Selvakumar, Veeramuthu Ashokkumar, Sneha Hariharan, Akila Manibharathi, Pau Loke Show, Cheng Tung Chong, and Chawalit Ngamcharussrivichai. 2021. "The COVID-19 Pandemic Face Mask Waste: A Blooming Threat To The Marine

Environment". *Chemosphere* 272: 129601.
doi:10.1016/j.chemosphere.2021.129601.

27   Hammerl, Michael. 2021. "Impfpflichten Sind Der Richtige Test Für Eine Klimaneutrale Zukunft". *Kurier.At*. https://kurier.at/meinung/mein-tag/impfpflichten-sind-der-richtige-test-fuer-eine-klimaneutrale-zukunft/401471353.

28   "What Is The Great Reset? | Davos Agenda 2021". 2021. *Youtube*. https://youtu.be/uPYx12xJFUQ.

29   Rankovic, Didi. 2022. "Fauci Reports Back To Davos That The US Has A Covid "Disinformation" Problem". *Reclaim The Net*. https://reclaimthenet.org/fauci-reports-back-to-davos-that-the-us-has-a-covid-disinformation-problem/.

30   "Dr. Christina Parks Full Highlights | Senator Ron Johnson COVID-19: A Second Opinion". 2022. *Rumble*. https://rumble.com/vt8o3u-dr.-christina-parks-full-highlights-senator-ron-johnson-covid-19-a-second-o.html.

31   Haislmaier, Edmund, and Abigail Slagle. 2021. "Obamacare Has Doubled The Cost Of Individual Health Insurance". *The Heritage Foundation*. https://www.heritage.org/health-care-reform/report/obamacare-has-doubled-the-cost-individual-health-insurance.

32   "Constitutional Economics 101: Left, Right Or Center?". 2009. *Web.Archive.Org*. https://web.archive.org/web/20090625205450/http://jpatton.bellevue.edu/print/direction.html.

33   Ibid.

34   Harari, Yuval Noah. 2022. "How To Survive The 21St Century | DAVOS 2020". Presentation, Davos, , 2022.

35   "German Government Concerned About Massive Anti-COVID Restriction Protests". 2022. *Europe Renaissance*. https://europerenaissance.com/2022/01/24/german-government-concerned-about-massive-anti-covid-restriction-protests/.

36   Convery, Stephanie. 2021. "Australia Covid Protests: Threats Against 'Traitorous' Politicians As Thousands Rally In Capital Cities". *The Guardian*. https://www.theguardian.com/australia-news/2021/nov/20/australia-covid-protests-threats-against-traitorous-politicians-as-thousands-rally-in-capital-cities.

37   "Mass Protests In Austria As Government Announces Forced Vaccinations: Nuremberg Code Violation?". 2021. *World Tribune*. https://www.worldtribune.com/mass-protests-in-austria-as-government-announces-forced-vaccinations-nuremberg-code-violation/.

38   "Worldwide Protests - Covid Crime". 2022. *Covid Crime*. https://covid-crime.org/worldwide-protests/.

39   Bingham, Jack. 2022. "Former NHL Star Theo Fleury Endorses Canadian Truck Drivers' 'Freedom Convoy' Protest - Lifesite". *Lifesite*. https://www.lifesitenews.com/news/former-nhl-star-endorses-canadian-truck-drivers-freedom-convoy-protest/.

40   Leibowitcz, Karen. 2020. "Of Course Fidel Castro Is Justin Trudeau's
      Dad. Nobody Has 'Debunked' Anything". *Medium*.
      https://medium.com/@leibowitt/of-course-fidel-castro-is-justin-trudeaus-
      dad-nobody-has-debunked-anything-4db6fc8a9042.

41   Fudzi, Liyana. 2019. "Trudeau's "Aladdin" Brownface Picture
      Controversy Reveals 2 More Instances Of Blackface". *Narcity*.
      https://www.narcity.com/trudeaus-aladdin-brownface-picture-
      controversy-reveals-2-more-instances-of-blackface.

42   Brody, David. 2022. "David Brody On Gab: 'This Is A MUST WATCH!
      Liberal Bari Weiss, A Self-…'". *Gab Social*.
      https://gab.com/dbrodyreports/posts/107671955514614120.

43   Tacopino, Joe. 2021. "NYC Mom And Her Child Kicked Out Restaurant
      By Cop Over COVID Vaccine Cards". *Nypost.Com*.
      https://nypost.com/2021/12/29/nyc-mom-and-her-child-kicked-out-
      restaurant-by-cop-over-covid-vaccine-cards/.

44   Borrink, Sallie. 2022. "Registered Nurse Nicole Sirotek Testimony To
      Senator Ron Johnson - The Horrors And Abuse Of Covid Patients - A
      Quiet Simple Life With Sallie Borrink". *A Quiet Simple Life With Sallie
      Borrink*. https://sallieborrink.com/registered-nurse-nicole-sirotek-
      testimony-to-senator-ron-johnson-the-horrors-and-abuse-of-covid-
      patients/.

45   Daniels, Cheyanne M. 2021. "Black Activists Split Over COVID-19
      Vaccine Due To History Of Racism In Medicine - Medill News
      Service". *Medill News Service*.
      https://dc.medill.northwestern.edu/blog/2021/01/20/black-activists-split-
      over-covid-19-vaccine-due-to-history-of-racism-in-
      medicine/#sthash.1HwR6hxf.dpbs.

46   "Advancing A New Social Contract". 2021. *World Economic Forum*.
      https://www.weforum.org/events/the-davos-agenda-
      2021/sessions/advancing-a-new-social-contract.

47   "Identity In A Digital World: A New Chapter In The Social Contract".
      2018. *World Economic Forum*.
      https://www.weforum.org/reports/identity-in-a-digital-world-a-new-
      chapter-in-the-social-contract.

48   MAJASKI, CHRISTINA, MICHAEL SONNENSHEIN, and ARIEL
      COURAGE. 2022. "What Is The Invisible Hand In
      Economics?". *Investopedia*.
      https://www.investopedia.com/terms/i/invisiblehand.asp.

49   Parker, Tom. 2022. "GETTR CEO Jason Miller Faces Questions On JFK
      Censorship, Banning Nick Fuentes, And "Hateful" Content". *Reclaim The
      Net*. https://reclaimthenet.org/gettr-ceo-jason-miller-jfk-nick-fuentes-
      hateful-content/.

50   Redshaw, Megan. 2021. "Foo Fighters 'Vaccinated Only' Concert
      Canceled After Band Member Gets COVID As Breakthrough Cases On
      The Rise". *Children's Health Defense*.

https://childrenshealthdefense.org/defender/foo-fighters-vaccinated-only-concert-canceled-covid-breakthrough-cases/.

51   Lavin, Will. 2021. "Skillet's John Cooper: "Rage Against The Machine Is Just 'Government Rock' Now"". *NME*. https://www.nme.com/news/music/skillets-john-cooper-rage-against-the-machine-is-just-government-rock-now-3110943.

52   Anslow, Louis. 2022. "Neil Young's Long Record Of Spreading Scientific Misinformation". *News.Yahoo.Com*. https://news.yahoo.com/neil-young-long-record-spreading-023237548.html.

53   Liebman, George. 2022. "The Blindness Of Blinken - The American Conservative". *The American Conservative*. https://www.theamericanconservative.com/articles/the-blindness-of-blinken/.

54   Norton, Benjamin. 2022. "Biden Admitted In 1997 NATO Expansion Would Cause Russian 'Hostile Reaction' - Multipolarista". *Multipolarista*. https://multipolarista.com/2022/03/08/biden-nato-expansion-russia-hostile-reaction/.

55   LaFleche, Grant. 2022. "How Vaccination Status Might Predict Views On The Russian Invasion Of Ukraine". *Thestar.Com*. https://www.thestar.com/news/investigations/2022/03/19/how-vaccination-status-might-predict-views-on-the-russian-invasion-of-ukraine.html.

56   "Bill Maher Says Zelensky Is Proof Some Toxic Masculinity Is Good & Sexy". 2022. *TMZ*. https://www.tmz.com/2022/03/26/bill-maher-zelensky-sexy-toxic-masculinity-real-time/.

57   Jones, E. Michael. 2014. *Barren Metal*. South Bend, Indiana: Fidelity Press. pp. 15-23.

58   Ibid.

59   COLLINGE, ALAN M. 2016. "President Obama's Horrible, Terrible Legacy On Student Loans". *Thehill.Com*. https://thehill.com/blogs/congress-blog/education/279512-president-obamas-horrible-terrible-legacy-on-student-loans.

60   Jones, E. Michael. 2014. *Barren Metal*. South Bend, Indiana: Fidelity Press. pp. 23-32.

61   "Federal Reserve Act Signed Into Law | Federal Reserve History". 2013. *Federalreservehistory.Org*. https://www.federalreservehistory.org/essays/federal-reserve-act-signed.

62   Biden, Joe. 2020. "2020 Fox News Presidential Debate". Debate, 2020.

63   Malpass, David. 2021. World Bank's Malpass on Vaccine Distribution, Debt Relief. TV. Bloomberg TV. https://www.bloomberg.com/news/videos/2021-04-07/world-bank-s-malpass-on-vaccine-distribution-debt-relief-video.

64   The World Bank. 2020. "Remarks By World Bank Group President David Malpass On G20 Finance Ministers Conference Call On COVID-19". https://www.worldbank.org/en/news/speech/2020/03/23/remarks-by-

world-bank-group-president-david-malpass-on-g20-finance-ministers-conference-call-on-covid-19?cid=ECR_TT_worldbank_EN_EXT.

65 Jones, E. Michael. 2014. *Barren Metal*. South Bend, Indiana: Fidelity Press.

66 Surz, Ron. 2021. "Money Printing And Inflation: COVID, Cryptocurrencies And More". *Nasdaq.Com*. https://www.nasdaq.com/articles/money-printing-and-inflation%3A-covid-cryptocurrencies-and-more.

67 Koa, Kane. 2021. "The Banker Super-Cycle Behind The Rise Of Bitcoin, Inflation, And The Great Reset". *Kanekoa.Substack.Com*. https://kanekoa.substack.com/p/the-banker-super-cycle-behind-the?s=r.

68 Todhunter, Colin. 2021. "The Fear Pandemic And The Crisis Of Capitalism". *Offguardian*. https://off-guardian.org/2021/10/08/the-fear-pandemic-and-the-crisis-of-capitalism/.

69 Cheng, Jeffrey, and David Wessel. 2020. "What Is The Repo Market, And Why Does It Matter?". *Brookings*. https://www.brookings.edu/blog/up-front/2020/01/28/what-is-the-repo-market-and-why-does-it-matter/.

70 Vighi, Fabio. 2021. "A Self-Fulfilling Prophecy: Systemic Collapse And Pandemic Simulation - The Philosophical Salon". *The Philosophical Salon*. https://thephilosophicalsalon.com/a-self-fulfilling-prophecy-systemic-collapse-and-pandemic-simulation/.

71 Mattera, Philip. 2017. "Pfizer: Corporate Rap Sheet | Corporate Research Project". *Corp-Research.Org*. https://www.corp-research.org/pfizer.

72 Adams, Ben. 2022. "COVID Vaccines Help Pfizer, Moderna Reign Supreme Reputation-Wise, But They're A Double-Edged Sword For J&J And AZ". *Fierce Pharma*. https://www.fiercepharma.com/marketing/vaccines-helps-pfizer-moderna-reign-supreme-reputation-score-but-it-s-a-double-edged.

73 The United States Department of Justice. 2009. "Associate Attorney General Tom Perrelli At Pfizer Settlement Press Conference". https://www.justice.gov/opa/speech/associate-attorney-general-tom-perrelli-pfizer-settlement-press-conference.

74 LETENYEI, DANIELLE. 2021. "Pfizer Paid The Largest Criminal Fine In U.S. History—Lawsuit Details". *Market Realist*. https://marketrealist.com/p/who-paid-largest-criminal-fine-in-history/.

75 Harris, Gardiner. 2009. "Pfizer Pays $2.3 Billion To Settle Marketing Case (Published 2009)". *Query.Nytimes.Com*. http://query.nytimes.com/gst/fullpage.html?res=9500E3D8143CF930A3575AC0A96F9C8B63&scp=2&sq=Pfizer+%2B+%242.3+Billion&st=nyt.

76 Wilson, Duff. 2010. "Pfizer Gives Details On Payments To Doctors (Published 2010)". *Nytimes.Com*. http://www.nytimes.com/2010/04/01/business/01payments.html.

77 Stephens, Joe. 2000. "Where Profits And Lives Hang In Balance". *The Washington Post*. http://www.washingtonpost.com/wp-dyn/content/article/2007/07/02/AR2007070201255.html.

78   Lewin, Tamar. 2001. "Families Sue Pfizer On Test Of Antibiotic (Published 2001)". *Nytimes.Com.* http://www.nytimes.com/2001/08/30/business/families-sue-pfizer-on-test-of-antibiotic.html.

79   Stephens, Joe. 2006. "Panel Faults Pfizer In '96 Clinical Trial In Nigeria". *The Washington Post.* http://www.washingtonpost.com/wp-dyn/content/article/2006/05/06/AR2006050601338.html.

80   Stephens, Joe. 2009. "Pfizer To Pay $75 Million To Settle Nigerian Trovan Drug-Testing Suit". *The Washington Post.* http://www.washingtonpost.com/wp-dyn/content/article/2009/07/30/AR2009073001847.html.

81   Farbstein, Susan. 2011. "Breaking News: Settlement In Abdullahi V. Pfizer | Human Rights @ Harvard Law". *Human Rights @ Harvard Law.* https://hrp.law.harvard.edu/alien-tort-statute/breaking-news-settlement-in-abdullahi-v-pfizer/.

82   Stephens, Joe. 2010. "Cable: Pfizer Hired Investigators To Press Nigeria To Drop Suit". *The Washington Post.* http://www.washingtonpost.com/wp-dyn/content/article/2010/12/11/AR2010121102884.html.

83   Molotsky, Irvin. 1985. "RECALL URGED OF HEART VALVE SAID TO HAVE A SERIOUS DEFECT (Published 1985)". *Nytimes.Com.* https://www.nytimes.com/1985/06/27/us/recall-urged-of-heart-valve-said-to-have-a-serious-defect.html.

84   "MANUFACTURER ENDS PRODUCTION OF HEART VALVE (Published 1986)". 1986. *Nytimes.Com.* https://www.nytimes.com/1986/11/28/us/manufacturer-ends-production-of-heart-valve.html.

85   Meier, Barry. 1992. "Maker Of Heart Valve Balks Over Some Warnings (Published 1992)". *Nytimes.Com.* https://www.nytimes.com/1992/04/26/us/maker-of-heart-valve-balks-over-some-warnings.html.

86   "Lawsuit Settled Over Heart Valve Implicated In About 300 Deaths (Published 1992)". 1992. *Nytimes.Com.* https://www.nytimes.com/1992/01/25/us/lawsuit-settled-over-heart-valve-implicated-in-about-300-deaths.html.

87   Meier, Barry. 1994. "Pfizer Unit To Settle Charges Of Lying About Heart Valve (Published 1994)". *Nytimes.Com.* https://www.nytimes.com/1994/07/02/business/pfizer-unit-to-settle-charges-of-lying-about-heart-valve.html.

88   Berenson, Alex. 2004. "Pfizer To Halt Advertising Of Celebrex To Consumers (Published 2004)". *Nytimes.Com.* https://www.nytimes.com/2004/12/20/business/20drug.html.

89   Berenson, Alex, and Gardiner Harris. 2005. "Pfizer Says 1999 Trials Revealed Risks With Celebrex (Published 2005)". *Nytimes.Com.* https://www.nytimes.com/2005/02/01/business/01drug.html.

90   Mathews, Anna Wilde, and Scott Hensley. 2005. "FDA Stiffens Painkiller Warnings,Pushes Pfizer To Suspend Bextra - WSJ". *WSJ*. https://online.wsj.com/article/SB111287924404900734.html.

91   Saul, Stephanie. 2008. "Pfizer To Settle Claims Over Bextra And Celebrex (Published 2008)". *Nytimes.Com*. https://www.nytimes.com/2008/10/18/business/18drug.html.

92   "$60 Million Deal In Pfizer Suit (Published 2004)". 2004. *Nytimes.Com*. https://www.nytimes.com/2004/07/03/business/60-million-deal-in-pfizer-suit.html.

93   Mattera, Philip. 2017. "Pfizer: Corporate Rap Sheet | Corporate Research Project". *Corp-Research.Org*. https://www.corp-research.org/pfizer.

94   Mooneyspecial, Richard E. 1958. "6 CONCERNS CITED BY F.T.C. ON FIXING ANTIBIOTIC PRICES; Charges Involve Production Of 'Broad Spectrum' Drugs Attacking Many Diseases ALL COUNTS ARE DENIED Agency Sets Oct. 1 Hearing Here To Seek Order For Companies To Desist 6 DRUG CONCERNS ACCUSED BY F.T.C. (Published 1958)". *Select.Nytimes.Com*. https://select.nytimes.com/gst/abstract.html?res=F30914F93D5A117B93C1A91783D85F4C8585F9.

95   Toth, Robert C. 1963. "U.S. AGENCY RULES 6 COMPANIES RIG ANTIBIOTIC PRICES; Trade Commission Reverses Examiner And Finds Plot In Tetracycline Case MAKERS DENY CHARGES Drug Concerns Are Ordered To End Conspiracy--'Bad Faith' In Patent Hit American Cyanamid Scored U.S. AGENCY FINDS DRUG PRICE FIXED Documents List Price. Critical Of Order (Published 1963)". *Select.Nytimes.Com*. http://select.nytimes.com/gst/abstract.html?res=F20614FE38541A7B93C3A81783D85F478685F9.

96   "6 DRUG COMPANIES GET PRICING ORDER; Told By Agency To Reset Fee On Antibiotic Independently (Published 1964)". 1964. *Select.Nytimes.Com*. https://select.nytimes.com/gst/abstract.html?res=F10C1FFB385C147A93C5A9178AD85F408685F9.

97   Toth, Robert C. 1963. "U.S. AGENCY RULES 6 COMPANIES RIG ANTIBIOTIC PRICES; Trade Commission Reverses Examiner And Finds Plot In Tetracycline Case MAKERS DENY CHARGES Drug Concerns Are Ordered To End Conspiracy--'Bad Faith' In Patent Hit American Cyanamid Scored U.S. AGENCY FINDS DRUG PRICE FIXED Documents List Price. Critical Of Order (Published 1963)". *Select.Nytimes.Com*. http://select.nytimes.com/gst/abstract.html?res=F20614FE38541A7B93C3A81783D85F478685F9.

98   Cray, Douglas W. 1968. "DRUG MAKERS GET MAXIMUM FINES; Bristol-Myers, Pfizer And Cyanamid Must Each Pay $150,000 On Charges THREE COUNTS INVOLVED Case Centers On Conspiracy To Control Production And Sale Of Antibiotics DRUG MAKERS GET

MAXIMUM FINES (Published 1968)". *Select.Nytimes.Com.*
http://select.nytimes.com/gst/abstract.html?res=FA071FFA3A5C147493
CBAB1789D85F4C8685F9.

99   Freudenheim, Milt. 1996. "Drug Makers Settle Suit On Price Fixing (Published 1996)". *Nytimes.Com.* http://www.nytimes.com/1996/02/10/business/drug-makers-settle-suit-on-price-fixing.html.

100   U.S. Department of Justice. 1999. "U.S. PHARMACEUTICAL GIANT AGREES TO PAY CRIMINAL FINES FOR PARTICIPATING IN TWO INTERNATIONAL FOOD ADDITIVES CONSPIRACIES". Washington, DC: US DOJ.

101   Peterson, Melody. 2002. "Pfizer's Chief Is Subpoenaed In An Inquiry On Drug Pricing (Published 2002)". *Nytimes.Com.* http://www.nytimes.com/2002/01/08/business/pfizer-s-chief-is-subpoenaed-in-an-inquiry-on-drug-pricing.html.

102   U.S. Department of Justice. 2002. "DRUG GIANT PFIZER & TWO SUBSIDIARIES TO PAY $49 MILLION FOR DEFRAUDING DRUG MEDICAID REBATE PROGRAM". Washington, DC: US DOJ.

103   U.S. Department of Justice. 2016. "Wyeth And Pfizer Agree To Pay $784.6 Million To Resolve Lawsuit Alleging That Wyeth Underpaid Drug Rebates To Medicaid". Washington, DC: US DOJ.

104   U.K. Competition and Markets Authority. 2016. "CMA Fines Pfizer And Flynn £90 Million For Drug Price Hike To NHS". https://www.gov.uk/government/news/cma-fines-pfizer-and-flynn-90-million-for-drug-price-hike-to-nhs.

105   Mattera, Philip. 2017. "Pfizer: Corporate Rap Sheet | Corporate Research Project". *Corp-Research.Org.* https://www.corp-research.org/pfizer.

106   "THE MEDIA BUSINESS: ADVERTISING; Pfizer's Pact On Plax Ads (Published 1991)". 1991. *Nytimes.Com.* http://www.nytimes.com/1991/02/21/business/the-media-business-advertising-pfizer-s-pact-on-plax-ads.html.

107   Mattera, Philip. 2017. "Pfizer: Corporate Rap Sheet | Corporate Research Project". *Corp-Research.Org.* https://www.corp-research.org/pfizer.

108   U.S. Department of Justice. 2004. "WARNER-LAMBERT TO PAY $430 MILLION TO RESOLVE CRIMINAL & CIVIL HEALTH CARE LIABILITY RELATING TO OFF-LABEL PROMOTION". Washington, DC: US DOJ.

109   Saul, Stephanie. 2008. "Experts Conclude Pfizer Manipulated Studies (Published 2008)". *Nytimes.Com.* http://www.nytimes.com/2008/10/08/health/research/08drug.html.

110   Feeley, Jef, and Janelle Lawrence. 2011. "Pfizer To Pay $142.1 Million Over Neurontin Marketing". *Bloomberg.Com.* http://www.bloomberg.com/news/2011-01-28/pfizer-ordered-to-pay-142-1-million-in-damages-over-neurontin-marketing.html.

111   Pfizer. 2012. "PFIZER REPORTS THIRD-QUARTER 2012 RESULTS". New York, NY: US Securities and Exchange Commission.

https://www.sec.gov/Archives/edgar/data/78003/000115752312005612/a
50457010ex99.htm.

112   U.S. Department of Justice. 2013. "Wyeth Pharmaceuticals Agrees To
       Pay $490.9 Million For Marketing The Prescription Drug Rapamune For
       Unapproved Uses". Washington, DC: US DOJ.

113   New York State Office of the Attorney General. 2014. "A.G.
       Schneiderman Announces Settlement With Pfizer To End Deceptive
       Advertising Practices And Off-Label Promotion Of Immunosuppressive
       Drug Rapamune". https://ag.ny.gov/press-release/2014/ag-schneiderman-
       announces-settlement-pfizer-end-deceptive-advertising-practices.

114   U.S. Securities and Exchange Commission. 2012. "SEC Charges Pfizer
       With FCPA Violations". Washington, DC: US SEC.

115   Mek, Amy. 2022. "Pfizer Offers Doctor $1 Million Hush Money: 'That Is
       How They Silence You, Put You On Pay Role' (Video) - RAIR". *RAIR*.
       https://rairfoundation.com/pfizer-offers-doctor-1-million-hush-money-
       that-is-how-they-silence-you-put-you-on-pay-role-video/.

116   Bird, David. 1971. "U.S. Demands Pfizer Clean Waste-Not Dump It At
       Sea (Published 1971)". *Select.Nytimes.Com*.
       http://select.nytimes.com/gst/abstract.html?res=F00F10FA345B137A93C
       2A8178BD95F458785F9.

117   "COMPANY NEWS; Pfizer Pays Fine (Published 1991)".
       1991. *Nytimes.Com*.
       http://www.nytimes.com/1991/05/02/business/company-news-pfizer-
       pays-fine.html.

118   Mattera, Philip. 2017. "Pfizer: Corporate Rap Sheet | Corporate Research
       Project". *Corp-Research.Org*. https://www.corp-research.org/pfizer.

119   "Amendment To Complaint Filed Against Pfizer By Shelby, Roden &".
       2003. *Bloomberg*. https://www.bloomberg.com/press-releases/2003-05-
       08/amendment-to-complaint-filed-against-pfizer-by-shelby-roden.

120   Koa, Kane. 2021. "How Pfizer Blackmails Countries". *Rumble*.
       https://rumble.com/vqkf0i-how-pfizer-blackmails-countries.html.

121   Guarascio, Francesco, and Panu Wongcha-um. 2021. "Refugees Lack
       COVID Shots Because Drugmakers Fear Lawsuits, Documents
       Show". *Reuters*. https://www.reuters.com/world/refugees-lack-covid-
       shots-because-drugmakers-fear-lawsuits-documents-2021-12-16/.

122   "J&J Tried To Not Paying $3.5BN To Victims Of Cancer Causing Baby
       Talc". 2022. *Mail Online*. https://www.dailymail.co.uk/news/article-
       10478957/How-I-J-tried-worm-way-paying-3-5BN-victims-cancer-
       causing-baby-talc.html.

123   Stonberg, Stephen. 2021. "Cryptocurrencies Are Democratizing The
       Financial World. Here's How". *World Economic Forum*.
       https://www.weforum.org/agenda/2021/01/cryptocurrencies-are-
       democratising-the-financial-world-heres-how/.

124   MICROSOFT TECHNOLOGY LICENSING, LLC. 2020.
       CRYPTOCURRENCY SYSTEM USING BODY ACTIVITY DATA.
       WO2020060606, and issued 2020.

475

125   "Nanotech In The Shots?". 2022. *Archive.Ph.* https://archive.ph/2022.01.29-225016/https://masksaredangerous.com/nanotech-in-the-shots/.

126   Cochran, Drew. 2021. "Why Is Bill Gates Buying So Much Farmland? - Farmland Riches". *Farmland Riches.* https://www.farmlandriches.com/bill-gates-farmland/.

127   "Blackrock Is Buying Up US Homes Like No Tomorrow - Strange Sounds". 2021. *Strange Sounds.* https://www.strangesounds.org/2021/07/blackrock-is-buying-up-us-homes-like-no-tomorrow-real-estate-market-housing.html.

128   Stahl, Lesley. 2022. "Would-Be Home Buyers May Be Forced To Rent The American Dream, Rather Than Buy It". *Cbsnews.Com.* https://www.cbsnews.com/news/rising-rent-prices-60-minutes-2022-03-20/.

129   "The Washington Flyer". 2017. *Aacs.Org.* https://www.aacs.org/wp-content/uploads/2017/02/WF-3_03_17Rev.pdf.

130   Camarota, Steven A., and Karen Zeigler. 2018. "63% Of Non-Citizen Households Access Welfare Programs Compared To 35% Of Native Households". Center for Immigration Studies. https://cis.org/Report/63-NonCitizen-Households-Access-Welfare-Programs.

131   Pear, Robert. 2018. "Medicare's Trust Fund Is Set To Run Out In 8 Years. Social Security, 16. (Published 2018)". *Nytimes.Com.* https://www.nytimes.com/2018/06/05/us/politics/medicare-social-security-finances.html.

132   "A New Report Says The COVID Recession Has Pushed Social Security Insolvency Up A Year". 2021. *Npr.Org.* https://www.npr.org/2021/09/01/1033151631/a-new-report-says-the-covid-recession-has-pushed-social-security-insolvency-up-a.

133   Pipes, Sally. 2021. "Sanders Proposal Brings Medicare Closer To The Brink Of Collapse". *Forbes.* https://www.forbes.com/sites/sallypipes/2021/04/12/sanders-proposal-brings-medicare-closer-to-the-brink-of-collapse/amp/.

134   Epstein, Richard A. 2019. "The Economic Trap Of "Medicare For All"". *Hoover Institution.* https://www.hoover.org/research/economic-trap-medicare-all.

135   Hammond, Jackson, and Gordon Gray. 2021. "The Future Of America's Entitlements: What You Need To Know About The Medicare And Social Security Trustees Reports - AAF". *AAF.* https://www.americanactionforum.org/research/the-future-of-americas-entitlements-what-you-need-to-know-about-the-medicare-and-social-security-trustees-reports-4/.

136   Chamie, Juan. 2021. "Ivermectin In Mexico.". *Juanchamie.Substack.Com.* https://juanchamie.substack.com/p/ivermectin-in-mexico.

137   Kim, Tae. 2018. "Goldman Sachs Asks In Biotech Research Report: 'Is Curing Patients A Sustainable Business Model?'". *CNBC.*

https://www.cnbc.com/2018/04/11/goldman-asks-is-curing-patients-a-sustainable-business-model.html.

138   Gusovsky, Dina. 2016. "Americans Consume Vast Majority Of The World's Opioids". *CNBC*. https://www.cnbc.com/2016/04/27/americans-consume-almost-all-of-the-global-opioid-supply.html.

Chapter 18

An Assault on Representative Government

As we discussed in the previous chapter, the global collusion facilitated by organizations like the WEF and WHO has led to a usurpation of representative government in nations around the world. The coordinated, lockstep behavior of world leaders on a range of issues has brought their motivations into serious question, but in many cases also their legitimacy as apparently-elected officials.

The reason why is simple: the political power available to any leader willing to seriously oppose this conspiracy has become tremendous. For an example besides the massive protests which have taken place, consider a *Des Moines Register* poll of Iowans which showed support for the requirement (without a doctor's note) of *all* childhood vaccines dropped from 59% in 2015 to just 34% in 2022.[1] In fact, 28% of Iowans (up from 16%) believed there should be no laws at all on childhood vaccinations, demonstrating the true extent of the exceptional failure on the part of the Covid collaborators to control opinions despite their unprecedented control of information.

Despite this significant pendulum shift, the US government continues to engage in the exceptional corruption of bailing out Pfizer and buying hundreds of millions of shots people clearly don't want— and not only that people don't want, but even that people aren't authorized to receive in the case of the 50 million shots purchased for under 5-year-olds, a group for whom there remains (as of April 2022) no even falsely-demonstrated benefit or risk.[2] It simply does not make any sense for this sentiment shift and corruption to have gone unaddressed naturally—the opportunity politically is too great. The most prominent example of its potential is the meteoric rise in the Covid era of Florida Governor Ron DeSantis. But even DeSantis has stopped short of outright opposing the inoculations, despite his respectable stance for alternative treatments and against passports, lockdowns, and other human rights violations.

One potential explanation for this is the possibility of an even more sinister, behind-the-scenes expression of the global power wielded by the Covid perpetrators. For example, take the Bill & Melinda Gates Foundation sponsored article in *the Guardian*, "It's time for Africa to rein in Tanzania's anti-vaxxer president."[3] This

479

brazen threat by foreign powers against the sovereignty of Tanzania was made in February 2021 against 61-year-old President John Magufuli. Magufuli, who you will recall exposed Covid testing in the earliest days of the alleged pandemic by showing a fruit can test positive, mysteriously died one month after these Gates-sponsored calls for him to be, "reined in."[4] By July 2021, Tanzania had a new president—the first woman president in the country's history—who just-so-happened to provide a, "major breakthrough," in supporting a mass inoculation campaign in, "one of the world's last countries to embrace COVID-19 vaccines."[5,6]

A convenient sequence of events, to be sure. While it seems obvious enough what happened here, there is admittedly not the kind of hard evidence to prove a coup without what is clearly a warranted investigation (one which will never come). It becomes more impossible to deny the obvious though when one realizes Magufuli wasn't the only inoculation-opposing world leader to mysteriously die in the lead-up to the global mass inoculation campaign. In fact, the following are two more examples of the same exact type of thing happening around the world:

- In June 2021 *Bloomberg* reported Haiti was, "the only country in the western hemisphere without Covid vaccines," due to the refusal of President Jovenel Moïse.[7] One month later, in July 2021, Moïse was assassinated in his home by mercenaries.[8] By August 2021, *NPR* reported the following[9]: *"In the wake of one of the most devastating moments in Haiti's arduous history, there has been a bright spot. One week after Haiti's president was assassinated, the country's first shipment of COVID-19 vaccines finally arrived."*

- In July 2020, ABC reported the new president of Burundi would, "take COVID-19 more seriously," after predecessor Pierre Nkurunziza died of a heart attack the month before.[10] Just prior to his death, Nkurunzia, "kicked out the World Health Organization's country director," and, "allowed large campaign rallies ahead of the presidential election." Burundi would go on to announce its mass inoculation campaign the same day as neighboring Tanzania.[11]

Again, the complete lack of political will to acknowledge the obvious truths of the Covid coup is only explainable by a fear of the consequences of doing so. Hundreds of millions of people have voiced and/or taken to the streets to demonstrate support for such acknowledgements, yet they go suppressed and ignored thanks to a demonstrably corrupt corporate media. Since this unprecedented censorship has taken place alongside a heinous campaign of mass murder, it makes no sense for the tremendous movement of political opposition to have failed to show up in the institutions—unless these institutions are fully under control of the collaborators already, which they obviously are.

To appease said Covid collaborators, countless leaders put their political lives and potentially their actual lives at risk by engaging in one of the most reckless mass betrayals of their respective citizenries in world history. And for the most part they did so without exercising the least bit of caution or restraint. So the next questions we must ask ourselves are: how did this control structure get in place? Who supports its operation? Which, "representatives," are beholden to it? And why are they beholden to it?

Agenda 2030

On September 25, 2015, the 193 countries of the United Nations adopted a resolution called, "Transforming our world: the 2030 Agenda for Sustainable Development."[12] The Resolution contained a list of 17 Sustainable Development Goals (SDGs), with 169 targets covering a broad range of sustainable development issues including ending poverty and hunger, improving health and education, making cities more sustainable, combatting, "climate change," and protecting oceans and forests. Its introduction declares[13]:

> *"We, the Heads of State and Government and High Representatives, meeting at the United Nations Headquarters in New York from 25 to 27 September 2015 as the Organization celebrates its seventeenth anniversary, have decided today on new global Sustainable Development Goals.* **On behalf of the people we serve** (my emphasis) *we have adopted a historic decision on a comprehensive, far-reaching, and people-centered set of* **universal and transformative Goals and targets. We commit ourselves to working tirelessly**

for the full implementation of this Agenda by 2030 (my emphasis)."

Agenda 2030 was, at the time, the newest iteration of global planning the un-elected UN purported for several decades to be doing on behalf of citizens of the entire world. Its passage is reported as having received a, "thunderous standing ovation," according to the UN Department of Public Information and was endorsed by a number of high-profile leaders.[14] Ruthless revolutionary and dictator of Zimbabwe Robert Mugabe, for example, said, "This agenda promises a brave new world, a new world that calls for the creation of a **global citizen** (my emphasis)."[15] US President Barrack Obama also spoke glowingly of it, calling it, "one of the smartest investments we can make in our own future."

While this plan not ratified by Congress as is required by the Constitution would certainly be an investment, the idea it would be either a smart one or one made for, "our own," future is debatable. In fact, the now-familiar World Bank actually provided a 2015 report in the lead up to the Agenda's passing called, "From Billions to Trillions," on the financial cost which would be associated with it.[16] In the report the World Bank conceded, "To meet the investment needs of the Sustainable Development Goals, the global community needs to move the discussion from 'Billions' in ODA [Official Development Assistance] to 'Trillions' in investments of all kinds: public and private, national and global, in both capital and capacity." Of particular note here are both the emphasis on public-private partnerships (monopoly) and the consistency of the economic message as far as capital expansion goes. If the Covid era sounds like a logical extension of these things, it should. What should also be familiar is the cozy relationship the UN, like the WEF and WHO it's associated with, has with China.

> *"Therefore, the efforts to jointly build the 'Belt and Road' can significantly push forward the implementation of 2030 Agenda and the achievement of the SDGs not only for the countries along the 'Belt and Road' but also for the world as whole."*
> —Archived UN webpage[17]

"[The Belt and Road Initiative] *is highly consistent with the UN 2030 Agenda for Sustainable Development. More than 10*

UN agencies have signed cooperation agreements with the Chinese side ... The UN stands ready to work closely with the Chinese side in the process of jointly building the Belt and Road Initiative."

—Archived Chinese Ministry of Foreign Affairs webpage[18]

Per *InfoGalactic*, the Belt and Road initiative is, "a development strategy and framework, proposed by Chinese paramount leader Xi Jinping that focuses on connectivity and cooperation among countries primarily between the People's Republic of China and the rest of Eurasia."[19] The stated goal of this initiative is to support, "China's push to take a bigger role in global affairs." A popular opinion during the Covid era pointed to China and Russia being nationalist governments which stood in opposition to the regime of the globalist US Empire; however, China's Belt and Road initiative and its support from and/or influence over the globalist UN seem to suggest otherwise. Russia is the same in this regard, as James Corbett comically pointed out in comparing a 2022 joint statement by Russia and China on, "global sustainable development," to the same rhetoric used by western globalist puppets.[20] Consider how similar the following excerpt from the Russia-China statement sounds to the rhetoric of someone like Justin Trudeau, for example[21]:

"Today, the world is going through momentous changes, and humanity is entering a new era of rapid development and profound transformation. It sees the development of such processes and phenomena as multipolarity, economic globalization, the advent of information society, cultural diversity, transformation of the global governance architecture and world order...

... The sides call on all States to pursue well-being for all and, with these ends, to build dialogue and mutual trust, strengthen mutual understanding, champion such universal human values as peace, development, equality, justice, democracy and freedom, respect the rights of peoples to independently determine the development paths of their countries and the sovereignty and the security and development interests of States, ***to protect the United Nations-driven international architecture and the international law-based world order***

(my emphasis), *seek genuine multipolarity with the United Nations and its Security Council playing a central and coordinating role, promote more democratic international relations, and ensure peace, stability and sustainable development across the world.*

*... **In order to accelerate the implementation of the UN 2030 Agenda for Sustainable Development** (my emphasis), the sides call on the international community to take practical steps in key areas of cooperation such as poverty reduction, food security, **vaccines and epidemics control** (my emphasis), financing for development, climate change, sustainable development, including green development, industrialization, digital economy, and infrastructure connectivity."*

The consistency of the message and causes of both the western and eastern arms of this globalist body might be surprising if not for the consistency of the Covid measures. As we've seen, China and Russia both took the same actions as every other country in the world in response to the alleged Covid pandemic. The reasons for this are both financial and political. Just like the business world has shifted to a government-facilitated monopoly, so too have the governments of the world shifted to a monopoly—a monopoly which respects the sovereignty and rights of other nations about as much as a business monopoly respects competition.

So where previous plans resulted in, "unfinished business," the UN promised this new Agenda would address the remaining challenges they perceived the world was facing. As stated by Mugabe, this included, "an ethic of global citizenship," which is a barely indirect call by this unelected, not-representative body for global governance. "Global citizens," would ultimately inhabit environmentally and financially, "sustainable," cities/settlements, which sound awfully adjacent to the smart cities proposed by the WEF. For these cities/settlements the resolution proposed lofty, utopian visions of a, "world free of poverty, hunger, disease, and want," where, "every child grows up free from violence and exploitation."

The realities of ~~global~~ foreign governance were quick to strike down this fantasy however, as less than a year after the passage of the resolution, reports surfaced of UN, "peacekeepers," in warzones forcing, "starving children as young as nine," to give them, "oral sex to get food."[22] But these war-crimes were not limited to the warzone, either. Memos about the sexual abuse were reportedly, "passed from desk to desk, inbox to inbox, across multiple UN offices, with no one willing to take responsibility." In this case, the UN's children agency, UNICEF, failed to act, as, "the welfare of the victims and the accountability of the perpetrators appeared to be an afterthought, if considered at all."

Again, these are the natural, nightmarish consequences of a government which isn't representative of or accountable to its people. It is clear the UN and its aims are precursors of and/or party to those of the WEF and its allies. In fact, as we've covered in the various WEF propaganda pieces on owning nothing and being happy, the year frequently identified for this objective to be accomplished by is 2030, in line with the aims of the UN Agenda.[23,24] Given the alignment of timeline and mission, it is impossible to imagine there is not at least an intimate connection, if not a direct assignment of the task to Schwab and the WEF.

The UN's WHO also factors prominently here, especially in the wake of its 2022 attempted, "Pandemic Treaty," power grab.[25] Yes, you read that correctly: the same historically corrupt organization which endorsed and/or recommended *every* inhumane, coercive measure in the name of combatting a, "pandemic," it fraudulently declared, is now requesting the nations of the world sign their rights away to it—this despite the unmitigated disaster those measures either caused and/or completely failed to mitigate. Per Shabnam Palesa Mohamed of the Steering Committee of the World Council for Health, the powers proposed to be, "legally binding under international law," in this despicable match paper include[26]:

- The power of the WHO to dictate how nations approach pandemics, guaranteeing the aforementioned one-size-fits-all approach to medicine all over the world
- The power of the WHO to conduct bio surveillance which, considering the restrictive measures taken in the Covid era, means the same as general surveillance
- This effective assumption of police power during *declared*, "pandemics," would effectively equate to world government in line with the UN's goals, considering the fraudulent

485

methods used by this organization to make such declarations and the annual, perpetual claims of, "variants"

- Allows the WHO to further pervert statistical methodologies in the interest of continuing to manufacture pandemics, which in the absence of would make it obsolete
- Allows the WHO to sanction those who do not sign on to the Treaty
- Assumption of authority on the part of the WHO to, "combat misinformation"
- In the Treaty committee's own words, seeks to, "enhance long-term public and private-sector support," which by now has been clearly established to mean: strengthen monopoly

This cannot be permitted. Representatives must be made to reject such a treaty in any form. In fact, any nation which values its sovereignty should demand all funding be withdrawn from the WHO, that the organization be abolished, and its Covid era leaders tried for crimes against humanity. Its behavior over the course of its entire existence and its control by the oligarchic Gates Foundation are further support for such demands. Next, we will see how Klaus Schwab also employs world leaders and prominent figures to accomplish this collective vision, many of whom have observably sold out at the expense of those they're meant to represent.

Klaus Schwab's "Young Global Leaders"

Recall Klaus Schwab's 2007 quote about the growing influence of the WEF, in which he admitted to having vast influence over governments and politicians, NGOs, tribunals, media, experts in science and academia, religious leaders, and social entrepreneurs. What Schwab was referring to here was *not* a variety of your typical, informal networking connections. Let's check in with Schwab himself during a talk at Harvard in 2017 to clarify[27]:

> *"When I mention **our names** (my emphasis), like Ms. Merkel—even Vladimir Putin, and so on—they all have been 'Young Global Leaders' of the World Economic Forum. But what we are very proud of now is the young generation like Prime Minister Trudeau, the president of Argentina, and so on, that **we penetrate the cabinets. So yesterday I was at a reception for Prime Minister Trudeau and I know that half***

of this cabinet—or even more than half of this cabinet—are
*actually **Young Global Leaders** of the **World Economic***
***Forum** (my emphasis) ... It's true in Argentina, and it's true*
in France now."

The, "Young Global Leaders," (YGL) program is, in its own
words, "an accelerator for a dynamic community of exceptional
people," who are, "aligned with the World Economic Forum's
mission," and, "seek to drive public-private co-operation in the global
public interest."[28] The program was comprised of people under age 38
and would host its own summits, usually in conjunction with the
annual WEF meeting at Davos.[29] Per Schwab himself, the leaders of
some of the largest global powers *and their cabinets* are alumni of this
program which is, "aligned with the World Economic Forum's
mission." Schwab is even so bold as to admit to, "penetrating," these
positions of power in national governments.

There is no longer any possibility of mistaking it—this is
dictator-led, one-world government under the façade of sovereign
nations with distinct interests. That Schwab could get away with
admitting this at an institution as prominent as Harvard without being
arrested for national security violations, treason, or some other
usurpation-related crime is a testament to the global coup d'état he has
not only engaged in, but has seemingly accomplished. During this
speech he only dropped three names—despite their being highly
prominent names, indeed. The following are just some of the most
recognizable names of other Young Global Leaders who had
prominent totalitarian roles during the Covid era[30]:

- Bill Gates
- Vladimir Putin (Russian President)
- Angela Merkel (German Chancellor)
- Justin Trudeau (Canadian Prime Minister)
- Emanuel Macron (French President)
- Sebastian Kurz (Austrian Chancellor)
- Matteo Renzi (Italian Prime Minister)
- Jacinda Ardern (New Zealand Prime Minister)
- Greg Hunt (Australian Health Minister)
- Stéphane Bancel (Moderna CEO)
- Gavin Newsom (Governor of California)

- Devi Sridhar (leading, "zero Covid," proponent in Britain)
- Rebecca Weintraub (regular corporate media proponent of coercing universal inoculations)
- Jens Spahn (German Health Minister)
- Mark Zuckerberg (*Facebook* CEO)
- Sheryl Sandberg (*Facebook* COO)
- Jeffrey Zients (White House Coronavirus Response Coordinator since 2021)
- Jeremy Howard (Co-founder of the lobby group, "masks for all")
- Eric Feigl-Ding (Covid *Twitter* personality)
- Leana Wen (CNN medical personality)
- Sanjay Gupta (CNN medical personality)
- Fareed Zakaria (CNN host)
- Anderson Cooper (CNN host)
- Andrew Ross Sorkin (*New York Times* columnist)
- Thomas Friedman (*New York Times* columnist)
- George Stephanopoulos (ABC host)
- Lachlan Murdoch (CEO of Fox Corporation)

World leaders (and their cabinets), public health officials, and propagandists alike—and this is just the fraction which would've had the biggest visible impact in the Covid era. All went through the Young Global Leaders program in their youth before going on to contribute to the WEF's Covid agenda, as the program states they are meant to. To be clear, I'm not saying all of these people are privy to and conspire to aid and abet Schwab's globalist coup. Many of them likely just joined an organization hoping to network with other professionals. Others perhaps are fully aware of the scheme and actually believe what they're doing is good, as Justin Trudeau's half-brother, Kyle Kemper, seems to think of Justin[31]:

> *"I think from—and this comes back to this condition of hypnosis—I truly believe that he believes what he's doing is the right thing, even if he knows that it's the WEF agenda—that he believes it's the right thing to do."*

I personally find the idea Trudeau doesn't realize what he's doing hard to believe. Take his actual quote, "Mandates are the way to avoid further restrictions," for example.[32] This is a phrase which makes no sense on its face, unless your goal is to trick people into thinking, "mandates," and, "restrictions," are different so you can make, "mandates," seem acceptable. So it is a deceptive thing to say, which benefits Trudeau's cause, implying he knows what he is doing to some extent. He further confirms this when in 2013 he actually said, "There's a level of admiration I actually have for China because their basic dictatorship is allowing them to actually turn their economy around."[33] If we were to for some reason ignore such blatant admissions, I suppose the only alternative would be that the aforementioned quotes were the words of a hypnotized madman. I also understand why Kemper wouldn't want to think of his half-brother as knowingly doing wrong. But whether or not Trudeau intended to inflict the damage he has is irrelevant to his having inflicted it and having done so in a coercive manner.

So Schwab's influence on puppets like Trudeau is explicit, which enables his pushing the situation in the direction of his agenda. And if it's still hard to understand, imagine if the Pope (more on him shortly) had a, "Young Catholic Leaders," program which was designed to align future leaders with the agenda of the Catholic Church. If countries around the world started behaving extremely Catholic at the drop of a hat and the Pope bragged about his influence over them, would it still be so hard to fathom the possibility of a global Catholic conspiracy? Again, it wouldn't even require specific direction, would it? All it would require is people who are trained to make decisions based on ideology (Bio Revolution, climate revolution, crypto revolution, cyber revolution—check, check, check, check), a network of others who share the ideology (WEF, Davos gatherings, Young Global Leaders—check, check, check), and as much control of information as humanly possible (censorship, "fact-checking," cancel culture, "misinformation"—check, check, check, check).

Sound like a religion? It should. It absolutely is a religion—one which has perverted the word, "science," into an all-encompassing justification to achieve its aims, no matter how little science is actually involved. It also certainly isn't as if the Young Global Leaders groomed to, "penetrate," positions of power are the full extent of the WEF's faithful members/contributors, either. A few additional WEF-adjacent figures who frequent what *Vanity Fair* calls

489

the, "billionaire circus," at Davos and have, "pillaged the global economy, exploited workers, plundered housing and healthcare, and dismantled government programs," include the likes of[34]:

- Anthony Fauci
- Adhanom Ghebreyesus (WHO)
- Antonio Guterres (UN Secretary-General)
- Richard Hatchett (CEO of Coalition for Epidemic Preparedness and Innovations)
- Chrystia Freeland (Deputy Prime Minister and Minister of Finance in Canada responsible for freezing bank accounts of peaceful protesters during Trudeau's crackdown against dissent ... also on WEF Board of Trustees[35,36])
- Peter Buttigieg (YGL)
- Nikki Haley (YGL)
- Chelsea Clinton (YGL)
- Tulsi Gabbard (YGL)
- Dan Crenshaw (YGL)
- Megan Rapinoe (YGL)
- Alexander Soros (YGL)
- David de Rothschild (YGL)

Speaking of religion, one thing which has been disheartening to Christians the world over is the extent to which Pope Francis has bowed to this globalist agenda. Rather than welcoming lepers as Christ did, the current Pope has heinously banned, "unvaccinated," Christians from the Vatican.[37] That's right, in a complete inversion of the religion itself, only those who wear the, "Mark," are welcome. The, "Holy See," has ordered this despite the shots not only being intended to literally reprogram the God-given immune system, but also despite their being acknowledged to contain aborted fetal cell lines.[38] This has always been a perfectly valid, if not necessary, reason for a Christian to refuse an inoculation. Still, the Pope inexplicably rejects these concerns and also ignores the utter lack of benefit the shots provide, demonstrating his ignorance of both Christianity and science.

The reason I said, "disheartening," above and not, "surprising," is because this type of anti-Christian behavior frankly isn't surprising at all from the current Pope. In fact, Francis is documented as having specifically called for a, "New World Order," *more than once*, among a papacy full of other strange statements and behaviors.[39,40] And not only has he verbalized such intentions, but he has also spearheaded an, "Inclusive Capitalism," initiative, which seeks to make the world, "fairer, more inclusive, and sustainable."[41] This sounds nice, doesn't it? In fact, if what the Pope was referring to was a way to address the real crises we discussed in the previous chapter, I'd be totally on board. Unfortunately however, this too is, "buzzword bingo."

The first tell of dishonesty is the use of the term, "inclusivity," by a pope we've already established is perfectly fine with entirely banning non-guinea-pigs from his pews and/or engaging in society. But when we peel back the layers on the aforementioned initiative itself, we can see its composition is just as dirty. The truth of the matter is the initiative was founded by Lynn Forester de Rothschild, whose son-in-law is YGL-alum David de Rothschild and who has been alleged as having ties to both Jeffrey Epstein and Ghislaine Maxwell.[42,43] Right off the bat, it is troubling the Pope would hand over the reins of an organization with this mission to such a controversial figure. However, even ignoring the allegations, I can't think of a worse representative in the entire world for a wealth-disparity focused organization than a Rothschild. In fact, it's downright insulting for the Pope to have permitted such a transparent sham, given the family is not only impossibly wealthy, but is also specifically known for both hiding the extent of that wealth and preserving its concentration in their hands.[44]

It doesn't end with the founder, either. Many of the same people and ideas present at the WEF Davos meetings are involved with the Inclusive Capitalism initiative, and this is even reflected in published praise by the WEF for the Pope to this end.[45,46] The WEF also specifically claimed that during a fall 2020 encyclical, "the Pope put his stamp on efforts to shape what's been termed a Great Reset of the global economy."[47] In this encyclical, the Pope is acknowledged as having declared the, "limits of market economics," he claims were revealed by the alleged pandemic.[48] One has to wonder based on this absurd claim if he is either ignorant or complicit in the inexplicable campaign of suppression of cheap, effective early treatments. The consequence of this suppression was medical mass murder and the, "limits of market economics," had nothing whatsoever to do with it.

491

In fact, the WEF, its allies, and its economic model are directly responsible for the entirety of the damages to human health in the Covid era, pandemic or no pandemic. In their blathering blog posts they insult the intelligence in claiming *more*, "active government intervention," is still necessary too.[49] This alleged pandemic saw the most government intervention of any in human history and yet, despite their attempts to portray it as an unprecedented disaster, they somehow simultaneously want you to believe measures more extreme than lockdowns, experimental medicines, concentration camps, surveillance, and anal swabs would have prevented it. Just please forget about the fact that all of these things observably failed and produced the opposite effect. Instead, focus on the enemy according to the WEF—namely, "neoliberalism," which they claim is a, "philosophy espousing austerity, privatization, deregulation, unbridled markets, and relatively weak labor laws." This is ironic coming from an organization which:

1. Vilifies an, "austerity," which hasn't been even remotely demonstrated in practice by the governments and economic actors the WEF simultaneously criticize and are comprised of
2. Is both comprised of some of the wealthiest benefactors of privatization and is illogically proposing a private-public power consolidation (one which has failed in the Covid era) as an alternative to separate public and private sectors with checks and balances
3. Has itself effectively nullified the concept of regulation, via its support and implementation of public-private monopoly mergers (i.e. pharma with the FDA, CDC, WHO, and NIH)
4. Has created/endorsed the single most massive, unbridled, reckless monopoly behavior ever witnessed in human history
5. Has expanded the wealth gap at the expense of labor in the Covid era, proposed a total wealth gap where labor is reduced to serfdom, and has sabotaged small business in favor of the conglomerate

We have already come to expect doublespeak of the WEF. What we cannot accept is for religious, government, or community leaders to tolerate it. The Pope is one among many representatives who have failed their mandate in the Covid era. This is the true conflict which is currently taking place today and which will define our time—namely, the battle between representative governance and governance by oligarchic imposition. Perhaps nowhere was this more evident than in totalitarian New York Governor Kathy Hochul's willingness to replace NY's, "unvaccinated," hospital staff with foreign workers—hospital staff who the same government lionized as, "frontline heroes," in 2020 in order to sell the seriousness of the alleged pandemic.[50] Equally bold were WEF YGL-alum Justin Trudeau referring to the, "unvaccinated," as, "racist and misogynistic extremists," WEF YGL-alum Emanuel Macron saying he no longer considered the, "unvaccinated," to be French citizens, or WEF YGL-alum Jacinda Ardern claiming New Zealand would become a, "two-tier society," based on inoculation status.[51,52,53]

Such statements—just like Joe Biden's about, "losing patience," with non-compliers—are not the statements of public servants. They are the statements of dictators. They lead to an institutionalized sentiment of psychopathy which can be seen in the additional example of Germany's Federal Constitutional Court, which was reported in 2022 as having admitted the Covid inoculations were harmful and even, "fatal," yet still upheld medical worker mandates because, "they are free to resign."[54] The fact that all major countries are led by such inhumane, well-connected tyrants also brings into question the mechanisms with which they are elected to begin with. That is, of course, not a topic for this book. However, the Covid era has revealed like never before the stark difference between those who seek power to rule and those who seek it to serve. One of the best examples in the entire world of the latter has been Wisconsin senator Ron Johnson.

A Lone Knight at a Round Table of Fools

As far as the United States federal government goes, there is only one man who truly and visibly opposed the WEF agenda and defended the human rights of the American people—that man is Senator Ron Johnson of Wisconsin. To date, Johnson has held two major hearings which have acknowledged the damage done by the conspiracy we have now laid out. The first was a November 2, 2021 hearing on the safety and efficacy of the inoculations, which included testimony by victims of severe adverse events, doctors who have treated victims of similar events, and scientists.[55] The second was a

January 24, 2022, "Second Opinion," panel, which featured more doctors and scientists, many of whom who have been inexplicably censored in the Covid era for opposing the conspiracy which has taken place.[56] Despite the victims and extensively-credentialed professionals present, all of the following were invited to both hearings and both times declined to show up to answer for the litany of disturbing anomalies identified:

- CDC Director Rochelle Walensky
- FDA Commissioner Janet Woodcock
- NIAID Director Anthony Fauci
- NIH Director (during majority of the alleged pandemic) Francis Collins
- NIH Director (newly appointed at the time) Lawrence Tabak
- White House Coronavirus Response Coordinator Jeffrey Zients
- Pfizer CEO Albert Bourla
- Moderna CEO Stéphane Bancel
- Member of Pfizer Board and former FDA Director Scott Gottlieb
- Former Director of BARDA Rick Bright

The names of these criminals are by now very familiar to us, as I have filled this book with tons of evidence of their misdoings. However, the inaction of elected officials both locally and in Washington has allowed them to run rampant in pushing the Covid conspiracy forward at the expense of science, health, and human rights. While there has certainly been opposition to tyranny, as demonstrated most popularly by Florida Governor Ron DeSantis, Senator Johnson is the one and only man who has been brave enough to honestly search and acknowledge the full truth without hesitation or gate-keeping.

During the Covid era it has generally been that Republicans were the ones fighting the narrative (either as, "conspiracy theorists," or, "truth-tellers," depending on your point-of-view), while Democrats were the ones supporting it (either as self-titled, "science believers," or, "sheep," depending on your point-of-view). There definitely is a degree of truth in this. Even, "progressive," Bill Maher eventually acknowledged liberal media was, "scaring the shit out of,"

Democrats, who surveys showed 41% of absurdly believed they had a 50% or higher chance to be hospitalized if they tested positive for, "Covid."[57] As stated previously, many of these people have been converted into technocrats via the hypnosis of one of the most intense propaganda machines in human history. We will cover much more on this propaganda machine in a future chapter. But this psychosis translated to Democrat politicians as well, seemingly universally. Here are just a few particularly disgusting examples of them betraying their constituents:

- House Speaker Nancy, "Good Morning, Sunday Morning," Pelosi was caught on video in a salon at a time when salons had been forced to close for months and indoor services in particular were forbidden in her home city of San Francisco.[58,59] Following her hypocritical violation of human-rights-violating regulations, Pelosi then had the nerve to claim the salon owner, "owes me an apology for setting me up."
- California Governor Gavin Newsom violated his own state mask mandate while attending an NFL playoff game, among other examples[60,61]
- New York Governor Andrew Cuomo was one of many officials who inexplicably sent sick people to nursing homes.[62] Cuomo later published a propaganda piece in which he tried to re-write the history of his disgraceful tenure during the Covid era.[63] He was ultimately ordered by an ethics panel however, to pay the state $5.1 million in book profits he made on the backs of taxpayers.[64]
- Austin, TX Mayor Steve Adler recorded a video at a Mexico beach resort telling Austinites to, "stay home if you can," during the Thanksgiving holiday[65]
- Popular Democrat Stacey Abrams took a dystopian picture sitting and smiling ear-to-ear with no mask in a room full of mask-abused children.[66] She then went on damage control despite having proudly posted the image to her social media page initially.

These are just a few examples of what would be far too many to list. That they occurred while human rights were being violated is not just hypocritical, it's criminal. Still, despite their tendency to be far more tyrannical, Democrats were certainly not the only ones guilty of deceit. To start with, there simply is not a prominent Republican outside of Senator Johnson who seriously questions the inoculations. Time and time again, prominent Republican figures like Senator Rand Paul would act tough with Anthony Fauci on origin theories, for example, but fail to acknowledge the failure and dangers of the inoculations. In fact, Senator Paul, a doctor, still in 2022 continues to insinuate the inoculations, "protect people from hospitalization and death," which is, beyond a shadow of a doubt, such an absurd claim it has to be knowingly untruthful.[67]

Back to the, "Second Opinion," panel though, we have also already covered many of the doctors and scientists who were given time to talk at these hearings, as well as their opinions. The words, "crimes against humanity," were stated several times at the panel, so it goes without saying their message is as dire as I've demonstrated it should be in this book. They acknowledged the extraordinary dangers presented by the inoculations, the censorship, the illegal and corrupt practices of the public health bureaucracies, the criminal suppression of early treatment, the uselessness of masks, the failure and devastation of lockdowns, and everything else in between. I would highly recommend going to the link where I cited it and watching the entire thing—it is riveting from beginning to end.

For now though, I will end this chapter with the testimony of New York City, "frontline," nurse Nicole Sirotek, given during the January 2022 panel.[68] As you read it, you might—if you've ignored my more than 1,000 citations to this point—first be surprised to notice how much this nurse's opinion corroborates my own assessment of the situation. What I really want to drive home here though is that Sirotek is a real nurse who was at the hospitals experiencing the circumstances governments used to declare, "Pandemic," in the spring of 2020. Despite this first-hand experience, the bureaucracies and companies involved declined to hear from Sirotek. And despite both this clearly suspicious refusal and the gravity of Sirotek's testimony, the vast majority of federal and state government officials in the US— outside of Senator Johnson—refuse to demand answers for the unspeakable crimes committed against their constituents. The testimony, in full, is as follows:

"Thank you, senator, for giving me an uninterrupted opportunity to represent the harm that is coming to the patients in the American hospitals, and the lack of early intervention.

My name is Nicole Sirotek. I'm a registered nurse—I've been a registered nurse for over a decade—my specialty is critical care, trauma, and flight. Since the start of the Covid pandemic I've actually been rebranded, I guess you could say, as a leading expert in early intervention strategies executed on a large, mass scale, using the FLCCC protocol, as well as Covid patient ventilator protective strategies to optimize Covid patients on the ventilators.

My story actually begins back in May of 2020. I was one of the original nurses that went to NYC to help with the Covid pandemic because, as we remember, they needed nurses and, most importantly, they needed ventilators. Well I was the whole package—a flight nurse that can manage ventilators.

And when I arrived there, the gross negligence and the medical malfeasance that happened in there and the complete medical mismanagement of these patients is what has led us to the situation that we're in right now. The pandemic and the hysteria that was created from poor public health measures and poor execution of appropriate early intervention strategies and the handicapping of medical professionals doing our job has led to where we are right now and into the crisis situation that we are in.

I will use several key case studies that will represent larger descriptive statistical information for what I am going to speak of. But when I was in New York, and what continues to happen today, is that many of them are not dying from Covid. Now what many people don't know about me is I am actually a Master's prepared biochemist and I have worked extensively with the HIV virus tracking genetic mutations, so I feel very comfortable going toe-to-toe with some of the doctors here, although I am not a doctor—I'm just a nurse.

But what we saw on these frontlines, we knew what was happening. And when we asked for the Ibuprofen they said, 'no it is counter-indicated.' When we asked, 'why aren't we giving them steroids,' 'oh, well it's not—we were just following orders.' Following orders has led to the sheer number of deaths that has occurred in these hospitals. **I didn't see a single patient die of Covid. I've seen substantial a number of patients die of negligence and medical malfeasance** (my emphasis).

When I was on the frontlines of New York I'm unfortunately known—globally viral—as the nurse that was in the breakroom sobbing saying that they were murdering my patients. The pharmaceutical companies had gone into those hospitals and decided to ... 'practice,' I guess you could say ... on minorities, on the disadvantaged, on the marginalized populations that we know that we had no advocates for, because the very agencies that should have been protecting them were closed because we were, 'sheltering in place.'

*Now while I was there, and I saw that the pharmaceutical companies were rolling out remdesivir onto the patients, I tried to get ahold of the IRBs, I tried to get ahold of my appropriate chain of command, I tried CMS, I tried the department of health—**and they rolled out remdesivir onto a substantial number of patients for which we all saw it was killing the patients. And now it's the FDA-approved drug that is continuing to kill patients in the United States*** (my emphasis).

*As nurses we collected a statistical, or descriptive, amount of information that you may not get from the doctors because where they do quantitative data, we do qualitative data with a humanistic, phenomenological approach in nursing research. And so we've collected the data from all these patients across the country from which we have been helping patients— because I formed the organization American Frontline Nurses and the Advocacy Network so nurses could advocate for these patients—**and all of this data pull shows is as these patients get remdesivir, they have a less than 25% chance of survival if they get more than two doses*** (my emphasis). *Now they're rolling it out on children as well, and into the nursing homes or school nursing facilities as, 'early intervention,' when as, Dr. Pierre Kory and Dr. Marik have already demonstrated that there are effective medications out there. And we are going to see the amplification of death across our country.*

And we haven't even touched on the vaccines, for which all of our expert panels have already very well described that situation so I won't touch on that since many of them are far superior to me—than even I could ever hope to be. **But I can tell you that two days ago I flew out my first ten-year-old with a heart attack. And I had to fight the doctor in the ER because he's like, 'ten-year-olds don't have heart attacks.' And I argued back and forth for 30 minutes to force his hand to get an EKG, to find out that he had almost a complete STEMI—which is ST-elevated myocardial infarction—for which you could see it lit up on the ... EKG. And he's like, 'well that's not possible.' And I'm like, 'well he was just vaccinated yesterday** (my emphasis)*—it is very much possible.'*

At any given time, people are getting ahold of me and the nurse advocates at American Frontline Nurses to help advocate, because as you've seen there is victim shaming—that, 'oh, it's anxiety—oh, it's this.' But in actuality, if they put down that it was a vaccine injury—the physician, the corporation, the hospital, the clinic—they actually won't get reimbursed, so it gets labeled as, 'anxiety,' or, 'neuropathy,' or, 'Guillian-Barré Syndrome,' when in actuality it's very realistically a vaccine injury.

Now I'm not—even though I founded American Frontline Nurses I've traveled extensively to South America, India, and South Africa working in hot zones, stopping the spread of the virus and working with early intervention. And nowhere in those countries, in developing nations, do I see these issues that we see here in the United States. It's actually—I'm a very proud American citizen, I come from a family of immigrants and my mother told me that the United States is the best country in the world—granted I am biased being an American—and our level of healthcare has been deteriorate to sub-standard, third-world-nation healthcare, whereas I tell people you are better off in South America in a field hospital than you are in level-1 trauma, designer hospitals in the United States.

As nurses we are getting reports across the country from our American Frontline Nurses about patients not getting food;

patients not getting water. 'How come a patient hasn't been fed in nine days?' 'Why do I need to get a court order to force a hospital to feed a person who isn't intubated and is literally telling you they would like food?' ... You know, if they're on a ventilator, they're not getting basic standards of care. I have patients that haven't been bathed; haven't been fed; haven't been given water; haven't been turned. And if you ask me, this isn't a hospital, this is a concentration camp—absolutely it is. Nowhere in the United States do we isolate people for hundreds of hours at a time with no human contact. It's not even allowed in the prisons. You are not allowed to isolate a prisoner beyond a certain, sensitive amount of time because it is horrible for their mental health and it is considered inhumane. However, in these hospitals now we are allowed to isolate patients from their families for days and you have to say goodbye to them over an iPhone, as Jennifer Bridges has just demonstrated to us—or, she has to shuttle people in to see. And personally, I was fired for sneaking a Hispanic family in to say the last rites to their family.

And so thank you, Senator Johnson, for giving nurses the opportunity to come and represent our patients because, as you can see, we're not often thought of as, 'leading professionals,' though we are the missing link between the doctors and the patients. So thank you so much for this time."

Endnotes

1   Leys, Tony. 2022. "Iowans' Support For Non-COVID Vaccine Requirements In Schools Erodes, Iowa Poll Finds". *Desmoinesregister.Com*. https://www.desmoinesregister.com/story/news/politics/iowa-poll/2022/03/13/iowa-school-mandatory-vaccine-requirements-non-covid-support-drops-poll/9442227002/.

2   Children's Health Defense. 2022. "CHD Says Pfizer Clinical Trial Data Contradicts 'Safe And Effective' Government/Industry Mantra". https://childrenshealthdefense.org/press-release/chd-says-pfizer-clinical-trial-data-contradicts-safe-and-effective/.

3   Tampa, Vava. 2021. "It's Time For Africa To Rein In Tanzania's Anti-Vaccine President | Vava Tampa". *The Guardian*. https://www.theguardian.com/global-development/2021/feb/08/its-time-for-africa-to-rein-in-tanzanias-anti-vaxxer-president.

4   Burke, Jason. 2021. "Tanzania's Covid-Denying President, John Magufuli, Dies Aged 61". *The Guardian*. https://www.theguardian.com/world/2021/mar/17/tanzanias-president-john-magufuli-dies-aged-61.

5   Nyeko, Oryem. 2021. "Tanzania: Human Rights Priorities For Tanzania's New President". *Human Rights Watch*. https://www.hrw.org/news/2021/05/20/tanzania-human-rights-priorities-tanzanias-new-president.

6   "Tanzanian President Gets COVID-19 Vaccine Dose, Urges Others To Follow Her Lead | CBC News". 2021. *CBC*. https://www.cbc.ca/news/world/tanzania-president-covid19-vaccine-promotion-1.6121008.

7   Wyss, Jim. 2021. "Hiati Is Only Country In Western Hemisphere Without Vaccines". *Bloomberg.Com*. https://www.bloomberg.com/news/articles/2021-06-08/haiti-is-the-only-country-in-western-hemisphere-without-vaccines.

8   "Haiti President's Assassination: What We Know So Far". 2022. *BBC News*. https://www.bbc.com/news/world-latin-america-57762246.

9   Beaubien, Jason. 2021. "A Bright Spot Amid Haiti's Woes: Its 1St Mass Rollout Of COVID Vaccines". *Npr.Org*. https://www.npr.org/sections/goatsandsoda/2021/08/03/1022776041/a-bright-spot-amid-haitis-woes-its-first-mass-rollout-of-covid-vaccines.

10   KANEZA, ELOGE WILLY. 2020. "New Burundi Leader Hints He'll Take COVID-19 More Seriously". *ABC News*. https://abcnews.go.com/International/wireStory/burundi-leader-hints-hell-covid-19-71553362.

11   KANEZA, ELOGE WILLY. 2021. "Burundi, In Reversal, Says It Will Accept COVID-19 Vaccines". *ABC News*. https://abcnews.go.com/Health/wireStory/burundi-reversal-accept-covid-19-vaccines-79135931.

12   "Sustainable Development Goals - Infogalactic: The Planetary Knowledge Core". 2022. *Infogalactic.Com*. Accessed March 31. https://www.infogalactic.com/info/Sustainable_Development_Goals.

13   United Nations General Assembly. 2015. "Resolution Adopted By The General Assembly On 25 September 2015 70/1. Transforming Our World: The 2030 Agenda For Sustainable Development". UN. https://www.un.org/en/development/desa/population/migration/generalassembly/docs/globalcompact/A_RES_70_1_E.pdf.

14   Newman, Alex. 2016. "UN Agenda 2030: A Recipe For Global Socialism". *New American*, , 2016. https://thenewamerican.com/un-agenda-2030-a-recipe-for-global-socialism/.

15   Little, Becky. 2018. "The Rise And Fall Of Robert Mugabe, Zimbabwe's Longtime Dictator". *HISTORY*. https://www.history.com/news/the-rise-and-fall-of-robert-mugabe-zimbabwes-longtime-dictator.

16   World Bank Group. 2015. "FROM BILLIONS TO TRILLIONS: MDB Contributions To Financing For Development".

https://documents1.worldbank.org/curated/en/602761467999349576/pdf/98023-BR-SecM2015-0233-IDA-SecM2015-0147-IFC-SecM2015-0105-MIGA-SecM2015-0061-Box391499B-OUO-9.pdf.

17   "Jointly Building The "Belt And Road" Towards The Sustainable Development Goals | United Nations". 2022. *United Nations.* https://web.archive.org/web/20220228123548/https://www.un.org/en/desa/jointly-building-%E2%80%9Cbelt-and-road%E2%80%9D-towards-sustainable-development-goals.

18   "Wang Yi Meets With Secretary-General Of The United Nations (UN) António Guterres | Chinese Ministry Of Foreign Affairs". 2019. *Archive.Ph.* https://archive.ph/alMXz.

19   "One Belt, One Road - Infogalactic: The Planetary Knowledge Core". 2022. *Infogalactic.Com.* Accessed April 1. https://infogalactic.com/info/One_Belt,_One_Road.

20   Corbett, James. 2022. "SHOCKING Document Reveals Trudeau's REAL Plan!". *Bitchute.* https://www.bitchute.com/video/WqHeBUFrsnHH/.

21   "Joint Statement Of The Russian Federation And The People's Republic Of China On The International Relations Entering A New Era And The Global Sustainable Development". 2022. *CNBC.* https://fm.cnbc.com/applications/cnbc.com/resources/editorialfiles/2022/03/31/Joint_Statement_of_the_Russian_Federation_and_the_Peoples_Republic_of_China_on_the_International_Relations_Entering_a_New_Era_and_the_Global_Sustainable_Development__President_of_Russia.pdf.

22   Bucks, Jonathan. 2015. "UN Officials 'Force Children To Perform Oral Sex For Food' In Warzones | World | News | Express.Co.Uk". *Express.Co.Uk.* https://www.express.co.uk/news/world/627783/Starving-children-as-young-as-NINE-forced-to-give-UN-officials-oral-sex-to-get-food/amp.

23   "Welcome To 2030: I Own Nothing, Have No Privacy And Life Has Never Been Better". 2016. *Forbes.* https://www.forbes.com/sites/worldeconomicforum/2016/11/10/shopping-i-cant-really-remember-what-that-is-or-how-differently-well-live-in-2030/.

24   Parker, Ceri. 2016. "8 Predictions For The World In 2030". *World Economic Forum.* https://www.weforum.org/agenda/2016/11/8-predictions-for-the-world-in-2030/.

25   "An International Treaty On Pandemic Prevention And Preparedness". 2022. *Consilium.Europa.Eu.* https://www.consilium.europa.eu/en/policies/coronavirus/pandemic-treaty/.

26   "Explained: The World Health Organization's Controversial 'Pandemic Treaty'". 2022. *Youtu.Be.* https://youtu.be/FQvAnmk5b04.

27   Jones, Alex. 2022. "Breaking! Klaus Schwab Confesses To Criminal World Domination Plan". *Banned.Video.* https://banned.video/watch?id=61f1a830c5d2221b863809b2.

28   "The Forum Of Young Global Leaders - World Economic Forum".
      2022. *The Forum Of Young Global Leaders*. Accessed March 31.
      https://www.younggloballeaders.org/.

29   "WEF/Global Leaders For Tomorrow - Wikispooks".
      2022. *Wikispooks.Com*. Accessed March 31.
      https://wikispooks.com/wiki/WEF/Global_Leaders_for_Tomorrow.

30   "The WEF And The Pandemic". 2021. *Swiss Policy Research*.
      https://swprs.org/the-wef-and-the-pandemic/.

31   "Covid Truth Network February 2022 - Kyle Kemper Western Standard
      Interview". 2022. *Telegram*. https://t.me/covidtruthnet/834.

32   Heilman, Zach. 2022. "Trudeau Doubles Down: 'Mandates Are The Way
      To Avoid Further Restrictions,' – He Really Said This
      [VIDEO]". *Redvoicemedia*.
      https://www.redvoicemedia.com/2022/02/trudeau-doubles-down-
      mandates-are-the-way-to-avoid-further-restrictions-he-really-said-this-
      video/.

33   "Trudeau Under Fire For Expressing Admiration For China's 'Basic
      Dictatorship'". 2013. *Ctvnews*. https://www.ctvnews.ca/politics/trudeau-
      under-fire-for-expressing-admiration-for-china-s-basic-dictatorship-
      1.1535116.

34   Goodman, Peter S. 2022. ""He Has An Incredible Knack To Smell The
      Next Fad": How Klaus Schwab Built A Billionaire Circus At
      Davos". *Vanity Fair*. https://www.vanityfair.com/news/2022/01/how-
      klaus-schwab-built-a-billionaire-circus-at-davos.

35   Tasker, John Paul. 2022. "Banks Have Started To Freeze Accounts
      Linked To The Protests, Freeland Says | CBC News". *CBC*.
      https://www.cbc.ca/news/politics/ottawa-protests-frozen-bank-accounts-
      1.6355396.

36   "Chrystia Freeland". 2022. *World Economic Forum*. Accessed April 1.
      https://www.weforum.org/people/chrystia-freeland.

37   Brockhaus, Hannah. 2021. "Vatican Requires Vaccine Pass For Visitors,
      Employees". *Catholic News Agency*.
      https://www.catholicnewsagency.com/news/249038/vatican-requires-
      vaccine-pass-for-visitors-employees.

38   North Dakota Department of Health. 2021. "COVID-19 Vaccines & Fetal
      Cell Lines."

39   Lancaster, Jessilyn. 2015. "Pope Francis Calls For New World Order—
      Again". *Charisma News*. https://www.charismanews.com/world/50444-
      pope-francis-calls-for-new-world-order-again.

40   LeClaire, Jennifer. 2015. "Why So Many People Think Pope Francis Is
      The Antichrist". *Charisma News*.
      https://www.charismanews.com/opinion/watchman-on-the-wall/50752-
      why-so-many-people-think-pope-francis-is-the-antichrist.

41   "Council For Inclusive Capitalism With The Vatican". 2022. *Council For
      Inclusive Capitalism*. Accessed March 31.
      https://www.inclusivecapitalism.com/.

42   "About Us | Council For Inclusive Capitalism". 2022. *Council For Inclusive Capitalism*. Accessed March 31. https://www.inclusivecapitalism.com/about/.

43   "Lynn Forester De Rothschild - Wikispooks". 2022. *Wikispooks.Com*. Accessed March 31. https://wikispooks.com/wiki/Lynn_Forester_de_Rothschild.

44   Harle, Benjamin. 2021. "Rothschild Family Net Worth: How Much Are They Really Worth? | Finance Friday". *Finance Friday*. https://thefinancefriday.com/2021/05/07/rothschild-family-net-worth/.

45   Hall, Kennedy. 2021. "Davos And The Great Reset". *Crisis Magazine*. https://www.crisismagazine.com/2021/davos-and-the-great-reset.

46   Letzing, John. 2020. "Here's The Pope's Prescription For Resetting The Global Economy In Response To COVID-19". *World Economic Forum*. https://www.weforum.org/agenda/2020/10/here-s-the-pope-s-prescription-for-resetting-the-global-economy-in-response-to-covid-19/.

47   "Fratelli Tutti (3 October 2020) | Francis". 2020. *W2.Vatican.Va*. https://w2.vatican.va/content/francesco/en/encyclicals/documents/papa-francesco_20201003_enciclica-fratelli-tutti.html.

48   Rocca, Francis. 2020. "Pope Francis Says Covid-19 Pandemic Shows Limits To Market Economics". *WSJ*. https://www.wsj.com/articles/pope-francis-calls-for-brotherhood-amid-covid-19-pandemic-11601806766.

49   Letzing, John. 2020. "Here's The Pope's Prescription For Resetting The Global Economy In Response To COVID-19". *World Economic Forum*. https://www.weforum.org/agenda/2020/10/here-s-the-pope-s-prescription-for-resetting-the-global-economy-in-response-to-covid-19/.

50   Hogan, Bernadette, and Bruce Golding. 2021. "Foreigners Could Replace NY's Unvaccinated Hospital, Nursing Home Workers". *Nypost.Com*. https://nypost.com/2021/09/22/foreigners-could-replace-nys-unvaccinated-hospital-nursing-home-workers/.

51   Mek, Amy. 2021. "'Fascist Psychopath': Justin Trudeau Calls The Unvaccinated 'Racist And Misogynistic Extremists' (Video) - RAIR". *RAIR*. https://rairfoundation.com/fascist-psychopath-justin-trudeau-calls-the-unvaccinated-racist-and-misogynistic-extremists/.

52   Snyder, Michael, and Tim Brown. 2022. "French President Labels "Unvaxxed" As "Non-Citizens" - Vows To "P*Ss Them Off" - The Washington Standard". *The Washington Standard*. https://thewashingtonstandard.com/french-president-labels-unvaxxed-as-non-citizens-vows-to-pss-them-off/.

53   "Jacinda Ardern Admits New Zealand Will Become A Two-Tier Society Between Vaccinated And Unvaccinated". 2021. *Uk.News.Yahoo.Com*. https://uk.news.yahoo.com/jacinda-ardern-admits-zealand-become-150600408.html.

54   Mek, Amy. 2022. "'Scandal': Germany's Highest Court Admits Covid Vaccines Are Harmful, Even 'Fatal' - Yet Upholds Mandate (Video) - RAIR". *RAIR*. https://rairfoundation.com/scandal-germanys-highest-

court-admits-covid-vaccines-are-harmful-even-fatal-yet-upholds-mandate-video/.

55   "Full Hearings - Ron Johnson's Expert Panel On COVID Vaccine Injuries". 2021. *Brandnewtube.Com.* https://brandnewtube.com/watch/full-hearings-ron-johnson-039-s-expert-panel-on-covid-vaccine-injuries_RJogrA87bWROhRG.html?lang=type.

56   "VIDEO RELEASE Sen. Ron Johnson COVID-19: A Second Opinion Panel Garners Over 800,000 Views In 24 Hours". 2022. *Ron Johnson Senator From Wisconsin.* https://www.ronjohnson.senate.gov/2022/1/video-release-sen-ron-johnson-covid-19-a-second-opinion-panel-garners-over-800-000-views-in-24-hours.

57   "Bill Maher: Liberal Media Scared 'S*** Out Of People' Over COVID, Democrats 'Afraid' To Leave Home | The Daily Wire". 2021. *The Daily Wire.* https://www.dailywire.com/news/bill-maher-liberal-media-scared-s-out-of-people-over-covid-democrats-afraid-to-leave-home.

58   Caplan, Joshua. 2020. "Nancy Pelosi Bizarrely Blurts Out 'Good Morning, Sunday Morning'". *Breitbart.* https://www.breitbart.com/politics/2020/09/21/nancy-pelosi-bizarrely-blurts-out-good-morning-sunday-morning-during-interview/.

59   Gregorian, Dareh. 2020. "'It Was A Setup': Pelosi Snips At Salon That Publicized Her Rule-Violating Visit". *NBC News.* https://www.nbcnews.com/politics/congress/it-was-setup-pelosi-snips-salon-publicized-her-rule-violating-n1239139.

60   Evans, Zachary. 2022. "California Mask Mandate: Gavin Newsom Violates State Mandate At NFL Playoff Game | National Review". *Nationalreview.Com.* https://www.nationalreview.com/news/governor-newsom-violates-state-mask-mandate-at-nfl-playoff-game/.

61   Ronayne, Kathleen. 2020. "Gov. Newsom Went To Party, Violated Own Virus Rules | KQED". *KQED.* https://www.kqed.org/news/11847570/gov-newsom-went-to-party-violated-own-virus-rules.

62   Hogan, Bernadette, Carl Campanile, and Bruce Golding. 2021. "Cuomo Nursing Home Order Caused More Deaths: Task Force". *Nypost.Com.* https://nypost.com/2021/06/15/cuomo-nursing-home-order-caused-more-deaths-task-force/.

63   Garber, Megan. 2021. "Portrait Of A Leader Humblebragging". *The Atlantic.* https://www.theatlantic.com/culture/archive/2021/03/andrew-cuomos-leadership-memior-did-not-age-well/618213/.

64   Campanile, Carl, and Bernadette Hogan. 2021. "Andrew Cuomo Ordered To Return Pandemic Book Profits To State". *Nypost.Com.* https://nypost.com/2021/12/14/andrew-cuomo-ordered-to-return-pandemic-book-profits-to-state/.

65   "'Stay Home,' Says US Mayor At Mexico Beach Resort". 2020. *BBC News.* https://www.bbc.com/news/world-us-canada-55168634.

66   "Stacy Abrams Scrambles To Delete Photo Of Her Grinning Maskless Surrounded By Masked Children". 2022. *Chad Prather*. https://chadprather.com/stacy-abrams-scrambles-to-delete-photo-of-her-grinning-maskless-surrounded-by-masked-children/.

67   "Rand Paul: COVID Edicts That Make No Scientific Sense Deserve A 'Massive Boycott'". 2022. *Fox News*. https://www.foxnews.com/media/rand-paul-boycott-of-government-covid-edicts.

68   "Frontline Nurse Nicole Sirotek's Testimony On The Abuse Of Patients". 2022. *Deep Roots At Home*. https://deeprootsathome.com/nicole-siroteks-testimony/.

Chapter 19

Propaganda and Political "Science"

"Congress shall make no law respecting an establishment of religion, or prohibiting the free exercise thereof; or abridging the freedom of speech, or of the press; or the right of the people peaceably to assemble, and to petition the government for a redress of grievances."
—The First Amendment to the US Constitution[1]

*"The United States remains in a heightened threat environment fueled by several factors, including an online environment filled with false or misleading narratives and conspiracy theories, and other forms of mis- dis- and mal-information (MDM) introduced and/or amplified by foreign and **domestic threat actors** (my emphasis)."*
—Department of Homeland Security (DHS) National Terrorism Advisory Bulletin, February 7, 2022[2]

Throughout this book we have covered how the term, "misinformation," has been utilized in a coordinated effort by a variety of public and private organizations in order to silence opposition to a clear, defined agenda to sell the public on mRNA inoculations. In fact, we saw Pfizer CEO Albert Bourla admit to working with the CIA and FBI to, "Combat misinformation," and heard Jen Psaki of the Biden Regime admit to having a similar partnership with *Facebook*.

The First Amendment of the US Constitution explicitly prohibits the creation of laws abridging the freedom of speech or prohibiting citizens from a redress of grievances. However, whether its bureaucracies like the DHS or private American companies like *Facebook*, the spirit of America's most important protection sadly does not seem to be one which is protected, in general, by the institutions of the United States—this despite public-private ties so intimate one could easily argue the same protections should legally have to exist in all spheres. But as the DHS bulletin makes perfectly clear, a key tactic toward turning, "misinformation," from protected

507

free speech into a danger worthy of censorship, is to simply make unsubstantiated claims of how it could inspire terrorism.

This tactic is hypocritical, obviously, since the vice president of the very regime pushing it, Kamala Harris, was openly expressing support for organizations which were bailing people out of jail who actually committed violent, domestic terror acts during the Covid era itself.[3] House Speaker Pelosi, for that matter, also said in 2018 in reference to an immigration issue, "I just don't even know why there aren't uprisings all over the country. And maybe there will be..."[4] The real reason the DHS publishes bulletins like they did is they realize that people are past the point of recognizing hypocrisy and are now rightfully fed up with the blatant, incessant lies. So instead of simply telling the truth for even a short period of time to gain a shred of credibility, these forces double down as if truth is not something they're even capable of. And this brings us to the topic of this chapter—propaganda.

Propaganda in the Covid Era

Per Merriam-Webster, the definition of propaganda is, "ideas or statements that are often false or exaggerated and that are spread in order to help a cause, a political leader, a government, etc."[5] The stereotypical images of propaganda tends to be splashy, exaggerated posters of soldiers or workers in support of a communist or fascist cause. Because of this stereotype, a common misconception today is that we can no longer be tricked by propaganda. Unfortunately, this cannot be further from the truth.

In the lead up to World War 1, one successful propaganda campaign was centered around, "The Rape of Belgium," which James Corbett summarizes as, "a catalog of scarcely believable atrocities, allegedly committed by the German forces in their invasion and occupation of Belgium."[6] This campaign included cartoon images of German soldiers bayonetting babies, which had no factual basis but which was used to stir up emotions against the Germans. A similar, if-more-sophisticated form of propaganda was seen as recently as 1990, when in the lead up to the Gulf War a 15-year-old girl identified only as, "Nayirah," testified before the US Congressional Human Rights Caucus about Iraqi soldiers taking babies out of incubators and leaving them to die.[7] The testimony was cited by the US government to get involved in backing Kuwait against invading Iraq. It turned out

508

to be false, however, and it was ultimately discovered Nayirah was the daughter of the Kuwaiti ambassador to the United States. Lastly, as recently as 2019, as the US withdrew troops from Syria, ABC News shared nighttime footage of large explosions, which they claimed appeared, "to show Turkey's military bombing Kurd civilians in a Syrian border town."[8] Despite an on-screen graphic reading, "Slaughter in Syria," which could have led to World War 3 however, the video was ultimately shown to be taken at a Kentucky gun range, with a crowd of onlookers having been cropped out from the bottom of the shot.

We've already discussed some of the more high-profile cases of Covid era propaganda throughout this book; we've also discussed how terms like, "misinformation," and, "fact-checking," have been used to stifle dissent under false pretenses; and Event 201 especially made clear that those looking, "to help the cause," of selling the mRNA inoculations knew how important the control of information would be. The combined power and influence of the forces behind these efforts ultimately allowed for the launch of one of the most intensive psychological warfare campaigns in history. The propaganda techniques utilized were all-encompassing and overwhelming. Still, to a sober mind which was open to asking even the simplest of questions, much of them were just as absurd and on-the-nose as the most colorful communist banner.

The truth is, what ultimately makes propaganda successful or not has little to do with weaving a complex scheme to trick people. What actually matters the most is whether or not enough emotion is stirred inside of them to think and act in the intended, irrational manner. The previous historical examples mentioned had three primary emotional targets, which are perhaps the most common to exploit in people: empathy, anger, and fear. For example, Iraqis were not a familiar people to the majority of Americans, and their way of living was certainly quite different. So—without any reason to doubt the account of a child in general, or an understanding that people with an agenda would exploit a child to provoke an emotional response—it would be easy to understand why a person unfamiliar with the situation there would feel empathy for the child's declared plight, a resulting anger at those alleged to be causing it, and a fear that if something isn't done a similar fate could come to their doorstep.

While all three emotional targets were taken advantage of, fear was by-far the most relevant in the Covid era. We will further discuss the psychology of how it was sustained in the next chapter, but for now, consider the opening days of the alleged pandemic. *Revolver News* covered a spate of videos which had been shared to social media in early 2020 of Chinese people collapsing dead in the streets, foaming at the mouth, and lined up in what appeared like body bags along sidewalks.[9] These videos also tended to include authorities in full-body Hazmat suits, which added to the fear as they spread rapidly on social media. However, time and time again, they turned out to be fake. Video of alleged body bags, "waiting for pickup," turned out to be vagrants in sleeping bags; a picture of a dead man with a bloody face and a loved one hunched over them in despair turned out to be a scooter accident with the scooter cropped out; training videos of, "coronavirus SWAT teams," were passed off as real encounters; and the fear-porn Hazmat suits turned out to be a routine outfit of Chinese first-responders. Of course, none of this type of thing ever materialized in the US, but that is irrelevant to the purpose it achieved. People around the world were sent into the panicked, stressed state which would be needed to make extreme, counterintuitive measures like lockdowns, masks, and experimental drugs seem reasonable.

From there, the propaganda campaign amplified by the day. Among the first salvos was the *Lancet* letter by, "public health scientists," pre-empting any discussion of an origin. Then came the use of symbolic military rhetoric such as, "frontline," as it related to nurses. The same nurses soon after became the subject of a viral-video campaign in which groups of mask-wearing nurses from around the country danced together, apparently while on the job in the very hospitals which were meant to be, "overwhelmed." This pandemic marketing campaign ultimately culminated in the Biden Regime inviting The Northwell Health Nurse Choir to the White House.[10] The *masked* choir serenaded Biden and his wife in song and dance, in celebration of both their work and of a Christmas 2021 holiday Biden had recently claimed would be a, "dark winter." In a truly poetic sign of the times, it seems *Twitter* removed the video of the event, "in response to a report by the copyright owner."

The best propaganda has a kernel of truth, and it certainly is true that nurses were sent into traumatic, warzone-like scenarios at hospitals, thanks to the misdirection of public health departments.

Nicole Sirotek described this exact situation in her testimony. The trauma she expressed in her own viral video is also far more comparable to an actual soldier's experience than Tik Tok dances could ever be.[11] This is telling as far as whose boots were really the ones on the ground. Also, Sirotek's acknowledgement that, "black lives don't matter here," was particularly apt, given what took place in 2020. We've already touched on the damage done in the wake of the George Floyd riots, how Democrat politicians voiced support even for those engaging in criminal acts during those riots, and how Covid collaborators like Fauci and the WEF exploited the events in their dishonest calls for, "social equity." Sirotek's whistleblowing, however, adds a particularly inhuman dimension to this dishonesty, as she alleges the same communities exploited for the political benefit of feigned compassion, were also intentionally experimented on by those doing the exploiting.

Even without such allegations and supporting data, the political-not-scientific nature of the CDC, NIH, WHO, FDA, and their collaborators has been incredibly obvious from the beginning. Their willingness to put media appearances and press conferences before scientific studies and proof alone, demonstrated as much. Once the riots began, however, the public health departments threw whatever crumbs of scientific credibility they had left out the window. It became clear their globalist economic and social ambitions took precedent over their nominal roles, when everyone from Rochelle Walensky, to Anthony Fauci, to John's Hopkins doctors encouraged race protests at the same time they vilified rival political rallies, as we've covered previously. And this leads us to quite possibly the defining quote of the entire Covid era.

Anthony Fauci and "The Science," But I Repeat Myself?

> *"So it's easy to criticize, but they're really criticizing science because I represent science. That's dangerous."*
> —Anthony Fauci, November 2021[12]

Megalomaniac Anthony Fauci has said some pretty outrageous things over the course of his career. But the above quote was a kind of, "shot heard round the world," uttered by a man who has earned the righteous indignation of the entire human race at this point. The disdain for Fauci is especially remarkable however, when considering the grotesque propaganda campaign attempting to lionize him was likely more incessant than for almost any figure in world history.

One example of propaganda upon propaganda upon propaganda surrounds the relationship between Fauci and *Facebook*'s Mark Zuckerberg. First off, the magazine *Inc.* published a propaganda piece about a FOIA-requested email exchange between Fauci and Zuckerberg in the opening days of the Covid response.[13] In the email exchange, Zuckerberg—who spent the entirety of the alleged pandemic censoring dissent and violating civil liberties on Fauci's behalf—said he, "wanted to share a few ideas of ways we could help you get your message out."[14] Instead of focusing on a redacted deal made in the email exchange including, "trade secrets and commercial or financial information," however, the *Inc.* stenographer decided to instead focus on how great Zuckerberg's, "persuasion skills," were.

In an interview between Zuckerberg and Fauci that seems to have been a result of this email exchange, Fauci also admitted, "This would not be the first time, if it happened, that a vaccine that looked good in initial safety actually made people worse."[15] *USA Today*, *Reuters*, *Snopes*, and many other, "fact-check," propagandists all seized on the opportunity to publish pieces afterward, noting that Fauci, "did not say COVID-19 vaccines make recipients more vulnerable to infection."[16,17,18,19] As always, this is entirely irrelevant to the significance of Fauci's statement. The Covid inoculations certainly did *not* and *could not have* completed safety trials by 2021— the first year they were rolled out and the year these propagandist, "fact-checks," were published. Therefore, despite Fauci's 2021 claims that they, "looked good in initial safety," his 2020 admission to Zuckerberg shows he knew there was always a possibility the shots could ultimately make people worse—a possibility which Fauci inhumanely ignored as he encouraged mass, indiscriminate inoculation and even criminal coercion of the inoculations via mandates in *year one* of the inoculation campaign.

This reckless endangerment was ignored by these corrupt outlets as always, along with Fauci's documented pre-meditation to commit it, but so too were the ever-devolving claims Fauci made in favor of efficacy. Transmission prevention proved false; a lack of significant adverse events, including now-on-the-package-insert myocarditis, proved false; usefulness against, "variants"—if one subscribes to the, "variant," narrative at all—proved false; and it is an outright, "fact-checker," lie that, "there is no publicly available evidence suggesting COVID-19 vaccines," make infection worse. We've not only covered a variety of seasoned virologists who claim they do just that, but we can also point to Israel or Scotland—among countless other places—where the data shows *increased* rates of death and hospitalization among the inoculated populations.

With many people having become increasingly aware of Fauci's incoherent lies despite the efforts of, "fact-checkers," *National Geographic* released a propaganda documentary called *Fauci* in September 2021. The piece reportedly received a 2% *Rotten Tomatoes* audience score and a predictable 91% critic score, with the *IMDB* score magically jumping from around 2/10 shortly after release, to 6/10 and a handful of 10 star reviews a few months later.[20,21] The documentary is an attempt to humanize Fauci, who claims to have, "post-traumatic stress syndrome," from his time during the AIDS debacle, for which he also faced rightful indignation (more on that later). Still, Fauci has remained in his position for decades despite this and despite threats he alleges have been made against his family. Susan Rice is also featured, saying of the highest paid government employee the ironic quip, "You don't do it because you want to make money." Given his, "PTSD," his constant failures, the disdain the public has for him, and the alleged danger he is putting his family in by remaining at his post, what reason other than money could there possibly be for Fauci to continue? There is none, which only serves to continue exposing people like Rice for the liars they are.

The above are just a few long, egregious examples of the media Fauci embraces above scientific debate holding water for him. The following is a non-exhaustive list of additional shameless cases:

- Kate Messner authored a children's propaganda picture book biography of Anthony Fauci[22]
- *The Guardian* in a social media post featured a serious-looking photo-shoot picture of the allegedly extremely busy, pandemic-facing, "scientist," in which it referred to him as the, "sexiest man alive"[23]
- MSNBC anchor Nicolle Wallace actually said the following[24]: *"I'm a Fauci groupie. I'm thrice-vaccinated, mask adherent, I buy N-95 masks by the caseload, they're in every pocket, I*

wear them everywhere except when I sit down, and I'm certain that this is not a variant I can outrun."

- *Yahoo* published, "Time to make space in your superhero merch drawer," in reference to Anthony Fauci merchandise popping up including candles, sweatshirts, and socks.[25] The *Yahoo* typist even seemed overwhelmed by the sheer volume of sock sales, noting that the company in question, "sold nearly 100 of the design in two days' time." Can you believe that!? *Nearly* 100! The company is noted by the devout Faucian author as calling their lord and savior, "a sign of hope for all of us and a trusted advisor."

- The totally, "science-focused," Fauci posed for an *InStyle* magazine photoshoot as the alleged pandemic raged on in the summer of 2020.[26] Fauci stayed cool by lounging poolside in sunglasses, looking totally chill and natural. The piece also featured words from his public-relations manager (bioethicist?) wife, who spoke to the magazine about how her PTSD-victim husband was holding up in fighting the terrifying, all-consuming pandemic.

Transitioning off of Fauci, the perversion of the word, "science," is by now very familiar to us as it relates to the technocrat Covid collaborators and their faithful flock. Absolutely nothing is sacred in the impossible, fluid-truth reality they choose to inhabit— not even the definitions of words. In early September 2021, for example, the CDC changed its definitions of both, "vaccination," and, "vaccine," as follows:

- Vaccination
  - August 26, 2021[27]: *"A product that stimulates a person's immune system* **to produce immunity to a specific disease, protecting the person from that disease** *(my emphasis). Vaccines are usually administered through needle injections, but can also be administered by mouth or sprayed into the nose."*
  - September 1, 2021[28]: *"A preparation that is used* **to stimulate the body's immune response against diseases** *(my emphasis). Vaccines are usually*

514

administered through needle injection, but some can be administered by mouth or sprayed into the nose."

- Vaccine
  - August 26, 2021[29]: *"The act of introducing a vaccine into the body **to produce immunity to** (my emphasis) a specific disease."*
  - September 1, 2021[30]: *"The act of introducing a vaccine into the body **to produce protection from** (my emphasis) a specific disease."*

Valid concerns were raised surrounding such a change being made not only in the midst of a mass, "vaccination," campaign, but also at a time when the inoculations were clearly failing to, "produce immunity," to positive tests in less than a single year of use. The CDC's PR team—I mean, the *Washington Post*—no … I mean, the CDC's PR team—came to the organization's defense to play down this change, asserting it wasn't a, "gotcha," moment because, "medical experts have long said that no vaccine … is 100 percent effective."[31] Once *again*, however, this is entirely irrelevant to the point. *WaPo* argues that the Covid inoculations still provide, "immunity," because they are allegedly greater than 0% effective. If this is true, however, what's the reason to change the definition?

While *WaPo* suggests without evidence it's an innocent one, even the slightest bit of journalism and unbiased reporting would have revealed otherwise. You see, the CDC is *not* a science-based organization. Its conflicts of interest reveal that it is a sales-based organization. Its actions show it is not focused on crafting a message based on disinterested studies, but rather on fitting studies to a predetermined message. This is further validated by the CDC's regular engagement in social activism, such as an April 8, 2021 statement from Rochelle Walensky on race disparities in health care.[32] Do such disparities exist? I'm sure they do. Want to know how I know? Because a nurse who experienced it first-hand testified to it. Does Walensky's social justice slobbering ever address these credible allegations that drug-company experimentation *caused* these disparities in outcomes? Of course it doesn't, because this would require her to stand against the pharmaceutical masters who fund her organization through the CDC Foundation, as we've covered.

Walensky's dishonest activism is also emblematic of deeper organizational issues at the CDC. It reveals the CDC suffers from an affliction which is common to many American institutions today. It is an affliction Vox Day diagnoses in his book, *Corporate Cancer*, called, "convergence."[33] As Day describes it, convergence, "describes the degree to which an organization prioritizes social justice," with, "fully converged," organizations devoting, "significant resources to social causes that have absolutely nothing to do with its core business activities."[34] One could argue the CDC is *not* fully converged as it relates to its unofficial *business* mission, i.e. it remains highly focused on its core business activity of selling inoculations on behalf of its parent companies. However, emails have revealed that convergence, *not* science or happenstance as the careless writers/editors at *WaPo* falsely and dishonestly imply, is what led to the CDC's decision to change its definitions.

Internal CDC emails acquired via FOIA request by *TechnoFog* show that in August 2021 an activist CDC employee (a classic source of, "corporate cancer," per Day) cited complaints that, "Right-wing covid-19 deniers are using your 'vaccine' definition to argue that mRNA vaccines are not vaccines."[35] What does a concern with a definition change and/or the consistent dishonesty of the CDC have to do with being, "right-wing?" Your guess is as good as mine. The use of this term would, however, seem to imply that the alternative in this activist's mind would be a, "left-wing covid-19 narrative accepter." Either way, this shows the CDC itself, as usual, is the one making the issue political, which has nothing to do with its intended function as a public health organization. So was this activist who invalidates the premise of the *Washington Post* propaganda piece fired on the spot for even bringing up this absurdity? Of course not. The activism-based request based on a, "problematic," (classic activist word) definition went all the way up the chain and is what directly led to the change.

Still, the CDC isn't even alone in its convergence. Despite another *WaPo* deception that Merriam-Webster hasn't changed the definition of, "immunity," recently, the definition of the word actually in question, "vaccine," *has* been changed in a similar fashion by even Merriam-Webster in 2021.[36,37] The famous dictionary also took their subservience to another level, however. In November 2021 it was reported Merriam-Webster's, "word of the year," for 2021 was chosen to be the very word which didn't even have a consistent definition over the course of the year in question—namely, "vaccine."[38]

These organizations also join the WHO, which has its own history of changing definitions. In fact, the WHO's own bulletin acknowledged the organization's ambiguity-in and reluctance-to even define the word, "pandemic," in the wake of the swine flu of 2009.[39] A heated debate took place at the time centered on whether there even should have been a swine flu, "pandemic," declaration, since the WHO had removed the criteria that a pandemic causes, "enormous numbers of deaths and illness."[40,41,42] There were also valid suspicions as to why it did so mere months before a pandemic was declared—a, "pandemic," which also ended up akin to a seasonal flu. Their excuse was that this was not meant to be a, "definition," per sé, but was better described as a, "description-definition," as if that doesn't make their admitted lack of a definition *more* confusing. Confusion has remained since and has continued with similarly convenient changes to the definition of, "herd immunity," by the WHO in late fall 2020 and, of "gain-of-function," by the NIH in fall 2021 as follows[43,44]:

- WHO definition of, "Herd Immunity"
  - June 2020[45]: *"The indirect protection from an infectious disease that happens when a population is immune either through vaccination or immunity developed through previous infection."*
  - November 2020 (as vaccines were about to roll out)[46]: *"... a concept used for vaccination, in which a population can be protected from a certain virus if a threshold of vaccination is reached ... Herd immunity is achieved by protecting people from a virus, not by exposing them to it."*
- NIH definition of, "Gain-of-Function"
  - Early October 2021 definition: *"A type of research that modifies a biological agent so that it confers new or enhanced activity to that agent ... This research poses biosafety risks ... these risks must be carefully managed."*
  - Late October 2021 definition (as pressure mounted on Fauci after lying to Congress)[47]: *"While ePPP research is a type of so called 'gain-of-function'*

> *(GOF) research, the vast majority of GOF research does not involve ePPP and falls outside the scope of oversight required for research involving ePPPs."*

Especially as it relates to the, "herd immunity," change, these are definitional differences which would fundamentally alter the framework for determining whether or not there's a pandemic, how pandemics work, and the possible ways they can be mitigated. The changes were all made at the exact times they were needed in order to justify the actions taken by those making them. Like with masking, lockdowns, and many other Covid era practices, they were made despite contradicting hundreds of years of common scientific understanding. They were also not made based on any new scientific information or studies, but rather on political, marketing, and legal grounds. Further, in the case of the CDC *at least*, no basis was given willingly to the public for such an important adjustment at all. The incoherence and/or criminality of the actions the definition changes sought to justify, would literally hinge on the public's unfounded acceptance of those changes. This undoubtedly serves to, "help a cause," and serves as one of the most corrupt, dystopian examples of propaganda in the Covid era.

Overt Propaganda Programs

Operation Mockingbird was but one example of how propaganda has become institutionalized in our world today. While that program is allegedly no longer, it is clear the same type of upside-down news coverage one would expect from it remains. Still, in the Covid era there were several examples of overt, Covid-specific propaganda operations the, "public-private partnerships," we've discussed are acknowledged as having engaged in.

In the US, we've already covered how many of the large media outlets rely on pharmaceutical company advertising and how this represents a tremendous conflict of interest. However, in response to a FOIA request filed by the *Blaze*, the DHHS revealed that it too purchased advertising from major news networks as part of a, "comprehensive media campaign," to encourage inoculation.[48] The networks in question included mainstream media companies like ABC, CBS, NBC, Fox, CNN, and MSNBC, as well as publications/blogs like the *Los Angeles Times*, the *Washington Post*,

BuzzFeed, and *NewsMax*. Additionally, according to the documents, "The government also relied on earned media featuring 'influencers' from 'communities hit hard by COVID-19' and 'experts' … to be interviewed and promote vaccination in the news."

Funds used seem to have included the at least $1 billion Congress appropriated as part of the American Rescue Plan Act to expressly spend on propaganda activities with the aim to, "strengthen vaccine confidence in the United States."[49] Again, this goes back to the idea of, "universal," government programs of any kind coming with an incentive on the part of the government to coerce the service provided and a disincentive to honestly scrutinize how, "safe and efficacious," the service actually is. In this case, the government buys the inoculations through the CDC and programs like Operation Warp Speed; it also profits off the inoculations through pharma kick-backs like the FDA's user fees, direct patents like those held by the NIH, royalties like those received by the CDC, and corporate taxation of the pharma company's massive profits; and finally, it strategically and coercively markets with propaganda like we've seen above, working with media outlets to stifle dissent/scrutiny where it exists. Those outlets are clearly happy to take the money and run with it too, as all of the aforementioned networks covered the inoculations with near universal positivity and without ever once disclosing the lack of independence in their reporting.

Another US example of institutionalized propaganda came on the part of the DHS and CISA, per a February 2022 report by *Uncover DC*.[50] The report outlines how the two organizations partnered to roll out terrorism advisories and a series of graphic novels called, "The Resilience Series," all focused on combatting Constitutionally-protected free speech mischaracterized as, "misinformation." The CDC also partnered with *Facebook* toward the same aims, per emails obtained by lawyer Aaron Siri.[51] Examples include *Facebook* directly becoming a CDC publishing company, as the government bureaucracy dictated the, "focused messaging for the next week," which *Facebook* was meant to display on its pages.

Patrick Howley of *National File* expanded on this mass-scale information laundering in an incredible report on the University of Pennsylvania's extensive involvement in inoculation propaganda, as well as its ties to the current regime via the Penn Biden Center think tank.[52] As outlined in the report, U Penn admitted the following in December 2020:

> *"The Pfizer/BioNTech and Moderna COVID-19 mRNA vaccines both use licensed University of Pennsylvania technology. As a result of these licensing relationships, Penn, Dr. Weissman and Dr. Kariko have received and may continue to receive significant financial benefits in the future based on the sale of these products. BioNTech provides funding for Dr. Weissman's research into the development of additional infectious disease vaccines."*

As part of this licensing agreement, U Penn secured civil legal immunity in its deal with BioNTech. This immunity included liability protection from any cases of, "bodily injury," and, "death," that might be associated with the inoculations their work developed. However, this is a familiar story. What isn't as familiar is that U Penn also just-so-happens to host the now-familiar, universally-inoculation-positive website *FactCheck.org*!

In none of the endless amount of, "fact-checks," this site provides on the Covid inoculations did I ever see a disclosure of the *fact* that it is hosted by the very people who profit directly off those inoculations. Still, the website validates this fraudulent inoculation marketing scheme via its own statement[53]:

> *"FactCheck.org is a project of the Annenberg Public Policy Center of the University of Pennsylvania. The APPC was established by publisher and philanthropist Walter Annenberg to create a **community of scholars within the University of Pennsylvania** (my emphasis) that would address public policy issues at the local, state and federal levels."*

The truth is, we can go on and on and on about all the propaganda and information laundering conflicts present today in the corporate media. They exist all over the world and have for some time turned what was once a useful fourth estate into a mere mouth piece of the day's desired psychological operations. However, there are a few particularly interesting additional stories worth covering outside the US before we move on. One includes Britain's Office of Communications (Ofcom), a type of, "Ministry of Truth," bureaucracy tasked directly with enforcing censorship, including of content which is not explicitly illegal.[54] Former *Sky News* Exec Mark Sherman blew the whistle on Ofcom in 2022, when he alleged[55]:

> *"It* [an early Covid era Ofcom bulletin] *was a warning to basically say, 'do not question the official government line.' Now to be fair to them, they said, you can have opposition voices on, but you must present as 'must intervene' if there's any danger of harmful or misinformation."*

We can also turn next to Young Global Leader Justin Trudeau's country of Canada. As reported by the *Ottawa Citizen*, a Canadian Forces report concluded Canadian military leaders used the pandemic as a, "unique opportunity," to test propaganda techniques on the public.[56] While this might not seem surprising since the US and many other countries obviously had propaganda campaigns of their own, the circumstances and types of operations acknowledged in the report are particularly disturbing.

First, the Canadian government never authorized the Canadian Joint Operations Command's initiative—a type of initiative meant only to be aimed at adversaries. Canadian military commanders didn't think they needed such authorization however, and carried on anyway in April 2020. The tactics utilized were reportedly similar to those used in the Afghanistan War. They called for, "shaping," and, "exploiting," information in order to, "head off civil disobedience by Canadians during the coronavirus pandemic and to bolster government messages about the pandemic." While the operation was allegedly halted a month later in May, a September 2020 scandal reported by the *Ottawa Citizen* told of military members in Nova Scotia blasting wolf noises on loudspeakers during, "propaganda training."[57] The terror inflicted on locals was then amplified by an officer who forged a document, "using the letterhead of the Wildlife Division of Nova Scotia's Department of Lands and Forestry," which, "was a warning to local residents, claiming wolves had been reintroduced into the area by the provincial and federal governments and were now roaming the Annapolis Valley." The letter managed to get passed around town and panic ensued until it was eventually identified as fake.

Mistake or not, the backdrop of an already fear-porn-laden pandemic qualifies these actions as psychologically abusive. Still, we know such behavior was not limited to the government. The, "public-private collaboration," the WEF championed was on full display in the media sphere as well, with a dystopian BBC-led propaganda operation called the Trusted News Initiative (TNI).[58] In August 29, 2021, the *Exposé* reported on the TNI in great detail, as follows[59,60,61]:

> *"**In July 2019** (my emphasis), before the pandemic, the UK and Canadian governments hosted the FCO Global Conference on Media Freedom, where then BBC Director-General Tony Hall announced:*
> *'Last month I convened, behind closed doors, a Trusted News Summit at the BBC, which brought together global tech platforms and publishers. The goal was to arrive at a practical set of actions we can take together, right now, to tackle the rise of misinformation and bias... I'm determined that we use that [BBC's] unique reach and trusted voice to lead the way – to create a global alliance for integrity in news. We're ready to do even more to help promote freedom and democracy worldwide.'*
> *The initial Trusted News partners in attendance were the European Broadcasting Union (EBU), Facebook, Financial Times, First Draft, Google, The Hindu, and The Wall Street Journal."*

Here, again, we have yet *another* massive, open conspiracy taking place in late 2019. This conspiracy also just-so-happened to be built around the same mission Event 201 called for—namely, a public-private partnership aimed at controlling the flow of information. For context about who was doing the conspiring, consider a June 2021 report by the Reuters Institute, which found that trust in the US media had fallen to an incredible 29%.[62] Rather than seek to understand the valid concerns of the overwhelming majority and adjust accordingly, the TNI sought to double-down on the same practices which led to the clearly terrible reputations of its collective member organizations. The *Exposé* even points out that initial wrong-think concerns of the TNI in 2019 included the growing influence of those slanderously dubbed, "anti-vaxxers," before continuing as follows[63,64,65,66]:

> "CBC/Radio-Canada publicly announced its participation in the TNI in September 2019, saying 'this includes a commitment to collaborate on source authentication, civic information, media education, and other responses to disinformation.' The Hindu announced the Indian program simultaneously.
>
> Two weeks after WHO announced the Covid-19 pandemic on March 11, 2020, Canada's CBC reported that the Trusted News Initiative had announced plans 'to tackle harmful coronavirus disinformation.'
>
> 'Starting today, partners in the Trusted News Initiative will alert each other to disinformation about coronavirus, including 'imposter content' purporting to come from trusted sources. Such content will be reviewed promptly to ensure that disinformation is not republished.'
>
> The media partners had now expanded to include Twitter, Microsoft, Associated Press, Agence France-Presse, Reuters, and the Reuters Institute for the Study of Journalism.
>
> The TNI next agreed to engage with a new verification technology called Project Origin, led by a coalition of the BBC, CBC/Radio-Canada, Microsoft and The New York Times – with a mandate to identify non-authorized news stories for suppression.
>
> In July, 2020, Eric Horvitz, Chief Scientific Officer for Microsoft, remarked about **authorizing the news** (my emphasis): 'We've forged a close relationship with the BBC and other partners on Project Origin, aimed at methods and standards for end-to-end authentication of news and information.'
>
> By December 2020, the BBC had reported that disinformation was 'spreading online to millions of people,' and included minimizing COVID-19 risks along with impugning the vaccine developers' motives."

And there you have it. An openly-admitted, named collaboration does exist between effectively the entire major corporate media, public media, and social media apparatus. These, "distinct," organizations have all signed on to exclusively blast the messages of the WHO, CDC, NIH, FDA, and WEF, while suppressing and censoring all dissent. Like each of the former organizations, they also invert the truth of what they actually do by claiming their aim is to, "protect democracy." Considering 71% disagree with their coverage, it is clear that literally the exact opposite is true. Still, the machine keeps on churning, and the result is what has led increasing numbers of people to brand this propaganda mafia, "clown world."

An Absolute Circus of Freak-Show Propaganda

So what was the result of this union of narcissist, technocrat propagandists known as the TNI? The following is a list of as many examples as I have been able to document during these past two years of just *some* of the most mind-boggling Covid era propaganda. These posts, pictures, videos, and other media insulted the intelligence of the entire world for two years straight. As shocking as it has seemed, these things really were spread without an ounce of shame. They are what inspired me to change the main title of this book from the working-title, "The Cost of Lies," to what is now, *Stranger than Fiction.* And despite their unmistakable absurdity, I must emphasize that *billions* of people's minds were clouded by enough fear, anger, and/or empathy to have prevented them from seeing through it. So this is a cautionary tale: you *can* be tricked; I *can* be tricked; and those who don't control their emotions, during trying times especially, *will* be tricked. Now, without further ado, enjoy the freak show:

- In the interest of starting things off with a bang, the following is the headline of a *Forbes* article which was an, "editor's pick," was in the, "science," section of the blog, and was quite possibly the most demented piece of propaganda of the entire alleged pandemic[67]: *"You Must Not 'Do Your Own Research' When It Comes To Science."* Still, the contents of the article itself are even worse, as it actually attempts to claim the layperson should simply have faith in what, "scientists," call, "science," whether it can be explained in a way that makes sense or not. The author then makes the ironic claim that the consequences of not having this blind faith could be, "deadly."

524

- The CDC's actual, not-ironic recommended tips around, "Preparing for a Hurricane," include first[68]: *"Prepare for a hurricane: Take basic steps now to ensure your safety should a storm hit."* And once you've prepared for the hurricane by preparing for the hurricane, you're ready for the second most important step in preparing for a hurricane: *"Get a COVID-19 vaccine as soon as you can."* Steps 3 and beyond include much less important things than step 2, such as getting emergency supplies, making a plan, preparing to evacuate, and protecting the weak.

- Propagandists *Vice* published in September 2021 a since-edited article and deleted social media post claiming, "There's no such thing as natural immunity"[69]

- *Bloomberg* defiled the good name of *The Lord of the Rings* by posting the obviously deceptive article, "What if your fourth Covid shot could last forever?" with the familiar line, "One Covid shot to rule them all, one Covid shot to find them, one Covid shot to bring them all and in the darkness bind them."[70] In a way this might actually be an astute connection to make however, since the Covid inoculations and their, "passports," are undoubtedly tools of social control used to, "rule them all," to, "find them," to, "bring them all," and, "in the darkness bind them."

- *Twitter*, "fact-checked," a 37-year-old mother's obituary in October 2021 as, "misleading," because it told of how she died of blood clots brought on by the inoculations.[71] The mother was reportedly, "vehemently opposed," to taking the shots but was mandated to by the state of Washington in order to continue teaching. Backlash about the absurd-as-usual, "fact-check," led to *Twitter*'s removing it without comment.

- On October 6, 2021, the *Jerusalem Post* shared the obvious about the benefits of doctors actually treating patients, which inexplicably stopped happening in the Covid era[72]: *"Aspirin lowers risk of COVID: New findings support preliminary Israeli trial."* Six days later, on October 12, 2021, the *New York Times* and the rest of the corporate media outlets gave Aspirin the, "horse dewormer," treatment[73,74]: *"Adults ... may face serious side effects if they start a daily regimen of low-*

dose aspirin." While this may seem to the untrained eye like it could be a coincidence, it comes despite the following remaining on the FDA's website to this day (spring 2022)[75]: *"Aspirin has been shown to be helpful when used daily to lower the risk of heart attack, clot-related strokes and other blood flow problems in patients who have cardiovascular disease or who have already had a heart attack or stroke. **Many medical professionals prescribe aspirin for these uses*** (my emphasis). "

- Similar to the previous misdirection, the public's increasing recognition of an explosion in heart conditions, "in younger and younger people," led to a spate of late-2021, early-2022 propaganda pieces theorizing all manner of hair-brained explanations.[76] Everything from, "climate change," to, "broken heart syndrome," to pandemic depression/anxiety, to eggs, to daylight savings time, to referee whistles—yes, *referee whistles*—were blamed for the spike in heart diseases and strokes.[77,78,79,80,81,82,83] "Climate change," a laughable explanation, was actually blamed specifically for child heart conditions in December 2021, a group that has almost never experienced such conditions historically and a time when the FDA had only months before authorized the experimental inoculations for children who Cal studies showed at the time would have greater risk of serious heart-related issues than of, "Covid," by a factor of 6.

- The *Washington Post* asked, "He's cute, but is he swab worthy?" as they suggested rapid testing had become a, "dating ritual."[84] The picture at the head of the article included a man and a woman smiling at each other as they're connected at the nostrils by a heart-shaped swab.

- On September 23, 2021 it was widely reported that Oregon, "health officials," let the public know that after a year and a half of not kissing anyone, "because of the virus," they could start kissing again … *if* both people were inoculated.[85] This is strange, considering Fauci's endorsement of Tinder hookups as early on as April 2020.[86] At that time, "public health officials," like Fauci deemed meeting up with strangers a risk the public should have the right to take or not, but not going to the gym. Strange as it is however, this starts to make more sense when you learn Fauci frequented gay bathhouses and bars during the AIDS scare, "to study the disease."[87]

- Speaking of these public health decrees, CNN reported in December 2021 on a poll it conducted and decided to go with the headline, "Nearly 4 in 10 Americans think Covid-19 precautions are here to stay, but others have already returned to their pre-pandemic normal."[88] It chose this headline despite the obvious, far more significant finding—namely, that more than 6 in 10 Americans were done with Covid-19 precautions, while some others had been scarred for life by the 24/7 fear porn CNN refers to as, "news."

- CNN's Brian Stelter, who might actually be the lowest IQ media figure I've ever witnessed, complained about podcaster Joe Rogan being trusted more than CNN.[89] In his segment, Stelter quipped, "Not all opinions are created equal." True, Brian. Very true.

- On the topic of censorship and political, "science," the *JAMA* and *NEJM* medical journals reportedly (per Malone on his since-banned *Twitter* account) blocked Dr. Robert Malone's (inventor of mRNA technology) IP address from accessing their medical journals[90]

- While prolific doctors and scientists like Malone were being banned for warning parents about the dangers the shots posed to their children, CNN and their chief medical correspondent Sanjay Gupta were shamelessly teaming up with children's show Sesame Street to propagandize children into getting the experimental mRNA inoculations and wearing masks for a disease of which they have zero risk[91,92]

- *Reuters*, after slandering ivermectin the entirety of the alleged pandemic, finally in January 2022 acknowledged its longtime, well-documented anti-viral effect[93,94]

- Per NBC News, "Colin Powell was vaccinated against Covid," but died from it because he, "was elderly," and he, "suffered from a cancer that makes the shots less effective."[95] The *New Yorker* magazine's *Intelligencer* blog at the same time pointed its readers to a, "HermanCainAward," *Reddit* board—named after the late, also-elderly Herman Cain—to, "dunk on," those

527

who died, "of Covid," despite being, "anti-vaccine," or, "anti-mask."[96] The typists at the *Intelligencer* might be wise to take a lesson on hubris from cardiologist Sohrab Lutchmedial, however.[97] Lutchmedial posted on social media of those who refused the shot, "for selfish reasons," that he, "won't cry at their funeral," before dying in his sleep two weeks after getting his booster inoculation. Lutchmedial was only 52 years-old.

- *LA Times* blogger and sociopath Michael Hiltzik published the column, "Mocking anti-vaxxers' COVID deaths is ghoulish, yes — but may be necessary," with the source link featuring the question, "why shouldn't we **dance on the graves** (my emphasis) of anti-vaxxers?"[98] I don't really have much to say about this, but Hiltzik might want to be careful of whose grave he dances on. For example, *Yahoo News* and others learned this hard way when they got footloose about the death of, "anti-vaxxer," and Olympic gold medalist Szilveszter Csollany, who reportedly died of, "Covid."[99] The only problem with the propagandist liars' headlines was that if you actually read the articles themselves you'd realize Csollany was actually, "vaccinated."[100] An, "honest mistake," *surely*.

- Hiltzik should also be careful as he continues to play Pharma Roulette and should consider examples like that of Indian actor, Vivekh. Vivekh, like Dr. Lutchmedial, urged others to get inoculated and wanted to help, "dispel rumors."[101] Within a day of receiving his shot however, he had his first and last heart attack.[102] Good for Hiltzik though, who has clearly been more fortunate than his fellow aggressive proponents.

- *NPR* coronavirus frequently asked (apparently) question[103]: *"I just got a booster. Can I ... go crazy?"* NPR answer: *"... keep your stash of masks ... In fact, after your booster, **you may be more at risk of catching a cold or flu** (my emphasis) than COVID-19 ... 'It's still the same precautions.'"* As a friendly reminder, "a cold," is supposedly still a coronavirus, "variant."

- In either an example of a person engaging in propaganda or the devastating effects of propaganda, charlatan Supreme Court Justice Sonia Sotomayor and her charlatan allied justices simply made things up during a trial which would define the official position of the US government on informed consent.[104] Sotomayor in particular was universally mocked for the fictitious claims that the inoculated can't transmit, "Covid," and that, "we have over 100,000 children, which we've never had before, in serious condition and many on ventilators."[105]

- Sotomayor wasn't alone in her statistical fabrications, as the *New York Times* was forced to correct a more than 10-times exaggeration of the number of children hospitalized *with*, "Covid"[106]

- *Google* played a vaccine propaganda song to Android users who simply asked to, "hear a song."[107] Speaking of songs, Columbia University partnered up with Darryl DMC McDaniels of Run-DMC to make a propaganda hip-hop track targeted at, "black individuals," who polls said, "were among the least likely to be vaccinated." They figured since logic and reason didn't work, they decided that to convince people they'd, "need to truly connect, culturally and **emotionally** (my emphasis)."[108] Other cringe-worthy music propaganda examples include a, "nerdcore," rap by University of Auckland staff called, "Vax the Nation;"[109] two separate inoculation jingles by mindless late-night shills James Corden and Jimmy Fallon (both featuring Ariana Grande);[110,111] a rendition of Jon Lennon's, "Imagine," led by actor Gal Gadot and including a bunch of, "celebrities," who thought it'd be a good idea to tell a bunch of dying old and obese people to imagine there being no heaven;[112] a rap song by Juvenile called, "Vaxx That Thang Up," which the *New York Post* suggested might be the, "unofficial summer anthem of 2021;"[113] a Zoom-recorded rendition of Dolly Parton's song, "Jolene," called, "Vaccine," by a Vancouver choir who were, "begging you please don't hesitate," in a highly risky medical experiment.[114]

- ABC News, January 24, 2022, 1:16 PM[115] *"Seattle hospitals at breaking point amid COVID crush of patients."* The *Seattle Times*, January 25, 2022, 2:13 PM[116]: *"Cases of the coronavirus are on the decline in the Seattle metro area."*

- *Project Veritas* revealed the extraordinarily unethical practice of incentivizing disadvantaged people, such as the homeless, to get, "five or six," shots in order to receive tax-funded $100 gift cards.[117] This comes after such, "public health," initiatives as free sex at brothels for those who get inoculated on site, free Krispy Kreme donuts, free Budweiser, free cheesecake, free hot dogs, and free White Castle fast food.[118,119,120] You will recall, "public health," departments recommended gym closures and didn't discourage the above incentives, despite deaths of the alleged disease overwhelmingly involving obese people with 4 or more co-morbidities.

- The *New York Times Magazine* in January 2022 pondered the divisive question of whether it'd be ethical to reveal a colleague's, "Covid," diagnosis, suggesting, "While it might be un-collegial to spread the word about a co-worker's medical condition, collegiality is a two-way street"[121]

- *Republic World*, "India's Fastest Digital News Source," reported on Covid protests in Germany using a stock picture of masked people with signs that included the slanderous term, "anti-vax"[122]

- An October 2021 compilation video demonstrated how inoculation, "efficacy," the media made confident claims about dropped over time from 100%, to 99%, to 97%, to 96%, to 95%, to … 84%, to 83%, to 82%, to … 70%, to … 50%, to … 20%, to, "you need boosters," to, "you need two boosters and a third dose," and so on[123]

- *Telegraph* writer Jack Rear wondered why he had, "caught Covid five times," despite following all the, "rules," and being, "fully vaccinated," and, "boosted."[124] Perhaps after his sixth positive, "test," he'll realize he's uprooted his life for the common cold, but at this point I doubt it.

- "Researchers," in Mexico produced nose-only masks, which shockingly didn't take off but were nonetheless un-ironically reported on as being a work of science[125]

- The *New York Times*, October 30, 2020[126]: *"Masks Work. Really. We'll Show You How."* The *New York Times*, January 14, 2022[127]: *"Cloth Masks Do Not Protect Against Virus as Effectively as other masks."* The *New York Times*, February 8, 2022[128]: *"The benefits of universal masking in schools remains unclear."* How can that which was clear to the point of enforcement in 2020 be unclear in 2022? Nevermind. We know the drill at this point.

- "Face masks make people look more attractive," *the Guardian* and several other corporate rags hilariously reported. Their staffs' must *really* not like who they see in the mirror.[129,130,131]

- Media outlets reported that only in late March 2022 was it finally, "confirmed," that exercise reduces your chances of dying from, "Covid."[132] Similarly, other outlets suggested whether or not you, "caught Covid," might come down to, "how attractive you are."[133] I reject this hypothesis however, because this implies physically fit people without co-morbidities are more attractive, which is bigoted, body-negative, and fat-phobic!

- The blog *Buzzfeed* claimed, "People are frustrated there isn't a COVID vaccine for babies," which they inexplicably didn't admit was a mental issue of the alleged, "people," they were referencing, since babies have zero risk associated with, "Covid," and significant risk associated with the failed, dangerous inoculations[134]

- In order to explain why people's, "unvaccinated," friends weren't all dropping dead, propagandists in March 2022 typed headlines like, "A hidden immune feature may have spared unvaccinated people from COVID-19 infections."[135] You mean to tell me human beings have immune systems? No way! That's gotta be misinformation!

- The most prominent figure of those who demand answers for the open, relevant questions related to vaccines in general is Robert F. Kennedy Jr., which I believe he would agree is fair to say. I would also believe he would agree it fair to say he is what most would consider, "left leaning," politically, if one were to describe him within the context of that binary. It is with this understanding we can label the following thesis by Kurt Anderson of the *Atlantic* a slanderous, evil lie and an attempt to dehumanize dissenters[136]: *"The Anti-Vaccine Right Brought Human Sacrifice to America."* This threat is in the same league as the DOJ's attempt to justify extrajudicial human rights violations against dissenters by branding them, "terrorists." It also comes from a propagandist who endorses experimental inoculations with a risk higher than the alleged reward for children and young people, *at least*, which unlike people choosing their own medical care is literally human sacrifice.

- Several blogs complained of, "anti-vaxx," graffiti sprayed on a new public school in Toronto.[137] The vandals wrote horrible, clearly anti-vaccine phrases like, "freedom," and, "respect the charter of rights." The Trusted News Initiative partner CBC Canadian radio network thankfully acknowledged, "why the word 'freedom' is such a useful rallying cry to protesters," going on to add, "the word has become common among far-right groups, experts say."[138] What would we do without these, "experts?" Without them we might actually desire to be free! Hold on, I need to go vomit from the nightmare induced by such a thought.

The Psychopaths Distance Themselves from their Atrocity

I started writing what would become this book in September-October 2021. At that time, only a strong faith in God and the truth's inevitability provided any kind of signal that the Covid narrative would collapse. Several relevant events in my own life also made this a particularly hard time. While I will go into the remainder at the end of this book, there was one which inspired me to starting telling this story in the first place.

Late-summer, early-fall 2021 was a time when the government/media pressure rhetoric was at an all-time high. It was at this time the, "delta variant," was just starting to be utilized to explain away the failure of the experimental inoculations. As such, the Covid collaborators did everything they could to double down, amplify the confusion, and weaken the resolve of the, "control group." The resulting pressure campaign led my then-fiancé's family-owned office to order her to work from home for refusing the shot. While this is not the worst punishment ever, being treated like a leper when you're the youngest, healthiest person in your workplace is not an easy thing to deal with mentally—especially when you're the *only* one it's being done to (the few others who refused to be experimented on all happened to, "test positive," as having antibodies).

My then-fiancé was certainly saddened to have been treated this way, and so I started writing this book initially as a thesis to provide her employer on why all these Covid policies were a mistake. At the time I was only going to discuss the business implications, specifically as they related to taking on the business risk of a scientifically senseless discrimination policy. Several weeks passed of furious typing and eventually our October 2021 wedding came and went. Perhaps because they experienced our joyous, mask-less wedding, or perhaps just because they realized what a wretched decision they'd made, her bosses soon after removed all senseless policies and asked my now-wife to return to the office.

From there things started to turn fast. The detrimental impact of the inoculations had reached the point of becoming impossible to hide, protest movements had become overwhelming, courts including the US Supreme Court had started rejecting illegal Covid policies, and governments around the world which still had tyrannical mandates had declared ends to them as well. And this is why I bring this history up, because as things stand today in (as I'm typing this) February 2022, the narrative has been flipped on its head to a point that would have been difficult to imagine only months ago. As that flip has occurred over the course of my writing this, so too has my intended purpose in doing so. As stated in my introduction, this purpose is to document the things that *did* happen. Now, as the script flips and the censorious psychopaths who committed this atrocity scramble to distance themselves from it, editing their webpages and deleting videos along the way, I have realized just how important such historical documentation will prove to be.

I say this not necessarily for the hope of justice being done— though it absolutely should be in this life and *will certainly* be in the next. I say it rather, for the hope of people not forgetting who did the lying, what lies they told, and how those lies were used to trick untold masses of people. Because those liars have shifted hard now in an attempt to appear reasonable and regain the trust they deserve to have permanently stripped from them, it is as important as ever to cast down their behavior in stone.

And don't get me wrong, those who were not directly involved who honestly acknowledge the error of their ways can be forgiven. Take Danish newspaper *Ekstra Bladet* for example, which admitted, "we failed," with respect to its lack of scrutinizing the government's statistics and contributing to a culture of fear.[139] This is a respectable step to take, especially when other culpable organizations are not, and it might even earn them back a degree of trust which the newspaper rightly deserves to have lost.

But such apologies/confessions are especially important because despite the immense wealth transfer which has taken place over the past two years, the most valuable asset in the entire world is trust. In fact, trust is the basis for the value of all currency. The Covid collaborators understand this perfectly well and used it to accomplish the events of the past two years. To those who continue to give it to them despite their abuse of it, they can and will do the same thing again. Here are a few examples of their attempting to take it back:

- Just as the CDC PCR test got revoked after almost 2 years of, "emergency," use, Rochelle Walensky admitted in late December 2021 that PCR tests can stay positive as long as twelve weeks (3 months!) and, "we would have people in isolation for a very long time if we were relying on PCRs."[140] Walensky therefore reduced the recommended, "quarantine," period people were apparently following from 10 days to 5 days. To make matters even worse, Walensky admitted to CBS this change wasn't scientific (as we know the CDC doesn't involve itself in), but it rather, "had a lot to do with what we thought people would be able to tolerate." In the same interview Walensky revealed that in the case of the PCR-substitute rapid antigen tests, which we've covered are even worse, "the FDA has not at all looked at whether … your positive antigen really does correlate with whether you're transmissible or not." Keep in mind, these are the tests used in tremendous numbers to identify the, "omicron spike," which was the largest case spike by far of the alleged pandemic.
- It also took until December 2021 for Walensky to admit that, "The overwhelming number of deaths, over 75%, occurred in people who had at least four comorbidities."[141] Still, Walensky to-this-day has completely ignored the Great Barrington Declaration's recommendation to set policy based on this long-known information, opting instead for a policy of universal tyranny, one-size-fits-all medicine, and coercion.
- Boris Johnson's aforementioned, scandal-following claim that the, "science," suddenly points to removing all mandates

While there are and will continue to be many more of these desperate heel-turns, I'd like to end this chapter by drawing attention to one—namely, that of Young Global Leader and WEF servant Leana Wen. You will recall, Wen is the CNN personality who in 2021 compared people simply existing in public without being inoculated to drunk drivers—effectively calling a person with the natural immune system they were born with a murderer for simply breathing in the presence of others. The vile psychopath also made this comparison without any pushback from her allied media slaves, despite its worse-than-Nazi-doctor, human-rights-violating implications.

However, the shift in narrative has forced the WEF and her daddy Klaus to order comrade Wen to pivot. Now, instead of the all-inoculation-all-the-time agenda, Wen has taken a 180 degree turn on every single stance she publicly babbled about mere months earlier.[142]

- CNN interview, July 2020: *"Yeah, at this point there absolutely should be that* [federal mask] *mandate because we know that if all of us wear masks we reduce the chance of transmitting or acquiring COVID-19 by 5 times."*
- CNN interview, August 2020: *"There is a real danger when we politicize science.* **That public trust is broken when we are politicizing science instead of following scientific process** *(my emphasis)."*
- CNN interview, May 2021: *"My kids are not eligible to be vaccinated—it's not that I don't want them to be vaccinated, it's that they can't be. And I do really worry."*
- CNN interview, June 2021: *"I have an almost 4 year-old and a 1 year-old. I cannot wait until they're eligible to receive the vaccine. I think until then mask wearing for kids, especially if we are living in high-transmission areas, is still going to be important."*
- CNN interview, July 2021: *"And what we really need to do at this point is to make vaccination the easy choice.* **It needs to be hard for people to remain unvaccinated** *(my emphasis)."*
- CNN interview, August 2021: *"We wouldn't imagine bringing together 20 or 30 unvaccinated adults, putting them in a single room together the entire day, and have them not wear masks. Why would we say that that's okay for our children?"*

535

- CNN interview, September 2021: *"Travel, and having the right to travel interstate—it's not a Constitutional right, as far as I know, to board a plane—and so, saying that, 'if you want to stay unvaccinated that's your choice. But if you want to travel, you'd better go get that vaccine.'"*

- CNN interview, October 2021: ***"There is no evidence whatsoever for any other vaccine causing long-term consequences*** (my emphasis). *We really should be a lot more worried about the virus and the short-term as well as long-term consequences on our children, as opposed to the vaccine."*

- CNN interview, October 2021: *"Make sure that you're wearing a mask.* ***Even though it's outdoors*** (my emphasis) *if there are lots of people packed around you—wearing a 3-ply surgical mask.* ***Don't wear a cloth mask—cloth masks are little more than facial decorations*** (my emphasis).*"*

- CNN interview, February 2022: ***"There actually is a harm that we should be discussing of children continuing to mask ... We should also be intellectually honest and say that masking has had a cost, especially for the youngest learners ... So the risk-benefit calculation has really changed*** (my emphasis).*"*

- CNN interview, February 2022: *"I'm the mom of two little kids under 5. I can't wait until my kids are vaccinated.* ***But I would wait until we find that the vaccines are safe and effective, and I'm not sure that we can say that at the moment because we just don't have the data*** (my emphasis).*"*

- CNN interview, February 2022: *"I'm not saying—I don't think anyone is really saying—that no one should ever wear masks. But rather, that* ***the responsibility should shift from a government mandate—imposed from the state of the local district of a school—rather, it should shift to an individual responsibility by the family*** (my emphasis).*"*

- Tweet, February 2022[143]: ***"In the coming days, we will see many Governors and local leaders lift mask mandates*** (my emphasis). *This is the right step, and marks a needed shift from government-imposed requirement to individual decision.* ***It***

536

helps to preserve public health authority for when it's needed again (my emphasis)."

Leana Wen, Anthony Fauci and many if not all of their Covid collaborators are people corrupted by varying but significant degrees of evil. They demonstrate a willingness to parrot lies without any remorse, hesitation, or regard for the consequences of their actions. When their stated opinion changes, it does not change with any apology or self-reflection on what they did wrong. Such changes occur on cue with the rest of their partners and are justified only with fictional claims, as opposed to utilization of the scientific method. This is self-refuting in that the actual, never-ending evolution of science is the very thing that makes the coercive actions they called for crimes against humanity. The obviousness of the lies only worsen these crimes, as their timing and coordination demonstrates an effectiveness in steering the masses toward their aims at any given time. That they were to some extent successful is the great travesty of propaganda in the Covid era.

Endnotes

1   *U.S. Constitution Amendment 1.* 1776.
2   U.S. Department of Homeland Security. 2022. "Summary Of Terrorism Threat To The U.S. Homeland". Washington, DC. https://www.dhs.gov/ntas/advisory/national-terrorism-advisory-system-bulletin-february-07-2022.
3   Binder, John. 2020. "Kamala Harris Promoted Bail Fund That Freed Six Domestic Abusers". *Breitbart.* https://www.breitbart.com/law-and-order/2020/09/23/report-kamala-harris-promoted-bail-fund-freed-six-domestic-abusers/.
4   Ernst, Douglas. 2018. "Nancy Pelosi Wonders Why There 'Aren't Uprisings' Across Nation: 'Maybe There Will Be'". *The Washington Times.* https://www.washingtontimes.com/news/2018/jun/14/nancy-pelosi-wonders-why-there-arent-uprisings-acr/.
5   "Propaganda Definition & Meaning - Merriam-Webster". 2022. *Merriam-Webster.* Accessed April 2. https://www.merriam-webster.com/dictionary/propaganda.
6   Corbett, James. 2018. "Babies On Bayonets - #Propagandawatch - The Corbett Report". *The Corbett Report - Open Source Intelligence News.* https://www.corbettreport.com/babies-on-bayonets-propagandawatch/.
7   "1990: Watch The Fake "Incubator Babies" Testimony Used By US Govt And Media To Create Public Support For The Gulf War". 2022. *TWO PLUS TWO EQUALS FOUR.* https://twoplustwoequalsfournews.wordpress.com/2022/01/24/1990-

watch-the-fake-incubator-babies-testimony-used-by-us-govt-and-media-to-create-public-support-for-gulf-war/.

8   Eustachewich, Lia. 2019. "ABC Mistakenly Aired Video From Kentucky As Kurds In Syria". *Nypost.Com*. https://nypost.com/2019/10/15/abc-news-airs-purported-syrian-war-video-but-its-really-from-kentucky/.

9   "How Phony Coronavirus "Fear Videos" Were Used As Psychological Weapons To Bring America To Her Knees - Revolver". 2021. *Revolver*. https://www.revolver.news/2021/02/how-phony-coronavirus-fear-videos-were-used-as-psychological-weapons-to-bring-america-to-her-knees/.

10   Huff, Ethan. 2021. "The Most Cringe-Worthy, Pathetic Medical Propaganda EVER: Masked-Up Nurses Dance And Sing Christmas Carols At The White House While Americans DIE From Hospital Homicide". *Vaccine Wars Com*. https://www.vaccinewars.com/2021-12-28-medical-propaganda-masked-nurses-white-house-christmas.html.

11   Sirotek, Nicole. 2020. "Nicole Sirotek, NYC Whistleblower Viral Meltdown". *The Great Ontario Fraud*. https://ontariofraud.org/video/2020/06/16/nicole-sirotek-nyc-whistleblower-viral-meltdown.

12   DOUGHERTY, MICHAEL BRENDAN. 2021. "Anthony Fauci: I Am The Science | National Review". *National Review*. https://www.nationalreview.com/2021/11/anthony-fauci-i-am-the-science/.

13   Stillman, Jessica. 2022. "This Email From Mark Zuckerberg To Dr. Fauci Is A Master Class In Effective Persuasion". *Inc.Com*. Accessed April 2. https://www.inc.com/jessica-stillman/mark-zuckerberg-anthony-fauci-email.html.

14   Wong, Julia Carrie. 2020. "Facebook Bans Some Anti-Lockdown Protest Pages". *The Guardian*. https://www.theguardian.com/technology/2020/apr/20/facebook-anti-lockdown-protests-bans.

15   Sadeghi, McKenzie. 2021. "Fact Check: Video Of Fauci Discussing COVID-19 Vaccine Safety Is From March 2020". *Usatoday.Com*. https://www.usatoday.com/story/news/factcheck/2021/12/15/fact-check-fauci-didnt-say-covid-19-vaccines-make-people-worse/8895253002/.

16   "Fact Check-Video Of Dr Anthony Fauci Discussing Vaccines With Facebook's Mark Zuckerberg Does Not Say COVID-19 Vaccines Make Recipients More Vulnerable To Infection.". 2021. *Reuters*. https://www.reuters.com/article/factcheck-fauci-zuckerberg-idUSL1N2T120Z.

17   MacGuill, Dan. 2021. "No, Fauci Did Not Say COVID Vaccines Are 'Making People Worse'". *Snopes.Com*. https://www.snopes.com/fact-check/fauci-covid-vaccine-worse/.

18   Gore, D'Angelo. 2021. "Viral Story Takes Fauci COVID-19 Vaccine Safety Comments Out Of Context - Factcheck.Org". *Factcheck.Org*. https://www.factcheck.org/2021/12/scicheck-viral-story-takes-fauci-covid-19-vaccine-safety-comments-out-of-context/.

19	Ford, Dana. 2021. "Fact Check: Fauci Did NOT 'Admit' That COVID-19 Vaccines May Make People Worse | Lead Stories". *Leadstories.Com*. https://leadstories.com/hoax-alert/2021/12/fact-check-fauci-did-not-admit-that-covid-19-vaccines-may-make-people-worse.html.
20	"Fauci - Rotten Tomatoes". 2021. *Rotten Tomatoes*. https://www.rottentomatoes.com/m/fauci.
21	"Fauci (2021) - Imdb". 2021. *Imdb*. https://www.imdb.com/title/tt13984924/.
22	Howley, Patrick. 2021. "Dr. Fauci Children's Book Takes Propaganda To Creepy New Level". *National File*. https://nationalfile.com/dr-fauci-childrens-book-takes-propaganda-to-creepy-new-level/.
23	Miller, Joshua Rhett. 2021. "The Guardian Proclaims Dr. Anthony Fauci 'Sexiest Man Alive'". *Nypost.Com*. https://nypost.com/2021/09/15/the-guardian-proclaims-dr-anthony-fauci-sexiest-man-alive/.
24	"MSNBC Anchor Reveals 6 Absurd 'Cult' Rules She Follows For Fauci | Tea Party Pac". 2021. *Teapartypac.Org*. https://teapartypac.org/msnbc-anchor-reveals-6-absurd-cult-rules-she-follows-for-fauci/.
25	Zaydenberg, Izabella. 2020. "From Candles To Socks, Dr. Fauci Merchandise Has Officially Arrived—Because It Was Only A Matter Of Time". *Yahoo.Com*. https://www.yahoo.com/lifestyle/dr-anthony-fauci-merchandise-222024228.html.
26	Harris, Jared. 2020. "As Americans Put Their All Into COVID Fight, Fauci Poses For Fashion Mag Photo Shoot". *The Western Journal*. https://www.westernjournal.com/fauci-poses-fashion-mag-photo-shoot-covid-engulfs-america/.
27	"Immunization Basics | CDC". 2021. *Web.Archive.Org*. https://web.archive.org/web/20210826113846/https:/www.cdc.gov/vaccines/vac-gen/imz-basics.htm.
28	"Immunization Basics: CDC". 2018. *The Centers For Disease Control And Prevention*. https://www.cdc.gov/vaccines/vac-gen/imz-basics.htm.
29	"Immunization Basics | CDC". 2021. *Web.Archive.Org*. https://web.archive.org/web/20210826113846/https:/www.cdc.gov/vaccines/vac-gen/imz-basics.htm.
30	"Immunization Basics: CDC". 2018. *The Centers For Disease Control And Prevention*. https://www.cdc.gov/vaccines/vac-gen/imz-basics.htm.
31	Blake, Aaron. 2021. "Vaccine Skeptics Claim A New CDC Gotcha Moment — But They Haven'T Got Much". *The Washington Post*. https://www.washingtonpost.com/politics/2021/09/09/vaccine-skeptics-claim-new-cdc-gotcha-moment-they-havent-got-much/.
32	The Centers for Disease Control and Prevention. 2021. "Media Statement From CDC Director Rochelle P. Walensky, MD, MPH, On Racism And Health". https://www.cdc.gov/media/releases/2021/s0408-racism-health.html.
33	Day, Vox. 2019. *Corporate Cancer: How To Work Miracles And Save Millions By Curing Your Company*. Castalia House.
34	Ibid. pp. 3-4.

35   "CDC Emails: Our Definition Of Vaccine Is "Problematic"".
      2022. *Technofog.Substack.Com.* https://technofog.substack.com/p/cdc-
      emails-our-definition-of-vaccine.

36   "Definition Of VACCINE". 2021. *Web.Archive.Org.*
      https://web.archive.org/web/20210118193104/https:/www.merriam-
      webster.com/dictionary/vaccine.

37   "Definition Of VACCINE". 2021. *Web.Archive.Org.*
      https://web.archive.org/web/20210226082308/https:/www.merriam-
      webster.com/dictionary/vaccine.

38   Schnell, Mychael. 2021. "Vaccine Picked As Merriam-Webster Word Of
      The Year". *Msn.Com.* https://www.msn.com/en-us/news/us/vaccine-
      picked-as-merriam-webster-word-of-the-year/ar-AARg3Eg.

39   Doshi, Peter. 2011. "The Elusive Definition Of Pandemic
      Influenza". *Bulletin Of The World Health Organization* 89 (7): 532-538.
      doi:10.2471/blt.11.086173.

40   Cohen, D., and P. Carter. 2010. "WHO And The Pandemic Flu
      "Conspiracies"". *BMJ* 340 (jun03 4): c2912-c2912.
      doi:10.1136/bmj.c2912.

41   Doshi, P. 2009. "Calibrated Response To Emerging Infections". *BMJ* 339
      (sep03 2): b3471-b3471. doi:10.1136/bmj.b3471.

42   Altman, Lawrence K. 2009. "Is This A Pandemic? Define 'Pandemic'
      (Published 2009)". *Nytimes.Com.*
      https://www.nytimes.com/2009/06/09/health/09docs.html.

43   "Why Did The WHO Alter Its Definition Of "Herd Immunity?"".
      2020. *Medium.* https://allswritewiththeworld.medium.com/why-did-the-
      who-alter-its-definition-of-herd-immunity-d701abeb5a77.

44   "NIH Quietly Changes Definition Of 'Gain-Of-Function' Amid Fauci,
      Wuhan Lab Scandal Fallout". 2021. *National File.*
      https://nationalfile.com/nih-quietly-changes-definition-of-gain-of-
      function-amid-fauci-wuhan-lab-scandal-fallout/.

45   "Coronavirus Disease (COVID-19): Serology | World Health
      Organization". 2020. *Web.Archive.Org.*
      https://web.archive.org/web/20201101161006/https:/www.who.int/news-
      room/q-a-detail/coronavirus-disease-covid-19-serology.

46   "Coronavirus Disease (COVID-19): Serology, Antibodies And
      Immunity". 2020. *Who.Int.* Accessed November 1.
      https://www.who.int/news-room/q-a-detail/coronavirus-disease-covid-19-
      serology.

47   "Research Involving Enhanced Potential Pandemic Pathogens".
      2022. *National Institutes Of Health (NIH).* Accessed April 3.
      https://www.nih.gov/news-events/research-involving-potential-pandemic-
      pathogens.

48   Pandolfo, Chris. 2022. "Exclusive: The Federal Government Paid
      Hundreds Of Media Companies To Advertise The COVID-19 Vaccines
      While Those Same Outlets Provided Positive Coverage Of The

Vaccines". *Theblaze*. https://www.theblaze.com/news/review-the-federal-government-paid-media-companies-to-advertise-for-the-vaccines.

49   *H.R.1319 - American Rescue Plan Act Of 2021*. 2021. Washington, DC: The 117th Congress.

50   Mahoney, Wendi Strauch. 2022. "DHS Attacks American Citizens Using Terrifying Tax Payer Funded Propaganda Campaign - Uncoverdc". *Uncoverdc*. https://uncoverdc.com/2022/02/10/dhs-attacks-american-citizens-using-terrifying-tax-payer-funded-propaganda-campaign/.

51   Becker, Kyle. 2022. "Exposed: Emails Show CDC Directed Facebook's Propaganda & Censorship Campaign On Covid 'Misinformation'". *Trending Politics*. https://trendingpolitics.com/exposed-emails-show-cdc-directed-facebooks-propaganda-censorship-campaign-on-covid-misinformation-knab/.

52   Howley, Patrick. 2022. "University That Funds Biden's Think Tank And Hosts Factcheck.Org Has Contract With Biontech, Gets Paid For Vaccine Sales And FDA Approvals". *National File*. https://nationalfile.com/university-funds-bidens-think-tank-hosts-factcheck-org-contract-biontech-gets-paid-vaccine-sales-fda-approvals/.

53   Ibid.

54   Hern, Alex. 2020. "What Powers Will Ofcom Have To Regulate The Internet?". *The Guardian*. https://www.theguardian.com/media/2020/feb/12/what-powers-ofcom-have-regulate-internet-uk.

55   Becker, Kyle. 2022. "Shock: Former News Exec. Reveals The Government 'Warning' Given To Networks To Air Covid Propaganda". *Trending Politics*. https://trendingpolitics.com/shock-former-news-exec-reveals-the-government-warning-given-to-networks-to-air-covid-propaganda-knab/.

56   Pugliese, David. 2021. "Military Leaders Saw Pandemic As Unique Opportunity To Test Propaganda Techniques On Canadians, Forces Report Says". *Ottawa Citizen*. https://ottawacitizen.com/news/national/defence-watch/military-leaders-saw-pandemic-as-unique-opportunity-to-test-propaganda-techniques-on-canadians-forces-report-says.

57   Pugliese, David. 2021. "Military Propaganda Exercise That Caused Panic About Wolves On The Loose "Lacked Oversight" - Investigation Finds | Ottawa Citizen". *Ottawacitizen.Com*. https://ottawacitizen.com/news/national/defence-watch/military-propaganda-exercise-that-caused-panic-about-wolves-on-the-loose-lacked-oversight-investigation-finds.

58   "The Trusted News Initiative - A BBC Led Organisation Censoring Public Health Experts Who Oppose The Official Narrative On Covid-19". 2021. *Dailyexpose.Uk*. https://dailyexpose.uk/2021/08/29/the-trusted-

news-initiative-a-bbc-led-organisation-censoring-public-health-experts-who-oppose-the-official-narrative-on-covid-19/.

59   "Global Conference For Media Freedom: London 2019 - GOV.UK".
        2019. *Gov.Uk*. https://www.gov.uk/government/topical-events/global-conference-for-media-freedom-london-2019.

60   Hall, Tony. 2019. "Media Freedom: What Is It And Why Does It
        Matter?". *Bbc.Co.Uk*.
        https://www.bbc.co.uk/mediacentre/speeches/2019/tony-hall-fco.

61   Abboud, Leila. 2019. "News Groups And Tech Companies Team Up To
        Fight Disinformation". *Ft.Com*. https://www.ft.com/content/6857149a-d0b2-11e9-99a4-b5ded7a7fe3f.

62   Edmonds, Rick. 2021. "US Ranks Last Among 46 Countries In Trust In
        Media, Reuters Institute Report Finds - Poynter". *Poynter*.
        https://www.poynter.org/ethics-trust/2021/us-ranks-last-among-46-countries-in-trust-in-media-reuters-institute-report-finds/.

63   "CBC/Radio-Canada Joins Global Charter To Fight Disinformation".
        2019. *Cbc.Radio-Canada.Ca*. https://cbc.radio-canada.ca/en/media-centre/trusted-news-charter-fight-disinformation.

64   "News Majors To Fight Disinformation". 2019. *Thehindu.Com*.
        https://www.thehindu.com/news/national/news-majors-to-fight-disinformation/article29356124.ece.

65   "Trusted News Initiative Announces Plans To Tackle Harmful
        Coronavirus Disinformation". 2020. *Cbc.Radio-Canada.Ca*.
        https://cbc.radio-canada.ca/en/media-centre/trusted-news-initiative-plan-disinformation-coronavirus.

66   Waters, Jo. 2020. "TRUSTED NEWS INITIATIVE STEPS UP
        GLOBAL FIGHT AGAINST DISINFORMATION AND TARGETS US
        PRESIDENTIAL ELECTION". *EBU | Operating Eurovision And
        Euroradio*. https://www.ebu.ch/news/2020/07/trusted-news-initiative-steps-up-global-fight-against-disinformation-and-targets-us-presidential-election.

67   Siegel, Ethan. 2020. "You Must Not 'Do Your Own Research' When It
        Comes To Science". *Forbes*.
        https://www.forbes.com/sites/startswithabang/2020/07/30/you-must-not-do-your-own-research-when-it-comes-to-science/?sh=4db82676535e.

68   "Preparing For A Hurricane Or Tropical Storm". 2022. *Cdc.Gov*.
        Accessed April 3.
        https://www.cdc.gov/nceh/features/hurricanepreparedness/index.html.

69   Rondón, Emmanuel. 2021. "VICE Causes Confusion After Denying
        Existence Of 'Natural Immunity' - El American". *El American*.
        https://elamerican.com/vice-natural-immunity-backlash-social-networks/.

70   "One Covid Shot To Rule Them All, One Covid Shot To Find Them, One
        Covid Shot To Bring Them All And In The Darkness Bind Them".
        2022. *Reddit*.
        https://www.reddit.com/r/AHomeForPlagueRats/comments/seyah2/one_c ovid_shot_to_rule_them_all_one_covid_shot_to/.

71   Crane, Emily. 2021. "Twitter Slammed After Flagging COVID Vaccine Death Obit As 'Misleading'". *Nypost.Com*. https://nypost.com/2021/10/04/twitter-criticized-for-fact-checking-seattle-moms-obituary/.

72   "Aspirin Lowers Risk Of COVID: New Findings Support Preliminary Israeli Trial". 2021. *The Jerusalem Post*. https://www.jpost.com/health-and-wellness/aspirin-lowers-risk-of-covid-new-findings-support-preliminary-israeli-trial-681127.

73   Rabin, Roni Caryn. 2021. "Aspirin Use To Prevent 1St Heart Attack Or Stroke Should Be Curtailed, U.S. Panel Says". *Nytimes.Com*. https://www.nytimes.com/2021/10/12/health/aspirin-heart-attack-stroke.html.

74   "Aspirin Use To Prevent First Heart Attacks Not Recommended For Most Older Adults -U.S. Panel". 2021. *US News*. https://www.usnews.com/news/top-news/articles/2021-10-12/aspirin-use-to-prevent-first-heart-attacks-not-recommended-for-most-older-adults-us-panel.

75   "Aspirin For Reducing Your Risk Of Heart Attack And Stroke". 2022. *U.S. Food And Drug Administration*. Accessed April 3. https://www.fda.gov/drugs/safe-daily-use-aspirin/aspirin-reducing-your-risk-heart-attack-and-stroke-know-facts.

76   Mazziotta, Julie. 2022. "Blood Clots Like Hailey Bieber's Are Happening In 'Younger And Younger People'". *PEOPLE.Com*. https://people.com/health/blood-clots-like-hailey-biebers-are-happening-in-younger-and-younger-people/.

77   Hirsh, Sophie. 2022. "How Climate Change Is Causing More Premature Births, Especially In Marginalized Communities". *Green Matters*. https://www.greenmatters.com/p/climate-change-preterm-birth-pregnancy.

78   Christensen, Thor. 2021. "Broken Heart Syndrome Is On The Rise, Especially Among Older Women". *Www.Heart.Org*. https://www.heart.org/en/news/2021/10/13/broken-heart-syndrome-is-on-the-rise-especially-among-older-women.

79   Hewitt, Tyler. 2021. "Study Finds Higher Heart Disease Risk During Pandemic Due To Increases In Anxiety, Depression". *UPR Utah Public Radio*. https://www.upr.org/utah-news/2021-11-15/study-finds-higher-heart-disease-risk-during-pandemic-due-to-increases-in-anxiety-depression.

80   Puttick, Helen. 2021. "Rise In Heart Attacks Attributed To Pandemic Stress And Poor Diet". *Thetimes.Co.Uk*. https://www.thetimes.co.uk/article/rise-in-heart-attacks-attributed-to-pandemic-stress-and-poor-diet-gdpn5bcgd.

81   Skidmore, Mark. 2022. "Irish Examiner: Referee Whistles May Be Causing All The Heart Problems On The Field". *Lighthouse Economics*. https://mark-skidmore.com/2022/02/11/irish-examiner-referee-whistles-may-be-causing-all-the-heart-problems-on-the-field/.

82   Houston, Muiris. 2022. "How Moving The Clock Forward This Weekend Could Kill You". *The Irish Times*. https://www.irishtimes.com/life-and-style/health-family/how-moving-the-clock-forward-this-weekend-could-kill-you-1.4827688.

83   Le Net, Solen. 2022. "Blood Clots: The Popular Breakfast Food That Could Enhance The Risk Of Blood Clotting". *Express.Co.Uk*. https://www.express.co.uk/life-style/health/1554078/blood-clot-risks-eggs-meats-choline.

84   Bonos, Lisa. 2022. "He's Cute. But Is He Swab-Worthy? How Rapid Testing Became A Dating Ritual.". *The Washington Post*. https://www.washingtonpost.com/lifestyle/2022/02/08/covid-test-dating/.

85   Acker, Lizzy. 2021. "Both Vaccinated? Oregon Health Officials Say You Can Kiss On Dates Again!". *Oregon Live | The Oregonian*. https://www.oregonlive.com/coronavirus/2021/09/both-vaccinated-oregon-health-officials-say-you-can-kiss-on-dates-again.html.

86   Cost, Ben. 2020. "Fauci Endorses Tinder Hookups — With A Caveat". *Nypost.Com*. https://nypost.com/2020/04/15/fauci-endorses-tinder-hookups-with-a-caveat/.

87   Rude, Mey. 2021. "Dr. Fauci Visited Gay Bathhouses And Bars To Study HIV". *Advocate.Com*. https://www.advocate.com/health/2021/2/08/dr-fauci-used-visit-gay-bathhouses-and-bars-study-hiv.

88   Edwards-Levy, Ariel. 2021. "CNN Poll: Nearly 4 In 10 Americans Think Covid-19 Precautions Are Here To Stay, But Others Have Already Returned To Their Pre-Pandemic Normal". *CNN*. https://www.cnn.com/2021/12/17/politics/cnn-poll-covid-pandemic/index.html.

89   "Brian Stelter Mocked After Complaining About Americans That Trust Joe Rogan More Than CNN | The Daily Wire". 2022. *The Daily Wire*. https://www.dailywire.com/news/brian-stelter-mocked-after-complaining-about-americans-that-trust-joe-rogan-more-than-cnn.

90   Menahan, Chris. 2021. "'They Have Blocked My IP Address': Mrna Vaccine Inventor 'Blocked' From Reading New England Journal Of Medicine". *Information Liberation*. https://www.informationliberation.com/?id=62596.

91   "DR. ROBERT MALONE's WARNING TO ALL PARENTS ON MRNA VACCINES - Freedom Of Speech". 2021. *Freedom Of Speech*. https://fos-sa.org/2021/12/13/dr-robert-malones-warning-to-all-parents-on-mrna-vaccines/.

92   Cox, Isa. 2021. "Watch: CNN Teams Up With 'Sesame Street' To Promote Vaccines For 5 To 11-Year-Olds". *The Western Journal*. https://www.westernjournal.com/watch-cnn-teams-sesame-street-promote-faucis-vaccine-propaganda/.

93   "Fact Check-2015 Nobel Prize For Ivermectin Intended For Treatment Of Parasitic Infections Doesn'T Prove Its Efficacy On COVID-19". 2021. *Reuters*. https://www.reuters.com/article/factcheck-nobel-ivermectin-idUSL1N2QB2XA.

94   "Ivermectin Shows 'Antiviral Effect' Against COVID, Japanese
      Company Says". 2022. *Reuters.*
      https://www.reuters.com/business/healthcare-pharmaceuticals/japans-
      kowa-says-ivermectin-effective-against-omicron-phase-iii-trial-2022-01-
      31/.
95   Lovelace Jr., Berkeley. 2021. "Colin Powell Was Vaccinated Against
      Covid, But Suffered From A Cancer That Makes The Shots Less
      Effective". *CNBC.* https://www.cnbc.com/2021/10/18/colin-powell-
      suffered-from-a-cancer-that-makes-covid-vaccine-less-effective.html.
96   Sicha, Choire. 2021. "How Mean Should We Be To Each
      Other?". *Intelligencer.* https://nymag.com/intelligencer/2021/08/anti-vax-
      coronavirus-deaths.html.
97   Laila, Cristina. 2021. "Cardiologist Who Said He 'Won't Cry At Funeral'
      For "Selfish" Unvaccinated People Suddenly Dies In His Sleep 2 Weeks
      After 3Rd Covid Jab". *The Gateway Pundit.*
      https://www.thegatewaypundit.com/2021/11/cardiologist-said-wont-cry-
      funeral-selfish-unvaccinated-people-suddenly-dies-sleep-2-weeks-3rd-
      covid-jab/.
98   Hiltzik, Michael. 2022. "Column: Mocking Anti-Vaxxers' COVID Deaths
      Is Ghoulish, Yes — But May Be Necessary". *Los Angeles Times.*
      https://www.latimes.com/business/story/2022-01-10/why-shouldnt-we-
      dance-on-the-graves-of-anti-vaxxers.
99   Latham-Coyle, Harry. 2022. "Anti-Vax Olympic Gold Medalist
      Szilveszter Csollany Dies Of Covid, Aged 51". *News.Yahoo.Com.*
      https://news.yahoo.com/anti-vax-olympic-gold-medalist-085354445.html.
100   Watson, Paul. 2022. ""Anti-Vax" Olympic Gold Medallist Dies Of
      COVID (But He Was Vaccinated)". *Summit.News.*
      https://summit.news/2022/01/25/anti-vax-olympic-gold-medallist-dies-of-
      covid-but-he-was-vaccinated/.
101   "Actor Vivekh Gets COVID-19 Vaccine, Urges Others To Do So".
      2021. *The News Minute.* https://www.thenewsminute.com/article/actor-
      vivekh-gets-covid-19-vaccine-urges-others-do-so-147156.
102   R, Nivedita. 2021. "RIP Vivek: Actor Passes Away After Suffering
      Severe Heart Attack". *India.Com | Top Latest News From India, USA
      And Top National Breaking News Stories.*
      https://www.india.com/entertainment/rip-vivek-actor-passes-away-after-
      suffering-severe-heart-attack-celebs-pen-emotional-tribute-4591869/.
103   Eldred, Sheila Mulrooney. 2021. "Coronavirus FAQ: I Just Got A
      Booster. Can I ... Go Crazy?". *Nevada Public Radio.*
      https://knpr.org/npr/2021-11/coronavirus-faq-i-just-got-booster-can-i-go-
      crazy.
104   "Despite Continued Idiocy, COVID Sense Is Finally Winning Out".
      2022. *Nypost.Com.* https://nypost.com/2022/01/08/despite-continued-
      idiocy-covid-sense-is-finally-winning-out/.
105   Downey, Caroline. 2022. "Sotomayor Fact-Checked: Justice Gets Four
      Pinocchios For 'Wildly Incorrect' Covid Claim". *News.Yahoo.Com.*

https://news.yahoo.com/sotomayor-fact-checked-justice-gets-150756972.html.

106   Schorr, Isaac. 2021. "Yahoo Is Part Of The Yahoo Family Of Brands". News.Yahoo.Com. https://news.yahoo.com/york-times-retracts-massive-exaggeration-163906675.html.

107   Miller, Andrew Mark. 2021. "Google Plays Vaccine 'Propaganda' To Android Users Who Ask To Hear A Song". *Fox News*. https://www.foxnews.com/politics/google-plays-vaccine-propaganda-android-users-who-ask-song.

108   "New Rap Videos Aim To Help Increase COVID-19 Vaccination In Communities Of Color". 2021. *Columbia University Irving Medical Center*. https://www.cuimc.columbia.edu/news/new-rap-videos-aim-help-increase-covid-19-vaccination-communities-color.

109   "Vax The Nation - The University Of Auckland". 2021. *Auckland.Ac.Nz*. https://www.auckland.ac.nz/en/news/2021/12/02/vax-the-nation.html.

110   Corden, James, Ariana Grande, and Marissa Jaret Winokur. 2021. "No Lockdowns Anymore W/ Ariana Grande & Marissa Jaret Winokur". *Youtube.Com*. https://www.youtube.com/watch?v=v7TarriXFME.

111   "Jimmy Debuts "It Was A…(Masked Christmas)" Ft. Ariana Grande And Megan Thee Stallion! | Tonight Show". 2021. *Youtube.Com*. https://www.youtube.com/watch?v=kX9luA0MTeo.

112   Isador, Graham. 2020. "Gal Gadot's Celebrity 'Imagine' Video Is Just Too Cringe". *Vice.Com*. https://www.vice.com/en/article/3a8yey/gal-gadots-celebrity-imagine-video-is-just-too-cringe.

113   Diaz, Adriana. 2021. "'Vax That Thang Up': Juvenile's Hit Song Gets 2021 Transformation". *Nypost.Com*. https://nypost.com/2021/07/07/vax-that-thang-up-juveniles-hit-song-gets-2021-transformation/.

114   Thomson, Cameron. 2021. "'I'M Begging Of You Please Don'T Hesitate': Vancouver Choir Creates Vaccine Parody Of Dolly Parton's Jolene (VIDEO)". *Vancouver Is Awesome*. https://www.vancouverisawesome.com/events-and-entertainment/im-begging-of-you-please-dont-hesitate-vancouver-choir-creates-vaccine-parody-of-dolly-partons-jolene-video-3782477.

115   Kekatos, Mary. 2022. "Seattle Hospitals At Breaking Point Amid COVID Crush Of Patients". *ABC News*. https://abcnews.go.com/Health/seattle-hospitals-breaking-point-amid-covid-crush-patients/story?id=82438895.

116   Takahama, Elise. 2022. "King County Omicron Cases Decline As 'Second Chapter' Of Surge Gains Steam In Eastern Washington". *The Seattle Times*. https://www.seattletimes.com/seattle-news/health/king-county-omicron-cases-decline-as-second-chapter-of-surge-gains-steam-in-eastern-washington/.

117   "Undercover Video Reveals Disadvantaged Populations Taking Excessive Vaccines For Tax Funded Gift Card Incentive: 'You Find People That Do It Five, Six Times…For The Incentive.'". 2022. *Projectveritas.Com*.

https://www.projectveritas.com/news/undercover-video-reveals-disadvantaged-populations-taking-excessive-vaccines/.

118 Cost, Ben. 2021. "Brothel Offers Vaccinations, And Free Sexual 'Session' In Bold Incentive Program". *Nypost.Com.* https://nypost.com/2021/11/09/brothel-offers-vaccinations-and-free-sexual-session-in-bold-incentive-program/.

119 Valinsky, Jordan. 2021. "Krispy Kreme Is Sweetening Its Free Doughnut Promotion For Vaccinated People". *CNN.* https://www.cnn.com/2021/08/25/business/krispy-kreme-free-doughnuts-vaccine/index.html.

120 Benveniste, Alexis. 2021. "Got Vaccinated? Here's All The Free Stuff You Can Get". *CNN.* https://www.cnn.com/2021/04/24/business/vaccine-freebies/index.html.

121 Appiah, Kwame Anthony. 2022. "Can I Reveal A Colleague's Covid Diagnosis?". *The New York Times Magazine.* https://archive.is/jSro8.

122 Shandilya, Aparna. 2022. "In Germany, Thousands Gather To Protest Against Country's COVID-19 Policies". *Republicworld.Com.* https://www.republicworld.com/world-news/europe/in-germany-thousands-gather-to-protest-against-countrys-covid-19-policies-articleshow.html.

123 Hannity, Sean. 2022. "Twitter User Video Showing The Shifting Narrative In Vaccine Efficacy". *Rumble.* https://rumble.com/vnouq3-twitter-user-video-showing-the-shifting-narrative-in-vaccine-efficacy.html.

124 Rear, Jack. 2022. "Why Have I Caught Covid Five Times?". *The Telegraph.* https://www.telegraph.co.uk/health-fitness/body/have-caught-covid-five-times/.

125 O'Neill, Natalie. 2021. "Researchers Produce Nose-Only COVID-19 Masks". *Nypost.Com.* https://nypost.com/2021/03/24/researchers-produce-nose-only-covid-19-masks/.

126 Fleisher, Or, Gabriel Gianordoli, Yuliya Parishna-Kottas, Karthik Partanjali, Miles Peyton, and Bedel Saget. 2020. "Masks Work. Really. We'Ll Show You How (Published 2020)". *Nytimes.Com.* https://www.nytimes.com/interactive/2020/10/30/science/wear-mask-covid-particles-ul.html.

127 Mandavilli, Apoorva. 2022. "The C.D.C. Concedes That Cloth Masks Do Not Protect Against The Virus As Effectively As Other Masks.". *Nytimes.Com.* https://www.nytimes.com/2022/01/14/health/cloth-masks-covid-cdc.html.

128 Leonhardt, David. 2022. "The Mask Debate". *Nytimes.Com.* https://www.nytimes.com/2022/02/08/briefing/mask-mandates-covid-new-jersey.html.

129 Morris, Steven. 2022. "Face Masks Make People Look More Attractive, Study Finds". *The Guardian.* https://www.theguardian.com/world/2022/jan/13/face-masks-make-people-look-more-attractive-study-finds.

130   "Face Masks Make You Look More Attractive, Study Says". 2022. *Msn.Com*. https://www.msn.com/en-us/health/wellness/face-masks-make-you-look-more-attractive-study-says/ar-AASUmZg.

131   Graff, Martin. 2022. "Can Wearing A Face Mask Make You More Attractive?". *Psychology Today*. https://www.psychologytoday.com/us/blog/love-digitally/202202/can-wearing-face-mask-make-you-more-attractive.

132   Patrick, Alex. 2022. "It's Confirmed, Exercise Does Reduce Your Chance Of Dying From Covid-19". *Sowetanlive*. https://www.sowetanlive.co.za/news/south-africa/2022-03-29-its-confirmed-exercise-does-reduce-your-chance-of-dying-from-covid-19/.

133   Chalmers, Vanessa. 2022. "Still Not Caught Covid? It Might Be Down To 'How Attractive You Are'". *The US Sun*. https://www.the-sun.com/health/4707931/how-attractive-you-are-covid-risk-beauty/.

134   Camero, Katie. 2022. "People Are Frustrated There Isn'T A COVID Vaccine For Babies — And It's Not Just Parents". *News.Yahoo.Com*. https://news.yahoo.com/people-frustrated-isn-t-covid-215947046.html.

135   Ozdemir, Derya. 2022. "A Hidden Immune Feature May Have Spared Unvaccinated People From COVID-19 Infections". Interestingengineering.Com. https://interestingengineering.com/immune-feature-covid19-infections.

136   Andersen, Kurt. 2022. "The Anti-Vaccine Right Brought Human Sacrifice To America". *The Atlantic*. https://www.theatlantic.com/ideas/archive/2022/01/human-sacrifice-ritual-mass-vaccination/621355/.

137   Landau, Jack. 2022. "Someone Just Vandalized Toronto's Newest Public School With Anti-Vax Graffiti". *Blogto*. https://www.blogto.com/city/2022/02/someone-just-vandalized-torontos-newest-public-school-anti-vax-graffiti/.

138   "Why The Word 'Freedom' Is Such A Useful Rallying Cry For Protesters | CBC Radio". 2022. *CBC*. https://www.cbc.ca/radio/checkup/what-s-your-reaction-to-the-ottawa-standoff-and-the-border-blockades-1.6349636/why-the-word-freedom-is-such-a-useful-rallying-cry-for-protesters-1.6349865.

139   Chung, Frank. 2022. "Newspaper Apologises For Covid-19 Reporting". *Heraldsun*. https://www.heraldsun.com.au/business/companies/we-failed-danish-newspaper-apologises-for-not-questioning-government-covid19-numbers/news-story/5f360ab5764cf9bcfb0d8edae7160658.

140   Dillon, A.P. 2022. "CDC Director: PCR Tests Can Stay Positive Up To 12 Weeks". *Apdillon.Substack.Com*. https://apdillon.substack.com/p/cdc-director-pcr-tests-can-stay-positive.

141   Berrien, Hank. 2022. "CDC Director: Over 75% Of COVID Deaths In Vaccinated Had 'At Least 4 Comorbidities' | The Daily Wire". *The Daily Wire*. https://www.dailywire.com/news/cdc-director-admits-over-75-of-covid-deaths-in-people-with-at-least-4-comorbidities.

142   "Dr. Leana Wen's Evolving Message On COVID-19". 2022. *Youtu.Be.*
        https://youtu.be/lkplCqbGM18.
143   Kruta, Virginia. 2022. "CNN Medical Expert Says It's Time To Lift The
        Mask Mandates — To Preserve 'Medical Authority' | The Daily
        Wire". *The Daily Wire.* https://www.dailywire.com/news/cnn-medical-
        expert-says-its-time-to-lift-the-mask-mandates-to-preserve-medical-
        authority?itm_source=parsely-api.

Chapter 20

The Psychology of the Covid Era

"If you have to be persuaded, reminded, pressured, lied-to, incentivized, coerced, bullied, socially shamed, guilt-tripped, threatened, punished, and criminalized... If all of this is considered necessary to gain your compliance – you can be absolutely certain that what is being promoted is not in your best interest."

—Quote Attributed to Ian Watson[1]

While this treatise has mostly been focused on scientific, evidence-based arguments to this point, I would like to make something very clear: science is not, under any circumstances, a justification for the violation of human rights. Even if the coercive violation of free speech, peaceable assembly, religious practice, expression, informed consent, and bodily autonomy *could* be demonstrated to save lives—which it has not remotely been because it cannot be—it would still not be justified to do so without the consent of the person to whom those rights are God-given. This is the beginning and end of any necessary argument for why the actions of public health organizations have been wrong over the last year and a half—the rest I've provided above is just fuel to the fire.

That said, there is also malice which can be attributed to these actions, using common psychological methods/understandings. To support this case, we turn to an overview by Narcissistic Abuse Rehab, on Biderman's Chart of Coercion.[2,3,4,5] The overview summarizes 8 tactics used by narcissistic abusers of all kinds to exercise coercive control. Coercive control in this case is defined as, "an act or a pattern of acts of assaults, threats, humiliation, and intimidation or other abuse that is used to harm, punish or frighten the target," into an action or series of actions. According to Biderman, these tactics have been used for centuries in authoritarian societies (for example, those based on slavery) to condition compliance. These tactics are listed below, along with summaries of how they directly relate to the narcissistic, abusive tactics used by public health organizations in 2020 and beyond:

1. **Isolation**
   a. Description: *"participation in recreational activities is denied. Contact with family and friends is restricted. Target is discredited to family and friends. Access to transportation, phone, and/or finances is restricted."*
   b. Applicable actions in the Covid era: quarantining the healthy; closure of gyms; "social," distancing practices; denial of family and friends to be present as patients die in hospital; "fact-checking," of any post in opposition to the Covid religion; gaslighting propaganda; "non-essential," business designations; removal of online accounts (including even transaction-based accounts like PayPal) for, "spreading misinformation."
2. **Exhaustion/Induced Debility**
   a. Description: *"disparages body image. Limits finances for necessaries and healthcare. Disruption of meals and rest. Verbal abuse and interrogation. Possible rape and assault. This weakens the target mentally and physically."*
   b. Applicable actions in the Covid era: the slander of natural immunity, the benefits of physical fitness, and nutrition; forced closure of, "non-essential," small businesses; dissenting doctors subject to psychological evaluations; refusal to provide or endorse proven, safe, alternative early treatments; politicians and media slandering and encouraging others to slander those who refuse inoculation; abusive bio-state police enforcement.
3. **Threats**
   a. Description: *"threatens to kill the target or their family or pets. Threatens to take children away. Threats of suicide or abandonment. Destruction of property. This causes anxiety and despair in the target."*
   b. Applicable actions in the Covid era: Chinese health workers killed pets, "in pursuit of zero Covid;"[6] guilt-shaming the young about putting the old/sick at risk by merely breathing/existing; "anti-vaxxers," considered unfit parents in custody hearings; threatening

propaganda claims about how to, "handle," those who choose to not be inoculated; threats of doctors losing licenses for going against the failing orthodoxy; threats of losing job over non-compliance with inoculations, masks, etc.

4. **Humiliation/Degradation**
   a. Description: *"public humiliation. Forced participation in degrading sexual acts. Verbal abuse, name calling. Demeaning punishments, insults, and taunts. Denial of privacy."*
   b. Applicable actions in the Covid era: anal swab testing; "anti-vaxx," "anti-science," and other name-calling slanders; "unvaccinated," unwelcome in public places and/or gatherings; "unvaccinated," subject to discriminatory screening procedures; inoculation passports and requirements to report inoculation status.

5. **Distortion**
   a. Description: *"monopolization of the target's perceptions. Blames target for the abuse, uses social and familial reinforcement. Unpredictable behavior. Dominates target's thoughts."*
   b. Applicable actions in the Covid era: "fact-checking," and 24/7 Covid propaganda, "flooding," the airwaves; censorship/suppression of all dissenting scientists/doctors; claims, "unvaccinated," cause the alleged pandemic and associated tyrannical intrusions to continue; propaganda pieces on how to address family who choose to not be inoculated; constant media presence by public health officials who publicly endorse the exclusion of dissenting family members (as Fauci did); projection of initial certainty followed by claim, "science is uncertain," when proven wrong; constant flip-flopping and disorientation on every single issue; continuous flow of new claims to distract from past lies and inconsistencies.

6. **Omnipotence**
   a. Description: *"physical assaults. Manipulation of legal system. Use of position and privilege. Stalking. Confrontation. Makes the target feel powerless."*

b. <u>Applicable actions in the Covid era</u>: abusive enforcement of absurd mandates by police; false approval of, "Comirnaty," to provide façade of legality to illegal experimental inoculation mandates; unprecedented, all-encompassing conflicts of interest; infallibility of public health officials without any apparent mechanism for audit, investigation, or consequences of bad behavior; "to question me is to question science," and other narcissistic claims by figures like Fauci.

7. **Intermittent Reinforcement**

   a. <u>Description</u>: *"occasional favors. Promises to change behavior. Charm then harm strategy. Unexpected burst of kindness or affection. Motivates the target to submit."*

   b. <u>Applicable actions in the Covid era</u>: ending and resuming of lockdowns, mask mandates, etc. on a whim; promises of privileges such as travel for inoculation; ever-shifting timeline of when we will be, "back to normal," with occasional suggestions of never going back ("new normal"); "vaccinated," don't and then do have to wear masks; suggestions of no boosters, followed by boosters being necessary, followed by additional shots not being necessary, followed by more boosters and additional primary doses; cheap incentives to inoculate like gift cards and doughnuts; admission of occasional truths like natural immunity being better than inoculation, for example.

8. **Enforcing Trivial Demands**

   a. <u>Description</u>: *"mind games. To make the target compliant, the abuser punishes non-compliance with a rigid set of ever changing rules. These rules may control the target's appearance, style of dress, housekeeping, parenting, punctuality, etc."*

   b. <u>Applicable actions in the Covid era</u>: mask-wearing to utilize services and enter stores amid admissions masks do not provide protection but are rather a psychological tool; "social," distancing despite admissions it's pointless; on-and-off quarantine and lockdowns despite admissions of psychological and economic damages; remote school learning and masking despite zero risk to young people; constant shifting on which masks to wear and even how many to wear; economic sanction mandates for enforcement including inoculation passports; ever shifting goal-posts on, "fully-vaccinated," status.

The above abuses can be directly tied to documented psychological operations engaged in by the abusers. Other than the Event 201 simulation as one example, consider a pre-mass-inoculation-campaign July 2020 study on, "COVID-19 Vaccine Messaging," conducted by Yale University.[7] Let's pretend for a moment the timing of this study doesn't imply a pre-determined inoculation campaign, and the content of it doesn't imply glaring conflicts of interest related to how Yale is operating as a pharmaceutical company marketing team. The study itself tested, "vaccine," messaging on people, including all the typical dishonest messages of how inoculation would result in community protection, personal freedom, economic freedom, and economic growth. However, they also included more intense psychological manipulations, such as:

- Social pressure messages like, "Imagine the guilt/embarrassment/anger they will feel if they don't get vaccinated and spread the disease"
- "Trust in science," messages like, "If one doesn't get vaccinated that means that one doesn't understand how infections are spread or who ignores science"
- Lack of bravery messages like, "Those who choose not to get vaccinated against COVID-19 are not brave"

These patterns of abuse have also led to an observable Stockholm syndrome amongst those who capitulated and/or bought into the illogical narratives of the narcissists and their immense pressure. Studies conducted by McGill University and the Montreal Neurological Institute-Hospital on cognitive ability unsurprisingly found the fearful people who accepted these narratives performed poorly on simple cognitive tests, were less able to process information, and had a distorted view of risks.[8] Another 2021 study by Deoni et al. in *medRxiv* found similar results for children, documenting, "Significant reductions in attained cognitive function and performance in children born over the past 18 months during the pandemic."[9] Such horrendous outcomes implicate abusers like the Event 201 participants, Yale University, and the complicit media, among others, in the damage their psychological operations have done. Observing the resulting psychosis of their victims was at times comical, at times frustrating, and at other times terrifying, as the behavior of those who suffered from it became exceptionally irrational in a very short period of time. Consider any of these few examples:

- A *Twitter* user shared a post as follows, including a picture of herself wearing a surgical mask, a decorative mask which read, "vote," and a face shield[10]: *"I'm flying today but I'm not f—ing around with omicron. [Checklist:] Pfizer x 3, Negative rapid test, Natural immunity, N95 sealed to my face with surgical tape, Secondary mask for displaying opinions, Face shield, Vinyl gloves, Touchscreen gloves, Shitton of Xanax."*

- Actress Katy Stoll said the following in a thread also on *Twitter*[11]: *"Look. This isn't intended to come across as antivax in any way. I am triple protected and would do it again. But, it has significantly affected my menstruation. It has significantly affected a lot of women's menstruation. There has been hardly anything written about this. The only thing I've seen about it said 'yes, it seems the vaccine affects menstruation but its minor' but I'm telling you- what I'm experiencing and what other people have shared with me is that this is not minor. **Excruciating symptoms, and delayed periods of up to two weeks. Again. I am grateful for the vaccine and would do it again** (my emphasis)."*

- One woman's reply to Stoll[12]: *"Fully vaccinated and boosted and **I've had two pregnancy losses since then** (my emphasis)- I would be lying if I said I wasn't scared and curious about if things could have been different pre-shot. **HUGELY grateful to not have had Covid thus far. Doesn't change what I'm scared about** (my emphasis)."*

- Stoll and her commenter certainly confirm the aforementioned McGill study, but they were not alone in their distortion of the

556

risks and resulting impact on cognitive function. Two French surveys, for example, found French citizens believed the infection fatality rate of, "Covid," to be around 16% on average, despite it actually being between 0.0% and 0.3%.[13]

- NBC News reported a story of a man whose, "wife died from Johnson & Johnson Covid vaccine complications,"[14] but who both continues to get inoculated and believes others should too. This tragic man also carries on this way despite admitting, "They're not taking time to explain the acceptable risk ... It's an absolute failure to some degree. The fear of scaring everybody away from the vaccines overran the ability to educate the public correctly."

- New York Governor Andrew Cuomo observably had the worst Covid response in pretty much the entire world since the beginning of the alleged pandemic. He also had a built-in propagandist at CNN in his brother, Chris Cuomo, who ended up being revealed as having run interference for also-corrupt Andrew in a variety of ways.[15] While much of this was readily apparent in spring 2020, an absurd cult of personality shielded the Democrat governor. In fact, it got so shameless that the term, "Cuomosexual," started to spread and was repeated as part of a full-blown propaganda campaign run in his defense, as supported in creepy fashion by Robert DeNiro, Rosie Perez, Billy Crystal, Ben Stiller, Chelsea Handler, Cher, Jada Pinkett Smith, Ellen Degeneres, Trevor Noah, Stephen Colbert, and the Emmy Awards.[16] Ironically and embarrassingly for all involved, beyond the nursing home genocide Cuomo also ended up with a sex scandal that saw him removed from office.

- The Democrat Party in general was also exposed on the manipulation of its constituents when in 2022 a leaked memo by a Democrat polling firm called *Impact Research* dictated it was time to, "declare the crisis phase of COVID over and push for feeling and acting normal."[17] This conclusion was not based on science at all, but rather on polling sentiment—not that any of their tyrannical human rights violations in the prior two years were actually based on science either.

- A viral cover song of the 1954 hit, "Mr. Sandman," hailing High Priest Fauci was shared, which featured the following

557

lyrics[18]: *"Dr. Fauci, give us vaccines. Help all the people who have been quarantined. We'll wear our masks and we'll have to stay distant. We'll wash our hands and we'll be more resistant. Fauci! (Yes?) Promise us, please! We'll have a cure that can fight off this disease! Restrictions will lift with some ease! Dr. Fauci, don't forget me!"*

- Mark P. Shea, a self-described, "Catholic," who, "lives the writing life and tries to be a disciple of Jesus, mostly badly," blogged about the, "self-pity," of people who disagree with their being denied services in their own community/country for not taking part in a medical experiment.[19] He then fantasized about those who he considers diseased and unfit for society getting, "immediately punched in the face," by the offspring of holocaust-era Jews, whose relatives suffered because they were considered diseased and unfit for society. This is strange when you take into account the opinion of actual holocaust survivor, Vera Sharav, who has spoken out and herself made the same comparison.[20] The post's final claim that, "The selfish do not have a right to spread disease to the innocent and vulnerable," should, of course, see the, "vaccinated," excluded from society as well, since they can obviously also, "spread disease." But at least Mr. Shea was honest about his being bad at emulating Jesus, who welcomed lepers with open arms.[21]

- A Melbourne doctor, Shane Huntington, posted the following on *Twitter*[22]: *"Sitting in the @RCHMelbourne* [hospital] *with my son hooked up to heart monitors post his second Pfizer shot, I have a message for parents: Get your kids vaccinated if you can. These side effects are rare and manageable. Help protect us all."* This cruel, lost father added: *"When vaccination is available for my 9-year-old son we will be first in line. Vaccines are safe and effective ... These things will keep them safe."*

- Comedian Heather McDonald passed out on stage mid-routine and fractured her skull, immediately following a joke about having gotten two Pfizer shots and a Moderna booster.[23] Upon recovery, she was interviewed by Dr. Drew, who she asked about the possibility of having had such an issue 3 weeks following her booster. Rather than deny a connection, Dr. Drew nodded knowingly, affirming such debilitating side effects were common *in his own personal experience*, and admitted the following: *"Two to three weeks is where you see a lot of this stuff. I have a friend that got the booster and he got really **destroyed by it, he still can't walk across the road. He's having all kinds of symptoms. Yeah there's a lot of funny stuff. We don't really know what it all is or where it's coming from but ... it's still worth doing it** (my emphasis)."* Fortunately for Dr. Drew, McDonald was a good sport despite not even knowing what myocarditis was, thus demonstrating her clear lack of prior informed consent. The TV doctor casually and outrageously ignored this. So, instead of lambasting him for his inhumanity in continuing to encourage people to take the poison that could have easily killed her and which, "destroyed," his friend, McDonald laughed, saying, "I think I'm done," in reference to a potential *fourth* shot. Despite not knowing, "what it all is or where it's coming from," and despite the Hippocratic oath's decree to, "first, do no harm," Dr. Drew and many others like him continue to inject people. And the reason why is simple: the consequences of admitting their mistake would/will be both internally and externally severe.

Yuri Bezmenov and Cultural Subversion

So how did we get to this point? How did we end up with people poisoning themselves and their children, publicly acknowledging they did so, and still believing in such a Jamestown-like cause? On a long-term basis, an explanation which seems to fit well comes from ex-KGB agent and Soviet defector, Yuri Bezmenov. In his 1984, "Love Letter to America," Bezmenov explains the Soviet concept of, "ideological subversion," as, "the process of changing the perception of reality in the minds of millions of people all over the world."[24] He makes it clear based on his own involvement in this work that unlike the Hollywood depictions of action-packed espionage, the vast majority of the KGB's operations involved ideological propaganda campaigns. This, he claims, is in line with the teachings of Sun-Tzu, the famous Chinese military philosopher, who said:

559

*"All warfare is based primarily on deception of an enemy. Fighting on a battlefield is the most primitive way of making war. There is no art higher than to destroy your enemy without a fight—by **subverting** anything of value in the enemy's country."*

Bezmenov also explains that, "in the context of the USA, most of these nasty things are done to America by Americans ... with the ideological help of the Communist subverters." These, "subverters," would engage in, "a long-term process," in order to deeply ingrain these ideological shifts. In fact, the process would be so, "stretched in time," that the average individual, "is unable to perceive the process of subversion as a consistent and willful effort." So the goal was not to impose a communist ideology on Americans by force, but to convince them via propaganda to support it themselves. And this goal would be achieved in four major stages as follows:

1. Demoralization – *"... to change your perception of reality to such an extent, that even despite an abundance of information and evidence about the danger ... you are unable to come to sensible conclusions in your own interests and in the interests of your nation ... One of the main tactics in this process is to develop, establish and consistently enforce a set of 'double standards' ... overt and covert propaganda; use of 'Agents of Influence,' faked 'International Forums' created by KGB/Novosti to bring the atmosphere of legitimacy and respectability to Soviet Operations; provoking and manipulating mass demonstrations and assemblies; spreading rumors and 'reliable information from circles close to Politbureau'; forgeries of USA Information Services press-releases; planting phony stories in local media; creating hundreds of tabloid newspapers subsidized by the USSR embassy through front organizations and fake 'advertising' companies for the purpose of 'legally' financing groups of subversives and radicals, etc. Other tactics, such as sabotage, character assassination of 'stubborn' Indians resisting Soviet subversion, terrorism and even occasional killings of 'reactionaries and counter-revolutionaries' for the psychological effect of 'paralyzing with fear' ... It is*

imperative that any sufficient challenge and counter-balance by the basic moral values and ideology of this country be eliminated."

I really could've emphasized that entire paragraph when considering how we've directly covered the involvement of the Covid collaborators in every single tactic mentioned above. Particularly jarring to me was the description of, "international forums," especially since Klaus Schwab is documented as having begun his Forum around the time Bezmenov was sounding this alarm in the 1970-1980s. To be clear here, I'm not saying the KGB is secretly behind our current world affairs. However, the tactics they had used and the goals they had set out to achieve remain relevant. I'd also highly recommend reading more of this letter to get a far more detailed background on how the same institutions Schwab bragged about, "penetrating," (media, influencers, religion, etc.) were also a primary focus of the KGB.

According to Bezmenov, it takes around 15-20 years for those tactics to alter a nation, since this is the amount of time a generation of youth take to have their minds shaped and then enter the institutions. So consider for a moment the rise of institutionally-ingrained, "cancel culture," censorship permissibility, "social justice," anti-second amendment sentiments, anti-informed consent, anti-medical autonomy, and end-of-the-world alarmism around, "climate change." About how long have these ideologies been the 24/7 topics of news agencies, colleges, and even workplaces? Does it seem to you like the generation sprayed with the firehose of these wretched, un-American ideas has now infiltrated the institutions? Because it certainly does to me. And this is what makes the next three stages possible.

2. Destabilization – *"Here the efforts of subverter narrow down to the 'essentials': the internal power structures of a target nation; the nation's foreign relations; economy and 'social fiber'. Now he gets to the 'spinal cord' of your country and helps YOU to bring your own society into the state of destabilization ... Traditional national institutions no longer appear efficient. They are replaced by artificially created 'citizen's committees' and 'boards' which acquire more and*

more political power. These bodies which are in essence, mirror reflections of the totalitarian structures of power, are more and more 'responsive' to mob-ocracy, the rule of the crowd of radicalized consumers. At the same time, the back of the economy – the free bargaining process – gradually yields to the principle of 'planned economy' and 'centralization'. With the final destruction of the free bargaining process the predominant economic power moves into the hands of 'Big Brother', the State, which functions more and more 'in cahoots' with mega-monopolies and monopolized labor unions. The famous 'division of powers' no longer governs the judicial, legislative and executive lines, but rather is replaced by bureaucracy in government, bureaucracy in business and bureaucracy in labor."

Over the course of the past decade or so, it has been disheartening to many people to see almost all companies and institutions bow to the seemingly illogical demands of, "social justice," and, "cancel culture." To Americans who believed their country was based on free-bargaining and the free market, it has been impossible to understand this shift from institutions being built to serve *them*, to institutions making demands *of* them. But this destabilized, "mob-ocracy," Bezmenov describes is exactly what we face with the aforementioned *technocracy* we have identified, along with its technocrat servants, who he refers to as, "radicalized consumers." Said technocrat consumers in our day are radical enough at times to knowingly poison themselves and demand others do the same, which our non-representative institutions have proven more than willing to, "respond to," as we've seen with their human-rights-violating coercions.

And this is only the tip of the iceberg as far as parallels to the Covid era itself go. When Bezmenov brings up the government being, "in cahoots," with mega-monopolies, the predominance of bureaucracies at the expense of division of powers, and the overall lack of representative government in general, these are all things we have identified in the technocrat endorsement, "public-private partnerships." In fact, he even mentions the fraudulent, "frictions," the US and USSR portrayed, as both cooperatively served the interests of multi-national monopolies—just like we see occurring via the WEF and its, "distinct," member governments today.

Another perhaps especially light-bulb-igniting mention for many people will also be the role of, "boards," given the prominent, despicable actions of school boards in implementing psychologically abusive policies for children. These policies were so overwhelmingly and publicly opposed, in fact, that the technocrat-serving Biden Regime saw fit to allegedly collaborate with the National School Board Association (yet another totalitarian power structure, as Bezmenov refers to) to label parents voicing concerns over these and other Covid-era policies as, "domestic terrorists."[25]

Before we continue, I'd like to highlight one final point made by Bezmenov on this stage. When referring to perceptions on America's violating international law, he says, "The average American may not even realize that the 'International Court' is nothing but an artificial creature of the Soviet-controlled General Assembly of the UN." I think this is particularly prudent because of our exploration of the actions of the UN and other global interests, as well as the charges which have been filed at the ICC against the Covid collaborators. In my opinion, understanding this control could lead to a few different outcomes—namely, the UN-controlled court could ignore the charges and sweep everything under the rug, or it could take up the charges and use the massive resulting tribunals to provide itself legitimacy/power over what it considers unruly national systems. Either way, a lack of UN/WHO culpability will point directly to this control over the ICC Bezmenov talks about.

3. Crisis – "... 'radicals' and Soviet 'sleeper' agents springing into action, trying to seize power as quickly and as ruthlessly as possible ... the majority of Americans will be so totally confused that they may even WELCOME some 'strong' leaders who 'know how to talk to the Russians'. Chances are these leaders will be elected and given almost unlimited 'emergency powers'. A forceful change of the U.S. system may or may not be accomplished through a civil war or internal revolution, and a physical military invasion by the USSR may not even have to take place at all. But change it will be, and rather a drastic one, with all the familiar attributes of Soviet 'progress' being instituted such as nationalization of vital

563

industries, the reduction of the 'private sector' of the economy to the bare minimum, the redistribution of wealth and a massive propaganda campaign by the newly 'elected' government to 'explain' and justify the reforms.

I perhaps don't even need to explain how every single one of the above sentences exactly describes the Covid era. From a ruthless seizure of power including even by, "strong," and, "nationalist," leaders like Trump; to the disorientation and welcoming of a seemingly limitless amount of, "emergency," powers; to tyrants who, "are the science;" to the radical intimidation and destruction of well-organized ANTIFA agents;[26,27] to nationalization of the pharmaceutical and media industries, among others; and the openly admitted and obvious election fraud which has taken place to prop up a clearly compromised regime.[28,29] This is an exact 1-to-1 comparison of what's taken place.

It's also not hard to understand why crisis is so readily attainable for such a society, if we look at a micro example. Imagine a person is raised in a Christian family with Christian values. Let's say they live according to those values all the way up until high school, where they start to be influenced by the wrong crowd. This crowd raises doubts about the importance of maintaining a sober mind, which they push until the person gives in and surrenders their belief in the inherent importance of sobriety (demoralization). Eventually the person partakes. It starts as once, but they continue and continue until it has become an addiction they suddenly are having to go the extra mile to hide and to find, "creative," ways to fund (destabilization). From here money gets tight and it becomes so stressful they get careless, culminating in some catalyzing event like a car accident, robbery, and/or arrest (crisis). It is easy to see in this example how the first two stages naturally lead to the third, and how possible it would be for an outside force to overwhelm the addict into the stage of crisis, before the final stage.

    4. Normalization – *"Any normal nation would definitely resist such a 'progressive change'. As I have just described. And according to the 'classics of Marxism-Leninism' there will arise pockets of resistance, shortly after the takeover consisting of the enemy classes and counter-revolutionaries who will physically resist the new system. Some Americans*

564

may take to arms and flee to the mountains (as in Afghanistan). Reforms (or destruction to be more accurate) of the security agencies, (police and military) by the new government may lead to a situation of 'split loyalties' among law enforcement officers and render the majority of the population defenseless. At this point, to avoid 'the bloodshed', the subverter moves to normalization ... the vanquished country was brought by force into the NORMAL state of SOCIALISM: namely, subjugation. This is when my dear friends you will start seeing 'friendly' Soviet soldiers in the streets of our cities working together with American soldiers and the 'new' police force to 'restore law and order'. Very soon your yesterday's American socialist radicals and do-gooders who were working so hard to bring 'progress' to their own country will find themselves in prisons."

One could argue that there are two groups of Bezmenov's, "useful idiots," in the case of the Covid era: 1) the Trump supporting election fraud resistance who were graciously allowed into the Capitol Building before being rounded up and sent to what have been alleged to be inhumane prison conditions, and 2) the twice or more, "vaccinated," who got injected for stupid reasons like self-aggrandizement and other, "particularly valuable human being," rewards (like travel), only to be maimed, killed, to find out they'd need more shots, or for their, "vaccine," passport systems to be cancelled entirely in less than a year.[30,31,32] Either way, a man with dementia who didn't campaign at all, who has a history of touching children inappropriately right out in the open, and who has a litany of damning corruption allegations, is said to have received the most votes ever in an American election by about 20 million.[33,34] He is said to have done so during a year when mail-in voting (well-documented as a primary means of fraud[35]) was at an all-time high and when vote counting stopped in the middle of the night (also a well-documented practice of fraudulent elections[36]). This absurd narrative has been accepted by the institutions for more than a year now. All of the above intimidation, related to Covid or otherwise, has sought to normalize in the minds of Americans (among others) the complete and utter lack of representative government, as we've covered.

Whether it's worked to this aim or has unwittingly awoken the consciousness of millions of people is another story. But overall, comparing these stages to our current state of affairs should make something abundantly clear: the United States has already become the society Bezmenov describes here. While this might seem scary, solace can be taken in that an understanding of the problem makes finding the solution possible. The solution in this case is also not violence or strife, as Sun-Tzu mentions—in fact, these things serve the enemy. Instead, a rediscovery of and return to our religious, societal, and moral principles can lead to a true freedom from this hectic, crisis-based society. By reverse-engineering these stages, American ideals can be restored and defended in the future. I will discuss this more at the end of this chapter.

Clear Cut Proof of Media Hypnosis

Moving into the short-term Covid era psychological triggers for this psychotic behavior we've observed, we will now turn to how the media directly uses hypnosis in its propaganda. But first, we need to define hypnosis. According to Mayo Clinic, hypnosis is[37]:

> *"A trance-like state in which you have heightened focus and concentration. Hypnosis is usually done with the help of a therapist using verbal repetition and mental images. When you're under hypnosis, you usually feel calm and relaxed, and are more open to suggestions."*

In her January 2019 publication in *Palliative Care*, "What is hypnosis and how might it work?"[38] Ann Williamson adds:

> *"Every day 'trance' states are part of our common human experience, such as getting lost in a good book, driving down a familiar stretch of road with no conscious recollection, when in prayer or meditation, or when undertaking a monotonous or creative activity. Our conscious awareness of our surroundings versus an inner awareness is on a continuum, so that, when in these states one's focus is predominantly internal, but one does not necessarily lose all outer awareness."*

We are all certainly familiar with the above scenarios, in particular driving on a familiar road and not retaining much of the memory of going from point A to point B. What people are not as familiar with is that this state is the equivalent of a hypnotic state, in which a person could be increasingly opened up to outside suggestion and internalizing that suggestion. Hypnosis does *not* require a watch on a chain, staring into swirly images, or putting someone to sleep and telling them to quack like a duck. Instead, it is simply the process of making suggestions to a person in a state of hypnosis. To this effect, Williamson continues:

> *"Hypnosis could be seen as a meditative state, which one can learn to access consciously and deliberately, for a therapeutic purpose. Suggestions are then given either verbally or using imagery, directed at the desired outcome. This might be to allay anxiety by accessing calmness and relaxation ... However, the main usefulness of the hypnotic state is the increased effectiveness of suggestion and access to mind/body links or unconscious processing."*

As explained, such a state is utilized by hypnotists typically to help a person reverse an internalized fear. The role of the hypnotist is to bring the patient to this state, and then to make corrective suggestions. For example, a person's fear of public speaking might come from a subconscious fear of something going wrong while speaking. This fear could be rational if based on a personal experience, or not. But the point is it can become instinctual, which is why suggestions of confidence and/or positive public speaking images presented to a person while they're in a hypnotic state can be an effective way to reverse that instinct.

Similar to getting lost in a good book as described above (I've got you right where I want you, dear reader!), smartphones are also a very common way people end up in this, "trance." In fact, research published in *Frontiers in Psychology* by Olson et al. in 2020 suggests that people who are frequent users of smartphones are more likely to be easily hypnotized[39]. This makes intuitive sense based on what we've discussed, since such people (myself included to some extent) would frequently find ourselves in a hypnotic state.

This brings us to the hypnosis tactics of the modern day media, and online media in particular, which exploit an increasingly smartphone-attached population. While this too could be the topic of its own book, I will provide the most dramatic example of blatantly hypnotic suggestion I've come across, courtesy of the *Associated Press*. Before I do, I find it necessary to remind you that the misconceptions of hypnosis might make it seem like I'm saying the *Associated Press* is using some kind of advanced, through-the-phone technology or something to brainwash people—I'm absolutely not. Once someone is in a hypnotic state as they tend to be when focused on their phone, all it takes is the right words (suggestions) in the right place to achieve the effect.

These suggestive words are what the *AP* used in spades when they published a, "fact-check," of Dr. Robert Malone's opinion that the media had the population under a form of, "mass formation psychosis."[40] Now, I'm not going to get into what, "mass formation psychosis," is, specifically because I find it irrelevant to the question of whether or not the media uses hypnosis techniques on the population. I will instead prove that they do use them, and do so excessively in this very article they claim not to. So let's go example by example:

1. "What you need to know:" – *Twitter*'s, "fact-checks," of, "mass formation psychosis," cited the aforementioned *AP* article. Above *Twitter*'s on-site, "fact-check," bullet-point summary of the article, they led with the headline, "What you need to know." This is a right-off-the-bat suggestion which signals that the reader can continue in their relaxed state and let the hypnotists take over from here. It assuages the anxiety of uncertainty, and it implies the reader won't need to dig deeper because they are about to be told the whole story. This is obviously untrue however, as neither the *AP* nor *Twitter* provide any of the context of the interview itself, nor do they appear to even provide a link to it.

2. "FACT FOCUS:" – The title of the *AP* article itself reads, "FACT FOCUS: Unfounded theory used to dismiss COVID measures." First off, it is interesting that unlike seemingly all other, "fact-check," articles I've ever seen, the word, "focus," is substituted for, "check." The effect is to center the reader's attention off the lengthy scientific credentials of Malone and onto the perceived authority of the propagandists slandering him. What also makes this even more effective is the

568

capitalization of the words. In the *European Journal of English Language and Linguistics Research*, Md. Mozaffor Hossain published a 2017 psycholinguistic analysis of language as a device for psychological manipulation, specifically as used in George Orwell's *1984*.[41] Hossain cites the well-documented effect of, "grandeur, pomposity, and aesthetic seriousness," intended by capitalization, both in *1984* and throughout history. To start the article with this manipulation establishes that effect before the reader even reads the content.

3. The very idea of a, "fact-check," is itself suggestive. It implies the content of the article is indisputable, which by the very nature of the article existing tends toward that not being the case. In fact, *Facebook* itself defended its actions in a 2021 court case by openly admitting its, "fact-checks," were actually opinions the whole time.[42] This type of fraud is permitted to exist because, as we saw in several prior examples, the federal government endorses and encourages it.

4. "An unfounded theory" – the article is opened with these words, which if its intention was honest would be a case it'd need to make. As I've demonstrated here clearly, however, the theory as *AP* states it that, "millions of people have been 'hypnotized' into believing mainstream ideas about COVID-19," is observably supported in this very article, among countless others, by their excessive use of hypnotic suggestion. This on top of outside exercises like Event 201 and the Yale study on the Covid inoculations, among others, which explicitly theorized how to make millions of people believe mainstream ideas about, "Covid."

5. "Here's a look at the facts … THE FACTS:" – at this point I think you're probably starting to get the point. The difference between actual scientists like Robert Malone and the corporate media is in this use of tone and narcissistic behavior. Science cannot be treated as fluid or debatable, given the objectives of a propagandist, despite its fundamentally being a method of fluid testing which is dependent on debate and peer-review.

I could continue with the incessant use of the word, "experts," despite those experts never offering to talk to and/or debate Malone, or the cherry picking of a strawman unrelated to the core issue to make the case seem closed, as we've previously discussed in this book. That such articles are so filled with this on-the-nose suggestion, however, in my opinion strongly *suggests* that these multimillion-dollar mass media outlets the intelligence community is documented as having had involvement in know what they're doing. That it has led to two-thirds of the population injecting themselves with an experimental serum claimed to reprogram your cells, and which pharma executives like Bayer's Stefan Oelrich admitted they wouldn't have accepted otherwise, suggests that their hypnosis tactics have been a resounding success.

The Ten Stages of Genocide

One could point to the suppression of safe and common medical treatments, the introduction and exclusive availability of experimental medications, and the psychological warfare coercion of dangerous experimental inoculations to make a case of Covid era genocide. However, the elements which comprise a genocide have been explicitly defined by Dr. Gregory H. Stanton, a professor and Vice President of the International Association of Genocide Scholars, whose model has been internationally recognized for its historical validity.[43] This model is the, "Ten Stages of Genocide," which are a, "formula for how a society can engage in genocide." Using this formula, we can back-solve to determine if the Covid era adds up to genocide and/or attempted genocide:

1. **Classification**
   a. Description: *"... categories to distinguish people into 'us and them' ... If societies are too segregated (divided) they are most likely to have genocide."*
   b. Classification in the Covid era: slanderous titles designated to those with logical questions/grievances such as, "science-deniers," "anti-maskers," "conspiracy theorists," and/or "anti-vaxxers."[44,45,46,47]

2. **Symbolization**
   a. Description: *"We give names or other symbols to the classifications ... We name people ... or distinguish them by colors or dress, and apply them to members of groups ... When combined with hatred, symbols may*

be forced upon unwilling members of minority groups ... Sometimes we impose symbols on ourselves ... That is the group's right but sometimes backfires..."

  b. Symbolization in the Covid era: mandated masks only for the, "unvaccinated," (the group that generally was most unwilling to wearing them) in workplaces and businesses.[48,49] Masks in general served as a primary symbol of either compliance or non-compliance. Manic hatred of the unmasked was widespread, thanks in large part to media encouragement, including verbal abuse and in some cases physical assault.[50,51,52,53,54,55] The irony is this is an example of embracing symbolism backfiring, since masks deteriorate health and so do the experimental drugs/inoculations they symbolize compliance with.

3. **Discrimination**

  a. Description: *"A dominant group uses law, custom, and political power to deny the rights of the other groups ... stripped ... citizenship and prohibited employment..."*

  b. Discrimination in the Covid era: companies required experimental, EUA-authorized inoculations to employees lacking informed consent and the knowledge that such mandates were illegal.[56] Countries proposed and imposed fines on people who weren't inoculated.[57] Aforementioned documentation of when YGL leaders like Emanuel Macron actually said he doesn't consider the, "unvaccinated," to be Frenchmen. Aforementioned documentation of free speech suppression, gaslighting, etc. of the, "unvaccinated," and dissenters in general.

4. **Dehumanization**

  a. Description: *"... when one group treats another group as second-class citizens. Members of a persecuted group may be compared with animals, parasites, insects, or diseases."*

  b. Dehumanization in the Covid era: aforementioned viewpoint held by those like blogger Mark P. Shea that the presence of the, "unvaccinated," in society is

571

somehow a danger to others and those people should therefore be isolated (imprisoned); or Leana Wen's aforementioned comparing this group to drunk drivers—implying they are guilty of murder for breathing in public; or Daniel Andrews' aforementioned explicit designation of them as second-class citizens in his planned, "vaccinated economy;" or, perhaps the most on the nose, vicious tyrant Justin Trudeau's saying the following[58]: *"We are going to end this pandemic by proceeding with the vaccination ... There is still a part of the population fiercely against it ... **They take up some space. This leads us, as a leader and as a country, to make a choice: do we tolerate these people** (my emphasis)?"* There is irony in the common person accepting these inhuman words, however, because those who do are themselves routinely dehumanized by the eugenicists benefitting from this cause like Bill Gates and other WEF allies, who openly call for their numbers to be reduced.

5. **Organization**
   a. Description: *"Genocide is always organized, usually by the state, though sometimes informally or by terrorist groups."*
   b. Organization in the Covid era: aforementioned, "public-private," organization by the WEF specifically, along with globalist collaborators like the UN/WHO, World Bank, and the WEF's allies in the national governments they admit to having, "penetrated," in the words of Klaus Schwab.

6. **Polarization**
   a. Description: *"Extremists drive the groups apart. Hate groups broadcast propaganda that reinforces prejudice and hate ... targets moderates, and intimidates them so that they are silent."*
   b. Polarization in the Covid era: extensive documentation on, "fact-checking," censorship, gaslighting, and online profile banning. Overt censorship of open non-compliers leads to a general lack of awareness in

moderates of relevant information negative to the inoculation agenda, as evidenced by comedian Heather McDonald's not knowing what myocarditis was despite having received three shots which can cause it. It also leads to a self-censorship by moderates trying to avoid the same consequences, whether that be in the workplace, social media, or society at large—self-censorship as evidenced by both Joe Rogan's downplaying his own experience-based opinions on the matter despite also talking to experts regularly, and *Project Veritas'* consistent call for moderate potential-whistleblowers to, "be brave," against the same type of consequences Rogan fears.[59] This culminates in polls such as one which is claimed as showing, "59% of Democrats favor government confining unvaccinated Americans to their homes."[60]

7. **Preparation**

    a. <u>Description</u>: *"... plan the 'Final Solution' to the ... targeted group 'question.' They often use euphemisms to cloak their intentions, such as referring to their goals as 'ethnic cleansing,' 'purification,' or, 'counter-terrorism' ... They indoctrinate the populace with fear of the victim group."*

    b. <u>Preparation in the Covid era</u>: Event 201, "epidemic preparedness," simulation of October 2019 and its illogical focus on, "misinformation," also known as logical questions or grievances. Rockefeller Operation Lockstep and John's Hopkins SPARS war games are additional examples conducted by largely the same group and with the same purpose. This has culminated in the CDC's aforementioned preparation of concentration camps using the euphemisms, "quarantine camp," or, "Green Zones," as well as in New York's proposed bill to allow the governor to detain anyone suspected as a, "threat to public health." Additional intention-cloaking euphamisms used by the Covid collaborators include, "public-private partnerships," "sustainability," "women's healthcare," and, "equity."

8. Persecution

    a. <u>Description</u>: *"Victims are identified and separated out ... lists are drawn up ... property is often confiscated. Sometimes they are even separated into ghettos, deported into concentration camps, or confined ..."*

    b. <u>Persecution in the Covid era</u>: aforementioned implementation of these, "Green Zone," concentration camps in places like China and Australia, where in the latter three teenagers were actually arrested for, "escaping."[61,62] Hospitals removing transplant patients from lists and denying care to the, "unvaccinated," and/or those who have not received a test (has happened to me personally, more on that later).[63,64] Canadians traveling back into their own country faced mandatory, "quarantine," confinement *at their own expense* in government approved hotels—hotels YGL Prime Minister Justin Trudeau *did not have to stay at* after a G7 Summit.[65] Lists of, "unvaccinated," were drawn up, including reports of the US Commerce Department keeping a record of all employees seeking medical and religious exemptions for proposed inoculation mandates.[66]

9. Extermination

    a. <u>Description</u>: *"Extermination begins, and quickly becomes the mass killing legally called, 'genocide.' It is 'extermination' to the killers because they do not believe their victims to be fully human (see dehumanization)."*

    b. <u>Extermination in the Covid era</u>: aforementioned documentation on disastrous, deadly consequences of lockdowns; mass mischaracterization of disease using faulty testing techniques; mass denial of early treatment throughout the alleged pandemic, which lead to expert and eyewitness claims of a hospital genocide; incentivized and required utilization of dangerous and experimental drugs as the sole medication options which, considering the aforementioned evidence, also contributed to this genocide; deadly and debilitating adverse side effects of the inoculations; VAERS underreporting factors which hint at the true death toll of the shots; identification of once-in-a-century mortality rates by insurance companies during the year of mass inoculation; observable deterioration of heart and general health, especially visible in athletes.

10. Denial

    a. <u>Description</u>: *"... always follows genocide. It is among the surest indicators of further genocidal massacres. The perpetrators dig up mass graves, burn the bodies, try to cover up the evidence and intimidate the witnesses. They deny that they committed any crimes, and often blame what happened on the victims.* ***They block investigations of the crimes, and continue to govern until driven from power by force, when they flee into exile. Leaders of the genocide continue to deny the crime unless they are captured and a tribunal (special court) is established to try them*** (my emphasis).*"*

    b. <u>Denial in the Covid era</u>: as reported by the *New York Times*, amid the mass medical malpractice and inhumanity which took place in New York City, as much as a tenth of the city's, "Covid dead," were, in fact, buried in mass graves at Hart Island.[67] Aforementioned documentation has shown the FDA and Pfizer attempted to cover up the evidence and block investigation, as they jointly asked a judge for 100 years to release the data used to authorize the inoculations. This on top of the CDC's dismissing their own warning system's incredible spike in reports while simultaneously calling it, "robust," their denying the public access to the, "v-safe," data they claimed was better despite its including over 119 million reports, their revising-down of data such as child, "Covid deaths," two years after those data were used to drum up fear, and the outright refusal of any of these public health organizations to face those at Senator Ron Johnson's panels who were either severely injured by or who lost a loved one due to the inoculations.[68] Public health officials continuously tell outright lies in an attempt to cover up the damages, such as when German Minister of Health Karl Lauterbach had the audacity to say the inoculations were free of side effects.[69] Blame placed on the, "unvaccinated," for inoculation failures. Testimony also given by doctors/nurses that inoculation injuries are being blamed on the, "vaccinated," because of their alleged, "anxiety." Aforementioned inoculation-coercing DOD attempt to cover up tremendous 2021 disease spikes in its own medical data system, DMED, which went as far as to admit its own egregious negligence in making the not-remotely-believable claim that all prior years used for comparison were understated, due to a, "glitch in the system." Speaking of fleeing into exile, this too has already begun, with Moderna's YGL hype-man Stéphane Bancel mysteriously deleting his *Twitter* account in February 2022 and having progressively sold his Moderna shares since late-2019, the same timeframe the contracts were being signed for the ultimately-utilized SARS mRNA inoculations with the NIH.[70]

As for the remainder of the Covid collaborators, they have and will continue to desperately cling to power until they are, in fact, forced from it. The aforementioned crimes against humanity charges being filed with the International Criminal Court are a big step in the right direction in this regard. In such courts, based on the evidence in this book and more, there are also many other legal bases beyond genocide with which the many people involved in these crimes can be clearly implicated.

1. Conspiracy[71]: *"An agreement between two or more persons to engage jointly in an unlawful or criminal act, or an act that is innocent in itself but becomes unlawful when done by the combination of actors."*
2. Accessory[72]: *"Contributing to or aiding in the commission of a crime. One who, without being present at the commission of an offense, becomes guilty of such offense, not as a chief actor,*

but as a participant, as by command, advice, instigation, or concealment; either before or after the fact or commission."

3. Accessory after the fact[73]: *"An accessory who assists a lawbreaker after the commission of a crime, as to avoid arrest, trial, or punishment."*
4. Fraud[74]: *"A deception practiced in order to induce another to give up possession of property or surrender a right."*
5. Racketeering[75]: *"To engage in an illegal business or other organized illegal activities."*
6. Reckless endangerment[76]: *"Behaving indifferently to the consequences in such a way as to create a substantial risk of serious physical injury or death to another person."*
7. Treason[77]: *"The betrayal of allegiance toward one's own country, especially by committing hostile acts against it or aiding its enemies in committing such acts."*

But still, while it might sound like an ideal outcome, ICC prosecution including of the WHO and UN members involved in this atrocity cannot be depended on for a just result, when corruption is as global and widespread as it is today. The people in positions of authority would essentially be prosecuting themselves, which they will not do. It is this reality which makes the following quote, attributed to R. Buckminster Fuller, ring true[78]:

"You never change things by fighting the existing reality. To change something, build a new model that makes the existing model obsolete."

With this in mind, my 2 cents on the matter for the average person would be: be fruitful, multiply, build strong local communities, demand representation of your representatives (such as verbalizing calls for usurpations like the aforementioned WHO treaty to be rejected), and above all, tell the truth. There are two main reasons these things are the best counters to the demented UN/WHO/WEF agenda:

1. They are the exact opposite of that agenda
2. They are in each person's control to enact in their own life

Strong, independent communities and families are ultimately the best shield because even if the controllers initiate crises in the global system, such communities are best positioned to carry on without incident. Take the Amish as a perfect example, who memes astutely portrayed as, "immune," to Covid because they didn't have televisions. Now, I'm not saying people need to eliminate *all* technology or convenience. But it is simple to understand how controlling an isolated person who doesn't know where their food or information originates would be much easier than a community-insulated person who does. A community full of like-minded people who are as familiar with each other as possible would, of course, have the easiest time rejecting, "mandates," without a second thought. And this alternative ecosystem can even be seen sprouting in the tech space, where platforms like *Gab* and others have absolutely refused to back down on free speech.

The more this type of mindset continues to expand, the better. Because the scarcity/victimhood mindset the WEF collaborators of the world seek to imprison people with is neither good, nor is it true. Claims of an unsustainable human population are the unfounded ramblings of greedy, immoral narcissists who we have demonstrated time and time again to be lying, as opposed to simply being wrong. But we can choose to instead live with abundance and a victor mindset, knowing now that both the fear they spread and the fear *of* them are things we can choose to live without. While it won't be an easy life to live—it will come with its own unique challenges—it sure is better than covering your breathing hole, injecting yourself with experimental poison, being discriminated against by cowardly fools, and waiting for a cabal of wicked psychopaths to, "give you your rights back." As for me, I have been and will continue to distance myself from all of that as much as humanly possible.

Endnotes

1   "Think Of The Current Time As The World's Largest Ever Human IQ... - Samim". 2021. *Samim.Io*. https://samim.io/p/2021-07-31-think-of-the-current-time-as-the-worlds-largest-ever/.

2   Biderman, Albert D. "Communist attempts to elicit false confessions from Air Force prisoners of war." *Bull*. N.Y. Acad. Med., 1957, 33, 616-625

3   Biderman, Albert D. "Effects of Communist Indoctrination Attempts: Some Comments Based on an Air Force Prisoner-of-War Study." *Social Problems, Volume 6, Issue 4*. Spring 1959, Pages 304-313, https://doi.org/10.2307/799363.

4   "Amnesty International Report on Torture." London. *Gerald Duckworth & Co.* 1975. Page 53

5   "Biederman's Chart Of Coercion - Narcissistic Abuse Rehab". 2019. *Youtu.Be.* https://youtu.be/k6RuFq8TAZk.

6   Feng, Emily. 2021. "Health Workers In China Are Killing Pets While Their Owners Are In Quarantine". *Npr.Org.* https://www.npr.org/2021/11/15/1055831581/health-workers-in-china-are-killing-pets-while-their-owners-are-in-quarantine.

7   James, Erin K., Scott E. Bokemper, Alan S. Gerber, Saad B. Omer, and Gregory A. Huber. 2021. "Persuasive Messaging To Increase COVID-19 Vaccine Uptake Intentions". *Vaccine* 39 (49): 7158-7165. doi:10.1016/j.vaccine.2021.10.039.

8   Manno, Adam. 2022. "Study Shows Worrying About COVID Leads To People Making Bad Choices". *Mail Online.* https://www.dailymail.co.uk/news/article-10362429/Study-shows-worrying-COVID-leads-bad-choices-performing-poorly-cognitive-tests.html.

9   Deoni, Sean CL, Jennifer Beauchemin, Alexandra Volpe, and Viren D'Sa. 2021. "Impact Of The COVID-19 Pandemic On Early Child Cognitive Development: Initial Findings In A Longitudinal Observational Study Of Child Health". doi:10.1101/2021.08.10.21261846.

10   "OMICRON INSANITY! Check Out This Image. – Investment Watch". 2021. *Investmentwatchblog.Com.* https://www.investmentwatchblog.com/omicron-insanity-check-out-this-image/.

11   Trent, John F. 2022. "Actress Katy Stoll Claims Covid-19 Vaccines "Significantly Affected My Menstruation," Says She's Experiencing "Excruciating Symptoms"". *Bounding Into Comics.* https://boundingintocomics.com/2022/03/29/actress-katy-stoll-claims-covid-19-vaccines-significantly-affected-my-menstruation-says-shes-experiencing-excruciating-symptoms/.

12   Ibid.

13   Attema, Arthur E., Olivier L'Haridon, Jocelyn Raude, and Valérie Seror. 2021. "Beliefs And Risk Perceptions About COVID-19: Evidence From Two Successive French Representative Surveys During Lockdown". *Frontiers In Psychology* 12. doi:10.3389/fpsyg.2021.619145.

14   Hawryluk, Markian. 2022. "His Wife Died From Johnson & Johnson Covid Vaccine Complications. Why He's Still Pro-Vaccine.". *NBC News.* https://www.nbcnews.com/health/health-news/complications-johnson-johnson-covid-vaccine-caused-oregon-womans-death-rcna18200.

15   "CNN's Chris Cuomo's Interference For Brother Andrew Laid Bare". 2021. *RT International.* https://www.rt.com/usa/541686-cuomo-covered-brother-cnn-harassment/.

16   Hays, Gabriel. 2021. "'Cuomosexuals,' The 20 Celebs Who Were 'In Love' With Accused Sex Pest/Granny Killer Gov. Cuomo". *Newsbusters.*

https://www.newsbusters.org/blogs/culture/gabriel-hays/2021/03/11/cuomosexuals-20-celebs-who-were-love-accused-sex-pestgranny.

17 Carroll, Conn. 2022. "We Found The Science Behind Democrats' COVID Flip-Flop". *Washington Examiner.* https://www.washingtonexaminer.com/opinion/we-found-the-science-behind-democrats-covid-flip-flop.

18 Mogavero, Zachary. 2021. "Dr. Fauci Song". *Genius.* https://genius.com/Zachary-mogavero-dr-fauci-song-lyrics.

19 "The Fathomless Self-Pity Of The Anti-Vax Cult - Stumbling Toward Heaven". 2022. *Stumbling Toward Heaven.* https://markpshea.com/2022/01/26/the-fathomless-self-pity-of-the-anti-vax-cult/.

20 Sharav, Vera. 2022. "Vera Sharav: "Never Again Is Now: Unless We All Resist" (Video + Transcript)". *Childrens' Health Defense Europe.* https://childrenshealthdefense.eu/eu-issues/vera-sharav-never-again-is-now-unless-we-all-resist/.

21 Mayfield, Emily. 2021. "JESUS AND THE LEPER". *Servants Of Grace.* https://servantsofgrace.org/jesus-and-the-leper/.

22 Huntington, Shane. 2021. "Father Determined To Vaccinate His 9-Year-Old Even After His 14-Year-Old Son Developed Heart Inflammation From The Pfizer Vaccine". *Ifunny.* https://ifunny.co/picture/father-determined-to-v-father-determined-to-vaccinate-his-9-xsmod2p29.

23 Pinsky, Drew. 2022. "Heather Mcdonald LIVE: Onstage Collapse, Skull Fracture Recovery & Tour Update – Ask Dr. Drew | Dr. Drew Official Website - Drdrew.Com". *Dr. Drew | Official Website.* https://drdrew.com/2022/heather-mcdonald-live-onstage-collapse-skull-fracture-recovery-tour-update-ask-dr-drew/.

24 Bezmenov, Yuri. 1984. "Bezmenov: LOVE LETTER TO AMERICA". *Internet Archive.* https://archive.org/details/BezmenovLoveLetterToAmerica.

25 Ashworth, Nate. 2021. "Why Did Merrick Garland Lie About Targeting Parents As Domestic Terrorists? - Election Central". *Uspresidentialelectionnews.Com.* https://www.uspresidentialelectionnews.com/2021/11/why-did-merrick-garland-lie-about-targeting-parents-as-domestic-terrorists/.

26 Levy, Janet. 2021. "The Roots Of Insurrection: Antifa Exposed". *Americanthinker.Com.* https://www.americanthinker.com/articles/2021/03/the_roots_of_insurrection_antifa_exposed.html.

27 Cheong, Ian. 2020. "BREAKING: DHS Leaked Email Confirms Antifa Is An Organized Group". *The Post Millennial.* https://thepostmillennial.com/dhs-leaked-email-confirms-that-antifa-is-an-organized-group.

28   Ball, Molly. 2021. "The Secret History Of The Shadow Campaign That Saved The 2020 Election". *Time*. https://time.com/5936036/secret-2020-election-campaign/.

29   Morse, Brandon. 2020. "Even A Large Number Of Democrats Believe Biden Stole The Election". *Redstate.Com*. https://redstate.com/brandon_morse/2020/11/30/even-a-large-number-of-democrats-believe-biden-stole-the-election-n286942.

30   "Watch - Trump Supporters Were Allowed In The By Capital Police They Did NOT Forcethere Way In". 2021. *Rense.Com*. https://rense.com/general96/trump-supporters-allowed.php.

31   Atkinson, Grant. 2021. "Alleged Conditions Of Jan. 6 Prisoners Revealed In Shock News Briefing". *The Western Journal*. https://www.westernjournal.com/alleged-conditions-jan-6-prisoners-revealed-shock-news-briefing/.

32   Goddek, Simon. 2021. "Covid Truth Network". *Telegram*. https://t.me/covidtruthnet/1113.

33   Baker, Brian. 2022. ""Mommy, I'm Scared": 7 Joe Biden Photos That Are Guaranteed To Frighten Your Child - 93.1FM WIBC". *93.1FM WIBC*. https://www.wibc.com/blogs/breakdown-with-brian-baker/mommy-im-scared-7-biden-photos-guaranteed-to-upset-your-child/.

34   Lord, Jeffrey. 2021. "Joe Biden: The Most Corrupt President Since Warren Harding". *The American Spectator | USA News And Politics*. https://spectator.org/joe-biden-the-most-corrupt-president-since-warren-harding/.

35   Liptak, Adam. 2012. "Error And Fraud At Issue As Absentee Voting Rises". *The New York Times*. https://www.nytimes.com/2012/10/07/us/politics/as-more-vote-by-mail-faulty-ballots-could-impact-elections.html.

36   "Tense Vote In Chavez Fiefdom In Venezuela Amid Interference Claims". 2022. *RFI*. https://www.rfi.fr/en/tense-vote-in-chavez-fiefdom-in-venezuela-amid-interference-claims.

37   "Hypnosis - Mayo Clinic". 2020. *Mayoclinic.Org*. https://www.mayoclinic.org/tests-procedures/hypnosis/about/pac-20394405.

38   Williamson, Ann. 2019. "What Is Hypnosis And How Might It Work?". *Palliative Care: Research And Treatment* 12: 117822421982658. doi:10.1177/1178224219826581.

39   Olson, Jay A., Moriah Stendel, and Samuel Veissière. 2020. "Hypnotised By Your Phone? Smartphone Addiction Correlates With Hypnotisability". *Frontiers In Psychiatry* 11. doi:10.3389/fpsyt.2020.00578.

40   FICHERA, ANGELO, and JOSH KELETY. 2022. "FACT FOCUS: Unfounded Theory Used To Dismiss COVID Measures". *AP NEWS*. https://apnews.com/article/coronavirus-pandemic-science-health-joe-rogan-ap-fact-check-a87b1044c6256968dcc33886a36c949f.

41 Hossain, Mozaffor. 2017. "LANGUAGE AS THE DEVICE FOR PSYCHOLOGICAL MANIPULATION IN GEORGE ORWELL'S NINETEEN EIGHTY-FOUR: A PSYCHOLINGUISTIC ANALYSIS". *European Journal Of English Language And Linguistics Research* 5 (8): 25-31. https://www.eajournals.org/wp-content/uploads/Language-as-the-Device-for-Psychological-Manipulation-in-George-Orwell%E2%80%99s-Nineteen-Eighty-Four-A-Psycholinguistic-Analysis.pdf.

42 Bokhari, Allum. 2021. "Facebook Admits In Court That 'Fact Checks' Are Just Opinion". *Breitbart*. https://www.breitbart.com/tech/2021/12/13/facebook-admits-in-court-that-fact-checks-are-just-opinion/.

43 "Ten Stages Of Genocide | The Genocide Education Project". 2016. *Genocideeducation.Org*. https://www.genocideeducation.org/wp-content/uploads/2016/03/ten_stages_of_genocide.pdf.

44 MCINTYRE, LEE. 2022. *HOW TO TALK TO A SCIENCE DENIER*. [S.l.]: MIT PRESS.

45 Austin, Daryl. 2020. "Opinion: Anti-Maskers: A Group Of People Whining So Much Over Something So Little". *CNN*. https://www.cnn.com/2020/11/13/opinions/utah-covid-cases-anti-maskers-austin/index.html.

46 COOK, JOHN, SANDER VAN DER LINDEN, STEPHAN LEWANDOWSKY, and ULLRICH ECKER. 2020. "People Who Believe COVID-19 Conspiracies Have These 7 Tendencies". *Fast Company*. https://www.fastcompany.com/90506252/people-who-believe-covid-19-conspiracies-have-these-7-tendencies.

47 Canal, Gabriella. 2017. "Understanding Anti Vaxxers And Their Opposition To Vaccines". *Global Citizen*. https://www.globalcitizen.org/en/content/everything-you-need-to-know-about-the-anti-vaxxer/.

48 Keenan, Alexis. 2021. "Can Employers Legally Require Unvaccinated Workers To Wear Masks? The Answer Is Likely Yes". *Msn.Com*. https://www.msn.com/en-us/news/us/can-employers-legally-require-unvaccinated-workers-to-wear-masks-the-answer-is-likely-yes/ar-AAKccUs.

49 Ferré-Sadurní, Luis, and Jesse McKinley. 2021. "New York Businesses Ordered To Require Masks Indoors Or Vaccine Proof". *Nytimes.Com*. https://www.nytimes.com/2021/12/10/nyregion/ny-mask-mandate-covid.html.

50 Walker, K. 2022. "WATCH: Elderly, White 'Mask Karens' Assault Unmasked Black Man While Yelling 'Black Lives Matter' In An Elevator". *Clash Daily*. https://clashdaily.com/2022/01/watch-elderly-white-mask-karens-assault-unmasked-black-man-while-yelling-black-lives-matter-in-an-elevator/.

51 Schwartz, Ian. 2021. "Watch: Maskless Woman Assaults Man For Not Wearing A Mask On Plane, Yells "Put Your Fu*King Mask

On"". *Realclearpolitics*.
https://www.realclearpolitics.com/video/2021/12/27/watch_maskless_wo
man_attacks_man_for_not_wearing_a_mask_on_plane_yells_put_your_f
uking_mask_on.html.

52   T., Brett. 2022. "Assistant Principal Says It Will Be Considered
Trespassing If Unmasked Kids Set Foot On School
Property". *Twitchy.Com*. https://twitchy.com/brettt-
3136/2022/02/02/assistant-principal-says-it-will-be-considered-
trespassing-if-unmasked-kids-set-foot-on-school-property/.

53   Montgomery, Mimi. 2020. "People Are Calling Out Runners Who Aren't
Wearing Masks. When Do They Actually Need To Wear One? |
Washingtonian (DC)". *Washingtonian*.
https://www.washingtonian.com/2020/05/07/people-are-calling-out-
runners-who-arent-wearing-masks-when-do-they-actually-need-to-wear-
one/.

54   Arama, Nick. 2020. "Watch: Angry Masked Mob Of Shoppers Scream
Obscenities At Another Shopper For Not Wearing A Mask In Grocery
Store". *Redstate.Com*. https://redstate.com/nick-arama/2020/05/25/watch-
angry-mob-screams-obscenities-at-non-mask-wearing-customer-in-
staten-island-grocery-store-n138108.

55   Schneiderman, Matt. 2020. "It's OK To Yell At Strangers Who Don't
Wear Masks". *Yahoo.Com*. https://www.yahoo.com/lifestyle/ok-yell-
strangers-don-t-134608959.html.

56   Messenger, Haley. 2022. "From Amex To Walmart, Here Are The
Companies Mandating The Covid Vaccines For Employees". *NBC News*.
https://www.nbcnews.com/business/business-news/amex-walmart-are-
companies-mandating-covid-vaccine-employees-rcna11049.

57   "These Countries Are Slapping The Unvaccinated With Fines And Bans".
2021. *Bloomberg.Com*. https://www.bloomberg.com/news/articles/2021-
12-01/these-countries-are-slapping-the-unvaccinated-with-fines-bans.

58   "Liberal Comedian Compares Canadian PM To Hitler". 2022. *RT
International*. https://www.rt.com/pop-culture/549186-bill-maher-
trudeau-hitler-truckers/.

59   McCarthy, Tyler. 2022. "Joe Rogan Addresses Spotify Scandal In First
Stand Up Show Since Controversy: 'I Talk S--- For A Living'". *Fox
News*. https://www.foxnews.com/entertainment/joe-rogan-spotify-
scandal-stand-up.

60   Gournell, Jack. 2022. "Dems Overreach? Poll Says 59 Percent Want Govt
To Confine Unvaxxed In Homes". *Newsmax*.
https://www.newsmax.com/politics/democrats-unvaccinated-hesitancy-
lockdowns/2022/01/17/id/1052760/.

61   Brown, Lee. 2022. "China Sending People To 'Quarantine Camps' Ahead
Of Olympics". *Nypost.Com*. https://nypost.com/2022/01/12/china-
sending-people-to-quarantine-camps-ahead-of-olympics/.

62   Davis, Jack. 2021. "Three COVID Detainees Escape Quarantine Camp In
Australia, Are Arrested After Foot Chase". *The Western Journal*.

https://www.westernjournal.com/three-covid-detainees-escape-quarantine-camp-arrested-foot-chase/.

63   MCKNIGHT, PATRICIA. 2022. "More Hospitals Are Removing Transplant Patients From Lists Due To COVID Vaccine Status". *Newsweek*. https://www.newsweek.com/more-hospitals-are-removing-transplant-patients-lists-due-covid-vaccine-status-1672946.

64   Foster, Ally. 2021. "Controversial Plan For Unvaxxed Goes 'Too Far'". *News*. https://www.news.com.au/world/coronavirus/australia/why-controversial-plan-for-unvaccinated-aussies-is-a-bad-idea/news-story/7a0a3084e43cef91af90bfc1fc173c1a.

65   FUNG, KATHERINE. 2021. "Canadian PM Justin Trudeau Faces Backlash For Not Staying At Designated Quarantine Hotel After G7 Summit In The UK". *Newsweek*. https://www.newsweek.com/canadian-pm-justin-trudeau-faces-backlash-not-staying-designated-quarantine-hotel-after-g7-summit-1599541.

66   Lucas, Fred. 2022. "EXCLUSIVE: Government Lists Track Medical And Religious Exemptions". *The Daily Signal*. https://www.dailysignal.com/2022/01/26/exclusive-government-expands-list-of-unvaccinated-now-tracking-both-medical-and-religious-exemptions/.

67   Slotnik, Daniel E. 2021. "Up To A Tenth Of New York City's Coronavirus Dead May Be Buried In A Potter's Field. (Published 2021)". *Nytimes.Com*. https://www.nytimes.com/2021/03/25/nyregion/hart-island-mass-graves-coronavirus.html.

68   "CDC Deletes 24 Percent Of Child COVID-19 Deaths, Blames Coding Error". 2022. *Great Game India*. https://greatgameindia.com/cdc-deletes-covid-deaths-coding-error/.

69   Schwarz, Peter. 2021. "German Left Party Politician Sahra Wagenknecht Denounces COVID-19 Protection Measures". *World Socialist Web Site*. https://www.wsws.org/en/articles/2021/11/08/left-n08.html.

70   "How Much Moderna Stock Stephane Bancel Owns And Why He Just Sold $1.8 Million Of It - News Nation USA". 2022. *News Nation USA*. https://newsnationusa.com/news/finance/stock-market/how-much-moderna-stock-stephane-bancel-owns-and-why-he-just-sold-1-8-million-of-it/.

71   "Conspiracy". 2022. *Thefreedictionary.Com*. Accessed April 6. https://legal-dictionary.thefreedictionary.com/conspiracy.

72   "Accessory". 2022. *Thefreedictionary.Com*. Accessed April 6. https://legal-dictionary.thefreedictionary.com/accessory.

73   "Accessory after the fact". 2022. *Thefreedictionary.Com*. Accessed April 6. https://legal-dictionary.thefreedictionary.com/accessory+after+the+fact.

74   "Fraud". 2022. *Thefreedictionary.Com*. Accessed April 6. https://legal-dictionary.thefreedictionary.com/fraud.

75   "Racketeering". 2022. *Thefreedictionary.Com*. Accessed April 6. https://legal-dictionary.thefreedictionary.com/racketeering.

76   "Reckless endangerment". 2022. *Thefreedictionary.Com*. Accessed April 6. https://legal-dictionary.thefreedictionary.com/reckless+endangerment.

77   "Treason". 2022. *Thefreedictionary.Com*. Accessed April 6. https://legal-dictionary.thefreedictionary.com/treason.

78   Fuller, R. Buckminster. 2022. "A Quote By R. Buckminster Fuller". *Goodreads.Com*. Accessed April 6. https://www.goodreads.com/quotes/13119-you-never-change-things-by-fighting-the-existing-reality-to.

Chapter 21

Important Historical Context and the Germ Theory Debate

"[Claude] Bernard was correct. I was wrong. The microbe is nothing. The terrain is everything."
—Attributed to Louis Pasteur, on his deathbed[1]

Before we close we must make an additional point that is pivotal to highlight as historical and scientific context on the topic of public health organizations and the pandemics they identify: **the germ theory of disease v. the terrain theory of disease**. Though we won't go into the level of detail necessary here to come to any kind of resolution, the point of view one takes on this topic makes all the other scientific points either necessary follow-up (germ theory point of view), or moot (terrain theory point of view).

Because the general public is largely not aware of the difference and because the germ theory prevails as a societal norm, earlier chapters have mostly assumed the germ theory is valid and have demonstrated the faults of Covid era public health policy in the context of the germ theory. For those doctors and scientists who do not presume that to be the case however, the validity of the terrain theory would imply an inherent absurdity in the entire philosophy of the public health approach. And given how wildly inaccurate those bureaucracies have been about seemingly every single thing—their tests don't work, their recommendations don't work, and their drugs either don't work or worse—it's definitely worth exploring to see if the cracks go deeper.

When you do, you begin to notice Covid isn't the first time this madness has happened—not in this century, or even in this decade. From the Spanish flu to AIDS and seemingly everything in between, there is so much background on the responses and declarations of public health organizations—background which provides a helpful context when trying to further understand the Covid era. For a much deeper dive on this than I can possibly provide in one chapter, one can find much more on the history and debate in resources (among others) like *Virus Mania* by Torsten Engelbrecht and Claus Kohnlein and/or *Goodbye Germ Theory* by Dr. William P. Trebing.[2,3] To begin this discussion for our purposes though, we first need to define a scientific theory[4]:

> *"A theory that can be tested and **potentially disproved** (my emphasis); failure to disprove or refute it increases confidence in it, but it **cannot be considered as proven** (my emphasis)."*

Before we even bother to continue, the point must be made here again that the actions of the vast majority of public health organizations (all actions related to Covid) are/were justified using the assumption that the germ *theory* holds. As we can see in the definition above, however, because this is a scientific *theory*, as opposed to a scientific *law*, it "cannot be considered as proven." Therefore, it should go without saying, this further muddies the waters of whether any mandate or law or coercive measure of any kind in its name can truly be legal, moral, or just. Certainly under the Nuremberg Code they cannot, since any, "unproven," scientific practice can only become, "proven," via further experimentation, for which it is illegal to coerce a subject to be involved in.

Next, we define germ theory[5]:

> *"... in medicine, the theory that certain diseases are caused by the invasion of the body by microorganisms, organisms too small to be seen except through a microscope. The French chemist and microbiologist Louis Pasteur, the English surgeon Joseph Lister, and the German physician Robert Koch are given much of the credit for the development and acceptance of the theory."*

And finally, terrain theory[6]:

> *"... states that diseases are results of our internal environment and its ability to maintain homeostasis against outside threats ... believes if an individual maintains a healthy terrain, it can handle outside invaders or threats which cause diseases. When terrain is weak, it favors the microorganisms. Hence, the health depends on the quality of an individuals' terrain ... initiated by Claude Bernard and was later developed by Antoine Bechamp."*

The fundamental difference between the two theories comes from the question: **does the presence of specific microorganisms (such as viruses, bacteria, etc.) during an illness imply causation of said illness?** The relevance of this question could almost never have been made clearer to the average person than to the extent demonstrated during the Covid era. The reason why is that for the first time of this magnitude in history, the topic of asymptomatic, "spread," has been alleged by public health organizations.

This concept of asymptomatic infection also raises another very important question: **if the virus is the *cause* of the disease, how can it be present in a person who isn't in a state of disease?** This reasonable question has even been pondered with bewilderment by mainstream sources like *National Geographic*, when they admit, "we have little idea who among us is spreading the disease," right before acknowledging, "people who are old, obese, or have other health conditions such as asthma or diabetes are more likely to develop a severe form of Covid-19."[7] The truth of the matter is, *National Geographic*'s admission implies they also have, "little idea," if the disease is *spreading* at all. The reason for this is viruses, such as corona viruses, and other microorganisms (like bacteria, parasites, and fungi) are in each of our bodies at all times and in tremendous quantities. So since old, obese, or otherwise unhealthy people (weakened terrain) are so much more likely to get sick, it seems logical that the terrain itself could just as easily—or perhaps, more easily—be argued as the *true* cause.

In this regard you will recall Dr. Ryan Cole's message that cold and flu season should rightly be called, "low vitamin D season," and that they occur in the months of least sunlight (vitamin D supplier) for this reason. To add to this thesis, the NIH published a 2014 study which estimated 35% of adults and nearly 50% of infants are vitamin D deficient.[8] The study determined this deficiency to be a, "major global public health problem." Anthony Fauci has also admitted to taking 6,000 IU of vitamin D supplements per day, and has even acknowledged the connection of low vitamin D to Covid, despite not making this cheap, simple solution part of his official federal public health investment recommendations at all.[9,10]

With all this in mind, we are brought right back to the same question: what then, is the *cause* of cold/flu? Is it the virus's presence when sick? Or is it the condition of vitamin malnutrition, as stated by

589

all of the above doctors, which in the absence of said malnutrition the person likely wouldn't be sick at all? The more obvious answer seems to me to be the latter. There is a clear cause and effect there which isn't there for the virus explanation. Could the lack of nutrients lead to an increased prevalence of the viruses already in the body? Yes. Does this imply the increased prevalence of viruses in the body caused the sickness? No.

Another issue this presents is the question of whether the one-cause model is even relevant to disease. Consider, for example, the time of year cold/flus are known to occur—namely, the low-sunlight months of winter. What else occurs during these months? Well, in the US at least, this is peak holiday season, which for many people includes over-eating, excess drinking, less exercise, and increased stress levels. The impact of over-eating and exercise on health is mostly obvious, but a November 2021 study by Reinold et al. in *Frontiers in Cellular and Infection Microbiology* has actually concluded a pro-inflammatory gut biome to be directly related to poor, "Covid," outcomes.[11] Stress also leads to increased cortisol levels, which have been demonstrated in many studies to be highly correlated to disease risk.[12,13,14] In fact, stress is so potent that qualitative analysis has even linked it to cancers, such as breast cancer.[15] So taking all these things together, it is perfectly reasonable to imagine several factors can combine to lead to the internal conditions which cause the body to need to flush out toxic buildup, as it does during a cold/flu. In fact, to me it seems far *more* reasonable and allows one to take far more responsibility for their health than to simply conclude, "Someone else breathed near me, so now I'm sick."

I won't go any deeper on this topic as I am not involved in microbiology and the books I've already mentioned do a much better job of it than I could in the short time I have left. Four other fantastic resources for more I would also recommend if you'd like to learn more, are Doctors Tom Cowan, Andrew Kaufman, Stefan Lanka, and/or Dr. Tom Barnett.[16,17] But I will end this discussion by saying virology and infectious disease, like all other sciences, have to be questioned until they are explained in a way that makes sense. Until that happens, the lack thereof isn't our problem or fault—it's the microbiologist's. What we do know by our own experience is illness overwhelmingly dominates in a stressed (emotional or physical), malnourished (diet and nutrients), unfit (exercise and posture), and/or toxic (drugs and chemicals) environment. Meanwhile, mass gatherings and human interaction are *not* observably correlated *at all* to disease or death, in the absence of the aforementioned environmental factors. Next, we will touch on a variety of historical events which both provide support for this hypothesis, as well as context for the Covid era.

The Smallpox Vaccine Campaign of 1888

The common understanding that modern medicine consists of vaccination bringing us out of a dark age of plagues is, frankly, a myth. People in the 1800s and before did not remotely enjoy the sanitation we benefit from today.[18] By the time the Industrial Revolution rolled around, populations shifted into cities where they faced dangerous living conditions. These cities tended to have sewage and sanitation systems so poor that in 1832 one doctor is cited as saying only 10% of the city of Leeds was actually in full health.[19] Disease therefore can be presumed to have increased not by indiscriminate aerosols carrying viruses, but specifically in urban, lower-class populations living in squalor.

It is this cause and effect which brings us to the absurdity of vaccination as a medical miracle. This myth can be traced to the mid-1800s, when smallpox fluctuated in England and Wales from an average of 50 deaths per 100K per year in 1838-1850, to 20 deaths per 100K per year from 1850-1875, and essentially continuing the downward trend to close to 0 by the turn of the century.[20] While this is popularly credited to vaccination, Smallpox vaccination was not made compulsory until 1853, when the downtrend was already firmly established. In fact, comparing Smallpox mortality to that of the lesser-known Scarlet Fever at the time shows the latter was more than twice as deadly on average and was also trending down. This general downtrend of disease including for those without vaccination campaigns (such as Scarlett Fever), is therefore much more easily traceable to improvements in sanitation over time as the industrial age developed.

In her book *Dissolving Illusions*, Dr. Suzanne Humphries explains how physician Edward Jenner on May 14, 1796 inoculated an 8-year old boy with disease matter from a milkmaid he believed had cowpox.[21] In July of the same year, Jenner inoculated the boy with smallpox. When the boy did not catch smallpox from the inoculation,

Jenner declared his vaccine would be 100% effective for life. Mirroring public health today, he would later revise this to 10 years of protection, before revising it again to 1 year. No controlled experiments were done at the time, but initial doctors who tested it found reason to doubt Jenner. One doctor in particular inoculated three boys and all three subsequently developed smallpox. Still, also mirroring today, physician skepticism shifted as vaccination demonstrated itself to be a reliable income stream. Though some continued to speak out and published literature demonstrating dangers, popularity took over.

From there came the aforementioned compulsory vaccination legislation in both the UK and US in the 1850s.[22] These campaigns were facilitated by the same rejection of documented injuries and vaccine failure we see today, with Dr. Humphries even citing public officials' now-familiar goal-post-shifting from, "perfect," immunity to, "milder disease." Resistance to reports of harsher enforcement grew in the late 1800s, including an 1874 quote by Emeritus Professor F.W. Newman, who decried, "the commanding of vaccination on a second child of a family, when vaccination has killed the first; and then sending the father to prison for refusal."

As we have seen, the technocrats of our day literally justify these same types of atrocities by calling them, "incentives," or, "tools." They then hideously ban the victims on social media for sharing their stories. Tremendous protests in places like Leicester in 1885 ultimately shredded the political capital of the government so badly that, "the government was replaced, mandates were terminated, and by 1887 vaccination coverage rates had dropped to 10%." As we are today at the midway point of February 2022, it seems the two-year Covid era was almost an exact replica of the century-long Smallpox era. It is yet to be seen if it will end the same, though the apparent collapse of the Covid narrative suggests it might.

The Spanish (Vaccination-Caused) Flu of 1917

> *"The vaccine is one of the greatest achievements of mankind. We would've have had a 1917—remember the Spanish Flu killed perhaps 100 million people—actually it ended the first World War because the soldiers were so—a lot of people don't*

know that because the soldiers got so sick. There were no vaccines. There was no anything."

—Donald Trump, 2021[23]

To quote the movie *Billy Madison*, what Donald Trump said in this interview is one of the most insanely idiotic things I have ever heard. At no point in his rambling, incoherent response was he even close to anything that could be considered a rational thought. Everyone who heard him utter it is now dumber for having done so. I award him no political points, and may God have mercy on his soul.

In all seriousness, it is untrue that Operation Warp Speed was relevant in any way in *developing* the inoculations. They were already developed, as we've covered, and the Operation was simply a government commitment to engage in a redistribution of wealth to the pharmaceutical companies. It is also untrue that the inoculations had even a remote role in preventing anything, as we've already seen excess mortality *worsen* in 2021, especially in highly inoculated places. But there are additional falsehoods said by Trump which seem to slip under the radar—namely, that there weren't vaccinations during the Spanish Flu and that 100 million people died due to the Spanish flu.

Starting with the latter claim, it is supported only by the abstract of a 2002 paper which made an offhand suggestion its own estimate of 50 million was, "perhaps as much as 100 percent understated."[24] However, even the 50 million number actually cited in this paper is a largely blind estimate, based on a series of assumptions which lead to a more than 100 percent difference from the estimates cited at the time in the 1920s of 21.5 million. Medical researcher John Varoli opined that even the 21.5 million number is likely over-counted, as documented exaggerations of the death toll in China and India both suggest the number to be lower than 15 million.[25] In fact, Varoli also points out the curious phenomenon that India's coastal regions were the *least* impacted by this so-called viral pandemic, despite the narrative being that the flu arrived by ship. He goes on to mention historian David Hardiman's explanation that poverty, poor sanitation, diet and water, all plagued the northern and interior regions of India, leading naturally to poor health outcomes.

About 15 million people globally is a somewhat significant amount and the true number is clearly debatable, so we can maybe let

Trump slide on this one even if he is unintentionally misrepresenting things. However, Trump's second falsehood is much less acceptable. Not only were there vaccinations at the time of the Spanish Flu (as we saw with the *prior* Smallpox incident), but the same World War 1 soldiers Trump cited as coming home sick were actually subjected to one of the most intensive vaccination campaigns in history at the time of the war.[26] In fact, Professor G. Dennis Shanks even acknowledged in the *Lancet* how much this campaign benefitted the Pasteurian worldview of infectious disease (and thus, the pharmaceutical industry), despite going on to admit its having been followed by a pandemic, which, "killed more people than died during the entire war."[27]

Perhaps you picked up on the connection I just made between the vaccination campaign and the large increase in disease which followed, referred to as the Spanish Flu. Perhaps you think I'm reaching by making such a connection. We have, in our chapter on masks, already discussed the *primary* role bacterial infections had during this time. In the words of Fauci and the CDC themselves, these bacterial infections were far more of a factor in the deaths than the flu in question. So maybe it was just the mask-wearing at the time, poor sanitation, and/or some other causes.

While those things could have and likely did have some role, there is a very specific reason I directly connect the vaccine campaign to the onset of disease, beyond the conspicuous timing. It is one of the main inspirations for my writing this book: primary sources. One of the most fascinating things in the book *Virus Mania*, in my opinion, is the first-hand account of American author Eleanora McBean, who lived at the time of the Spanish flu.[28] McBean shows that even then people understood the connection I now extrapolate. The value of her experience is also incalculable today in developing an understanding of current events. It is recounted as follows:

> *"All the doctors and people who were living at the time of the 1918 Spanish Influenza epidemic say it was the most terrible disease the world has ever had. Strong men, hale and hearty, one day would be dead the next. The disease had the characteristics of the Black Death added to typhus, diphtheria, pneumonia, smallpox, paralysis and all the diseases the people had been vaccinated with immediately following World War 1.*

Practically the entire population had been injected/'seeded' with a dozen or more diseases—or toxic serums. When all those doctor-made diseases started breaking out all at once it was tragic.

That pandemic dragged on for two years, kept alive with the addition of more poison drugs administered by the doctors who tried to suppress the symptoms. As far as I could find out, the flu hit only the vaccinated. Those who had refused the shots escaped the flu. My family had refused all the vaccinations so we remained well all the time. We knew from the health teachings of Graham, Trail, Tilden and others, that people cannot contaminate the body with poisons without causing disease.

When the flu was at its peak, all the stores were closed as well as the schools, businesses—even the hospital, as the doctors and nurses had been vaccinated too and were down with the flu. No one was on the streets. It was like a ghost town. We seemed to be the only family [that] didn't get the flu; **so my parents went from house to house doing what they could to look after the sick, as it was impossible to get a doctor then. If it were possible for germs, bacteria, virus, or bacilli to cause disease, they had plenty of opportunity to attack my parents when they were spending many hours a day in the sick rooms. But they didn't get the flu and they didn't bring any germs home to attack us children and cause anything** *(my emphasis). None of our family had the flu—not even a sniffle—and it was in the winter with deep snow on the ground. When I see people cringe when someone near them sneezes or coughs, I wonder how long it will take them to find out that they can't catch it—whatever it is. The only way they can get a disease is to develop it themselves by wrong eating, drinking, smoking or doing some other things which cause internal poisoning and lowered vitality. All diseases are preventable and most of them are curable with the right methods, not known to medical doctors, and not all drugless doctors know them either.*

It has been said that the 1918 flu epidemic killed 20 million people throughout the world. But, actually, the doctors killed them with their crude and deadly treatments and drugs. This

is a harsh accusation but it is nevertheless true, judging by the success of the drugless doctors in comparison with that of the medical doctors.

While the medical men and medical hospitals were losing 33% of their flu cases, the non-medical hospitals such as Battle Creek, Kellogg and MacFadden's Health-Restorium were getting almost 100% healings (my emphasis) *with their water cures, baths, enemas, etc., fasting and certain other simple healing methods, followed by carefully worked out diets of natural foods. One health doctor didn't lose a patient in eight years.*

If the medical doctors had been as advanced as the drugless doctors, there would not have been those 20 million deaths from the medical flu treatment.

There was seven times more disease among the vaccinated soldiers than among the unvaccinated civilians, and the diseases were those they had been vaccinated against. One soldier who had returned from overseas in 1912 told me that the army hospitals were filled with cases of **infantile paralysis** [polio] *and he wondered why grown men should have an infant disease. Now we know that paralysis is a common after-effect of vaccine poisoning. Those at home didn't get the paralysis until after the world-wide vaccination campaign in 1918."*

Then as now. McBean's experience is further substantiated by Anne Riley Hale in her 1935 book *The Medical Voodoo* in which she acknowledges, "the world has never witnessed such an orgy of vaccination and inoculation of every description as was inflicted by army-camp doctors upon the soldiers of the [First] World War."[29] This, "Voodoo Medicine," as Hale calls it would continue on for the next century, as documented in books like *Virus Mania*. Whether it's Polio's near 1-to-1 correlation with DDT production, or bird-brained theories about how sunlight and nutrient-deprived chicks would spread, "bird flu," to humans, this for-profit anti-science has gone on in a well-organized manner thanks largely to public health departments like the CDC. We will cover the troubling history of that organization next.

The Centers for Crying, "Disease!" But Never Controlling It

Despite my lambasting the current makeup of government bureaucracies in this book, I am absolutely *not* opposed to the government's role to regulate. For example, I believe the FDA to be a necessary organization to ensure the safety and accurate advertising of the corporate products consumed by Americans. What we consume *is* what determines our health (or lack thereof) and throughout this book we've clearly seen people are more than willing to destroy human health if there's profit and/or power to be gained. So since government representatives themselves cannot reasonably be expected to complete such a task, delegation makes sense in this case.

Is the FDA a corrupted, broken organization? Absolutely, without question. The February 2022 *Project Veritas* release we've covered shows FDA executive Christopher Cole directly admitting as much. What we didn't mention before is he also said authorization of the inoculations for babies was a foregone conclusion, despite there being no supporting data whatsoever or risk to this population.[30] According to Cole, the reasons to coerce the inoculations were political via the Biden regime's agenda and financial via pharma profit, as in his own words, "the drug companies, the food companies, the vaccine companies—they pay us hundreds of millions of dollars a year to hire and keep the reviewers to approve their products." This type of corruption demands criminal punishment of the current FDA leadership who are responsible and dramatic organizational reform to remove the industry capture it currently suffers from. Also, whatever capacity of enforcement which has been granted to it should be removed, in my opinion, leaving it as a body to make recommendations to representatives.

With all this in mind, I believe the CDC and NIH serve the opposite of a beneficial regulatory purpose and need to be eradicated as organizations. I will focus first on the CDC to explain why, before pivoting into Anthony Fauci and the NIH.

Following World War 2, many prominent diseases once known to cause mass fatalities faded away, as industrialized nations like the United States benefited from affluence and improved living conditions.[31] This became a problem for the CDC however, since redundancy became such a threat that in 1949 a majority voted to eliminate it completely. Instead of acknowledging the most beneficial truth, however—namely, that the organization is redundant because consumption, living conditions, and sanitation are the keys to disease control—the CDC adopted the policy of, "finding," diseases through a method called, "clustering."

Clustering is simply looking for any collection of sick people in relative proximity and assuming it to result from a new, infectious cause. It is the CDC's primary tactic in everything from declaring new diseases to claiming the predominance of a, "variant." The most famous utilization of this technique came in the early 1980s, when five severely ill homosexual young men became the first, "AIDS," patients.[32] These men suffered from a known immune system disorder not typically seen in people of this age, but rather in babies with an immune defect or older people on immunosuppressive medication. Instead of exploring their lifestyle habits, the mania of discovering a new disease took over. It became so absurd, in fact, that the CDCs James Curran referred to the thesis as, "hot stuff, hot stuff," with the CDC going on to speculate the disease was the result of sexual contact.[33]

In reality, none of these men knew each other or had the same sexual partners.[34] What they *did* have in common—what the CDC conveniently ignored—was a different lifestyle habit—namely, the use of a, "nitrate inhalant," drug referred to as, "poppers."[35] Poppers were popular amongst gays at the time for their muscle-relaxing effect, which made sodomy easier to tolerate, as well as their prolongation of a man's stamina. Unfortunately however, they can also produce neural damage similar to multiple sclerosis, can severely damage the immune system including several vital organs, can have carcinogenic effects, and can lead to, "sudden sniffing death."[36]

Besides gays, AIDS overwhelmingly effected drug abusers in general, with the *New England Journal of Medicine* several times making the connection of drugs to already-known diseases (like Kaposi's sarcoma, Hodgkin's disease, herpes zoster aka shingles, or tuberculosis) all newly referred to as, "AIDS."[37,38,39,40] It also presented as entirely different in the, "African version of AIDS." Unlike in the US where an antibody test labeled one an AIDS patient, in Africa the WHO defined an AIDS patient as anyone suffering from weight loss plus diarrhea and itching—symptoms which were common in mass-malnourished, poor African countries.

As you can see in the above example, but also over and over again in our modern day, the role of the CDC is only to find *infectious* disease. Whether or not the disease is actually infectious is irrelevant.

Alternative causes are dismissed because there is no profit and therefore no funding incentive in the CDC simply advising gays to stop taking poppers, for example—something the simplest advertising campaign could accomplish. As a data scientist I can also attest to the fact that if you tasked me with finding a new disease—with or without significant financial gain on the line, but *especially* with financial gain on the line—it wouldn't be difficult at all to, "find," a slightly anomalous looking cluster or two and craft a narrative around them.

This is the CDC today—only it gets worse, because with redundancy as it relates to disease, the organization transformed via convergence into a subversive political body. We've already covered this in some detail, including inoculation as the most important step of hurricane preparation, depiction of racism as a, "public health crisis," leading to double-standard recommendations, and a general aversion to logic or consistency displayed most prominently by Director Walensky. But the racism example is also matched in its absurdity by the CDC's intention to subvert the Second Amendment, with their September 2021 labeling of, "gun violence," as a, "public health threat," and stating its aim to, "craft swift interventions, as they have done to contain the coronavirus pandemic and other national health emergencies."[41]

For one thing, it is astonishing (from *any* point of view) to see the CDC claim to have, "contained," the alleged pandemic. But to then double down on the human rights violations so egregious they resulted in the theorizing of concentration camps, the CDC is well beyond the classification of redundant and has now become a proxy-organization for the enforcement of Constitution-violating authoritarian tyranny. It needs to stop and the CDC should, in my opinion, be abolished. The information it was *actually* intended to present (not what it presents today) on health and disease are now available in the public square, if only that information is spared the wrath of the censor. Any determination about how this translates into treatment must be returned to the discretion of the treating physician. Until then, the CDC only serves to destroy the doctor-patient relationship and centralize medicine into a one-size-fits-all approach that has resulted in genocide in the Covid era.

Anthony Fauci: An Evil Man

"When I was looking at this data with our team the other night, it was reminiscent of 34 years ago in 1986 when we were struggling for drugs for HIV—and we had nothing. And there was a lot of anecdotal reports about things that maybe they work, maybe not, and people were taking different kinds of drugs. **And we did the first randomized placebo controlled trial with AZT, which turned out to give an effect that was modest, but that was not the end game** *(my emphasis). Because building on that every year after we did better and better. We had better drugs of the same type and we had drugs against different targets.*

—Anthony Fauci from the White House, April 29, 2020[42]

It almost seems a subtle, wicked brag that Anthony Fauci would bring up AZT in the same breath he first hailed remdesivir. AZT was to AIDS what remdesivir, sedatives, and ventilators have been to Covid—namely, the cause of the deadliest symptoms most commonly and falsely attributed to the, "novel," disease itself, and a drug fast-tracked by Fauci specifically, using seriously flawed data. And just like in the Covid era, this isn't nearly my assessment alone of the AIDS situation. It's one that's been shared by many, including the likes of prominent journalist, Harvard analyst, and gay rights activist John Lauritsen, as well as the now-familiar Kary Mullis.[43] For example, consider the following public accusations from Dr. Robert Willner from 30 years ago[44]:

"We're talking about probably the most horrible scandal and scam ever perpetrated—not only in the name of science, but in humanity and all history.
Today is December 7th, and I was 12 years old when the attack on Pearl Harbor came. And I remember World War 2 very well. And it's a very significant day today, because I see an incredible parallel between what is going on in the so-called 'AIDS epidemic' and what happened in the year preceding and resulting in World War 2—the great lies of Hitler. It's amazing—I think he would envy the job being done by members of the National Institutes of Health and even the media—especially in this country.

And I will put the lie to the individuals of the NIH—
particularly [Robert] *Gallo and* [Anthony] *Fauci and*
[William] *Haseltine and* [Max] *Essex, and the rest of these*
scoundrels of the worst order. Criminals guilty of genocide,
without a doubt.

I invite them to take me to court. I wish Burroughs Wellcome
would take me to court because they have been putting out a
killer drug knowingly. Because in a court of law I would have
the opportunity to provide the absolute proof and evidence, as
I have in my book, Deadly Deception.

Now, I'm not alone in what I'm doing here today. How does
the press escape such obvious truths? Why would the most
famous virologist in the world—the most notable virologist—
member of our National Academy of Sciences, Peter
Duesberg—why would he put his name and entire career on
the line? What did he have to gain? He's already lost his
laboratory and his funding."

Besides the fact that Dr. Willner also wrote a book about a
time very similar and connected to my own, I very much relate to his
incredulity at how such blatant crimes are allowed to continue. How
many more prominent scientists, doctors, and journalists can make
such grave accusations of this man before they become worthy of
criminal investigation by authorities in a place to bring justice?
Whatever the number, the truth remains: Anthony Fauci hasn't just
failed his way up to untouchable status—he's mass murdered his way
there.

And AZT is just the beginning. In November 1989, *SPIN*
Magazine's Celia Farber would publish a report which founder of
SPIN Bob Guccione Jr. would later say should have earned her, "the
Congressional Medal of Honor for her brave and relentless
reporting."[45] The report was titled, "Sins of Omission," and it
provided, "Hard evidence of the cold-bloodedness of the AIDS
establishment pushing a drug that was worse than the disease, and
killed faster than the natural progression of AIDS left untreated."

That drug was AZT, a then-quarter-century old cancer
chemotherapy drug which had been shelved and forgotten about due
to its extreme toxicity, expensiveness to produce, and total
ineffectiveness. Still, a study which suggested AZT reduced death

relative to a placebo group caused the FDA to convene in January 1987 and consider giving, "lightning-quick," approval to the highly-toxic drug. The FDA's Ellen Cooper at the time worried its approval would represent, "a significant and potentially dangerous departure from our normal toxicology requirements." Two doctors on the FDA's panel, Calvin Kunin and Itzhak Brook, also acknowledged the bind the FDA was in. Each noted in particular the same indiscriminate cellular destruction which made AZT a short-term benefit in the study could lead to potentially, "disastrous," results, "a year from now." Still, thanks to the desperation of activists for any possible medication, the pressure won out and the FDA granted the approval to the Burroughs Wellcome drug.[46]

Dr. Brook, who had been the only vote against approval, later acknowledged the mistake of the panel, noting he was, "struck by the fact that AZT does not stop deaths," as the study suggested it would, and that, "even those who were switched to AZT still kept dying." He also would go on to claim FDA leadership made an, "extremely unusual," intervention midway through the process, applying, "political pressure," when it appeared his doubts were winning out. Burroughs Wellcome promised, "they would not let the drug get out of its intended parameters: as a stopgap measure for very sick patients."

By the summer of 1989, however, "newspapers across America banner-headlined that AZT," had been proven effective, regardless of symptoms or disease stage. And guess who was pushing to expand prescription? Anthony Fauci. Despite there being no new evidence of benefit and the promised follow-up data falling by the wayside, Fauci's endorsements led to a complete lack of investigation on over, "100 other promising," potentially less toxic alternatives. It also led to tremendous profits for Burroughs Wellcome, which was then selling the drug at $8,000 per patient, making it, "the most expensive drug ever marketed."

The story gets worse—though perhaps more familiar—when the details of the original study are reviewed. That study was intended to be double-blind and placebo-controlled, but was, "unblinded on all sides, after just a few weeks." Burroughs Wellcome and the FDA both inexplicably accepted and confirmed this result prior to approval. Patients in the trial even admitted to analyzing their capsules to figure out whether or not they were in the placebo group. Some of those who were, Farber explains, "bought the drug on the underground market." Other reports told of patients pooling pills out of solidarity to each other. With these things together, it should have hardly been surprising that those in the placebo group taking such risks were dying. Either way though, the study was corrupted and its results would therefore be worthless. But the biggest issue came when it was ended early, "due to ethical reasons," and all the participants were then put on AZT.

We in the Covid era are by now used to hearing of un-blinded studies prevented from reaching completion for, "ethical," reasons. Fauci has proven to be a leading proponent of these anti-scientific concepts as he ironically discusses them in the same breath he refers to himself as, "the science." What his reckless actions inevitably led to then was as catastrophic as what they've led to today. The same year AZT was approved, the *New York Times* was already interviewing doctors who were giving it to healthy people who tested positive with antibody tests. Dr. Harvey Bialy, scientific editor of the journal *Biotechnology*, decried this practice on multiple grounds. In addition to the worthlessness of the sole study used to support it, Bialy found the drug actually accelerates the process it was said to prevent— namely, the loss of T-4 cells. He stated:

> *"Undeniably, AZT kills T-4 cells. No one can argue with that. AZT is a chain-terminating nucleotide, which means that it stops DNA replication. It seeks out any cell that is engaged in DNA replication and kills it. The place where most of this replication is taking place is in the bone marrow. That's why the most common and severe side effect of the drug is bone marrow toxicity. That is why they [AIDS patients] need blood transfusions."*

In the summer of 1989, Anthony Fauci proudly announced that a trial had been going on for, "two years," which had, "clearly shown," that early AZT intervention would keep AIDS at bay. Based on this, he made a recommendation that around 1.4 million healthy people take low-dose AZT, now that after two years of its high dose use its toxic effects were too significant to ignore (all patients in the original AZT trial mentioned were dead within 3.5 years). Like we see today, Fauci and the NIH produced this study—referred to by one doctor in

Farber's report as, "terribly dishonest"—and made these claims despite a preceding December 1988 French study in the *Lancet* which found AZT to be too toxic for most to tolerate. Farber goes on to point out the obvious about Fauci's recommendation to use such a substance in healthy people—namely, that, "it seems criminal."

In a 2014 piece in the *Huffington Post*, Sean Strub further documented Fauci's attempts to whitewash his, "shameful role," in delaying promotion of alternative treatments which, "would have prevented tens of thousands of deaths in the first years of the epidemic."[47] Like AZT has a historical mirror in today's remdesivir, today's ivermectin and/or HCQ have a mirror in yesterday's Bactrim. Strub tells of how AIDS activist Michael Callen, "begged," Fauci as early as 1987 to promote Bactrim, a drug Dr. Joseph Sonnabend was already widely and successfully using as early treatment to prevent the recurrence of the pneumonia AIDS was known for. Fauci himself claims he couldn't have done so without a trial, despite having done the exact same thing for AZT two years later based on a trial he hadn't yet published at the time. He is even alleged as having, "Encouraged people with AIDS to *stop* taking treatments, like Bactrim, that weren't specifically approved for use in people with AIDS."

The truth of the matter is that Bactrim was much cheaper and more readily available, like every safe, common drug Fauci slanders in the name of promoting exceptionally expensive known-poisons.[48] Senator Ron Johnson documented the murderous career Fauci has built on engaging in this pattern of behavior in a January 2022 presentation, acknowledging, "Dr. Fauci—he's using the exact same playbook for Covid as he did for AIDS—ignoring therapy like Bactrim, or the cornucopia of cheap, generic, repurposed drugs that are available, that are being used successfully to treat Covid and save lives."[49] Johnson even cited a 1983 *JAMA* article authored by Fauci, stating:

> *"The possibility that routine close contact, as within a family household, can spread the disease … if indeed the latter is true, AIDS takes on an entirely new dimension. And then, if we add on this possibility that non-sexual, non-blood-borne transmission is possible, the scope of the syndrome may be enormous."*

Johnson makes note of the fact that these were not off-the-cuff remarks, but were written with forethought during a delicate time when fear was already beginning to simmer. Fauci, in the type of move we've already discussed is entirely contrary to public health, exploited and stoked that fear in an abuse of his authority. The media the following day ran stories presenting these baseless theories as truth, with headlines such as, "Household Contacts May Contract AIDS," and, "Does AIDS Spread by Routine Contact?" The *New York Times* also cited Fauci's article when reporting, "Family Contact Studied in Transmitting AIDS."[50] However, only two months after authoring the *JAMA* article, Fauci engaged in another character trait of his—namely, reversing course and pretending he never said the thing he just said—when he claimed:

> *"It is absolutely preposterous to suggest that AIDS can be contracted through normal social contact like being in the same room with someone or sitting on a bus with them."*

This playbook of using fear to pimp expensive drugs previously shelved for being too dangerous, too useless, or both is at this point a common marketing tactic. It is by all accounts the business model and mission of, "public health," organizations like the NIH and CDC, which they can get away with perpetually by claiming they do what they do for health and/or science. Nevermind the fact that the health outcomes of those who follow their advice needlessly worsen over time. But whether we're discussing vaccines, remdesivir, Tamiflu, AZT, Truvada, mRNA inoculations, or a mess of other expensive poisons, the strategy and the players executing it are the same.[51]

A 2014 report by journalist Terry Michael goes deeper on other examples of this tactic he refers to as, "profiteering," and, "medical science research-gone-wild."[52] Specifically on Tamiflu, like remdesivir, it too was a drug produced by Gilead Sciences, which was also considered worthless for its intended purpose—namely, as a flu palliative. However, just after Fauci placed Gilead CEO John C. Martin on his NIAID advisory council in March 2000, Gilead's then-chairman Donald Rumsfeld resigned to go serve as Secretary of the Department of Defense under George W. Bush. Under Rumsfeld's tenure, the administration used the fear-mongering of a bird flu that never came to pass as an excuse to use taxpayer dollars to stockpile millions of units of the useless Tamiflu, providing Gilead windfall profits.

On a similar note, despite AZT's diminished popularity thanks to years of death, Michael summarizes how this game continues to be played with AIDS, as follows:

> *"The Fauci-Gilead connection is a textbook example of oligarchic capitalism, the legal bilking of taxpayer dollars for the benefit of a single, politically well-connected business enterprise, provided with potentially millions of new customers in a rigged game of confirmation-biased clinical trials, used to justify FDA new-use approval for one of Gilead's top-selling old drugs, which in turn led to May 2014 CDC encouragement of doctors to 'PrEP' patients with the company's extremely expensive ($12-$14 thousand per year) big blue pills, known as Truvada."*

Beyond facilitating this format of scheme, Fauci also has a habit of allocating his tremendous budget to shocking causes. For one, *Changing America* reported Fauci's NIH division, "shipped part of a $375,800 grant to a lab in Tunisia to drug beagles and lock their heads in mesh cages filled with hungry sand flies so that the insects could eat them alive," as well as locking, "beagles alone in cages in the desert overnight for nine consecutive nights to use them as bait to attract infectious sand flies."[53] The 44 beagle puppies involved even, "had their vocal chords removed, allegedly so scientists could work without incessant barking."

Considering all Fauci has done to destroy *human* health over the course of his entire career, this story almost feels tiny in comparison. Holocaust survivor Vera Sharav acknowledged this when questioning the, "irony," that, "it's these little puppies bringing the outrage."[54] And the reason why is that Fauci's NIAID also funded AZT (you will recall, a chemotherapy drug) experiments on children who were, "wards of the state," in the late 1980's and early 1990's.[55] Those experimented on were, "the most vulnerable, disadvantaged children," who were, "exploited by powerful entities and used as guinea pigs as if they were not human beings."[56] This should serve as a disturbing reminder of Fauci's dishonest calls to address, "social inequities," as it is also noted that, "most of the children were Black, Hispanic and poor, often born to drug-addicted mothers."[57]

The best biography you will likely find on Anthony Fauci is Robert F. Kennedy's book *The Real Anthony Fauci*.[58] My own book was not intended to be such a biography, but Fauci is a great focal point for understanding the greater problem it presents. The truth is, there are many Fauci-like characters in the world today. From Christian Drosten in Germany, to Christopher Whitty in the UK, and so many other, "public health," narcissists, the same problems I've outlined mostly in the context of the US have, "infected," public health departments all over the world. The reason for this is ideological as much as it is financial and control-based. The goal of this book was to summarize this in a meaningful, thorough enough way such that the Covid era as a whole could be understood. Because only in understanding what has happened here can we develop ways to oppose it, in the hopes of achieving a healthier, freer future.

Endnotes

1   Dorey, Susan. 2011. "Louis Pasteur Recants His Germ Theory". *Susandoreydesigns.Com*. http://www.susandoreydesigns.com/insights/pasteur-recant.html.

2   Engelbrecht, Torsten, Köhnlein Claus, Bailey Samatha, and Scoglio Stefano. 2007. *Virus Mania*.

3   Trebing, William P. 2006. *Good-Bye Germ Theory*. 6th ed. Xlibris.

4   "Scientific Theory". 2022. *Thefreedictionary.Com*. Accessed April 6. https://medical-dictionary.thefreedictionary.com/scientific+theory.

5   "Germ Theory | Definition, Development, & Facts". 2022. *Encyclopedia Britannica*. Accessed April 6. https://www.britannica.com/science/germ-theory.

6   Wolfe, Karen. 2022. "Germ Theory Or Terrain Theory Of Disease? - Dr. Karen Wolfe". *Drkarenwolfe.Org*. Accessed April 6. https://www.drkarenwolfe.org/germ-theory-or-terrain-theory-of-disease/.

7   RICHARDS, SARAH ELIZABETH. 2020. "Why Do Asymptomatic COVID-19 Cases Even Happen?". *National Geographic*. https://www.nationalgeographic.com/science/article/why-do-asymptomatic-coronavirus-cases-even-happen-cvd.

8   Palacios, Cristina, and Lilliana Gonzalez. 2014. "Is Vitamin D Deficiency A Major Global Public Health Problem?". *The Journal Of Steroid Biochemistry And Molecular Biology* 144: 138-145. doi:10.1016/j.jsbmb.2013.11.003.

9   "Dr. Fauci Takes 6,000 IU Of Vitamin D Daily – Sept 2020 | Vitamindwiki". 2020. *Vitamindwiki*.

https://vitamindwiki.com/Dr.+Fauci+takes+6%2C000+IU+of+Vitamin+D+daily+%E2%80%93+Sept+2020.

10   Scipioni, Jade. 2020. "Dr. Fauci Says To Take Vitamin D If You're Deficient — Here's How To Know". *Msn.Com*. https://www.msn.com/en-us/health/nutrition/dr-fauci-says-to-take-vitamin-d-if-you-re-deficient-here-s-how-to-know/ar-BB19rGVQ.

11   Reinold, Johanna, Farnoush Farahpour, Christian Fehring, Sebastian Dolff, Margarethe Konik, Johannes Korth, and Lukas van Baal et al. 2021. "A Pro-Inflammatory Gut Microbiome Characterizes SARS-Cov-2 Infected Patients And A Reduction In The Connectivity Of An Anti-Inflammatory Bacterial Network Associates With Severe COVID-19". *Frontiers In Cellular And Infection Microbiology* 11. doi:10.3389/fcimb.2021.747816.

12   Konkel, Lindsey, and Robert Jasmer. 2018. "Cortisol: The Stress Hormone". *Everydayhealth.Com*. https://www.everydayhealth.com/cortisol/guide/.

13   "Chronic Stress Puts Your Health At Risk". 2021. *Mayo Clinic*. https://www.mayoclinic.org/health-lifestyle/stress-management/in-depth/stress/art-20046037.

14   Schoorlemmer, R. M. M., G. M. E. E. Peeters, N. M. van Schoor, and P. Lips. 2009. "Relationships Between Cortisol Level, Mortality And Chronic Diseases In Older Persons". *Clinical Endocrinology* 71 (6): 779-786. doi:10.1111/j.1365-2265.2009.03552.x.

15   Chiriac, Valentina-Fineta, Adriana Baban, and Dan L. Dumitrascu. 2018. "PSYCHOLOGICAL STRESS AND BREAST CANCER INCIDENCE: A SYSTEMATIC REVIEW". *Medicine And Pharmacy Reports* 91 (1): 18-26. doi:10.15386/cjmed-924.

16   Stilwell, Kathleen. 2021. "Drs. Tom Cowan, Andy Kaufman & Stefan Lanka: On The Myth That Virology Is Real Science & What We Don't Yet Know About These Highly Toxic Covid "Vaccines" - Truth Comes To Light". *Truth Comes To Light*. https://truthcomestolight.com/drs-tom-cowan-andy-kaufman-stefan-lanka-on-the-myth-that-virology-is-real-science-what-we-dont-yet-know-about-these-highly-toxic-covid-vaccines/.

17   "Dr. Tom Barnett". 2022. *The Big Virus Hoax*. Accessed April 6. https://thebigvirushoax.com/dr-tom-barnett.

18   "Graphs & Images - Dissolving Illusions | Disease, Vaccines, And The Forgotten History". 2022. *Dissolving Illusions | Disease, Vaccines, And The Forgotten History*. Accessed April 6. https://dissolvingillusions.com/graphs-images/.

19   Wilde, Robert. 2019. "How Did Public Health Develop During The Industrial Revolution?". *Thoughtco*. https://www.thoughtco.com/public-health-in-the-industrial-revolution-1221641.

20   "The Smallpox Pandemic Response Was Eerily Similar To COVID". 2022. *Amidwesterndoctor.Substack.Com*.

https://amidwesterndoctor.substack.com/p/the-smallpox-pandemic-response-was.

21   Humphries, Suzanne, and Roman Bystrianyk. 2013. *Dissolving Illusions.*

22   "The Smallpox Pandemic Response Was Eerily Similar To COVID". 2022. *Amidwesterndoctor.Substack.Com.* https://amidwesterndoctor.substack.com/p/the-smallpox-pandemic-response-was.

23   Owens, Candace. 2021. "Ep. 40 - Unscripted With Donald J. Trump". *The Daily Wire.* https://www.dailywire.com/episode/ep-40-unscripted-with-donald-j-trump2.

24   Johnson, Niall P. A. S., and Juergen Mueller. 2002. "Updating The Accounts: Global Mortality Of The 1918-1920 Influenza Pandemic". *Bulletin Of The History Of Medicine* 76 (1): 105-115. doi:10.1353/bhm.2002.0022.

25   Varoli, John. 2021. "Debunking 5 Popular (And False) Notions About The 1918 Spanish Flu". *John365.Substack.Com.* https://john365.substack.com/p/debunking-5-popular-and-false-notions.

26   "Medicine In World War I: Diseases At The Battlefield · Yale University Library Online Exhibitions". 2022. *Onlineexhibits.Library.Yale.Edu.* Accessed April 6. https://onlineexhibits.library.yale.edu/s/wwi-medicine/page/diseases-at-the-battlefield.

27   Shanks, G Dennis. 2014. "How World War 1 Changed Global Attitudes To War And Infectious Diseases". *The Lancet* 384 (9955): 1699-1707. doi:10.1016/s0140-6736(14)61786-4.

28   MacBean, Eleanora. *Swine Flu Expose.* 1977. www.whale.to/a/mcbean2.html#CHAPTER%202.

29   Hale, Annie. *The Medical Voodoo.* Gotham House. 1935.

30   "FDA Executive Officer On Hidden Camera Reveals Future COVID Policy: 'Biden Wants To Inoculate As Many People As Possible…Have To Get An Annual Shot'". 2022. *Projectveritas.Com.* https://www.projectveritas.com/news/fda-executive-officer-on-hidden-camera-reveals-future-covid-policy-biden/.

31   Engelbrecht, Torsten, Köhnlein Claus, Bailey Samatha, and Scoglio Stefano. 2007. *Virus Mania.* p. 58.

32   Ibid. p. 101.

33   Gottlieb, Michael. "Pneumocystis Pneumonia—Los Angeles". *Morbidity and Mortality Weekly Report.* 5. June 1981. pp. 250 – 252.

34   Engelbrecht, Torsten, Köhnlein Claus, Bailey Samatha, and Scoglio Stefano. 2007. *Virus Mania.* p. 102.

35   Duesberg, Peter. *Inventing the AIDS Virus.* Regnery Publishing. 1996. p. 148.

36   Engelbrecht, Torsten, Köhnlein Claus, Bailey Samatha, and Scoglio Stefano. 2007. *Virus Mania.* p. 104.

37   Masur, Henry. "An outbreak of community-acquired Pneumocystis carinii pneumonia: initial manifestation of cellular immune dysfunction". *New England Journal of Medicine.* 10 December 1981. pp. 1431 – 1438.

38   Siegal, Frederick. "Severe acquired immunodeficiency in male homosexuals, manifested by chronic perianal ulcerative herpes simplex lesions". *New England Journal of Medicine*. 10 December 1981. pp. 1439 – 1444.

39   Durack, David. "Opportunistic infections and Kaposi's sarcoma in homosexual men". *New England Journal of Medicine*. 10 December 1981. pp. 1465 – 1467.

40   Engelbrecht, Torsten, Köhnlein Claus, Bailey Samatha, and Scoglio Stefano. 2007. *Virus Mania*. p. 93.

41   Nightingale, Hannah. 2021. "CDC Implements Gun Violence Study After Naming It A 'Public Health Threat'". *The Post Millennial*. https://thepostmillennial.com/cdc-implements-gun-violence-study-public-health-threat.

42   Rosen, Len. 2020. "Is The Remdesivir White House Announcement To Be Taken Seriously?". *21St Century Tech Blog*. https://www.21stcentech.com/remdesivir-white-house-announcement-seriously/.

43   Lauritsen, John. 1995. "HIV & AIDS - Talk On Risk-AIDS Hypothesis". *Virusmyth.Com*. http://virusmyth.com/aids/hiv/jlrisk.htm.

44   "(Video): Dr Robert Willner Accused Anthony Fauci Of Genocide". 2022. *Herald.Ng*. Accessed April 6. https://www.herald.ng/video-dr-robert-willner-accused-anthony-fauci-of-genocide/.

45   Farber, Celia. 2021. "AIDS And The AZT Scandal: SPIN's 1989 Feature, 'Sins Of Omission'". *Stateofthenation.Co*. https://stateofthenation.co/?p=69117.

46   Kramer, Larry. 1988. "An Open Letter To Dr. Anthony Fauci - The Village Voice". *The Village Voice*. https://www.villagevoice.com/2020/05/28/an-open-letter-to-dr-anthony-fauci/.

47   Strub, Sean. 2014. "Whitewashing AIDS History". *Huffpost*. https://www.huffpost.com/entry/whitewashing-aids-history_b_4762295.

48   Bramhall, Stuart. 2022. "Fauci's Fatal Mismanagement Of The AIDS Epidemic". *The Most Revolutionary Act*. https://stuartbramhall.wordpress.com/2022/02/10/faucis-fatal-mismanagement-of-the-aids-epidemic/.

49   Koa, Kane. 2022. "Sen. Ron Johnson Blast Fauci For Track Record Of Blocking Effective AIDS Treatment". *Rumble*. https://rumble.com/vsrxz6-sen.-ron-johnson-blast-anthony-fauci-for-blocking-effective-aids-and-covid-.html.

50   "Family Contact Studied In Transmitting AIDS (Published 1983)". 1983. *Nytimes.Com*. https://www.nytimes.com/1983/05/06/us/family-contact-studied-in-transmitting-aids.html.

51   Godlee, Fiona. 2020. "Covid-19: The Lost Lessons Of Tamiflu". *BMJ*, m4701. doi:10.1136/bmj.m4701.

52   Michael, Terry. 2020. "AIDS War Profiteering. NIH's Fauci And Gilead's Martin: Junk Science And Oligarchic Capitalism.". The HIV-

AIDS Industry. Thirty Years Of Political Science. Carter Heavy
Industries.
https://carterheavyindustries.files.wordpress.com/2020/06/aids_war_profi
teering_by_terry_michael_may2014.pdf.

53   Spencer, Christian. 2021. "Bipartisan Legislators Demand Answers From
Fauci On 'Cruel' Puppy Experiments – The Hill". *Thehill.Com*.
https://thehill.com/changing-america/well-being/medical-
advances/578086-bipartisan-legislators-demand-answers-from-fauci.

54   "Holocaust Survivor: Don'T Let Authorities Use Fear To Turn You Into
A 'Robot'". 2020. *Children's Health Defense*.
https://childrenshealthdefense.org/defender/holocaust-survivor-vera-
sharav-covid/.

55   Varma, Sumeeta, and David Wendler. 2008. "Research Involving Wards
Of The State: Protecting Particularly Vulnerable Children". *The Journal
Of Pediatrics* 152 (1): 9-14. doi:10.1016/j.jpeds.2007.07.039.

56   Montero, D. "AIDS Tots Used as 'Guinea Pigs'". *New York Post*. 2004
February 29. 2004 Sect. 005.

57   Rosen, Ann Tomoko. 2021. "'Guinea Pig Kids': Fauci's Legacy Of Cruel
Experiments On Kids". *Children's Health Defense*.
https://childrenshealthdefense.org/defender/guinea-pig-kids-aids-fauci-
experiments/.

58   Kennedy, Robert Francis. 2021. *The Real Anthony Fauci*. Skyhorse.

Chapter 22

From the Author Pt. 2: Final Reflections on the Covid Era

When 2020 began I had planned three trips for my then-girlfriend and I—one to Disney Orlando in February, another to Boston in June, and then to San Francisco in October. What she pretty much knew at the time was that I was going to propose to her, but she did not know on which trip it would happen. In order to throw her off the scent, I was in contact with one of her best friends about a fourth trip to Seattle in August. This trip was going to be played off as entirely the friend's idea for us to go with her and her husband, and that's where I was going to ask. Fortunately, we got to go to Disney without any issue. Then the Covid era began …

By now you know, "two weeks to slow the spread," turned into a month, turned into a year, turned into forever. However, at the time it still seemed hard to believe it wouldn't be over by June. That didn't happen obviously, so Boston got cancelled. Then in June there were race protests around the country because of something that happened in Minnesota, so naturally Seattle turned into literally an anarchy zone called, "CHAZ."[1] I didn't want to propose in CHAZ though, I wanted to propose in Seattle. So in the end, all three of the remaining trips were cancelled. Fortunately, however, I continued to talk to her friend and had her push for us to instead take a local trip. We did that and I honestly am glad it worked out that way because the nearby town I asked in is now a great place to visit for the memory.

So I proposed to and married my best friend during the Covid era. While that might seem chaotic, I am convinced there couldn't have been a better time. You see, when this all began in March 2020, my now-wife was understandably scared as pretty much everyone was. During that month I recall distinctly a blog post she had sent me by the internet rag *Vox* about how much more infectious, "Covid," was than the flu, blah, blah, blah. Knowing that being stressed and fearful basically guarantees you will make yourself sick, I knew I needed to help this woman see through this charade the way I immediately did, thanks to my training in what does and doesn't constitute statistical fraud. In a way, it might have been a challenge to prove to myself I was ready to be a husband and protect her.

So I started posting regularly about it on my *Instagram* page, specifically on my, "stories." Stories are basically pictures or videos which disappear after 24 hours. The reason I chose this avenue is because it doesn't have a comment section (a cancerous hellhole for people to slander each other without any substance at all) and because if someone wanted to reply they'd have to message me directly. Given that she loved me, believed in me, and knew this was my job, it didn't take much convincing for my now-wife. In fact, even if she hadn't known me like that, the absurdity of the public health reaction alone probably would've gotten through to her eventually. Still, we were bonded simply by information we now had that the average person didn't.

Things didn't always go as well with people who were less close to me however, despite my background in the subject and their lack thereof. The following are a few hilarious slanders and absurdities I'd receive in messages:

- "Science denier" – the number of times people would say this in response to me presenting data and evidence is astounding. I mean, other than the fact that they never once presented a single study or substantiated claim, the word "scientist," is actually in my job title!
- "You're not an expert" – I literally am the definition of an expert...
- "Religious nut" – First of all, science cannot exist without a basis in morality and religion is the only defined code of morality which exists. If I haven't made it clear by this point that immoral people can call whatever they want, "science," no matter how nonsensical, then I never will and we just will not agree on that. Either way, this kind of slander is ironic because slander isn't, "science," either. Lastly, creation is more logical than something coming from nothing, which is impossible, but that's a topic for another book.
- "You must be a Trump fan" – They would say this despite me continuously posting things that Trump clearly would not agree with. Full disclosure, I *was* a Trump fan prior to his horrendous cowing in the Covid era to the very same,

"globalists," he claimed previously to oppose. However, Donald Trump both failed to meaningfully counter those responsible for this travesty and even came to support them as he shamelessly shilled the not-vaccines. The main thing I really appreciated about him before the Covid era was that he made people cry who had become the abusive, pro-censorship political zealots we now refer to as, "technocrats." I thought he was funny and I liked some of the more nationalist things he did, since I'm an American and why the hell wouldn't a leader of a *nation* be a *nationalist* (someone who puts the needs of that nation first)? Isn't that their entire job, else they are a traitor? Anyway, whatever. Politics are for imbeciles to argue endlessly about and this is just another non-argument.

People who said these types of things were swiftly blocked or called out on their empty slander. There is simply no point in trying to convince people willing to degenerate to this level of anything—they are too emotionally invested in something else entirely and that needs to be disarmed first. For example, one person gave me the classic, condescending, "you *do* know that *fill in the blank* right?" This person was not starting from a place of respect, so instead of respond to the point they were making, I simply said, "what a condescending way to ask a question." Their tact changed awfully fast when they realized they were in fact being pointlessly rude and once they were disarmed we actually had a very positive conversation.

Another close friend was initially rattled by my posts, since his mom was sick in the early days of the alleged pandemic. During this time of frustration he messaged me very angrily, so I simply replied to everything he was saying with questions. It turned out his mom was a hypochondriac (a person very stressed about getting sick as is), which must be a living hell when the media and public health are shouting, "pandemic," every single day. Unsurprisingly to me, she was the only one in a large household who, "tested positive." But I didn't argue. Again, I just asked questions related to how that would make sense during a super infectious pandemic. A few weeks later, he messaged me out of the blue saying that since I was, "a smart guy," and since I, "couldn't have been saying this stuff for no reason," he had looked into it more and acknowledged I was right about the things I was calling out. This is another reason I wrote this book, since convincing someone of any of this in a conversation is simply impossible. There is *way* too much background.

But again, this is a key lesson for anyone struggling to, "wake people up," from the mainstream haze: *if you don't gain someone's trust first, you won't convince them of anything.* This is a common thread in all three examples I provided, as well as something that didn't happen in the cases that didn't work out. During a time as stressful and intense as the Covid era has been, it becomes an even tougher challenge to get to that point. Some people will never get there, and that's fine. For the most part I've been the most focused on keeping my immediate family and anyone else who wants to listen informed, however few or many that might be at a given time.

Today in early 2022 it seems that number is growing. In fact, it seems to be growing so fast it's made writing this book somewhat stressful. It was awfully hard to imagine a year ago that non-mainstream-narrative points of view such as Robert F. Kennedy Jr.'s would end up featured in best-sellers, but here we are. It is entirely possible this story will be close to common knowledge by the time anyone reads this book in full and if that's the case, I'm completely fine with it. As long as people are freed from the mental prison that monsters like Fauci have condemned them to and human rights are reaffirmed/restored, that's all I care about.

What can be taken from this book, if nothing else, is that what we lived through is not to be understated. It was a traumatic time to be alive thanks to the psychopathic actions of a wicked few. Much of the damage done has been documented in previous chapters. Still, my stated goal is to include bits of my own story here as well, since I know now how important that is to do. The sad reality of what took place is that people simply didn't want to listen during this time. They would simultaneously tell experts they're not experts, but should listen to experts who were considered experts only because they were the experts who the TV said were experts. They would use words like, "conspiracy," to deny real, documented, at times on-video conspiracies as if the mere act of conspiring was an impossibility. It was a time when the same hypocrites who spent the previous decade pushing, "body positivity," acceptance of unhealthy lifestyles, and "my body, my choice," continued to degenerate into advocating for one-size-fits-all medicine, boundless corporate-government control, and no choice for *anyone* when it comes to what goes into their body.

Despite what the same self-styled, "pro-science," bunch preach however, not one of the people closest to me who I've convinced not to get the shot have had the flu or hospital malfeasance damage (collectively, "Covid") in the entire two years since this began. Even my breast-cancer-surviving, permanently immunocompromised mother has been at the top of her game health-wise, thanks to diet changes, lifestyle changes, and a move to Florida, which has become a haven of humanity more than anywhere else in the entire world. She has not worn masks, has not physically avoided other human beings, nor has she lived in fear at any time during the Covid era. I've hugged her throughout, gone on trips with her throughout, and have not needlessly abandoned her to a life of miserable solitude only for her to end up in a hospital that would murder her like they did so many others.

So that's even the case for the immunocompromised and elderly. What about healthy, young people like myself? Outrage doesn't begin to describe the emotions I have for how they shut down our ability to be productive for no reason at all. Even if there had been a pandemic, they could have put us to use to serve the needs of the elderly and at-risk who did choose to shelter in place. But they didn't, because we too were targets of the mRNA marketing campaign. This is the *only* possible explanation for those abuses. And the idea that public health was, "compassionately," abiding by the, "if it prevents even one death," mantra to justify human rights violations is a load of absurd bullshit which would never be warranted under any circumstances. Not only did their actions not save a single life, what they did in every area undoubtedly constitutes pre-meditated genocide, in my opinion.

Also, what about when it comes to inoculations? If those kill one person aren't they also not worth it, if that's the philosophy of these God-playing psychopaths? How is it not *more* evil to proactively give someone something that you know can kill them in the false name of the, "greater good," than the objectively good, Western concept of providing human beings their own autonomy to make their own health decisions and determine their own risks? It absolutely is more evil, as was every action taken and justified by the cowards who, without question, betrayed my generation and those that have followed it in unprecedented fashion.

I have always eaten better, been in better physical shape, and paid more attention to my health than the majority of people around me. I do not eat fast food on more than a rare occasion; I do not drink a significant amount on more than a rare occasion; I do not take even prescription drugs on more than a rare occasion; I exercise 2-5 times per week; and I eat organic and low sugar foods as much as possible. This was also the case before, during, and after, "Covid." So why the hell did people who don't live anywhere near the lifestyle I live think it was alright to advocate that I be forced to do anything? They were given choices. This is a benefit of living in a society that believes in human autonomy, which technocrats were happy to enjoy until they were hypnotized into think my breath threatened their life. Diseases like those bucketed into the brand name, "Covid," are the result of many things. But to pretend bad choices don't have some role to play in those diseases is simply insane as we clearly can observe from the obese/unhealthy majority who filled the hospitals/morgues during this time.

A sane public health policy would have accounted for this and would have made *recommendations* such that people like me were not equally limited, since I wasn't a risk to others or at-risk myself. But as we now know, we don't have sane public health departments. In fact, if you go to the section on obesity at the CDC's website, you can see from the, "Notes on Language and Images," that they as-usual seem more concerned with using nice language than solving the problem.[2] They even link to a document titled, "Guidelines for Media Portrayals of Individuals Affected by Obesity." This absurd document ironically complains of, "bias and discrimination," based on certain portrayals of obese people. Yes, you heard that right: the same CDC which exclusively practiced medical discrimination with every policy it recommended during the Covid era thinks discrimination is a bad thing for obese people. Apparently, in their case only, one size doesn't fit all and discrimination will hurt their feelings, but when it comes to healthy people who acknowledge the mRNA shots have no benefit and are dangerous, discrimination is simply an, "effective policy tool."

Imagine if any successful fitness coach ever adopted the CDC's policy on obesity. Let's say you're healthy and I'm obese and we're at the same gym. On average, you can run a 7 minute mile and I can run a 15 minute mile. If the CDC was our coach, it seems they'd

618

have both of our treadmills set to 15 minute miles, since showing the differential in speed could lead to, "harmful stereotypes," and/or, "discrimination." In fact, the CDC might even recommend we not work out together in the same room at all, so that I don't have to be emotionally scarred by how much faster than me you are. Their policy during the Covid era suggests that even if we *were* separated into different rooms, they'd have still had you running a 15 minute mile. You'd never improve, but at least you'd be serving the greater good ... somehow. And this might seem like a tongue-in-cheek example, but the CDC literally had gyms closed down entirely for periods of time, so they are even more absurd in action than in theory.

Back to my personal experiences, the people I know that did comply with testing, fear, and inoculations have both, "had Covid," and worse. In fact, within a year of getting the gene therapy both my grandpa and my wife's grandpa have had cancers recur which they'd overcome in the past. Unfortunately, my grandpa recently died because of that cancer recurrence. While the inoculation cannot be considered the cause with absolute certainty, the spike protein *has* been connected to interrupting cancer suppressors as we've touched on previously. So there's at least an observational correlation occurring here in my family, and the public health agencies responsible for studying these types of things have always refused to do so because they know the consequences of finding such a connection. I also tangentially know of several other people who have died of strokes immediately following the shot, know of young and healthy people who died immediately following the shot, and certainly know of *many* of people who've gotten sick with, "Covid," despite having the shot.

In fact, ask yourself this question whether you've had the shot or not: whenever you've had/heard a conversation about the mRNA inoculations, what question *always* comes after, "so did you get vaccinated?" If your answer isn't, "how bad were your symptoms?" then you're lying. Whether or not one dies due to complications of the shot, people have come to accept that immediate, debilitating symptoms are so commonplace that they are actually expected to occur. Somehow—some incomprehensible (if not for the media fear porn campaign) way—people have been convinced to accept almost *guaranteed* bad symptoms in order to theoretically (not actually) avoid a *dis-ease* of which the CDC claims perhaps a majority of people can have without any symptoms at all.

This has to have been one of the most brilliant marketing campaigns ever to have accomplished such backward thinking. It was. And it's been mastered over the course of more than a century as we covered in the previous chapter. The following are some societal abuses I've personally experienced thanks to the aforementioned psychosis it created, and despite my well-above-average healthy lifestyle:

- Having had diarrhea for two straight weeks following my bachelor party, a tele-doctor told me to go to an urgent care clinic to get a fecal test done. When I got to one, I filled out a form and put down that my symptoms were diarrhea as well as a mild cough. Thanks to the CDC's declaration that as little as diarrhea or a cough can be evidence of, "Covid," the urgent care clinic I went to denied care to me, since I was, "unvaccinated," and didn't previously get a, "Covid," test. Mind you, I was already inside the building and all they needed to do was send me home with a cup to fill and then drop off. Apparently this was too much to ask. It took another week for me to get an appointment at an ethical doctor, who did send me home with a cup despite my not having a, "Covid," test. Turns out I had a parasite as expected, which, thanks to the unethical urgent care clinic, went untreated an extra week longer than it should have.
- The same urgent care clinic featured positive reviews on *Google* of people waiting two hours to get a, "mask fit test." Somehow this is a real thing which people go do where they ensure their mask is tight enough to ~~suffocate themselves~~, "ensure viruses can't get in." This was somehow considered more, "urgent," than a parasite.
- Was cursed out at a grocery store for not wearing a mask … *on July 4th*!
- Was denied entry at several other stores for not wearing a mask
- Denied the ability to go to work functions because of my lack of inoculation, despite the fact that inoculation does not prevent transmission. Also despite the fact that the venues these functions are held at do not and cannot legally require

proof of inoculation in Texas, so the other patrons very well might not have been inoculated either.

- Workplace policy was that non-inoculated workers in the office have to wear masks. While I work from home, this is just another humiliating discrimination taking place at a corporation which requires annual re-education, "anti-discrimination trainings"
- Found out day-of that a concert my wife and I were supposed to attend required proof of inoculation or test. This was not advertised beforehand when the ticket was bought.

Many people have obviously had it way worse than me, given the hospital genocide which took place. Still, this was a historic psychological warfare campaign we went through. The shock of seeing masked people present their, "vaccine passports," to go see the new Matrix movie and the shift in perspective one comes to have about the nature of reality after witnessing such a thing are not insignificant. Those who refused to comply with these backward policies were treated as enemies in their own counties, states, communities, and even families in some cases. Fortunately, many of us came out far stronger and less compliant. As stated previously, the resistance to nonsensical tyranny strengthened the bond my wife and I share as a unit and also brought us closer to God. Without believing in something greater to fight for, this very likely would have been an impossible hill to climb without being consumed by fear, whether of the virus itself or the consequences of non-compliance.

Fear is, of course, the primary weapon employed by the culprits of this crime against humanity. They admit this openly. This is because their enforcement powers are incredibly weak. In reality they are Oz behind the curtain—little men (in Fauci's case, literally and figuratively) who serve their own interests at any cost. They are limited in their capability, however, by their near-sightedness, especially when facing those who do believe in a higher power.

For me and many others the Covid era was a Great Awakening. The Great Reset offered to us has been rejected and I wish the best of luck to anyone who took the offer. All in all though, the cost of those lies now seems pretty clear: an overall fear of your fellow man, a willingness to suffocate yourself, a health and financial indentured servitude to the disturbing will of psychopathic shepherds, and a fundamental changing/poisoning of the very body you inhabit. The great news is that if you're reading this it's not too late to reject the next offer, and I hope this book has helped arm you with some of the information you'd need to do so.

Endnotes

1   "Seattle's Anarchist Utopia Breaks Down, Residents Report 'Screams Of Terror' On The Streets". 2020. *RT International*. https://www.rt.com/usa/491883-seattle-autonomous-zone-anarchy/.
2   "Overweight & Obesity". 2022. *The Centers For Disease Control And Prevention*. https://www.cdc.gov/obesity/index.html.

Interested in more from N.B. Austin?

Continue to Amazon to buy more books:

https://www.amazon.com/author/nbaustin

Need more than that?
Check out the author's website and/or link page!

www.nbaustinbooks.com

About the Author

N.B. Austin is the author, songwriter, and blogger behind the Civilands fantasy series, Stranger Than Fiction standalone synthesis of the Covid era, and songwriting under the name, "OldWiseBear," with composer OliveTreeBear. His first novel, Crimson River, was a finalist for the 2016-2017 BooksGoSocialDaily Book of the Year Award.

Based in Austin, Texas, but hailing originally from Long Island, New York. University of Texas at Austin educated. His experience in all things writing has expanded into a prolific library of more than 5 books and many more songs to-date.

Find more about N.B. Austin at:

www.nbaustinbooks.com

Made in the USA
Coppell, TX
13 May 2024

32335846R00351